THE CENTURY SOCIAL SCIENCE SERIES

EDWARD ALSWORTH ROSS, Editor

The Ways of Men

The Ways of Men

AN INTRODUCTION TO ANTHROPOLOGY

BY

JOHN GILLIN

Professor of Anthropology
University of North Carolina
Research Professor
Institute for Research in Social Science

APPLETON-CENTURY-CROFTS, INC.

NEW YORK   LONDON

438

TO MY FATHER

JOHN LEWIS GILLIN

Preface

Most books which purport to be "Introductions" to a field of knowledge are probably inspired by the fact that the author has been unable to find among published works a single volume which presents the material in a manner completely satisfactory to himself. By attempting to resummarize significant findings, to bring extant material up to date, and to rearrange it in terms of new orientations in theory and point of view he hopes in some measure to satisfy his own needs and to be useful to other persons interested in the field. It is doubtful that such an author ever entirely satisfies either himself or his audience. But this is the spirit in which the present volume has been written.

Those who are familiar with extant books on general anthropology will find in the present work some departures from the conventional outline both in materials and in point of view. Two of the more general may be mentioned. One is that an attempt is made to place the Primate order and the human species in a functional relation to culture, and the data are arranged with this in mind. I feel that the somewhat negative relationship which has existed between the study of the human organism and its zoölogical kinsmen, on the one hand, and the cultural and social life of man, on the other hand, has tended to block that overall comprehension of human ways which is essential to scientific progress in the understanding of mankind. Another innovation for a book of this type is a systematic attempt to weave psychological theory and findings into a functional approach to culture. The aim is not only to consider "culture as culture," but also to relate culture to actual human behavior. These two objectives are approached only in an elementary manner in the present volume, but it is hoped that some points may be suggestive to readers beginning the study of mankind.

None of the following persons can be held in any way responsible for the shortcomings of the present book. However, the least I can do is to record appreciation. Professor Ralph Linton first roused my interest in anthropology and has stimulated it consistently ever since. He was good enough to read the manuscript of this work in its entirety after its completion, and I am much indebted to him for penetrating and sympathetic

vii

comments. Professor Earnest A. Hooton opened my eyes for the first time to physical anthropology and, although he has had nothing directly to do with the present volume, his indirect influence will be seen in some portions. Professors William W. Howells, Gabriel Lasker and S. L. Washburn were kind enough to read and criticize several chapters dealing with the human organism in the first part of the book. For a special grant which enabled me in 1940-41 to take a year's leave from teaching duties to spend at Yale University in exploration of the meeting grounds of psychology and anthropology I am greatly indebted to the Carnegie Corporation of New York. A number of institutions have provided the opportunity to acquaint myself at first hand in the field with human beings and their products in diverse cultures. These institutions have at various periods financed me and entrusted me with field investigations in the following areas: Algeria, Europe, New Mexico, Utah, Northern Wisconsin, British Guiana, Ecuador, Peru, Amazon Valley, Guatemala, Colombia, and the South. Space does not permit individual mention of dozens of professional colleagues whose writings and personal discussions have influenced my thinking. I am, of course, grateful to all of them.

The only actual collaborators, if they may be so called, in the writing of this volume have been my students, both graduate and undergraduate. During the past fourteen years I have "professed" anthropology to a considerable range of student audiences at one time or another in the following institutions: the University of Utah, Ohio State University, Duke University, the University of North Carolina, the Peruvian universities of Cuzco and Trujillo and (in summer sessions) in New York University and the University of Michigan. Also as a graduate assistant at Wisconsin and Harvard I had previously gained some insight into the reactions to anthropology of students at those institutions. Whether I have actually benefited sufficiently by what my students have tried to teach me I am unable to say, but they have at least endeavored to sharpen my wits and to keep me in touch with current trends of interest in human relations in a way that would not have been wholly possible without their collaboration and interest.

J. G.

Contents

PART I

THE HUMAN ANIMAL

PART II

SOCIAL LIFE AND CUSTOMS

PART III

SOME STRUCTURES OF HUMAN RELATIONSHIP

PART IV

PATTERNING AND COÖRDINATION OF CULTURE

PART V

INDIVIDUALITY AND CONFORMITY

PART VI

EPILOGUE AND PROLOGUE

Reasonable Expectations

One of the patent facts of our time is that mankind the world over yearns for a life of peace and abundance, so far as it is within the ingenuity of man, with the help of God, to provide it. It is apparent to all but the most benighted inhabitants of the planet that the technical proficiency of what has been called the present "neotechnic" era has achieved a mastery over the natural environment and the processes of nature which *could* bring surcease from drudgery, freedom from dire want and illness, and relief from many current fears and anxieties, were technical possibilities alone to be considered. The serviceability of the machine and of the laboratory are self-evident to all who have seen their performances, and are constantly brought to the attention of the common man by the illustrated press, even in regions as yet unindustrialized and among social groups with little immediate hope of actually participating in the benefits of modern technology. I have recently seen this yearning for the advantages of the modern life, even among penniless and illiterate peons in South America, even among half-civilized Indians of the jungle, who, if they had not personally come in contact with the new mastery over nature, had heard of it by word of mouth or had seen examples of its marvels in illustrated papers whose captions they were in some cases too ill-educated to spell out. In our own country, the prevalent day-dreaming during the war on the subject of the brave new world of postwar gadgets and inventions was so general as to be commonplace and was, of course, heartily abetted by the advertisers.

The marvels of the machine and the test-tube, in short, are now so familiar as no longer to partake of the freshness of spot news. If technics could become the servant of all mankind, not merely of a few men; if men could devise ways of using this servant for the enrichment of their own lives and cease using it for the perfection of homicide and human suffering, it is no idle dream to foresee an era of peace and abundance. Freed of the frustrations of the age-long struggle for mere existence, mere subsistence, masters at last in our more significant relations with material things, we would have reasonable expectations of seeing the energies of mankind devoted to a full realization of the potentialities of human personality and of human culture. At the present time we have the means to live at peace with nature and to command artifacts to our service on a scale never before possible, but, we have as yet evolved no settled means of "getting along" with each other, generally speaking. And in our failures in the realm of human relations, our accomplishments in the realm of material technology are being put to grossly inefficient use, considered from any point of view of human value or purpose.

For example, we are accustomed to think of modern warfare as the most grimly efficient display of modern technology, and all due credit must be given to modern man for his ingenuity in devising, producing, and using methods and machines of homicide and destruction. Yet even if we granted that homicide were a worthy objective, and if we merely reckoned its cost in the crass terms of dollars and cents, we should have to admit that modern warfare is a most inefficient means of reaching that objective. In terms of dollars and cents alone it cost the American armed forces a great deal more to kill an enemy than it cost the enemy country to rear him from infancy, educate and feed him, and prepare him for slaughter. Modern war is one of the most expensive and inefficient means of killing men which has yet been developed. And there is nothing to show that the atomic weapons so far devised are cheaper. I mention this, not in criticism of military men who do the best they can, but merely to point up the need for a science of human relations: the methods which we apply to our dealings with other individuals and groups of our own species are at present so unscientific and inefficient that we cannot even kill them without an expenditure of energy and treasure out of all proportion to our technical accomplishments in handling the other fauna and the flora of the earth, to say nothing of the inanimate substances and processes of nature.

Of course, a well-developed and applied science of man would render unnecessary such efforts at organized slaughter, whether efficient or not. But we must face the fact that with all our vaunted cleverness the hardest problem to handle at the present time is man himself.

The late President Franklin D. Roosevelt, in his last public address, a prepared speech which was delivered by proxy two days after his unexpected death, said that one of our greatest needs following World War II was the development of a "science of human relations" which would enable us to live at peace with our fellow-men and with the nations of the earth in reasonable expectation of freedom from war for ourselves and our posterity. So far as I am aware, this is the first time that a President of the United States, or any prominent "practical politician," has suggested publicly that the relations of human beings might be amenable to scientific treatment. It is a very significant forward step and is comparable to the period when "practical men" in charge of industry and commerce first admitted what is now a commonplace to the majority of successful businesses, namely, that scientific industrial and market research might be profitably applied to their enterprises.

Science has different values for different individuals. To some it is a respectable means of satisfying idle curiosity. For others it is an efficient technique in the solution of immediately pressing problems of a practical nature. Some see in it only a way of getting or holding a job, while still others are not above using scientific techniques for the exploitation of their fellow-men.

It is not necessary here to argue the pros and cons of such views, other than to point out that, whatever may be the subsidiary, uses to which it may be put, the great and outstanding value of science is the ability it confers upon men to *make reliable predictions*. The ability to predict the outcome of situations has been sought since before the beginning of recorded history, for thereby men would be enabled to control the situations in question to their own interest.

The alleged techniques of prediction with which we are perhaps most familiar are based either on magic or on inspiration. Neither of these techniques has shown a sufficiently high record of "hits" to be considered reliable in the crucial situations of our time, and for this reason they have, on the whole, been discarded long since in most matters which concern us, with the outstanding exception of the adjustment of the interrelations of human beings. In the latter realm, magical divinations, unexplained inspirations, and sheer fantasy are still accepted as respectable by the general public and, all too often perhaps, by responsible leaders and formulators of public policy.

One of the characteristics of scientific prediction is that it is never properly made at random. No scientific man is legitimately able to "rear back and pass a prediction" at the drop of a hat. To be sure, a scientific diagnosis and analysis may give this appearance, because of the speed with which it is delivered in certain cases. But one may be sure that a great deal of fact-finding and reasoning has gone before. *A scientific prediction concerning a specific event is properly made only in terms of the conditions under which the event is predicted to take place.* "If P, then Q." Once the conditions are reliably known and understood, prediction is merely a matter of logic, and control of situations is largely a matter of techniques of manipulating said conditions. It is, of course, in the collection of information about conditions, their analysis, and the determination of their relationships with the events in which we are interested that much of the hard work of science is involved, and generalizations permitting ready prediction are possible only after an adequate amount of this laborious spade work has been accomplished. This is the way in which your physician works when you fall ill of a mysterious fever. He must first "diagnose the case," in other words ascertain under which conditions the fever is operating in your body (for example, he may identify certain microörganisms in your blood), before he can make a prediction concerning its probable course and, perhaps by altering the conditions (for example, by administering chemotherapy), effect its disappearance and your "cure." But the ordinary physician's "diagnosis" and treatment is based upon a long record of research and experience by himself and other scientists concerning the conditions he observes in you, the patient.

In simple and general terms, then, it is desirable that we inquire into the condition of man and the conditions under which he operates, so that we may place in his hands the scientific tools whereby he may abolish or avert certain of the disagreeable events of his own making. And it is the purpose of this book to set down certain of the principles of the science of man which seem to have validity at the present time and to suggest how they may be used to human advantage. At the same time we shall suggest certain other principles whose validity remains to be "proven" by further investigation in the hope that those who read this book will be stimulated to carry on such investigations or to encourage them to the end that "man unto his fellow-man may be a friend forever."

Let no one, therefore, who takes up the science of human beings feel that he is embarking upon an arm-chair excursion. This science is something like an Olsen and Johnson show—the audience must participate and will be well advised to keep its wits about it. No statement made in this work should be taken for granted if you can adduce acceptable evidence against it, and no explanation should suffice if another simpler one, more closely fitting the data, can be found. The author and all other students of man will be grateful for any such truly scientific and reliably tested contributions, for the understanding of ourselves is an enterprise which vitally affects us all, and the end in view requires the collaboration of every man and woman of good sense and good will.

This book is not an encyclopedia of anthropology. The reader must search elsewhere for much of the primary data upon which the argument and conclusions are based. For this purpose bibliographies and references are provided as a means of putting the beginner and the layman "on the scent," but it is frankly expected that, once he is started down the trail, he will do a little sniffing for himself.

A word should be said to teachers and students who may use this book in classroom instruction and to professional anthropologists generally. The attempt has been made to arrange the material in a "functional" sequence which differs in some respects from the traditional compartments of the older orthodox presentation of anthropology. Although the conventional divisions of the field into physical and cultural anthropology and their respective subdivisions such as human evolution, race studies, anthropometry, archaeology, linguistics, ethnography, and ethnology, are explicitly set forth in the discussion contained in the first chapter, it has been the writer's experience that presentation of material strictly in terms of these technical and professional "fields" of specialization is confusing and meaningless to students and laymen who lack much previous understanding of the science of man. Therefore I have tried to arrange a more logical and meaningful approach, although the reader is introduced to all of the usual fields of specialization by the time he comes to the end of the book.

It should be clear that a general introduction to the science of man must of necessity leave much unsaid. Many details of human biology and of human culture cannot be mentioned in a work of this scope. Numerous valuable contributions remain uncited for sheer lack of space. The bibliography at the end of the text is intended to serve two purposes: the documentation of certain text statements the evidence for which may be unfamiliar to the reader, and the guidance of the student who wishes to pursue a certain aspect of subject-matter or theory more thoroughly. The bibliography, taken as a whole, is neither exhaustive nor, in some respects, representative of all aspects of anthropological and related literature. It is an introductory lead whereby, one may hope, the student may enter the more specialized literature and perhaps discover for himself some of the notable papers and books which are not cited here. For pedagogical reasons, a number of propositions seemingly basic to the present point of view have been repeated at intervals throughout the text. It was thought that these "reminders" might be of value to the beginner. The advanced reader will, of course, be able to skip over them.

J. G.

The Ways of Men

CHAPTER 1

The Science of Man

A MILLION years ago no one was studying man for the excellent reason, of course, that there were at that time no human beings. But at about that period, or shortly thereafter, certain definitely manlike animals began to appear in the Old World and the first chapter opened in the long story of human development and striving. It is a story, however, which was not to be told in words for hundreds of thousands of years. The actors, proto-men and early hominids, groped about the "set," as it were, with neither scenario to guide them nor camera to record the rôles which they lived. Only fortuitous records did they leave of their slowly moving drama—their own bones occasionally preserved by chance from complete disintegration; a few of their more durable tools buried in the debris of ancient camp sites; the remains of wild animals they had learned to slaughter by guile and brute force. From the geological evidence and these few clues, as in some gigantic detective case, the early episodes of the mystery of man have had to be reconstructed. It would be too much to say that the evidence is now all in; perhaps it never will be; but enough has been learned to go a long way toward dispelling the mystery.

In the last million years, of course, "times have changed." The earth itself presents a different appearance from that of those remote days. The relative level of oceans to land masses has altered and oscillated, creating islands out of certain areas then parts of continental blocks. Elsewhere the Pliocene islands have become attached to the larger land areas or have disappeared below the sea. Land bridges connecting continents have risen and disappeared. Four great climatic oscillations which we call the Glacial Periods ushered in four far-reaching cyclic alterations of the earth's face during the last million years, leaving their mark in ice-borne and water-borne deposits and erosions. New forms of animals and plants have replaced many now extinct. During all these terrestrial cycles of change the manlike creatures struggled with the earth and its creatures for their existence. Slowly, through hundreds of thousands of years, they learned new tricks of adaptation, reproduced themselves and multiplied, and spread over the earth's face. Several species of these early men died out and became extinct; others may have mingled their blood with succeeding more adaptable forms. At all events, we are sure that the face of man, as well as the face of nature, has changed during the thousand thousand years of our story. But about twenty-five thousand years ago the present species of man, later hopefully self-named *Homo sapiens*, appeared in Europe and around the Mediterranean. All the more brutish forerunners were extinguished or absorbed, and since that time the affairs of earth, in so far as they have been amenable to human activity, have been in the hands of the "wise" species of man.

It is with this species that we are most concerned in the following pages. All of us are living specimens of this group. During the period of its sway no glacial periods have contorted earth's seasons and climatic zones, nor have hemispheric ice-caps sealed the surfaces of continents, except in Antarctica and Greenland. Yet the landscape has been altered in many parts of the earth almost as startlingly as it was during the great natural cycles of the preceding nine hundred thousand-odd years. Forests of continental scope have disappeared before the axe. Rolling prairies of natural grass have been turned into park country with clumps of trees interspersed amid orderly cultivated fields. Elsewhere the prairies have become arid dust bowls nearly devoid of vegetation. Rivers have been diverted; large lakes have been created even in deserts; mountains have been literally moved. New, domesticated types of animals and plants which could never survive the harsh competition of raw nature, occupy thousands of square miles from which their sparser wild predecessors have been driven into remote hiding or extinction. All of this in a general way should be familiar to the reader. We wish to emphasize, however, that these changes have not been wrought by the slow processes of un-manipulated "nature." They are the direct result of human activity, the stupendously varied activity of the *sapiens* type of man.

It is necessary to grasp what the advent of this peculiarly adaptable animal has meant in world affairs, in terms of natural history. Numbering at the present time some two billion members, the species of man is the most numerous of the larger mammals. Representatives of the species live in all parts of the earth, adjusting at least sufficiently for survival to all the environments offered by the globe. Never before has a single species shown such versatility. Never before has an animal shown such success in modifying environments to its own basic needs. It is truer now than in Shakespeare's time that "Man bestrides the world, like a Colossus." Yet the greater part of the secret of man's "adaptability" does not lie in mysterious biological metamorphoses which provide ready-made adjustment to new conditions. Man *invents* solutions to problems, and *learns* ways of satisfaction. Other animals, to be sure, develop adaptive habits and modify their environments to some extent, but man differs from other creatures in his greater *degree* of inventiveness and learning ability. This is part of the secret. An invention can be discarded; a habit learned can also be unlearned. Placing relatively greater dependence on inventiveness and learning, man thus maintains a more flexible "stance" than other animals. As conditions change, man changes his ways to adapt to them. But man has one other great advantage. He is able to communicate and to teach what he has invented or learned to other individuals and to following generations. Again, it appears that certain other animals are able to transmit simple muscular habits to one another, but no other animal has developed any facility in *symbolic* learning. Every human group has developed a vast armory of symbols—verbal, gestural, sometimes written and otherwise—whereby the solutions of problems may be transmitted without the necessity for a wearying trial-and-error period. Because of this trick of *storing experience in symbols* the adaptive habits of other individuals and of other times become the heritage of the average human individual; the trial-and-error solutions of many lifetimes may be absorbed in a few years.

THE MODERN SCENE

Man's past, if viewed in the proper perspective, is more fascinating than any romance of fiction. It forms, in fact, the raw material from which romancers construct their invented plots. But we have to live in the present. Our children, we hope, will mold the future. Two billion of us "wise" animals occupy the earth, grouped into tribes and nations with the widest variety of ideals and values. The behavior of the tribes and nations of men is far from uniform throughout the world and activities of various groups frequently seem to run at cross purposes one to another. War and revolution, group aggression and internecine strife, instead of absorbing less of the energies of men than in the early days, seem in recent times to absorb more. The plain fact is that many tribes of man— and most spectacularly those of "Western Civilization"—have evolved culture which enables them to live on advantageous terms with their physical environments. But they have not developed satisfactory means of living on good terms with other men or groups of men. The difficulties arising from these deficiencies are often designated the "social problems" of our time. Yet no problem is solved simply by naming it. Therefore, one of the tasks of the science of man is to explain human difficulties, and by searching for solutions which have been successful in other times and places, as well as in our own backyard, to show the way toward the end of these "problems."

The habits, customs, traditions, values, goals, and artifacts of a human social group are collectively called its *culture*. Cultures vary, and the culture of one group is often diametrically opposed to that of another. Most of the human difficulties of the present day, as we shall see, are traceable to cultural maladjustments of one sort or another. It therefore behooves us to learn something of this phenomenon. Do other animals have culture, or is it a distinctively human possession? How do cultures develop? Why do they vary so widely? How are they passed on from one generation to another? How do cultures change? Can a culture be changed by rational planning? These are some of the questions which interest all modern men perplexed by the difficulties of our time.

We shall try to investigate man the animal and his cultural behavior with a dispassionate, but roving, eye. We shall not be content to study men of only one color, or men of only one culture. Our gaze must sweep the world, unimpeded by any artificial myopia produced by looking through the eye-glasses of our own society. As the botanical scientist, seeking the general laws of plant life, does not content himself with examining a single plant from his own garden, so the anthropological scientist, searching for the general principles of human culture, must try to understand it wherever it exists. *Anthropology, in short, takes the whole species of man as its subject-matter and the entire inhabited planet as its field of investigation.*

TOWARD A SCIENCE OF MAN

The business of subjecting the human species to scientific scrutiny is a relatively new development. One hundred years ago there were few anthropologists in our sense of the term, although by that time there was an ample number of human beings—perhaps a billion of them organized into several thousand societies each with its own somewhat distinctive culture. The first written records had been set down some six thousand years earlier and in the succeeding interval a vast accumulation of documentary material relating to men and their activities had been collected. But most of these documents were based on speculation, emotion, inadequate information, or faulty observation. The fantastic anecdote, the dogmatic pronouncement, the sage epigram were more popular than facts or sound systems of interpretation. Although some of the learned men of ancient Greece had suspected as much, a hundred years ago there were still few Western scholars who were prepared to accept the idea that man was an animal, developed over a comparatively long period of time, and not a "ready-made" creation. Not knowing exactly what man was ("a little lower than the angels"?) scholars were unwilling to apply scientific principles of study which two centuries of experience had already proved increasingly successful when applied to other phenomena of the universe. Confusion continued to be confounded. Let us sketch very briefly some of the landmarks along the road toward the development of a science of man

MAN'S DISCOVERY OF HIMSELF

One of the enigmas of human history has been man's indifference, during most of it, to himself as an object of study. He has avoided the inquiry into his origins and his normal activities as if they were a disease or a form of morbid indecency. Even today many persons lack an objective understanding of their own species or its cultural variations and developments. Anthropology is one of the sciences which has labored to produce a clearer comprehension of human beings and their problems the world over, and in this section we shall touch the high points of the slow emergence of man's proper study of mankind.

The ancient world. Foreign contacts of a more or less cosmopolitan nature are necessary for the appreciation of the fact of racial differences, and many early groups, as well as certain "backward" contemporary societies, lived in such isolation that the possible existence of human beings differing from themselves in appearance never occurred to them. *Egypt* was one of the first societies to develop contacts outside of its own boundaries and to leave us any record of them, and in Egyptian carvings and paintings we first discover a definite capacity for identifying alien types. Even as early as the Predynastic period (fourth millennium B.C.) and certainly during the early dynasties, non-Egyptian types are represented. And on the reliefs of the Royal Tombs of the Nineteenth Dynasty (1321-1198 B.C.) we have the first real attempt at racial classification. The four main types, as the Egyptians classified them were: Semites, painted yellow and supposed to be representative of Asiatics; Negroes, painted black; Northerners or Europeans, with white skins, blue eyes, and light beards; and the Egyptians themselves, who were painted red. As time went on the Egyptian repertory of racial and national types increased, but no attempt was made to study them scientifically nor to generalize upon them.

The *Greeks* first fully realized the variety of human types and developed the beginnings of a scientific interest in their origins and varieties. The spread of Greek civilization and commerce about the Mediterranean and northward and eastward to the Black Sea and to Asia Minor provided opportunities for travel and observation of foreign peoples. Especially in Miletus in Ionia during the eighth and seventh centuries B.C. a school for scholars grew up, devoted to the production of accurate maps and guide-books for the assistance of mariners and commercial travelers, and into these "Sailings Round" went all the available information concerning the physical appearance and mode of life of the "Barbarians." The learned men of Ionia not only compiled such information, but developed a philosophical basis for speculation and science. Ignorant of later theological doctrines which were to remove man from nature, they asked that he be examined objectively and his origins uncovered. Two of these philosophers, both of Miletus and of the sixth century B.C., stand out. They were *Anaximander* (610-546? B.C.) and *Archelaus*. Both postulated the biological evolution of man from lower animals and, in fact, the evolution of the earth itself. These Greek philosophers of the sixth century did not, of course, establish the theory of evolution, even though the observations of man and nature upon which they based their speculations were amazingly accurate, but they did anticipate the great discoveries of the nineteenth century, and in fact laid the basis for much of the science of modern Europe, not only in anthropology but in other fields as well.

Herodotus (c. 490-409 B.C.) was the first anthropologist and ethnographer. He was a wide traveler, an accurate observer, and an indefatigable compiler of information gathered from other travelers. Although his principal object was the writing of history, his books were filled with elaborate notes and lengthy intercalations concerning the "Barbarians." He attempted to illustrate in detail in his Histories the advice of Socrates that "man should know himself." Not only did he provide a systematic compilation of the extant knowledge concerning the known peoples of his time, but many of his reports, for example that on the Scythians, constitute the only accurate and detailed accounts available to the present day. He recognized that mode of dress is no criterion of race, and he did not confuse language with physical type. He set down the facts and forswore sentimentality. Herodotus was acquainted with the work of the Miletians and regarded man as simply a better kind of animal than others. Greeks in his view were not the only men in the world, and it was their duty to look at some of the more backward examples so that they should not be surpassed by them. This was a point of view which lapsed almost entirely from human thinking between the fifth century B.C. in Greece and the nineteenth century A.D. in Europe.

Other outstanding Greek contributors to anthropology may be summarized briefly.

Hippocrates of Cos (460-357? B.C.), the "Father of Medicine," compiled some ethnography and, in his *Airs, Waters and Places*, a treatise primarily on town planning, developed a theory that environment influences human society and customs. Hippocrates and his followers made the first scientific classification of animals, dealing with some fifty types, and human anatomy was compared briefly with animal anatomy, although not on the basis of dissection.

Aristotle (384-322 B.C.), the "Father of Science," made few contributions to cultural anthropology, other than the collection of political constitutions in his *Politics,* but in his books on natural history he anticipated the concept of species and set a long-time standard for close and methodical observation and recording. His method and objective viewpoint, despite their limitations, were of more influence than any specific contributions to the classification of races or to the inquiry into human evolution.

Following Aristotle the tendency of Greek thought with respect to man was to turn toward metaphysical inquiry with decreasing interest in the objective aspects of human life and behavior as represented in different societies. *Thucydides* (471-399? B.C.), in his history of the Peloponnesian War, gives a short account of the prehistory of Delos, basing his resumé upon archaeological evidence obtained "during the purification of Delos by Athens when all the graves in the island were taken up, and it was found that half their inmates were Carians, identified by the fashion of the arms buried with them, and by the method of interment." Otherwise we hear nothing of archaeological research in ancient Greece. Although occasional mention of the discovery of relics is made, they seem to have been regarded with idle curiosity rather than scientific interest.

In Rome the spirit of first-hand investigation was scarcely developed at all.

The Elder Pliny (23-79 A.D.) compiled in his *Natural History* the first encyclopedia, but its value for the advancement of scientific knowledge was doubtful because it was put together with no regard for accuracy or for the distinction between fact and fancy. He drew from every source of information, good and bad, and so far as ethnography is concerned probably did more than any one else to lay the basis for numerous myths concerning primitive peoples which are still current in our culture. For Pliny was read and reread for centuries during the intellectually impoverished period of the Dark Ages in Europe.

Tacitus (55-120 A.D.) wrote a book, *Germania,* which was the first attempt in antiquity to produce a rounded study of a culture outside the borders of civilization. Although Tacitus himself never "worked in the field," but obtained his information at second hand, his work is well composed and arranged; and it provides a remarkably full account, which stands today as our only source on the tribes of Germany in ancient times. The book contains numerous omissions from a modern anthropological point of view, but the arrangement of the material is as follows:

geographical description of Germany; brief account of the people and their own legends of origin; racial type; account of customs and institutions, arms, modes of warfare, kings and aristocracy; list of gods; methods of divination; German village life; absence of cities and towns; clothing; marriage rites and home life; the popular rally; food; standard of living for slaves; agricultural practices; funeral customs; and finally a regional description of the tribes.

Claudius Ptolemy of Alexandria compiled his geographical treatise in the first half of the second century B.C. This marked the peak of the geographical knowledge of the time, but showed little interest in peoples. Nor did his followers or successors.

A Hellenistic Greek of the second century A.D., *Galen* (131-201 A.D.) summarized the extant medical knowledge and his works served as the basis of most medieval medicine. Although he dissected apes, his exposition of human anatomy was based upon analogy with the apes, with the result that his actual contributions to the knowledge of the human organism and its varieties were almost nil, despite the great influence his works exerted.

The Middle Ages. During the so-called Dark and Middle Ages, roughly from the fourth century to the fifteenth century A.D., the intellectual climate of Europe was such as to inhibit interest in the scientific study of man. During this period the outstanding scientific contributions were made by *Muslims* in the Near East, North Africa, and Spain, but, so far as anthropology is concerned, their principal contributions were primarily of a geographical nature. Nevertheless they were wide travelers and in many cases accurate observers of the customs and characteristics of the people among whom they traveled. The travel memoirs of the early Muslims concerning the Orient were edited by *Abu Zaid* about 920 in his *Information about India and China*, which remained the most important work of its kind prior to Marco Polo. One of the most versatile of the Mohammedan scholars was *Ibn Khaldun* (1322-1406) whose works on the anthropology and sociology of early Arabian institutions and whose ethnographic descriptions of North Africa remain among the best existing sources in these fields. Much of anthropological value can be gleaned from geographical and historical books of other Muslim writers of this period. But the Muslims, although characterized by a free intellectual curiosity which was almost completely inhibited in European scholars by the contemporary theological atmosphere, seem not to have been primarily interested in anthropology. Meanwhile in Europe, the light of science in general and of scientific inquiry concerning man especially, was practically extinguished for more than a thousand years. Scholars were not motivated by curiosity concerning strange peoples nor by a consideration of the human species as a whole, so absorbed were they in theological hair-splitting and speculation concerning the future of the soul.

The age of discovery. About the thirteenth century Europe began to break out of its self-imposed shell of isolation and to realize that it was neither the center of the universe nor of the world of men. During the Middle Ages it was unthinkable to question the biblical dogma that mankind was a single and special creation, and, although Aristotle was read extensively, his biological studies were completely ignored. But gradually Europeans began to travel and thus to become aware of cultural phenomena and racial groups of which they had never dreamed. *Marco Polo* (1254-1324) opened the door to Asia and China. *Cyriac de Pizzicolli* (b. 1391) was the first learned man to go to Greece and actually excavate and study the ancient remains there, and for this reason he has been called by some the "Father of Archaeology." Both were Italians. The mariner's compass, based on a Chinese invention, is first mentioned as being used by Muslim navigators in 1282, although it was used as early as the twelfth century, and Christian navigators learned of its use from the Muslims by the beginning of the thirteenth century. With this instrument and the astrolabe a great period of discovery by European navigators began, the details of which we do not need to set forth here. Suffice it to say that the extended exploration of the outlying parts of the world which began under the stimulus of the Portuguese Prince, Henry "The Navigator" (1394-1460) in the fifteenth century, resulted in a great in-pouring of books and reports to Europe concerning peoples strange both in physique and in culture.

At the same time the revival of the critical outlook in human affairs and of humanistic interests which we associate with the time of the Renaissance swept away many of the medieval intellectual fetters and laid the basis for a new scientific spirit. *Vesalius* (1514-1564) in 1542 published his book *De humani corporis fabrica* (*On the Construction of the Human Body*) the first anatomical work based upon dissection of the human body itself, thus constituting the only substantial advance in human anatomy since the days of Hippocrates. *Las Casas* (1474-1566), a Spanish monk who had accompanied the conquerors to the New World and became acquainted with their brutality to the Indians, published his *Brief Account of the Destruction of the Indians* in 1542, a work which was widely read and had great influence in awakening Europeans to the fact that even American Indians were people. *Garcilasso de la Vega* (1540-1616), a descendant of a Spanish father and a Peruvian woman of royal Inca blood, published his *Royal Commentaries on the Origin of the Incas* in 1617; it remains an outstanding source on the culture of the

Inca Empire and its history. In 1655 *Isaac de la Peyrère* published *A Theo-logical System upon the Presupposition that Men Were Before Adam.* Peyrère was not a scholar or a specialist, but simply an educated layman. His book is significant in indicating that even non-scholars were beginning to discard the old theories of creation and to speculate on a more realistic conception of man's origin. His views were of course mercilessly attacked by many orthodox scholars. Shortly after this in 1674 *John Scheffer* of Upsala University in Sweden published the first competent ethnological treatise by a European, *History of Lappland.**

Although museums † are a common aspect of the modern scene, they were unknown until modern times. Organized curiosity in Europe began to show itself, after its awakening through the great discoveries, in the formation of collections of "curios." One of the earliest collections of ancient remains to be made in Great Britain was that formed by Thomas Howard, *Earl of Arundel* (1586-1646). Before this, under the stimulus of the Renaissance, the great potentates of Europe had begun collecting ancient works of art, fired by chance discoveries in Italy and Greece. Arundel, however, sent special agents through the Near East, excavating and buying antiques, and shortly thereafter the Duke of Buckingham started a rival collection. But the idea of public museums had not yet been born, and during the Civil Wars and subsequent to the death of Arundel most of his collection was dispersed or lost. Although a small part was placed by his heirs under the care of Oxford University, the University did not for a long time give it the care it deserved. One hundred and thirty-six stones bearing Greek inscriptions were built into

* The English translations of these titles are given here.

† *Museum* in ancient Greece meant "temple of the muses," and could by extension be applied to any place where literature and the arts were cultivated. The most famous museum of antiquity was that supposed to have been founded by Alexander the Great in Alexandria as a great library and home for scholars. Hammurabi of Babylonia is said to have maintained a collection of archaeological relics, and Alexander the Great is reputed to have sent back numerous collections from his conquests. The application of the term "museum" to a systematic collection of antiquities or of natural history or science is, however, quite modern. So far as modern anthropological collections go, it seems that Ole Worm (1588-1654), a Danish physician after whom the "Wormian" bones of the skull are named, established one of the earliest collections of archaeological specimens in Europe in the early seventeenth century. The Charleston (S.C.) Museum, founded in 1773, was the first in the United States, although its anthropological collections were insignificant. Among museums supporting work in anthropology, the Peabody Museum of Harvard was founded in 1861; Peabody of Yale, 1866; American Museum of Natural History, 1869; New York State Museum, 1873; United States National Museum, 1876; Public Museum of the City of Milwaukee, 1882; Field Museum of Natural History (now the Chicago Museum of Natural History), 1893. There are now about 7,000 museums in the world, of which Germany and the United States have about 1,500 each. Of the 1,500 in the United States, 125 are science museums, and of these at least 48 employ one or more full-time qualified anthropologists.

the wall of the Sheldonian Theatre and only in the nineteenth century were they rescued and placed in the Ashmolean Museum. The foundations of the *public museum idea* were laid in England by *John Tradescant*, a keeper of the royal gardens. Starting about 1637 he began to collect what he called his "Closet of Curiosities," a catalogue of which he published in 1656. Although the collection consisted in the main of botanical and natural history specimens, it also contained a section of "war-like instruments" which is actually the first ethnological collection ever made. Tradescant willed his collection at his death to his friend Elias Ashmole, who turned the specimens over to Oxford University on condition that a building be erected to house them. This was the start for the famous Ashmolean Museum, the foundations for the first building of which were laid in 1679 and finished in 1683. In the 1840's a new building was built, but Tradescant's collection remains intact, and the Ashmolean Museum is the oldest public institution of its kind in England. The importance of public museums of course lies in the educational opportunities they offer to the public and also in the fact that the collections are not broken up at the death of the original collectors. With these stimuli during the Age of Discovery, travel increased and interest spread in the study of antiquities and foreign and savage customs during the sixteenth, seventeenth, and eighteenth centuries.

"The Age of Reason." Modern science in most of its branches began to make its most important steps forward during the eighteenth century. In 1735 *Linnaeus* (1707-1778) published the first edition of his *Systema Naturae*, in which for the first time since Aristotle *Homo sapiens* was classified as one of the animals. In the first edition man appears among the Quadrupeds together with the ape and the sloth. In the tenth edition the Primates are made to include man, apes, lemurs, and bats. Man himself was classified under the headings *Homo sapiens, H. ferus, H. americanus, H. asiaticus, H. afer,* and *H. monstrosus.* Although the Linnaean system still forms the basis of modern taxonomy, we shall see later that the classification of man has been considerably revised and refined as a result of later research. The important thing in the present connection is, however, that the revolutionary system of Linnaeus was followed by little attack from authority. The free scientific attitude toward man was reviving for the first time since the days of Classical Greece, after a decline of some twenty-two centuries. Contemporary with Linnaeus, *Buffon* (1707-1788), a French scholar, had the boldness in his widely read work, *Natural History of Animals,* to maintain that it was possible for horse and donkey, ape and man to have a common ancestor.

Meanwhile new ethnological discoveries continued to be made. In 1772 Captain James *Cook* set out for Oceania where he discovered Hawaii,

New Caledonia, and many another of the South Sea Islands. His reports on the customs and material culture of the natives of New Zealand, Australia, and other islands are of the most accurate and competent kind, and he also made large collections of objects representing all the activities of native life. Most of these collections are preserved in the Pitt-Rivers Museum at Oxford. In 1771 *De Bougainville* published the report of his own voyage around the world, which is of almost equal importance to anthropologists, especially for his observations in Melanesia and Polynesia.

The variety of mankind was now almost commonplace and the stage was set for the systematic study of his origins and varieties, both from the physical and the cultural point of view.

Nineteenth-century advances. Neolithic objects had been worn by Greeks, Romans, and early Christians as charms with, however, no attempt to explain their existence. In the Middle Ages such trinkets were usually declared to be works of the Devil, and later the common man regarded them as "thunderbolts," a designation which is still used in some backward parts of Europe and America. Everything before the beginning of written history was disregarded, and most people, following an ecclesiastical calculation, believed that the world itself had been created in 4004 B.C. Yet evidence was accumulating which awaited interpretation in the second half of the nineteenth century. In 1797 John *Frere* published a report on a collection of flint implements which he had unearthed in Suffolk, England, twelve feet below the surface, and which he identified as of human fabrication; but the majority of scholars still regarded such an inference as preposterous. In 1825, *MacEnery*, a Catholic priest, carried out a careful excavation of a cave in which he found an extinct rhinocerous tooth directly associated with a flint weapon, the first recorded proof of the immense antiquity of man.

About the same time an obscure customs official in France, named *Boucher de Perthes*, started studying both cave and river deposits. In the vicinity of Abbeville, in cuttings in river gravels made for industrial and military purposes, he made elaborate studies of the numerous Paleolithic implements which he found. The geological association of the flints proved without doubt the antiquity of the men who made them. Boucher also had the vision to grasp the meaning of this evidence and to picture a long period of human development extending over hundreds of thousands of years. He first propounded this hypothesis in 1838, but it was more than twenty years later, after the Darwinian theory had suddenly opened the minds of scientists, that Boucher finally received the recognition which his work deserved. Boucher de Perthes, then, is the founder of modern prehistoric archaeology and of human paleontology. Several fossilized human skeletons had also been discovered whose importance was not at once realized, for example, the Gilbraltar skull (a Neanderthaloid, found 1848) and the Neanderthal type of skull itself found in Germany in 1857. The acceptance of the antiquity of man following Boucher de Perthes was also furthered by important advances which had been made in the science of geology during the first half of the nineteenth century, but it remained for Charles Darwin to raise the final curtain on the drama.

In 1859 *Darwin* published *The Origin of Species*. To the confused and groping scientists of the time, this vast and all-inclusive hypothesis seemed to open the door to the solution of a wider array of problems than any previous work. The probability became obvious that man, like the other developed animals, had evolved from previous and simpler forms of life. Darwin formulated clearly and precisely the unknown law which explained the whole outline of biological development. The evidence for man's development was already present in the gravel and cave flints, in the fossilized bones, and the wide collections of ethnological material concerning primitive peoples. And anthropology was not slow to take the hint. In 1866 the Berlin Museum of Ethnology was founded; in 1879 at Washington the Bureau of American Ethnology, the first government-sponsored research organization for anthropology. Anthropology, the study of man, had become respectable, and from the sixties we can speak of it as a science.

In the past eighty years anthropology has developed many theories to explain the evidence which has accumulated concerning the human species and its modes of life. It is not our purpose to describe and analyze these trends of modern anthropology in this chapter. We have discussed some of the more important mile-posts on the long road of groping advance to the point where human beings could look at themselves with clear eyes and candidly ask how they are made and "what makes them tick."

THE PRESENT STATUS OF ANTHROPOLOGY

The science of man has grown up and become a respectable member of the family sciences in the past eighty years. It would lead us much too far afield at this point to review either its mistakes or its accomplishments during that period of time, but it may be of some interest to glance at its status at the present moment.

General divisions of the field. From what has gone before it is apparent that one may study man from two general points of view: the biological and the social. We may approach man as an animal and also as a producer and user of culture. No more than a slight acquaintance with human beings is necessary to convince one that these two general aspects are closely linked in actual life, but for the solution of certain problems the division between biological and social aspects is desirable. Consequently the two large fields of anthropology have come to be called, (1) *physical anthropology* and (2) *cultural anthropology*. The first is distinguished by an emphasis upon the biological features of the species, the second by an emphasis upon the processes and products of man's life in groups.

While anthropology logically may be thought of as embracing all of the sciences dealing with man and his activities, a number of specialities have become primarily associated with anthropological study. In physical anthropology are the specialties of *human evolution* and *human paleontology,* concerned primarily with unraveling the story of the early development of manlike creatures through a study of their skeletal remains and the comparison of these with other animals. *Racial anthropology* is primarily a study of the varieties of the present species of man and their interbreeding. *Human ontogeny* or *growth study* is devoted to discovering the physical changes of the human organism from birth to death. *Anthropometry* is the science of measuring the human body in its anatomical aspects, for example, stature, diameters of the head, and the like. *Constitutional studies* are concerned with body build and physique and their relation to personality, illness, and so forth.

Cultural anthropology likewise has developed a number of specialities. Among these we may mention the following: *ethnography* is the study of the distribution of peoples and cultures throughout the world. *Ethnology,* sometimes called *social anthropology,* devotes itself to intensive analysis of living societies and their cultures, together with the drawing of generalizations therefrom. *Linguistics* is the study of languages, whether written by the societies speaking them or not. *Archaeology* is the science which endeavors to reconstruct extinct cultures and societies in their proper time sequences, largely through the excavation and study of the recoverable material remnants of such bygone cultures.

Each of these special fields proliferates into numerous subspecialities. Thus we might mention *human genetics* and *criminal anthropology;* or *technology, aesthetics, folklore, religion,* and *ethics.* Like all other sciences, the study of man also has its *theoretical,* its *methodological,* and its *applied* aspects. But, like other practitioners of scientific method, students of man have discovered that in the final analysis it is fatuous to separate theory, method, and applications in actual investigations. Also they have learned the futility of trying to build a high fence around the field of anthropology thereby to shut it off from other sciences. Everything significant to an understanding of man is welcome and since the majority of human beings are not misanthropes, but on the contrary are vitally interested in their fellow-men, we may say that *most of us are in fact anthropologists to some degree, whether we wear the label or not.* This, of course, does not mean that every one is scientific.

Professional anthropologists. As has just been intimated, if you scratch an average man the chances are good that you will find an anthropologist. The majority of human beings are, in a manner of speaking, anthropologists "under the skin," because they are interested in humanity. On the other hand, professional anthropologists—those who try to earn a living by studying the human species and its cultures according to specialized scientific methods—are relatively few. And the stock pictures of them as portrayed in cartoons and Sunday feature articles are not very helpful in identifying them. Sun helmets, Vandyke beards, and thick eye-glasses are no more characteristic of your run-of-the-mill anthropologist than are silk hats, bloated faces, and enormous abdomens the identifying marks of the average banker, except perhaps in cartoon and fancy.

In the popular mind the romantic aspect of anthropology is associated with expeditions, and many a layman sighs with envy as he imagines the lucky scientist pursuing his investigations under the palms of some tropic isle surrounded by bevies of bare-breasted savage beauties or dramatically uncovering the skull of the "missing link" from the dust of millennia in a remote cavern far from the madding crowd. We should point out here that whatever of drama and romance the investigator does enjoy in the field is properly only incidental to a long, planned campaign of library and laboratory investigation aimed at uncovering significant secrets of man's nature, past or present. However spectacular or sensational an anthropological expedition may be in some respects, it is worthless scientifically unless it results in an addition to our knowledge of mankind.

In actual fact, there are no permanent jobs for anthropologists as "expedition leaders." Field work is carried on at intervals as part of the regular work of the employed anthropologist who usually has other responsibilities as well. We do not intend to go into the technical aspects of the employment situation of the profession at this point, but in the year 1941, before the war scattered them about, it appears that there were in the neighborhood of four hundred trained anthropologists holding permanent paid positions which were recognized as anthropological in the United States, Hawaii, and Alaska. Among these, about 126 were on the staffs of the 48 museums of the country that employ anthropologists. About 175 held regular positions as instructors or professors of anthropology in colleges and universities. About 50 more were employed by research organizations on a permanent basis, and 52 others were in the employ of the United States Government. In addition there were 80 to 100 others, who would be recognized by training and accomplishment primarily as anthropologists, who held scientific positions with non-anthropological labels, for example, in sociology, anatomy, psychology, and so forth.*

There were three or four hundred other trained or partly trained anthropologists in the country who for one reason or another were not employed as anthropologists. Some had gone into business and other lines of endeavor; some were married women carrying on anthropological work supported by their husbands; some had private incomes enabling them to continue their work without a paid position; some were graduate students just finishing their training; and some, regrettably, were simply unemployed. The American Anthropological Association in 1939 had a membership of 1,101.

Professional anthropology is international. Science is, of course, a part of Western Culture or Civilization, and practically all modern countries where this culture has obtained a foothold have professional anthropologists. Some 737 journals and serial publications were regularly published before the outbreak of war in 1939 in all the national languages of Europe, except Albanian and Bulgarian, and also in Japanese and Chinese.† Anthropological societies flourished in most of the countries of the world, including those of Latin America, South, East, and North Africa, Australia, New Zealand, Asia, and Russia, as well as Europe and North America. Numerous local societies, in part supported by interested amateurs, exist in all parts of the United States and play a large part, not only in scientific progress, but also in the avocational life of numerous laymen. A list of journals and other publications will be found in the bibilography at the end of this book.

---

* These figures are not accurate to the last digit, but have been computed by the present writer from his own knowledge of the field and from a tabulation based upon the *International Directory of Anthropologists*, 2nd. Ed., Vol. I: "The Western Hemisphere," National Research Council, Division of Anthropology and Psychology, Washington, D.C., 1940. The National Research Council maintains a card index of all recognized professional anthropologists at its headquarters in Washington and endeavors to keep it up to date.

† Based on Donald Scott, *Seventy-fourth Report of the Peabody Museum of Archaeology and Ethnology of Harvard University*, Cambridge, Mass., 1941. The library of this institution maintains one of the most complete files of current anthropological publications in the world. Says Scott in his report, "The extent to which the Museum succeeds in keeping in touch with anthropological work throughout the world is reflected by the geographical distribution of the serial publications which it receives. Three hundred and twenty came from Europe, many of which are now interrupted by the war; 290 from North America; 59 from Asia; 45 from South America; 25 from Middle America; 26 from Africa; 37 from Oceania; 6 are international." P. 1.

The spread and applications of anthropology. In the foregoing paragraphs we have suggested something of the professional cadres of the science, the organization of the "detective bureau," as it were, devoted to solving the mysteries of the human species and its cultures. In any science basic research is fundamental to more "practical" applications and uses. The influence of anthropology, however, extends beyond its own professional boundaries, and, indeed, it would not be worth much as a science if this were not true.

The "anthropological point of view" has come to be increasingly appreciated. We will not try to define this point of view here, for it is one of the objectives of the book as a whole to present it, but some hint is given in the statement that the anthropologist endeavors objectively to take the whole planet as his field of investigations and the whole species and its cultures as his subject-matter. Data and principles thus derived have been found useful and fundamental in other sciences dealing more especially with the social life of our own society. Most universities and colleges which offer reputable programs in social science also offer courses in anthropology in connection or in separate departments. The use of anthropological materials in textbooks and research reports in sociology, psychology, geography and other social sciences has also shown a great increase. It is generally recognized, in short, that the competent social scientist should have a minimum acquaintance with anthropology, even though his primary interests may be restricted to a very small area of contemporary society.

The importance of *human resources* in the anthropological sense has thus become established in academic circles. It is also coming to be noticed in connection with programs concerned with human adjustments in the practical world. Thus the British Colonial Service in Africa and Melanesia has appointed government anthropologists to assist in solving the problems of contact between native and European peoples. Anthropologists have also been involved in colonial administration in Italian East Africa and in the handling of native populations within the Soviet Union. When the Wheeler-Howard Act of 1934, providing for tribal self-government of the reservation Indians of the United States, was put into action, anthropologists were called in to make studies of the Indian cultures and to make recommendations for the administration of the act. Wherever two societies with differing cultures come into contact—and in the modern world of rapid transport and travel this is becoming a world-wide phenomenon—it appears that scientific procedure along anthropological lines will be found increasingly useful—and somewhat cheaper than brute force and ruthless exploitation.

The "science of custom" also has its applications in planning for other types of human relationships. For example, a study by Roethlisberger and Dickson in the Hawthorne Plant of the Westinghouse Electric Company used the anthropological approach and discovered that cultural and social relationships among the workers had a determining influence upon their efficiency and output in the plant. The Resettlement Administration of the United States Department of Agriculture likewise uses anthropological studies in solving problems of adjustment for groups moved from one habitat to another. In the long view, the general principles which govern the functioning, growth, and interrelations of cultures, the principles of the culture-environment relationship, and the principles governing the relationship of the individual to his culture are either applicable to our own time and place or they are inadequate.

Anthropologists in the war. During the war of 1939-1945 the need and value of a "practical" science of human relations became increasingly evident in many quarters. Professional anthropologists showed a versatility in the war effort which can probably be exceeded by the members of no other profession. The record is not complete at this writing. A preliminary report prepared by a committee of the National Research Council at the beginning of 1943 provides the following partial summary. The committee says "the demand for anthropologically trained personnel, which is increasing and will probably soon exhaust the supply, indicates the desirability of broadening and intensifying the teaching of this subject in our colleges and universities." At the beginning of 1943 the following functions were being performed by anthropologists in the war effort, without mentioning those who served in the armed forces as citizens whose special training was not at the time being used.

1. In world-wide *planning and intelligence work*, requiring primarily a detailed knowledge of world regions and peoples, fifty men were employed by the Army, Navy and Office of Strategic Services. The State Department had two, and thirty-eight others were engaged by the Board of Economic Warfare (later, Foreign Economic Administration), Office of the Coördinator of Inter-American Affairs, and the Office of War Information. In addition about forty-five anthropologists were employed by peacetime institutions on special war work of this type; among these institutions were the American Council of Learned Societies, the National Research Council, the Social Science Research Council, the Smithsonian Institution, the Ethnogeographic Board, the Office of Indian Affairs. The work of the general group in this class is broken down as follows: (*a*) Forty anthropologists were being used as advisers and researchers in military warfare on problems ranging from field intelligence to problems of supply in obscure theaters. (*b*) Another fifteen were engaged in economic warfare and planning. (*c*) Political warfare and national morale

used the services of thirty more anthropologists, and in addition the anthropologists on the staffs of eighteen universities were coöperating. (d) Some thirty anthropological linguists, familiar with exotic and un-written languages, were at work in the war effort. (e) Ten additional members of the profession were occupied with compiling basic regional information for armed and civilian agencies.

2. Some forty anthropologists were serving in action programs in the war effort. (a) These included ten who, because of their knowledge of customs and social problems in particular regions, were engaged in the facilitating of strategic war material production in foreign communi-ties. (b) Ten more were involved in worker-management relation pro-grams aimed to increase production in the United States. (c) Community resettlement and regional rehabilitation absorbed the services of fifteen more, while (d) seven anthropologists remained with the Indian service in the interests of securing the coöperation of this sector of our popula-tion in the war.

3. Five anthropologists were engaged to help set up special training courses, primarily for military or naval officers being trained for the administration of occupied territories.

During the last two years of the war the number of anthropologists engaged in such specialized activities increased about 100 per cent and the number of special activities to which they adapted about one-third. Practically all of the professionally qualified anthropologists who entered the armed services were assigned special duties before the end of the war because of their experience or qualifications as anthropologists. The Na-tional Research Council committee in 1943 summed up the opinions of the armed services and other war agencies as to the special values of anthropologists under the following heads: first-hand experience of for-eign regions, knowledge of cultural interrelations, technical ability to analyze social structure, ability to understand human relations, experience in translating knowledge into action.

Anthropologists are on the whole no more intelligent or heroic than other men. Their versatility in the war effort is worth mentioning only because it seems to reflect the fact that a professional experience in dealing with people in all their aspects turns out to have unusual "practical" use-fulness, after all. Furthermore, one does not necessarily have to be a professional to be able to work effectively in the field of human relations, provided one has training in the basic principles and techniques.

The crisis of the postwar years, apparently somewhat different in kind, will be no less acute than that of the period of active hostilities. It is evident that a reliable science of human relations is desperately needed, call it anthropology or what you will. Shortly before the war a

Society for Applied Anthropology was organized and at present publishes a journal called *Applied Anthropology*, devoted largely to "practical" aspects of human relations.

All of our knowledge concerning man will have to be focused on the human problems of our age, if we are to have a future worth contemplating. Thus it is that the studies of mankind's past must be sharpened and coördinated with knowledge of his present condition in all parts of the world. One may expect to see a new science of man develop during the coming years. It is hoped that the following pages will provide a groundwork for those who wish to participate in this development.

SUMMARY

At the risk of "talking shop" rather early in the day, we have endeavored in this chapter to show something of the need for a science of man, the long slow process whereby the systematic approach to an understanding of man developed, and something of the present status of the study of man which calls itself anthropology.

Our main objective, however, is an understanding of mankind in general, not of anthropologists alone. There is nothing sacred about anthropology as such, and its present status or past vicissitudes are significant only in setting the stage for our study. Man has so many potentialities, so many variabilities, that as we come to know him better we may find that present programs for his study and for application of the findings fall far short of the needs in the present and the future.

Let us therefore look at ourselves in the mirror. Unprepossessing as the sight may be, each of us sees there a specimen. Try to shear off for the time being our local ideas of beauty, smartness, and "personality." Let us try to compare this specimen with the millions of other more or less similar specimens about us, in our country, on our continent—all over the face of the earth. Let us see how they are made, how they behave, and why.

NOTES TO CHAPTER 1

For further readings on the subject-matter of this chapter the following are recommended, among others: Beardsley, 1929; Casson, 1939; Lowie, 1937; Marett, 1908; Penniman, 1936.

PART I

The Human Animal

Introduction to Part I

ALTHOUGH HUMAN beings are animals, there are a good many respects in which man differs from other animals, especially in "what he does with his life." From a strictly physical and zoölogical point of view man differs from other mammals and particularly from the other primates only in degree. In non-scientific language you might say that he "is made of the same stuff, but he has more of it," at least as regards certain traits. Also the "stuff" as put together in man is organized along lines which, if not distinctive in kind, are nevertheless unique in result. This is especially true of the nervous system, for example, which is of the general mammalian type and which is composed of the same kind of tissues and interconnections as in other animals. Even the basic plan of the nervous system is typical of that of other mammals, particularly the Primates, but there is more of it, particularly in the brain, and the complexity of organization and function far outshadows that of any other animal.

It would be a matter of only academic interest to understand how man is made, if it were not for the fact that his physical structure and the functions of which that structure are capable are significant in understanding what man *does*. For it is what man *does* which is of most significance to him and to the remainder of the world of nature as well. Man's body, in other words, is "what he has to work with." He has to get along with this Primate type of body as best he can. It sets limits on what he can accomplish, so far as such matters are controlled by biological factors.

Since man is an animal, it follows that he is possessed of certain animal needs for nutrition, reproduction, and the like. Since he is a certain kind of animal, these needs are derived from his ancestry and his genetic constitution.

The most important things about the human species are its cultural accomplishments and its patterns of behavior and thought. But culture, we must remember, is a product of the human species and it is also a servant of the species. Men everywhere live in groups and develop systems of customs characteristic of those groups, but these systems must be generated and manifested by the biological body which God and nature have given to the species. And everywhere these customs must satisfy to some

23

extent the purely animal needs of the creatures we call men, regardless of the elaborations which are reared above the level of these crude biological requirements.

In this part of the book, therefore, we shall discuss the zoölogical position of the human species in the animal kingdom. We shall inquire into man's resemblances and differences as compared with his closest relatives, the Primates. We shall explore briefly among the bones of our fossil ancestors in order to appreciate better the qualities of the present species. We shall look into the hereditary variations which exist within the present species of man and we shall examine the question as to whether these hereditary variations have in fact any function significance from the cultural point of view. We shall consider certain constitutional features of present-day man, derived from differences of sex, age, and other factors, and we shall contemplate their functional importance in the development and operation of cultural patterns.

The reader will readily grasp that this is not a zoölogical review based on idle curiosity. We are not interested in fondling skulls and classifying organisms merely for the sensual pleasure involved or for the logical exercise possibly to be derived therefrom. The functional relationships of human biology with human culture are our primary concern, and we are constantly asking ourselves, "What has this to do with culture?"

CHAPTER 2

The Primate Patterns:
Zoölogical Classifications and Skeletal Comparisons

MAN AMONG THE ANIMALS

Life. If we depend upon our natural senses and upon them alone—thereby ignoring for the time being such possibilities as ectoplasm, ghosts, and fairies—we conclude that the world as we know it consists of two great classes of objects: living beings, and things without life. We recall that living things are composed of protoplasm organized into small units called cells, each with its wall around it and its nucleus within it. Living beings maintain themselves by transforming non-living substances into the protoplasm which constitutes their own bodies and by excreting wastes. Living beings may change in form through processes of growth, and although eventually they die, they are capable of reproducing themselves. These, to mention only a few, are qualities of living things and of them alone. When we apply these criteria to ourselves we conclude that man belongs in the class of living things and that, simply as a material object, he must be studied in the light of what is known about that class.

Man an animal? Living things fall into two major groups: plants and animals. There are some intertypes, such as certain protozoa and bacteria, which may be either animals or plants so far as formal classification goes, but these microscopic creatures are so unlike man that we do not have to be concerned. Man is definitely either an animal or a plant, and common sense as well as science tells us that he is an animal. In animals the cell walls are composed of nitrogenous materials, whereas in plants the cell walls are of carbohydrate material, frequently in the form of cellulose. Animals can fulfil their carbohydrate and protein needs only by absorbing carbohydrates and proteins already formed, that is, in the shape of dead plant or animal tissue. Green plants, on the other hand, build up these substances directly from inorganic salts, and even those

NOTE: References for this chapter will be found at the end of the following chapter. All notes for the two chapters on *The Primate Patterns* are numbered consecutively.

plants lacking chlorophyl, such as funguses, can synthesize their food from simpler chemical compounds than can animals. If we apply these two criteria—character of cell wall and of the absorption of starches—we find that man is definitely animal.

It may now be apparent that by proceeding with the zoölogical identification of the animal we are studying, we may obtain some hints concerning the type of behavior to expect and what not to expect. Where does man belong in the animal kingdom? And how may we identify his relatives?

Man a primate? Some two million kinds of animals have been studied and classified, and the range of variation in structure and behavior is very wide indeed. Thus, merely determining that man is an animal is not in itself going very far in laying down the biological possibilities of his behavior. The zoölogists have classified the greater part of the animal life of the world into groups for study and understanding. One group of this kind is called a race or subrace; next comes the species, the genus (pl., genera), the subfamily and the family and the superfamily, the suborder and the order, the class, and, finally, the phylum. Thus the members of a single species have more significant physical features in common with each other than with the members of the several species composing the genus; and so on up through the series until we find the members of a phylum with only a few features in common which distinguish them from other phyla.

What does the zoölogist hope to prove by thus sorting out the tribes of the animal kingdom? Aside from the fact that classification of material is one of the basic steps in any scientific study, we may get an answer by considering very briefly the general principles that govern these classifications. Animals are placed in groups on the basis of *structural similarities*. This fact is to be borne in mind, because the naïve observer frequently tends to group animals either on the basis of superficial appearance or on the basis of similarity of function alone. Thus, in South America the tapir is called the "bush cow," although structurally it is more closely related to the elephant than the cow, which, however, it resembles more closely in size and general appearance. On the same structural grounds a whale is not a fish but a mammal, a bat not a bird but a mammal. Structural similarities are the basis of zoölogical classification, but only *inherited structural features* are significant to the zoölogist. This point is often ignored in unscientific consideration of the so-called races of mankind. The zoölogical classification of the animal kingdom is thus in the nature of a geneological tree expressing the actual blood relationships between the animals, however remote those relationships may be. The animals grouped into an order, for example, are considered on zoölogical grounds to be more closely related to each other than to the animals in any other order.

It is not necessary to go through the animal kingdom in detail here in order to locate the position of man. This has already been done and the position is well established. Let us summarize.

Animals are of two kinds: single-celled (*Protozoa*) and many-celled (*Metazoa.*) Man, of course, belongs with the latter. Although there are recognized to be some eighteen to twenty-four phyla of *Metazoa*, they also may be divided into two broad divisions: invertebrates and verte-brates (or *Cordata*, usually regarded as a phylum). Man, with an internal segmental skeleton, is among the vertebrates. These, in turn, fall into five classes: fish, amphibians, reptiles, birds, and mammals. Mammals, in distinction to the other four classes, are covered with hair and nourish their young from milk-giving breasts in the female. They are also warm blooded. That is, internal body temperature is maintained relatively constant when the animal is in full health and function. This feature, however, is shared with the birds. Among the five classes of vertebrates, man qualifies only as a mammal.

The mammals have been differentiated into three large subclasses: (1) the *Prototheria* or Monotremes, of which there are only two species, the duckbill (*Ornithorhynchus*) and the spiny ant-eater (*Echidna*) confined to the Australian zoölogical region. They lay eggs and hatch them outside of the maternal body, but suckle the young; (2) the *Metatheria* or Marsupials are pouched animals such as the kangaroo, bandicoot, and oppossum, which, because of peculiarities of the reproduc-tive process, bring forth their young in semi-foetal condition to be reared for some time after birth in the "incubator" of the pouch; (3) the *Eutheria* or placental mammals gestate the young through the mechanism of a deciduate placenta and during life have two successive sets of teeth. Since these are the choices available, we have to place man among the Eutherian mammals. Of these there are several orders, for example, the *Edentata* (sloths, armadillos, ant-eaters), the *Cetacea* (including whales), the *Sirenia* (manati, dugong), the *Ungulata* (deer, pigs, horses, rhinoceri, and so forth), the *Carnivora* (cats, dogs, bears, seals), the *Rodentia* (rats, rabbits, squirrels), the *Cheiroptera* (bats) and the *Insectivora* (moles, hedgehogs, tree shrews). Without going into details, none of these groups is strikingly like man, except in the qualities which make them all Eutherian mammals. When we come to the *Primate* order, however, resemblances indicating closer relationship appear.

The Primate order includes all lemurs, tarsiers, monkeys, and apes. In general the Primates are less specialized in their physical adaptation to specific natural environments than are the members of other orders.

Among the common characteristics of this group of mammals are their prehensile (grasping) hands and (often) prehensile feet which characteristic depends upon their ability to oppose the innermost digits of at least one pair of extremities. All have five digits on each extremity. They also have a developed collar-bone, or clavicle, which provides a stabilized strut for the shoulder, permitting the rotation of the arm in three dimensions, and flat nails instead of claws on at least some of the digits. The penis is pendulous and the testes are scrotal, and two mammary glands on the chest are characteristic. Most important, the Primate brain always has a development of the posterior lobes and the order as a whole evinces an unusual tendency toward cerebral development. As Zuckerman says, "These morphological characters are generally believed to represent a primitive mammalian condition, so that it may be truly said that the Primate, except for its general tendency to cerebral development, is relatively a non-specialized animal." [1] In other words, man is able to adapt to a wide range of situations.

The zoölogists unhesitatingly place man among the Primates. As we saw in an earlier chapter this was done as long ago as 1735 [2] by Linnaeus without very audible objection. At that time it was believed that each group of animals represented a separate and special creation. It was not until the latter part of the last century, after the enunciation of the Darwinian theory of evolution, that different and more naturalistic implications of animal classification began to become apparent. According to Darwin, [3] the similarities that led zoölogists to classify man in the same category as the monkeys and apes were due to common inheritance. Immediately an outcry of injured human pride burst forth in some quarters, an outcry which has not entirely subsided even yet. In view of this fact we should state at once that man has not descended from any living species of Primate. That much is clear from all scientific evidence. No monkey or ape, as we know such creatures today, is even the remotest grandfather of any of us. On the other hand, all the evidence points to the probability that the monkeys and apes and—yes—we ourselves could trace our common ancestries back to a remote common progenitor were all the records available. Since, on the basis of geological reckoning, this hoary ancestor must have first appeared some sixty million years ago, we see that the present Primates are at best (or worst) our cousins several thousand degrees removed. Yet the family resemblance remains, and some of our "cousins" look and act just enough like men in a grotesque way to injure human vanity occasionally when this fact and the reasons for it are mentioned.

If we accept the apparently inescapable fact that man is zoölogically a Primate, it is to our interest to investigate the structure and function of this type of animal as a basis for our understanding of human accomplishments. When one steps behind the controls of a machine, it is well to know whether it is an airplane or a tank. Although there are many different kinds of planes, some capable of performances utterly impossible for other types, nevertheless the potentialities of any kind of plane are somewhat different from those of any tank. Any plane can do things which no tank can do, and vice versa. Likewise, any Primate can, by virtue of Primate structure and function, do things which no Ungulate, for example, can do; and the reverse is also true. Therefore, if man is a Primate, we need to know what are the limitations and the potentialities of animals with such specifications.

CLASSIFICATION OF THE PRIMATES

Although in the wild state many Primates live either in moist tropical or fairly warm arid regions, these animals have been known to human beings since antiquity, as pets, as sources of humor, or as evil spirits. Primates of various African species were imported into Egypt over a long period of time. They included the green guenon, the red guenon, the white-throated guereza, the yellow baboon, the hamadryas baboon, and others. The hamadryas baboon usually appeared in Egyptian art as the holy animal of the god Toth and was often mummified. Monkeys were imported into Mesopotamia from Egypt, but strangely no Indian or Asiatic species seem to have been brought into the Near East. Trading contacts spread a certain familiarity with African Primates through Asia Minor, Syria, Palestine, Crete, Phoenicia, and even to the Etruscans of Italy. In the Western Mediterranean the so-called barbary ape (actually a species of monkeys), was the best-known Primate and it appears in Carthaginian and Etruscan art. Both Aristotle and Pliny knew the barbary ape, as well as various monkeys and baboons, and Aristotle noted their resemblance to man, although he did not suggest human descent from them. Some type of ape was encountered and described by Hanno, the Carthaginian explorer, on the Sierra Leone Coast of West Africa in the fifth century B. C. Scientific knowledge of the large apes dates from the time of Galen (131-201 A.D.), the Alexandrian anatomist, who dissected certain monkeys and baboons and also, perhaps, at least one type of great ape (orang-utan or chimpanzee).[4] Systematic study of the Primates, however, began only in the eighteenth century to clarify much of the confusion which had existed since ancient times concerning this group of mammals.

The suborders. The Primates fall into three suborders: *Lemuroidea*, *Tarsioidea*, and *Pithecoidea* (sometimes called *Anthropoidea*). The

Lemuroids and Tarsioids are least like ourselves and need not detain us unduly long.

The *Lemuroids* are small, furry, fox-like animals living in the tropical forests of Africa, Madagascar, the Mascarene and Indonesian Islands as far east as the Philippines. They have a projecting, pointed snout like that of a dog, with a moist muzzle bearing an external mucous area and a split upper lip. The lower front teeth project outward and are rather specialized as are those of certain rodents. The skull shows many peculiarities of an unhuman nature. For example, the orbit of the eye does not have a back wall, but the eye rests merely in a ring of bone. The eyes of most species are placed on the sides of the head rather than in front, which prevents the visual areas of the two eyes from overlapping to any extent and precludes stereoscopic vision. Likewise the retina of the Lemuroid eye is of the nocturnal type, lacking a fovea, macula, and probably cones. These are structures which in eyes of the diurnal type (with which man and higher Primates are equipped) enable clear definition of sharply focused visual objects. The Lemuroids are also unhuman in their dental equipment, having only two pairs of incisor teeth (four pairs in man), but three pairs of premolar teeth on each side as compared with two pairs of premolars on each side in man. The low, slanting skull is suspended from the end of the vertebral column rather than being balanced on the upright column as in man, and the cerebral hemispheres are insufficiently developed to overhang the cerebellum, or lower part of the brain. The frontal lobes of the brain are relatively stunted. The Lemuroids have long tails which the mothers sometimes wrap around their young when in movement, for locomotion is usually of the four-footed type. Two or three offspring are brought forth at a single accouchement, at least in some species, and the lorises, at least, have a second pair of nipples in the groin which the infants, grasping the fur of the mothers' belly in an inverted position, hold in their mouths perhaps as "pacifiers," certainly to give additional support. The Lemuroid sub-order of the Primates includes two series of superfamilies: the Lemuriformes of Madagascar and the Mascarene Islands and the Lorisiformes of the African mainland and the Indonesian Islands. The Lemuriform series includes the families of lemurs proper, indrises, and daubentones. The Lorisiform series includes the families lorises and galagoes.

The *Tarsioids* superficially appear to be even less like men than the lemuroids, but in a number of structural details they show vaguely human traits. They are small rat-sized animals inhabiting the tropical forests of southeast Asia and Indonesia. The orbit of the eye is more manlike, with the eyeball lying in a partially formed bowl of bone. The eyes themselves face directly forward, although it is said that the axes of the actual bony orbits lie at an angle of 90 degrees to each other. The retina, however, is of the nocturnal type but differs from that of the lemuroid in possessing an area lateral to the entrance of the optic nerve which is thought to increase visual acuity.[5]

Stereoscopic vision seems to be doubtful in view of the fact that the two eyes are apparently incapable of coöperative movement, for lack of the necessary nervous mechanisms.[6] The occipital lobes of the brain, where the visual area of the cortex is located, are, however, relatively well developed and overhang the cerebellum, while the olfactory centers of the brain are reduced in size. One of the characteristic trends in primate evolution has been the progressive reduction of smelling equipment and progressive improvement of the seeing equipment. The tarsier normally maintains a semi-erect posture and uses its hands to convey food to the mouth. Thus it exhibits a certain specialization of function as regards the fore and hind limbs. These animals also have the unusual ability to rotate the head on the spinal column so that they can look behind them without having to turn the body, a feature which, perhaps regrettably, only a few talented human beings possess. The tarsiers, however, are not men. They differ in size, in furriness of coat, in possession of a long, sometimes partially hairless tail, primitive vision, poorer brain development, and so forth. They also show certain definite specializations for life in the trees, for the digits are equipped with sucker pads, the function of which is perhaps to enable these tiny animals to maintain their hold on tree branches too large to be grasped.

The *Pithecoids* include the true monkeys, apes, and man. They fall into two divisions: the New World monkeys (*Platyrrhini*: "nostrils widely spaced and directed outward"), and the Old World monkeys (*Catarrhini*: "nostrils narrowly spaced and directed downward"). All have eyes in true frontal position, stereoscopic vision, and relatively well-developed brains. A number of structural and functional differences indicate that the two divisions of the Pithecoids diverged from a common stem at an early date.

The *New World monkeys* are confined to the tropical forest regions of Central and South America and two families may be distinguished, the *Hapalidae* and the *Cebidae*. The *Hapalidae*, or marmosets, are small monkeys with furry covering and often with bushy tails. They have two or three young at a birth, their nails are clawlike except on the great toes, and they are unable to oppose their thumbs to the other digits. Usually they have an extra premolar tooth on each side, above and below. The *Cebidae* are also from Central and South America and are frequently seen in captivity, partly because they are the *only* Primates with prehensile, grasping tails, which are used for manipulating objects and for suspending the animals in trees. Only certain species of Cebidae are provided with this convenient appendage. Included in this family are capuchin monkeys, spider monkeys, howler monkeys, squirrel monkeys, and teetees. On the whole the New World monkeys are more primitive than the Old World Pithecoidea. They show weaker reactions to anti-human blood sera than Old World monkeys, and they are unable to inter-breed with the Old World group, perhaps because they have fifty-four chromosomes as compared with forty-eight, the number standard with all Old World Pithecoids from monkeys to man.[7]

The *Old World monkeys* or *Catarrhines* have the same number and kinds of teeth as man, flatter nails than in New World monkeys, and in various other structural and functional details show closer affinity to ourselves than do the New World Pithecoids. They may be grouped into two superfamilies: the Simian superfamily, or monkeys proper, and the Anthropoid superfamily including the apes and man. The Simian group contains one family, the *Cercopithecidae*, which is in turn divided into two subfamilies, the *Cercopithecinae* which have cheek pouches but no stomach pouches, large and brilliant callosities on the buttocks, and developed thumbs, and the *Colobinae* (or *Semnopithecinae*) which have sacculated stomachs but no cheek pouches as a rule, small ischial callosities, and thumbs small or absent. The *Ceropithecinae* include the macaques, the mandrills, baboons of the rocky hills of Arabia and Africa, Black Apes of Celebes, the mangabeys, the guenons of West and Central Africa, and the talapoin monkeys. The *Colobinae* include the langurs of Southeast Asia, the guerezas of Africa, the proboscis monkeys of Borneo, and the snub-nosed monkeys of Chinese Tibet.

In the anthropoid group of the Catarrhines are three families: *Hylobatidae* (gibbon and siamang), *Pongidae* (orang-utan, chimpanzee, gorilla), and *Hominidae* (extinct and living species of man).

The anthropoid group. All members of the anthropoid division resemble man more than any other members of the Primate order. For example, they are the only Primates without external tails. Cheek pouches are absent, the pelvis is laterally more expanded or widened out than in other Primates, and adaptation to semi-erect posture at least for short periods is common to all of them.

The *Hylobatidae* are the smallest of the anthropoids and comprise at least two genera, the gibbons (*Hylobates*) and the siamangs (*Symphylangus*); they differ chiefly in that the latter have large throat sacks, capable of inflation, and are in general body size somewhat larger than the gibbons. Perhaps twelve species of gibbons have been recognized and three of siamangs. The group is represented in southern China, the Malay Peninsula and Archipelago, and the Island of Hainan. The favorite habitat is in tropical but upland forests, ranging to an altitude of 5,000 feet. The animals are covered with fine wooly hair in contrast with the coarse hair of the other apes. Color may be white, gray, or black with combinations of these, and skin color is brown or black. The head is small and oval, with large orbits and well-marked supra-orbital ridges, but otherwise relatively smooth. The ears are comparatively large, but without lobes, and the nose is small, but somewhat more prominent than in other apes. The Yerkes rank the larynx second to that of the chimpanzee in resemblance to the human vocal mechanism.[8] Average weight of the adult male gibbon is about 13 pounds (6 kg.) and of the siamang about 24 pounds (11 kg.).[9]

Turning to the *Pongidae*, we find that the *orang-utan* is represented by a single species with several races all of which are confined to the lowland jungles of Borneo and Sumatra. The animal is relatively short and stocky in build, with a globular abdomen larger than the chest. Average height is about four feet and average weight about 158 pounds (72 kg.). The orang is covered with straight, long, coarse hair, light to dark reddish in color. The skin is usually brown, sometimes purplish or grayish. The skull is relatively high and pointed toward the rear, with prominent supra-orbital ridges, as well as a heavy transverse ridge across the back for the attachment of neck muscles and a crest running down the center. The ears are relatively small and without lobes. The nose is extremely flat and usually characterized by a small pointed flap of skin at the end. Laryngeal sacs are conspicuous and give a goiter-like appearance when inflated. The arm is very long, and the hand is long and slender with a diminutive thumb. The legs are short, while the foot is as flexible as the hand.

The gibbon and the orang are the most specialized of the apes for life in the trees. While the gibbon is agile and quick, the orang is, despite its slowness and caution, more confined to the trees than its smaller relative. When forced to the ground the gibbon stands erect and walks bipedally, more closely resembling man in this respect than any of the other apes. The orang, on the other hand, stands erect with the greatest difficulty and then only for short periods of time awkwardly on the outer edges of its flexed feet. When forced to move on the ground its natural position is quadrupedal, resting its weight on the outer edge of its foot and on the knuckles of its hand.

The *chimpanzee* is found in Equatorial Africa from the West Coast to the Belgian Congo, inhabiting the lowland and upland jungles and forests. It is possibly represented by at least two species, although some authorities name as many as eight. In build it is stocky, with well-developed chest and abdomen. Average stature is perhaps a little over four feet and average weight varies from 88 to 132 pounds.[10] The chimp is relatively sparsely covered with straight, coarse hair which may be black, grayish, or dark brown. Skin color is usually dark brown but may vary to a slaty gray. The head is elongated with heavy supra-orbital ridges but no central crest. The ears are large and prominent, occasionally with a small lobe. Nostrils are large and the nose is more conspicuous than in the orang, although less so than in the gorilla. Laryngeal sacs are present but inconspicuous and the voice box itself is most like that of man. The arm is longer than the leg, but the two are more nearly equal than in other apes. The hand is relatively broader than in the orang and gibbon and the thumb is better developed. The leg is short and bent as in the orang, but the foot is shorter and broader than in the orang or gibbon and also than the hand. The large toe is longer than the orang's.

The *gorilla* is the largest of the great apes, living in the Camaroons, Gaboon, and the Belgian Congo of tropical Africa. Two species or sub-species have been recognized, the lowland and highland, and a few possible races. The upland or mountain species (*Gorilla berengei*) lives up to altitudes of 10,000 feet. The gorilla is a massive animal with huge shoulders, barrel-like chest, broad back, and huge abdomen. Average height is about five feet, although six-foot adult males are not rare. Average weight, sex and species variations included, is about 300 pounds,[11] but the male mountain gorilla may exceed 400 pounds. The hair is coarse, black or grayish in color, and quite thick. The skin is black or dark brown. The skull is the largest among the apes and extremely craggy with enormous supra-orbital ridges, occipital and sagittal crests. The ears are small and inconspicuous with well-developed lobes. The hand is relatively shorter and broader than in the other apes and the arm long and heavy. The fingers are short and thick and the thumb large. The leg is larger than in other apes, but less developed than the arm. The foot is short and broad as in man. The gorilla moves about the trees, but spends more time on the ground than any of the other apes. It is slow and deliberate in its movements, except when angry. It stands erect and walks two-footedly more naturally than any other ape except the gibbon, but its usual method of locomotion on the ground is quad-rupedal. The bulk of the weight is borne on the sole of the foot, which is the most manlike ape foot, while the animal leans forward supporting its upper body on its knuckles.

The Hominidae. On morphological grounds as well as from the point of view of self-esteem, it is preferable to consider the human types as a separate family. At present, only one species of this family survives, namely, *Homo sapiens*, but in a later chapter we shall give some attention to various extinct species which have appeared and died out during the past million years. There is no question that the great apes as a group are more closely related to man than are any of the other Primates, but it is a somewhat moot question as to which of the apes is our closest relative. One may compare man with the ape trait for trait to answer this question, but the result of such comparisons depends somewhat upon the traits used and the weighting given to them. Thus Hooton [12] states that the chimpanzee shares ninety-eight traits with man, the gorilla eighty-seven, the gibbon eight-four, and the orang-utan fifty-six, while the Old World subanthropoid Catarrhines share only fifty-three traits with man. Schultz,[13] on the basis of comparison of fifty-seven anatomical and functional traits among the apes and man, gives the following tabulation:

NUMBER OF CHARACTERS OF CLOSEST RESEMBLANCE AMONG HIGHER PRIMATES

Number of Characters Regarding Which:	Man	Gorillas	Chimpan- zee	Orang- Utan	Hylo- batidae
Man most closely resembles	57	23	12	7	15
Gorilla most closely resembles	13	57	30	12	2
Chimpanzee most closely resembles .	4	28	57	15	10
Orang-utan most closely resembles ..	5	16	19	57	17
Hylobatidae most closely resemble ..	11	8	15	23	57
Number of characters showing highest degrees of specialization (total = 82)	27	17	6	16	16

Schultz comments:

These figures show chiefly the order in which the higher primates must be arranged according to their general resemblance, namely: man—gorilla—chimpanzee—orang-utan—*Hylobatidae*.... It is certainly not to be doubted any more that the gorillas and chimpanzees became phylogenetically divided *after* an independent branch for the orang-utan had appeared. That even the orang-utan diverged from an ancestral stock common to the great apes, *after* the separation of an evolutionary branch for man is the only admissible conclusion from the result...that the general, average differences between the three great apes are smaller and less significant than those between any of the latter and man."

Furthermore, the data show that man has carried out evolutionary specialization in twenty-seven characters as compared with only seventeen for his closest rival, the gorilla. Other data bearing upon man's relationships with the other Primates will be discussed in following sections.

STRUCTURAL CHARACTERISTICS OF PRIMATES AND MAN

In the preceding section we have dealt with the classification of the Primates and we now turn to a more detailed consideration of structural differences and similarities among the various species. Our object will be to illuminate the evolutionary changes within the Primate pattern which have eventuated in the present structure of man and which may determine to some extent his behavior. Necessarily we shall have space to deal with only a selected number of features.

Brain size. The general Primate tendency toward enlargement of the brain has been remarked. In man this tendency has gone to extremes. The average capacity of the adult male European skull is about 1,450 c.c., while that of the gorilla, the largest-brained of the apes, averages between 400 and 500 c.c. Although there are animals with larger brains than man (for example, elephants), in brain size *relative* to body weight man outshines most of the animal kingdom and also the other Primates, with a ratio of 1:40-60. The ratio of brain to body weight in the macaque, an animal typical of the unspecialized Catarrhine type, is 1:94 for males; in the gibbon, 1:61; in the siamang, 1:86; in the gorilla, 1:157 (on the basis of one male).[14] The general structure of the brain is similar in plan in all Primates, including the lemurs, and even the most primitive Primate brains have a cortex considerably more differentiated than those of other mammals of similar size.[15] The evolutionary changes in the manlike direction have involved increase in brain surface (cerebral cortex), its greater folding and convolution, and expansion of the visual, auditory, tactile, and motor functions of the cortex at the expense of the olfactory functions. Thus the brain of the lower Primates is "in its essential features and in its finer structure a simplified replica of the human brain."[16] From the functional point of view the evidence seems to indicate that as we go through the series toward man an increasing amount of the animal's behavior is controlled by the cortex rather than by lower brain or spinal centers. These matters have been studied by means of operations on monkeys and apes in which various portions of the cerebral cortex were removed. Relatively rapid and complete recovery of ability to move the legs after an operation on the cortex has been noted in monkeys, indicating that such movements are not under strong cortical control, but are mediated by lower centers in these animals. Similar operations show progressive decline in recovery, however, in the series baboon—gibbon—chimpanzee—man.[17] The sign of Babinski is an uncontrollable curling of the toes upward when the sole of the foot is stroked. It occurs, among humans, only in infants and in adults suffering lesions of the cerebral cortex, indicating that it is under cortical control in the normal human adult. This is not the case in the lower Primates, except in the ground-dwelling baboon. Zuckerman suggests that cortical dominance at least of motor limb responses may be correlated with terrestrial habit and modes of locomotion on the ground.[18] He also points out that the "known morphological differences in the essential structure of the brains of the Catarrhine group have not as yet been shown to have far-reaching significance in the problem of learning." [19] The significant advantage of man is apparently in his ability to use symbols.

Structural features of posture and locomotion. Three types of loco-motion and associated posture occur among the various species of Primates: quadrupedal (pronograde posture), bimanual (semi-upright or upright hanging posture), and bipedal (upright posture). Lemuroids and lower Pithecoids use quadrupedal locomotion for the most part; those species which live in the trees walk along the branches on all fours and spring with the help of all four limbs, while ground-dwelling species, such as baboons, walk on the ground on all fours. The *Hylobatidae* and the *Pongidae*, on the other hand, tend to be bimanual; they hang on branches from their hands, move along the branches overhand in a hanging position, and swing trapeze fashion. The legs are also used for support, in climbing, and in walking on branches or on the ground. When using the hind limbs for locomotion, however, the apes tend to be bipedal or semi-bipedal. In this connection, we have already remarked that the three larger apes partially support themselves in the semi-upright posture on the flexed knuckles of their hands. Lower Catarrhines, such as the macaque, gibbons, and man (particularly human infants), however, support their weight in quadrupedal position on the wrists and on the completely extended hand which is placed flat on the supporting surface. The orang-utan, chimpanzee, and gorilla are anatomically unable, because of shortness of the apposite muscles and ligaments, to extend the hand and the fingers at the same time, hence "walk on their knuckles".[20] This peculiarity of the three great apes may very well be a specialization to life in the trees; at least, the automatic flexure of the fingers when the hand is extended provides a never-failing grip when swinging about the branches.

Whether the support is from the two arms grasping a tree branch overhead (as is common for the apes) or from two feet planted firmly on the ground (as in man) the resulting tendency is to bring the body into an upright or orthograde posture perpendicular to the earth's surface and gravity pull. In describing characteristic stances of gibbons as observed in their native habitat, Carpenter observes that, "Whereas most animals have one normal position of arrested locomotion, gibbons have two. One position at rest is that of swinging from the branch of a tree. In this position the long arms act as supports and the trunk is dropped earthward while the legs are somewhat flexed. . . . Another position of rest is shown when a gibbon stands partially upright, supporting its weight on its feet and legs." [21] In short, this "orthogradizing" of the posture is a significant tendency of the great apes which has culminated in man in complete upright bipedal locomotion and posture.

SOME SKELETAL COMPARISONS BETWEEN THE ANTHROPOIDS

It is now generally agreed among students of human evolution, that man "came down out of the trees," in other words, that his ancestors were tree-dwelling Primates who either through chance mutations or environmental pressures took to living on the ground and developed through selection the structures adapting them to this type of life. This quite possibly took place during the early Pliocene period and may have been associated with extensive changes toward drier climatic conditions in certain parts of the Old World at that time. During the same period that the human stem was making this evolutionary experiment, the other apes (and some now extinct) were continuing their own separate ways of evolutionary development.[22] We may compare the end results as regards the skeleton in a cursory fashion to indicate how far man has differentiated.

The vertebral column. One of the most obvious and unique characteristics of the human vertebral column is its S-shape as viewed in profile from the side. The spine is curved forward in the small of the back (lumbar curve) and in the neck region (cervical curve) and it is curved backward in the region of the upper back (thoracic curve) and just above the buttocks (sacral curve). These curves give resiliency and permit the balancing of the weight of the body in an upright position without muscular strain by placing the center of gravity and mass vertical to the area covered by the feet. The most distinctively human of these curves is the lumbar curve which is present in no ape. The spine of the primitive pronograde animal is constructed so as to bend backward (or upward, in the pronograde position) like a bow, and the animal progresses in leaps and bounds by alternately arching and straightening its vertebral column. In the bipedal mode of locomotion, on the other hand, stability, rather than elasticity is the desideratum. One of the requirements of stability in the upright position is that the vertebral column be firmly attached to the pelvic girdle. As we come up the Primate series we note an increasing number of sacral vertebrae, those wedge-shaped, fused elements of the spine which articulate with the large bones of the pelvis. The average number in the macaque (lower Catarrhine monkey) is 3; in the gibbon, 4.4; in the orang-utan, 5.1; in the chimpanzee, 5.4; in the gorilla, 5.6; and in man, 5.2.[23] The greater attachment, however, of the spine to the pelvis in man is shown by comparative measurement of the sacral surface of the ilium (the area which actually joins the sacral vertebrae of the spine). In man the breadth of this surface is 12 per cent of the trunk height; in the macaque, 5; in the gibbon, 5; in the orang-utan and chimpanzee, 6; and in the gorilla, 8. Numerous other skeletal details could be cited to indicate the evolutionary changes in the human pelvis which give it stability and firm connection with the spinal column, changes associated with the mechanical requirements of upright posture.

The higher Primates are also distinguished by the suppression of the tail vertebrae. Although all the apes and man are devoid of external tails, they normally retain a few small, fused coccygeal vertebrae at the end of the spine. The average number of tail segments in the macaque is 17, in the gibbon, 2.7; in the orang-utan, 2.8; in the chimpanzee, 3.2; in the gorilla, 3; and in man, 4.2. Thus we see that taillessness has proceeded farther in the apes than in man. This condition is explained by Hooton with the observation that the tail muscles in man have spread out over the perineal floor like a hammock for the support of the viscera in the upright posture, a feature which has not occured in the apes and is not functionally required due to their semi-stooping stance.

While man, developing toward upright posture, has seen the lower part of his vertebral column more firmly knit to the pelvis and made more rugged, he has preserved and even extended the length of his neck. Schultz reports that in man the cervical region of the spine comprises 26 per cent of the height of the trunk; in macaques the neck is only 18 per cent of the trunk; in gibbons, 17; in orang-utans and highland gorillas, 24; and in the chimpanzee, 23.

The pelvis. The pelvic girdle is the means whereby the lower limbs are fixed to the trunk. It is directly articulated to the sacral portion of the spine and requires a certain stability in man because it must bear the stresses of the support of the whole body and because the excretory and genital organs require a firm framework. The primitive type of vertebrate pelvis is elongated in the same axis as the vertebral column. It is, as Hooton has expressed it, a sort of hollow bone tube with parts cut away, always having a greater length than breadth. Likewise, the dorso-ventral (back-to-front) diameter of the primitive, pronograde pelvis is always greater than the transverse (side-to-side) diameter. In the upright posture, however, the weight of head, trunk, and upper limbs rests upon the pelvis. It is desirable that a wider, more basin-like skeletal assembly be provided, and that is what has happened in man, probably through mutation and natural selection. The width of the human pelvis is practically always at least 6 per cent greater than is its sagittal diameter. The so-called "hip-bone," which reasonably slender people can usually feel on themselves, is a part of the pelvis called the ilium. The iliac plates in man are broad, laterally branching slabs of bone which help to support the viscera. Also, to their upper edges are attached some of the muscles which counteract side-sway in the trunk and assist in maintaining the upright posture. The quadrupedal animal has iliac bones which are long and narrow, extending headward along the back. Man possesses broad pelvic and broad iliac bones for the support and muscular balance of his body. The large apes are rather intermediate between the two conditions, although the gibbon is able to walk upright without an anthropoid type of pelvis because of its light body weight. The human tendency for the ilium to broaden out is shown by the fact that in men the breadth of the hip bone (ilium) averages 122 per cent of its height, whereas in the macaque breadth is only 42 per cent of height; in the gibbon, 46 per cent; in the chimpanzee, 60 per cent; in the orang, 72 per cent; and in the gorilla, 90 per cent. Breadth of the hips in man averages 58 per cent of trunk height, the same as for the lowland gorilla; in chimpanzee, 55 per cent, in orang-utan, 50 per cent; in gibbon, 43 per cent; and in the macaque, 33 per cent.

The pelvis tends to be broader in women than in men, and in the white race than in colored races.

Other changes in the pelvis concomitant with the development of upright posture include the following: The structure has not only been widened, but also lengthened antero-posteriorly, a feature which provides increased leverage on the thigh bone (femur). The human pelvis is rotated or tilted forward and downward as compared with its position in other Primates, so that the upper opening lies at a 50- to 60-degree angle with the horizontal, and the genital organs lie under the sub-pubic arch. Likewise, the socket for the hip bone (acetabulum), as a result of this rotation, lies in the same verticle plane as the vertebral column.

The leg. Man's leg is greatly hypertrophied and overgrown in comparison with that of other Primates. In the monkeys and apes living an arboreal life the evolutionary line has led to the over-development of the arms as compared with the legs, and this is especially true of the apes as illustrated by the following figures from Schultz. The average total upper limb length expressed as a percentage of the lower limb length is 111 for macaques, 162 for gibbons, 172 for siamangs, 170 for orang-utans, 137 for chimpanzees, 137-140 for gorillas, but man's arms are only 88 per cent the length of his legs. A good part of the comparatively greater length of the human leg is in the upper segment, skeletally the thigh-bone or femur, which is proportionately longer and slenderer in man. The thickness of the thigh-bone in the three larger apes averages between 32 and 34 per cent of the length, but in *Homo sapiens* between 18 and 20 per cent, although certain extinct species of

man approach more closely the ape condition. A distinctively human
feature of the femur is the *linea aspera,* a sharp ridge which runs up the
back of the thigh bone. This bony ridge is the insertion of the quadri-
ceps extensor femoris, a muscle which is involved in supporting the
femur in an upright position. Apes are devoid of this feature.

Two-footed walking is accomplished with the aid of enlarged calf
muscles which in man are enormously larger than in any other Primate,
and this condition is reflected in the hypertrophy of the fibula (the
smaller bone of the lower leg to which some of the calf muscles are
attached), which is proportionately larger in man than in any other
Primate.

The foot. The lowly human foot, which seldom comes into view or
receives flattering attention in civilized life, is actually one of the most
distinctively human features of man's body. The flexible hand-like foot
of the typical Primate has been replaced in man by a relatively solid,
stable organ adapted to supporting the whole body weight on a flat
surface. The great toe is not opposable, but lies firmly and flatly on the
supporting surface parallel to the other toes. The bones of the middle
foot (metatarsus) have developed into heavy wedges intricately fitted
together to provide both resiliency and stability, and they are arched
both transversely and antero-posteriorly. The heel bone is elongated
posteriorly so that the lifting muscles used in walking operate on a
greater leverage than in a climbing Primate foot. The large toe's increase
in relative length and its straight, non-divergent position also contribute
to the leverage mechanics of the foot: the fulcrum is in the ankle and the
line of leverage runs between the great and second toes. The other four
toes, on the other hand, have degenerated to the point where it often
appears that their only function is the growing of corns. Among the
apes, the gorilla has the most manlike foot, although it is still predominately apelike in character. The increased importance of the great
toe in bipedal locomotion is shown by comparing the distance from
heel to point of great toe in terms of length of the body trunk. In man
the average distance from heel to the end of the great toe is 48 per cent
of the trunk length; in the macaque and the orang-utan, 31; in the
gibbon, 47; in the chimpanzee, 46; and in the gorilla, 44. In all of the
apes the third toe is longest. If the phalanges of the third toe are measured
and compared to trunk length, they amount to only 8 per cent of the
trunk length in man; but 27 per cent in the orang-utan; 23 per cent in
the gibbon; 20 per cent in the saimang; 18 per cent in gorilla and chimpanzee; and 15 per cent in the macaque. If the length of the tarsus (the foot
without the toe bones) is expressed in terms of trunk length, we find that
man has proportionately the longest tarsus of the Catarrhine division;

it is 23 per cent of the length of his trunk; in the gorilla, 21 per cent; in the chimpanzee, 18; in the orang-utan, 16; in the gibbon, 15; and in the macaque, 12. We thus see that in the human foot the great toe has increased at the expense of the other four; the anthropoid prominence of the third toe has disappeared; and the middle portion of the foot, which contains the arches, has increased in relative length and stability.

The chest. The wide, shallow chest is a characteristic human feature. often more admired in the breach than in actuality. The thorax of the pronograde animal is deep and bowed out ventrally; the contents of the cavity depend downward against the ventral wall, but as animals tend toward a more upright posture, the condition changes. In the macaque, the chest breadth is only 87 per cent of its depth; in the apes and man, however, the chest is always wider than it is deep; in the gibbon, chest breadth is 118 per cent of depth; in the orang-utan, 126 per cent; in the chimpanzee and man, 129 per cent; and in the gorilla, 125 (lowland species) to 146 (highland species). Diaphragmatic breathing tends to replace external muscular expansion of the chest in man. Muscular attachments of the ribs still retain some of their pronograde configuration, however, as is evidenced in ourselves by the fact that when we are out of breath and desperately in need of expanding the lungs we bend forward in the quadrupedal position. Although man has proportionately as broad a chest as any of the Primates (except possibly the highland gorilla), the rib cage is not as large, body size considered, as in some of the apes. Thus the chest girth in man averages 162 per cent of the trunk height, while in the lowland gorilla it is 223 per cent; in the orang, 185 per cent; in the chimpanzee, 176 per cent; in the gibbon, 149 per cent; and in the macaque only 103 per cent. To some extent these figures reflect the compact, stocky trunk of the larger apes, as compared with the more elongated human trunk. In lower primates eight or nine pairs of ribs are attached to the sternum (breast-bone), whereas the usual number in man is seven, a fact which indicates an evolutionary shortening of the rib cage in man.

Shoulder girdle and arms. The clavicle, or collar-bone, is characteristically well developed in all Primates and seems to be adaptively correlated with brachiation in the trees; it serves as a strut to hold the shoulder out from the side of the body so that the arm can be rotated above the head for grasping branches. The scapula ("shoulder-blade") in man has developed certain distinctive features apparently correlated with decreased brachiating ability. The glenoid fossa, where the head of the arm-bone articulates, tends to be parallel to the spinal column in man, but faces anteriorly in apes, a difference mechanically correlated with the difference between normally swinging the arms at the side versus swinging the body by the arms from an overhead support. The part of the scapula blade above its spine (supra-spinous fossa) is only 48 per cent of the lower part (infra-spinous fossa) in man, but 97 per cent in gorillas and 148 per cent in gibbons. In man the spine tends to lie perpendicular to the main axis of the body (90 degrees), whereas in apes the angle is more acute (32 degrees in the gibbon). In general the blade of the scapula in man averages 67 per cent of trunk height, 65 in highland gorilla, 59 in the orang, 57 in the chimpanzee, 53 in the gibbon, and 35 in the macaque.

The bone of the upper arm (humerus) also shows distinctive human qualities. We have already remarked that man's arm is proportionately shorter than his leg, whereas the reverse is true of other great apes, whose arms are relatively enormous in length and strength. Arm length in proportion to trunk height is lowest in man of all the great apes; man's arm is 150 per cent of his trunk length; but in the gibbon, the arm is 238 per cent of trunk length; in the lowland gorilla, 184 per cent; in the orang-utan, 182 per cent; and in the chimpanzee, 175 per cent. The macaque has arms only 107 per cent of trunk length. The decrease in robustness of the upper arm as compared with the leg in man is shown by comparing the size of the head of the humerus with the head of the femur. In man the diameter of the humeral head is only 90 per cent of the diameter of the femoral head; in the gorilla, 125 percent; in the chimpanzee and siamang, 119 per cent; in the orang-utan, 117 per cent; in the gibbon, 113 per cent; and in the macaque, 102 per cent. The humeral head is eliptical in shape in man, but bullet-shaped in apes, while the cross-section of the shaft is prismatic in man, and round or oval in apes.

In apes the forearm is proportionately longer than it is in man, a feature associated with brachiation. In man the forearm length is only 77 per cent of the upper arm length, whereas in the gibbon it is 113 per cent; according to Schultz' figures, the lowland gorilla approaches most closely to man, with a forearm length 78 per cent of that of the upper arm; it is 83 per cent in the highland gorilla, 90 per cent in the chimpanzee, 101 per cent in the orang-utan, and 97 per cent in the macaque.

The function of the arm in brachiation may perhaps be grasped from Carpenter's description of the gibbon in the wild state.

...Imagine a gibbon seated at the base of a horizontal branch three inches in diameter but flexible and twenty feet in length. How does the gibbon travel in brachiating over this branch? ... The gibbon will rise slightly from the seated position and as it begins dropping to one side or other of the branch, it also moves forward and extends the hand and arm nearest the branch. The graceful and smooth downward glide of the animal's body is checked as the limb is grasped by the fingers. The first contact is made and a fulcrum is established for the first semi-cycle of the swing. The radius of the arc thus formed is equal to about two-thirds the length of the gibbon's arm. The forward movement is accelerated by the momentum of the downward swing and by the contraction of the group of arm muscles which bend the arm and bring the animal higher and somewhat closer to the limb. Next, the other hand and arm are brought up and forward to make a second contact with the branch at a point three or four feet beyond the point of the first grasp. The movement of this arm involves rotation at the shoulder to a high degree, perhaps to a degree normally impossible for man. The hand goes up at a sharp angle to the branch as the body of the gibbon is rising. The second grasp may not be completed until an instant after the first hand has released its hold. There is a brief period between each semi-cycle of a swing in fast locomotion, during which the gibbon glides *without actual support*. After the second contact, the animal is pulled forward by flexion of the arm and by the continued momentum.[24]

A normal part of the gibbon locomotion is that of jumping (with the arms).... Typically, jumps for short and average distances (up to twelve and fifteen feet) are made smoothly and without hesitation and almost as a part of the normal *swing*. Accumulating momentum, the ape releases its hold, throws itself through space and, after a gliding downward course in the air, grasps the opposing branch on the other side of the space.... Long jumps are usually made outward and downward with a considerable gliding quality about them. The direction of the body is usually that of an arc, the highest part of which is higher than the point on the branch from which the animal took off; i.e., the animal first swings upward then glides downward.[25]

The hand. In arboreal trapeze work, such as that of the gibbon, a long, narrow hand with strong fingers is a specialized adaptation. In the gibbon the hand breadth is only 24 per cent of its length, whereas in man it is 41 per cent. Man's hand is proportionately broader than that of other Catarrhines, with the exception of the gorilla. The generalized adaptability of the human hand for manipulating all kinds of objects is aided by the proportionately larger thumb. In man, length of the thumb is 68 per cent of the length of the hand; the poorly developed thumb of the orang-utan is only 44 per cent of the hand length; in the chimpanzee the figure is 47 per cent; in the gibbon, 54 per cent; and in the macaque, 56 per cent.

The complete opposability of the human thumb to each of the other four fingers and the flexibility of the human hand in general are prerequisites to much of human cultural activity. In the finer grasping movements, the great apes, perhaps because of the incomplete emancipation of their forelimbs, are less skilful. Wood Jones has pointed out that mere anatomical arrangement for opposability of the digits is not confined to Primates, but is found in certain arboreal Marsupials, phalangers, the chameleon, in some parrots, arboreal mice such as *Mus margarettoe*, and in the Koala (*Phascolarctus*) of Australia.[26] For the hand to attain the importance it does in human life it must be "emancipated" from responsibility for locomotion or support, an emancipation which is stimulated by conditions of arboreal life, but which reaches its culmination only in ground-dwelling upright posture and locomotion.

Gesell and Halverson have investigated the development of thumb opposition in the human child, and discover that perfected opposition of the thumb pad to the pads of the other four fingers is not structurally possible until about the thirty-second week of life at the earliest. The child goes through five periods of hand response in grasping: (1) fingers used primarily and thumb not pivoted around into opposing position (birth to 16 weeks); (2) thumb pivots but does not oppose other fingers, merely adducts (stage reached between 16 and 28 weeks); (3) mesial opposition in which the sides of the thumb and first finger come together for picking up an object (reached also between 16 and 28 weeks); (4) mesio-volar opposition, in which the pad of the thumb opposes the side of the first finger (24 to 36 weeks); and (5) full volar opposition (32 to 52 weeks).[27] Certain short-thumbed primates, for example, the orangutan, apparently never get beyond the fourth stage.

The os centrale is a small bone in the wrist which appears as a separate bone in all lower Primates. In man it is fused with the navicular bone during the third fetal month and never appears separately after birth except as an anomaly. In other apes the os centrale is usually a separate bone until old age, except in the chimpanzee in which fusion takes place during fetal or infantile life. The function of this bone is not clear.

The skull. The distinctively human features of man's skull involve primarily the comparative increase in the size of the brain case and the decrease in the size of the facial skeleton and jaws as compared with those of the apes. We have mentioned previously the great absolute and relative increase in the size of the human brain as compared with those of other Primates. A glance at comparative specimens will convey some idea of the diminutive size and fragile construction of the human facial skeleton as compared with that of the great apes. Although the olfactory part of the brain seems to have been the first to develop among vertebrates, there has been a tendency in Primates for it to shrink in size and importance. This is not wholly unconnected with the emancipation of the forelimbs, the decreased interorbital space, with eyes in the frontal plane, and the resulting ability of man to explore his universe by sight and by hand rather than by smell and by snout.[28] The advantages are numerous. As Stella Benson remarks, in another connection, "A smell casts no shadow before; dogs, therefore, who are led through life by the nose, have to be intensely conservative. They can tolerate no new departures because they know no destinations." [29] The recession of the snout in man has apparently carried in its train a decrease in size of teeth and a tendency toward a curtailment in their number (through tendency to suppress the third molars, or "wisdom teeth"). But the collapsing face has left standing the prominent nasal structure and the chin. The canine teeth which are elongated and interlocking in all apes, normally are level with the other teeth in man, a feature which makes man a less dangerous adversary in a biting match. Just in front of the socket on the skull into which the lower jaw fits is a small eminence called the glenoid tubercle, absent in apes, which plays an important mechanical rôle in the human chewing pattern. In human munching the coronoid process of the lower jaw is dragged out of its socket alternately on each side and onto the glenoid tubercle, thus setting the lower jaw awry, as it were, and permitting the lower grinding teeth to be dragged across the upper.

The skull of man is balanced nicely on the end of the spinal column and the neck lacks the heavy muscles required in apes to overbalance the heavy protruding snout. In man there are no heavy, high-placed ridges for the insertion of these muscles on the back of the head. In fact, the brain case of modern man is distinguished for its smoothness. In the gorilla, on the other hand, a heavy sagittal torus, or ridge, runs down the crest of the skull and to it are anchored the temporal muscles which activate the huge lower jaws. In the three larger apes these muscles cover the sides of the head almost completely. In the orang-utan the temporal muscles weigh 300 grams as compared to 20 grams in man, and the insertions in man reach only half way up the side of the skull. All apes have heavy overhanging brow ridges compared to those in man, although there is considerable variation among the races of the present species.

The foramen magnum is the hole in the bottom of the skull through which the spinal cord passes to the brain. The borders of the foramen magnum articulate with the first segment of the spinal column. In man the foramen is far under the head and the plane of the opening is tilted upward and forward; in lower Primates the head is hung from the end of the column to a greater or less degree, and the foramen magnum is correspondingly farther rearward and tilted downward and backward.

The mastoid process is a nobbin of bone behind each ear to which are attached balancing muscles of the neck (sternocleido-mastoideus) which are used to turn the human head from side to side. This feature is little developed among Primates, until we come to the gorilla. What man lacks in craggy occipital ridges for the attachment of heavy supporting muscles, he compensates for with mastoid processes and the attached muscles for movement of his balanced skull.

The protrusion of the snout (prognathism) is measured by the facial angle. The closer the angle approaches 90 degrees, the straighter (less prognathous) is the facial profile. This angle is 41 to 48 in the orang-utan, the most prognathous of the great apes, 55 to 58 in the gorilla, 55 in the gibbon, 56 in the chimpanzee, 66 in the cebus (New World) monkeys, and 73 in the marmoset. In man the angle varies in different groups between averages of 77 and 101 degrees. Thus we see that the least snouty of the other Primates is more prognathous than the most snouty of modern men and that extreme snoutiness is a specialty of the great apes (also the dog-faced baboons) among the Pithecoids.

The nasal bones in man are much shorter than in the great apes, a feature perhaps correlated with the reduction in height of the jaws. The bones are narrow and splint-like in the apes and tend to be pinched at the root. They lie flat and thus produce no noticeable bridge, with the exception of a rudiment in the gorilla. The bridged nose is, among the Anthropoids, a distinctive human feature. The suture between the two nasal bones rarely fuses in man even in old age, but in the macaque it is obliterated during fetal life, while obliteration occurs in the Hylobatidae, orang-utan, and chimpanzee in juvenile life soon after the eruption of the first molar tooth. In the gorilla fusion usually takes place during juvenile life, but sometimes not until subadulthood. The nasal aperture in man is always higher than it is wide, although in some monkeys the breadth equals the height. In the apes the lower borders of the nasal opening fade into the alveolar slope rather than forming a well-marked border as in man, and the spine of the human nasal septum is represented only by rudimentary tubercles in the ape. All in all, the relative size, structure, and shape of the human nose, racial differences included, is distinctive in detail among Primates.

As we have noticed, the lemurs lack a closed bony eye orbit, but as we come up the Primate series an increasing closure of the posterior wall is observed beginning with the tarsioids, concomitant with the frontal position of the eyes. The relative amount of space occupied by the orbits in the skull is shown by the following figures. In male Europeans the cranial capacity is 27.4 times the combined capacity of the two orbits while in the great apes the brain is only 5 to 6 times the size of the orbits.

The human palate is usually V- or U-shaped, but in the great apes, the greatest width is between the canine teeth. The lower jaw of man is widely sprung, particularly toward the rear end, while in the apes the two sides tend to be parallel. In man the "inside of the chin" is free and open, except for two small tubercles to which are attached tongue muscles; in apes a plate of bone, called the simian plate, lies across the angle of the chin and extends backward a short distance. Despite these hindrances to free movement of the tongue in the apes, it is probable that they could articulate words in a crude way if they had the neural organization necessary to speech; yet the lighter construction and greater roominess of the human jaw is not to be overlooked in connection with human speech ability.

The great size of the human brain is reflected in the size of the parietal bones, which form the sides of the skull vault. The median border of the parietal border in man averages 126 mm. in length, whereas the apes' range between 21 and 71 mm.

The mastoid process already mentioned is a functional feature which sometimes causes trouble when infected (mastoiditis). The frontal sinuses, hollow spaces in the forehead bone, are another, somewhat less functional, source of occasional trouble. Frontal sinuses occur only in man and the three larger apes, being absent in the gibbon and the lower Primates.

One final comparison, reflecting the increased size of the skull relative to the rest of the body in man, will suffice. The average diameter of the head in man is reported as 30 per cent of the trunk height, but only 21 per cent of trunk height in the macaque, 26 per cent in the *Hylobatidae* and the chimpanzee, 28 per cent in the orang-utan, and 22 to 29 per cent in the gorilla. Thus, even with their enormous supra-orbital ridges and cranial crests, the great apes do not equal man in relative size of the skull.

CHAPTER 3

The Primate Patterns:
Organic Structures and Functional Comparisons

Blood. Certain characteristics of the blood of men and apes show similarities which seem to indicate phylogenetic relationship. For example, the four blood groups of man occur also in the *Hylobatidae* and the *Pongidae*. Old World monkeys show no reactions to blood-group tests, but certain New World monkeys and lemurs have shown reaction to agglutinogens related to the B type. On the basis of blood types, then, it would appear that man and the apes are sharply differentiated from the Old World monkeys. Zuckerman remarks that "the fact of the anthropoid blood groups is of equal importance phyletically with the fact that man and the apes are among the very few mammals known to be incapable of carrying the oxidation of purine bases as far as allantoin. This metabolic process is possible for the 'monkey,' whereas in man, the chimpanzee, and the orang the process of purine metabolism ends with uric acid."[30] Tests of Primate blood sera, measuring the amount of precipitate resulting from mixtures, have repeatedly demonstrated that a wide gap in respect to this criterion exists between Lemuroids and Tarsioids on the one hand and the Pithecoids on the other. Rabbits are immunized against monkey, ape, and human sera in order to produce anti-sera in the rabbit blood. The anti-monkey, anti-ape, or anti-human sera thus obtained is then tested with the sera of other Primates to see what precipitin reactions result. While lemurs fail to give any positive reaction other than those produced in other mammals, the human affinities of the other Primates become closer as one passes from the New World monkeys to those of the Old World and from the latter to apes.[31] Other types of blood tests have indicated much the same things.

Diseases and parasites. The incidence of diseases throughout the animal kingdom has not yet been completely studied. The available evidence seems to show, however, that those Primates regarded as most closely related to man show symptoms most like those in man. For example, syphilis may infect monkeys, but produces manlike symptoms only in the larger apes. The same is true of yellow fever and malaria.

49

Chimpanzees show more or less human reactions to the following diseases, at least, a fact which is of considerable value in experimental medicine: syphilis, typhoid fever, cholera, bacillic and amoebic dysentery, typhus, yellow fever, poliomyelitus (infantile paralysis), plague, measles, scarlet fever, small pox, trachoma, pneumonia, grippe, trypanosomiasis, leishmaniosis, bilharziosis, and malaria.[32] -

A single, distinct family of lice (*Pediculus*) is restricted to the Primates, including man.[33] For what it is worth, man may console himself in his lousiness, when present, with the thought that this, too, is chargeable to his Primate ancestry, as well as to his individual lack of cleanliness. What evidence is available seems to indicate that certain pin worms occurring in the intestinal track of man are most closely related to intestinal worms of apes and less so to those of monkeys.[34] Further investigations may indicate still more far-reaching similarities between man and other Primates with respect to diseases and parasites.

Reproduction. Man shares the tendency to breed throughout the year with all other Primates, except the African and Mascarene lemurs (but including at least the slow loris among the Asiatic lemurs). Among certain of the Pithecoids, in contrast to man and other Pithecoids, the female is more receptive during certain phases of the monthly cycle than in others. This is apparently true of chimpanzees and gorillas, for example, whereas the gibbon and orang-utan females are said to be receptive at all times. Even the Tarsioids apparently bring forth young throughout the year. Menstruation is characteristic of the Catarrhine division from monkey to man. Until recently it was thought that this phenomenon did not occur in the New World monkeys, but it has now been reliably reported in at least two species of the *Cebidae*.[35] The evidence is not clear with respect to Tarsius, and menstruation seems to be unknown in the lemurs. In the macaque, as in man, the average duration of the complete cycle is twenty-eight days,[36] in the orang-utan the average cycle is 32 days,[37] in the chimpanzee 35-36 days.[38] The gibbon possibly has a cycle of 27 days.[39] A record has been published on eight complete cycles observed in a single lowland gorilla, with an average of 43 days, with the possibility that 39 days may represent the true cycle of this species.[40] Zuckerman points out that in menstruating Primates a non-menstrual period usually follows parturition, and menstruation ordinarily ceases during pregnancy.[41]

Continuous breeding and menstruation, also characteristic of man, are thus seen to be very widespread and presumably ancient characteristics of the higher Primates and they have had a determining influence upon certain aspects of human sexual and family behavior.

In several features of reproductive structure and function, however, man differs from some of the higher Primates. Thus, for example, a penis bone is generally present in the males of all species of the Catarrhine division, absent only in man. Among some species of the Catarrhine division occurs the phenomenon of the so-called sexual skin of females which reddens and swells usually during the first part of the menstrual cycle and subsides after ovulation has taken place, serving as a sort of sign, as it were, of the most fertile period of the cycle. This phenomenon has not been observed among the Platyrrhini and shows a somewhat uneven distribution among the Catarrhines. It occurs in macaques, but not in the *Colobinae* subfamily of the Old World monkeys. Among apes, it is absent in the gibbon, siamang, and orang-utan and has been reported only in the chimpanzee and gorilla. It is, of course, absent in man.[42] Yerkes has reported that in the chimpanzee, sex activity occurs most frequently during the postmenstrual swelling period.[43] It has been demonstrated that this visible response of certain cutaneous and epithelial areas is activated by the ebb and flow of estrin hormone in the blood, produced by the female reproductive organs in certain phases of the menstrual cycle. In man such visible response has been lost, but congestion and swelling of the nasal membranes appears in many women both premenstrually and in pregnancy. This reaction can be induced by injections of estrin,[44] and thus would appear to be the human vestige of Primate sexual skin.

In general we see that the reproductive and sexual activity of the higher Primates (Pithecoidea), and particularly of the Catarrhine division is somewhat distinctive as compared with other animals. In the absence of a yearly or semiannual rutting season, mating takes place frequently and apparently for pleasure as well as for reproduction. Situations suitable for sexual activity are far more varied and numerous for these animals than for other mammals. Homosexuality is relatively frequent and "normal", and weak males in certain species have been observed to assume a copulatory position when attacked by a stronger aggressor, apparently as a means of placation. Sexual solicitation has been observed to be used as a lure by males, followed by attack when the victim approaches. All Primates are notorious masturbators in captivity, which indicates a fairly constant level of sex drive.[45] In sum, sex drive is strong and constant, and serves other functions in addition to reproduction. These features which are shared by man are thus seen to be a part of his Primate background.

Rape has not been observed in infra-human Primates, possibly because copulation requires more coöperation from the female than in man. Copulatory position is usually dorso-ventral, except that the ventro-ventral position is occasionally used by apes. Giving birth requires more strain and exertion than in lower animals; delivery is usually in the crouching position and the placenta is often partially eaten by the mother.[46]

Maternal behavior is perhaps best known for the chimpanzee through the long continued studies of Yerkes and his students. On June 26, 1933, a twenty-year-old chimpanzee mother gave birth to twins, a male and a female; they were prematurely born and consequently small, under-nourished, and weak, but healthy. At present writing they are both flourishing. On the basis of study of sixteen confinements, it is reported that the gestation period in the chimpanzee ranged from 216 to 261 days, with an average of 236. Labor was short, often only one hour, and vertex presentation occurred in all cases. The tests commonly used for determining pregnancy in women are unreliable for the chimpanzee, probably due to difference in endocrine factors involved.[47] The mother chimpanzee usually cleans, grooms, and cares for her infant from the first. She actively exercises the babe in the early weeks and encourages it in creeping, standing, walking, and climbing. During the first three to six months she usually carries the infant against her abdomen, supported in her arms; after this period it learns to cling to her arm, leg, or back and is encouraged to take solid food. First mothers show a good deal of inefficiency as compared with those who have had previous infants, indicating that maternal behavior is to some extent learned, rather than being wholly "instinctive."[48]

The way in which the young are carried has been shown to have considerable influence on adult behavior among human groups, and may likewise be significant among primates. The Lemuroids carry the young in a horizontal position across the lower abdomen, and later on the back. The mother does not handle the young, and the males take no interest in them. The lorises have inguinal false nipples and the young rides with its head toward the mother's pelvis. Among the Tarsioids the infant hangs to its mother's fur without being handled by her. The New World monkey mother carries the baby on her back with its head toward her head and rarely handles it. Among the Hapalidae the fathers in some species carry the infant from birth, delivering it to the mother only for nursing. Among the Catarrhines, however, the baby is usually carried on the mother's belly and often supported by at least one of her hands. Even monkeys, among the Catarrhines, show a deal of maternal solicitude. The mother controls the infant's first walking, grooms it assiduously, and when it is larger carries it about on her back. Among the apes even more maternal care is normally manifested.

In this connection it should be remarked that the human adult female is the only Primate with permanently distended breasts. The human nipples are more widely set and lower on the trunk than in other Primates, features which are probably correlated with upright posture.

In general, the new-born Pithecoid is helpless at birth, except for its ability in some species of monkeys to cling to its mother's fur without other support. Mother Catarrhine monkeys and apes must carry the child in their arms for some time after birth, and this close bodily contact between infant and mother which is characteristic of all Catarrhines is significant in connection with their gregarious propensities in adult life. Almost all Pithecoid Primates prefer social life, and they are conditioned to association with others from birth, in part at least, due to the conditions of reproduction and infancy. This Primate infancy pattern is characteristic of human beings, although more elaborate and varied.

Much of the comparative difficulty in giving birth among human females is due to pelvic adaptations already discussed, associated with the upright posture. In the human pelvis a not entirely adequate compromise has been reached between the functions of bodily support, balance, and child-bearing. Another factor is the large size of the human infant at birth, particularly the skull. Although the human is not the largest of the great apes, it brings forth the largest infant at birth; thus, the average new-born human infant weighs 3,200 grams (about 7 lbs.), whereas the gorilla new-born averages 1,800 grams, the chimpanzee 1,600, the orang-utan 1,500. The new-born human is one twenty-third the weight of the adult (av. 75,000 g.), the chimpanzee infant is one twenty-eighth the weight of the adult (av. 45,000 g.), the orang-utan infant is one forty-eighth the weight of the adult (av. 72,000 g.), and in the gorilla the ratio is 1:111 (adult av. 200,000 g.).[49] Gibbons (ratio, 1:16) langurs (1:22), and macaques (1:21) on the other hand bring forth proportionately larger babies than man, but, as we have seen, none of them have to contend with the anthropoid type of pelvis, partially developed in the three large apes and fully developed in man.

Growth. Despite its large size at birth the human new-born is premature, in comparison with other new-born Primates. Schultz remarks that ". . . of the entire period of growth, from conception to completed eruption of the permanent dentition, 6.2 per cent represent intrauterine life in the macaque, 5.6 per cent in the chimpanzee, and only 3.5 per cent in man. In other words, in relation to the total duration of growth man is born much more early than the chimpanzee or macaque. . . . The author has . . . demonstrated that at birth man is very much less advanced in his ossification than the macaque."[50]

The duration of pregnancy in man is longer than in any other Primate except the orang-utan. The average for man is 266 days, for the orang 275 days, chimpanzee 236 days, gibbon 209 days, lower Catarrhines 150 to 180 days (166 for macaque), marmosets 150 days, and lemurs 145 days.[51] Obviously, the duration of gestation in apes is closer to that of man. After birth man matures more slowly than the other primates. The eruption of teeth is a reliable sign of maturation, and in man, on the average, the first milk teeth begin to appear at 6.5 months of age, in the orang-utan at 4.5 months, in the chimpanzee at 2.8 months, in the gibbon at 0.9 month, and in the macaque at 0.7 month. In man the average age at which the individual has all of his permanent teeth is 19.9 years; records are lacking for the orang-utan, gorilla, and gibbon, but in the chimpanzee this process is completed at 10.9 years and in the macaque at 6.8 years. Grether and Yerkes report that in the chimpanzee little further growth occurs in the male after 10 years of age and in the female after 9 years of age.[52] First menstruation occurs at from 7 years 4 months to 10 years and 2 months. Measured by rapidity of growth, the chimpanzee matures at about twice the rate of man.

The Yerkes point up the slow individual development of man by the following comparative facts. The lemur at birth is relatively very large, mature, and with functional senses. It is completely dependent upon the mother for only a few hours or days, and learns to walk within the first week. It is suckled for a few weeks and at the end of this short time is capable of social independence. Sexual maturity is reached within a year. The monkey, on the average, is also relatively mature at birth with well-developed senses. It is dependent upon the mother for a few days or weeks, learns to walk within the first month, is suckled for a month or so, is capable of independence within 2 to 4 months, and reaches sexual maturity within 3 years. The ape is relatively small and helpless at birth with senses only partially functional, is completely dependent on the mother for 3 to 6 months, learns to walk within 6 months, is suckled for several months, is sexually mature in 8 to 12 years. Man is also helpless, small and without developed sense function at birth; he is completely dependent for at least a year, and does not learn to walk for about 12 months after birth. The human is suckled for 1 to 2 years and cannot go about by himself safely until aged 6 to 8. Sexual maturity is not reached until 10 to 16 years.[53]

The Primates as a group are a long-lived brood. As Zuckerman says, "in spite of the limitations of the data, comparison with the records for other orders of mammals shows . . . that the Primates are among the longest-lived mammals. . . . Even when records relating to man are excluded, it is found that the Primates, *for their size*, form the longest-lived order of mammals. In the lemurs, the sexes seem to enjoy an equal longevity, but among monkeys, as in man, females seem on the average to live longer than do males." [54] Among the Primates, it appears that man is the longest lived. A few baboons and mandrills are on record which have lived in captivity for as much as 46 years. Yerkes estimates the full term of life for gibbon and siamang as 20 to 30 years, and for the three larger apes as 40 to 60 years.

It thus appears that man's slow maturity and comparatively long span of life is merely an exaggeration of a general pattern common to the higher Primates.

Body covering. Man is sometimes called "the hairless ape." Relative glabrosity, however, he shares with the *Pongidae*. Platyrrhine monkeys and the gibbon have the greatest hair density, apes and man the least. The average number of hairs per square centimeter on the human head exceeds that of the apes, but the apes of course outstrip the hairiest humans in amount of body hair, as a general rule. Men of hairy races may have more hair on the chest than does the gorilla, but no races are generally as hirsute as their Primate cousins.

NUMBER OF HAIRS PER SQUARE CENTIMETER OF SKIN IN ADULTS [55]

	Scalp	Back	Chest
Macaque	910	886	172
Gibbon	2,035	1,727	499
Siamang	718	429	251
Orang-utan	158	176	107
Chimpanzee	112	48	21
Gorilla, highland	440	127	5
Man	312	0	1

Only in the orang-utan does long hair occur, comparable to the length of human head hair. The orang is likewise the only great ape which grows a beard.

Skin and eye colors of all apes are brunet. Eyes are brownish in all Primates, except in some races of men, but light skin color occurs in some monkeys, for example the rhesus monkey, whose skin is as light as a blond human being's.

The relative hairlessness of man is, of course, one of the biological conditions of human culture. It renders him more susceptible to stimuli which arouse drives of pain and temperature; and no human group fails to make cultural responses to these drive-arousing stimuli.

The Catarrhine Primates in general are characterized by horny areas on the buttocks known as ischial callosities. In the macaque they are always present and appear early in life; in the gibbon they are always present but are small and appear late. In the orang-utan and gorilla they occur but rarely and are not really horny, but in chimpanzees they are present in 38 per cent of reported cases. As Schultz says, "in man alone have callosities never been discovered and never will be since the ischial tuberosities have become completely padded by muscles arising from their entire surfaces, a condition restricted to man and preventing the skin from being pressed directly against the bone." [56] These large gluteal muscles of man are functionally related to upright posture and locomotion.

Facial movements. The nose and upper lip of the lemurs represent the primitive mammalian type of smelling organ, naked and glandular. The lips and cheeks do not move, and emotional expression cannot appear on the blank visage of the lemur. These animals drink by lapping, whereas the Pithecoids suck in water by using their free moving lips and cheeks. Many Pithecoids drink in nature by sucking moisture off the vegetation or off their own fur, but in captivity they readily adapt to drinking from an open-mouthed vessel. In monkeys and apes a great variety of facial expression is possible and their pouting, smiling, and chattering are familiar to zoo visitors. The numerous social patterns which are concerned with motility of the face among all human groups are thus based upon muscular responses of the face referable to man's Pithecoid ancestry.

Receptor organs and processes.[57] We have already discussed the eye of the Pithecoids, pointing out that the retina is of the diurnal type in frontal plane and coördinated in movement to produce stereoscopic vision. The clear, sharp vision upon which so much social behavior of man depends is thus again a Pithecoid feature.

As to color vision, apparently lemurs are color-blind, but Pithecoids in general seem to be able to discriminate. Grether found that wavelength discrimination in Old World monkeys (Guinea baboon, green monkey, pigtailed monkey, and five rhesus monkeys) showed no difference from humans except for some slight deficiency at the long-wavelength end of the spectrum. Three New World cebus monkeys showed inferior discrimination in red and yellow shades, and two cebus monkeys were color-blind.[58] With respect to chimpanzees and rhesus monkeys, Grether concludes that their "color vision . . . is at an evolutionary position just short of human vision; the slightly deficient hue discrimination of these animals could be accounted for by less complete differentiation of red and green receptor mechanisms." Hess claims that monkeys are similar to man in sensitivity to wave lengths and that reduction in light intensity results in similar darkness adaptation.[59] Spense concludes that the visual acuity of the chimpanzee is the same as man's and superior to all animals with the possible exception of monkeys.[60] Kohts reports that her chimpanzee was able to discriminate objects of different sizes as well as man. It was able to differentiate thirteen different plane figures and ten different three-dimensional figures as well as a number of letters of the alphabet. Also the chimpanzee responded appropriately to the picture of a three-dimensional object if it was the same size as the object itself.[61] On the other hand, Kohler's chimpanzees, although they showed ability to allow for distance in estimating the size of an object, responded to mirrored objects as if they were real.[62]

It appears that Primates, except Lemuroids and Tarsioids, are outstanding among mammals as "see-ers," but rather poor as "smellers." The abilities of apes and monkeys to use various instruments, to rake in food, to jump to swinging ropes, and so forth, as well as the renowned aerialist performances of monkeys and gibbons in the trees speak for acute and readily adaptable visual capacities as well.

The contact senses, particularly of hands and fingers, are unusually acute in the higher Primates. A chimpanzee showed itself able to select objects of different shapes by inserting its hand into a closed bag.[63] Kluver reported a monkey able to locate by finger touch alone a thread of .204 mm. in diameter.

In the auditory field, it appears that chimpanzees are close to the human level of hearing in the lower ranges of sound and somewhat superior in the higher ranges. Elder, testing three chimpanzees, found sensitivity equal to man in the range of 128 to 8,192 cycles per second, except around 4,096 c.p.s., which inferiority is not normal in humans. Chimpanzees showed 50 per cent thresholds from 26,000 to 33,000 c.p.s., while three children tested showed no response at all above 25,000 c.p.s.[64] Somewhat similar results have been reported for rhesus monkeys. They are on a par with humans in the range of 64 to 1,024 c.p.s., inferior in the middle range (2,048 to 4,096 c.p.s.) and superior in the higher frequencies (8,192 to 16,384 c.p.s.).[65] Cebus monkeys are reported able to discriminate between a single and a double rap on a table, and the macaque can distinguish a single sound from two sounds in succession, but not from three successive sounds.[66] On the other hand, the evidence is conflicting on the question of infra-human Primates' abilities to learn and to "understand" human words. Cunningham thought she had taught a young gorilla to obey verbal commands, but admits that the actual stimuli may have been visual, rather than verbal cues.[67] Furness claimed to have taught a chimpanzee to identify wooden letters by command. Three other investigators, however, report that they were unable to teach the chimpanzee to respond discriminatingly to verbal commands.[68] The difficulty infra-human Primates seem to have in "understanding" human speech as such is apparently not, however, a matter primarily of auditory deficiency, but rather of neural and cortical inferiority. Various investigators have reported that chimpanzees use and distinguish a variety of affective, emotional sounds with each other.[69] Carpenter observed colonies of howling monkeys in their natural state in Panama and reports at least nine distinct sounds used by the monkeys themselves to which "meaningful" and distinct responses are made.[70] The apes seem to be weak in learning ability and "symbolic processes" as they are concerned in "understanding" human speech. Yerkes and Nissen, after long and varied training of individuals of the Yale chimpanzee colony, conclude that symbolic processes occasionally occur in the chimpanzee, but that they are relatively rudimentary and ineffective and show little increase in frequency and functional value with experience and age. Delayed response, "in the absence of spatial clues or with misleading cues is extremely difficult or impossible with most chimpanzees." In short, the apes can hear well enough, but from the human point of view, they are "just dumb." [71]

Senses of taste and smell, so far as known, seem to be about equal for men and the other Pithecoids. As we have seen, these senses are on the whole somewhat inferior to those in other mammals.

Most Pithecoids are rather more sensitive to changes in *temperature* than most other mammals, although due to their hairy covering their sensitivity is less than that of man. Most forest-dwelling Primates are subject to sunstroke when exposed to prolonged direct sunlight.

Apes and monkeys are similar to man in resistance to *electric shock*, so far as we know, and, judging by their climbing and balancing abilities in the trees, are at least not inferior to man in *statoreception* (adjustment to gravity and equilibrium). Chimpanzees and orang-utans can be trained to ride bicycles and the same species show definite learned preferences in postures, indicating good internal reception of stimuli in muscles and joints. Little is known of pain thresholds in the Primates.

Muscular responses of the infra-human Primates have not been exhaustively studied, but we may gather some suggestions from the material at hand. All of the apes are, relative to size, several times stronger than man, and in the gorilla, chimpanzee, and orang-utan, absolute *strength of muscles* exceeds man's several times over.[72] Strength of arm in the chimpanzee in a placid state of mind as measured by the dynamometer has been shown to be three to four times that of college athletes of the same weight (135 lbs.).[73] Man is apparently the puniest of his near relatives.

Monkeys and apes are outstanding among animals in *manipulatory ability*. They have been reported to have learned to use appropriately from the "civilized" point of view the hairbrush, toothbrush, wash basin, handkerchief, cup, spoon, hammer, saw, brace, and bit, clothing, screw driver, pencil and paper (for crude drawing), cigarettes, needle and thread, lock and key. In captivity they have used sticks and other suitable objects for digging, for obtaining objects otherwise out of reach, prying open boxes, "feeling" dangerous objects such as electric wires. Single-arm throwing and fair aim which are practically impossible for animals without "emancipated" forelimbs and prehensile hands, are fairly common among at least the apes.

In conclusion, we must recognize that man's manual abilities are simply a somewhat higher development of a generalized Primate characteristic, associated with structural adaptations of a tree-dwelling ancestry—prehensile hands, supple wrists, free forelimbs, and so forth.

Diet and feeding. Apparently the non-human Primates tend toward a vegetarian and insect diet with fruits supplying perhaps the bulk of the diet. Certain lemurs are apparently adapted to extracting grubs from trees with their projecting front lower teeth, and it is probable that insects, small mammals, and bird's eggs form a part of the diet of other Primates. Carpenter saw a gibbon rob a bird's nest and eat the eggs. Meat as an important part of the diet, however, is eaten only by human beings among the higher Primates. In this connection it is interesting to note that the kidney of man, an organ concerned with excretion of the products of nitrogen metabolism, has a unique structure which finds no close parallels among the other Primates.[74]

SOME BEHAVIORAL AND SOCIAL CHARACTERISTICS OF PRIMATES

The circus gorilla "Gargantua" seemed to be a singularly unsocial individual, perhaps because of an unhappy youth in captivity involving a number of traumatic experiences, but we have a record of another young gorilla which learned to adapt himself to human ways almost as well as a child. This is the case of "John Daniel" which was taken into Miss Cunningham's household when he was less than three years old and weighed only 32 pounds. He lived with his benefactress for two years and three months during which time he grew to weigh 112 pounds. After six weeks he was house-broken. He learned to use the toilet in the regular manner, slept in a bed, took warm baths in the bathtub, turned the light in his room on and off by himself when he got up at night, and ate at a table with the proper implements and with what are said to have been good manners. He is said to have been cleanly, friendly, and obedient, kept himself covered with bed clothes at night, and washed himself without urging. Surely, the accomplishments of this young ape indicate superior motor equipment and learning ability.[75] The question arises whether or not apes might be as smart as men, if only they had the chance.

In an attempt to discover if a human socializing routine would elicit human behavior in an ape, Mr. and Mrs. W. N. Kellogg raised an infant female chimpanzee with their own son for nine months. When first adopted the chimpanzee, named "Gua," was seven and one-half months old and the boy, Donald, was 10 months old. Both were treated the same, as children of the family, and they ate, slept, and played together. In general, during their nine months together, Gua proved herself to be much the better learner of motor activities, in part because of the fact that she developed physically at a faster rate than Donald. She showed greater speed of movement and vastly more facility at climbing and acrobatics. She also excelled in learning some of the "civilized" motor activity thought proper for children in our society. She learned to eat adroitly with a spoon, to drink out of a glass, to open doors, and to skip rope. Her deportment was better as well, and she was less given to sulking and temper tantrums.[76] In view of all this one might ask why the Kelloggs or any one else would not place their human children in the zoo and raise chimpanzees in their stead. The answer is that although the ape develops rapidly and reaches the limits of its learning ability before the more slowly developing human infant really gets started, the child passes the ape's peak when barely under way. The ape never seems to get much farther in learning ability than a three- to four-year-old child. In the crucially important matter of language, Gua never got anywhere at all, whereas Donald had a vocabulary of four words by the age of eleven and one-half months. This experiment seems to demonstrate the constitutional limitations of the ape which even the best socializing routine cannot overcome.

Vocal behavior. The Primates in general are a noisy breed and this is particularly true of monkeys and apes. In nature as well as in captivity they spend a good deal of energy in hand-clapping, rattling of objects together, shouting, and chattering. On the other hand, language, except in man, seems to consist merely of disarticulated emotional signals. The sounds themselves made by non-human Primates are probably not learned during life, but may be modified. There is little or no evidence of apes imitating each other vocally.[77] Nor has any notable success been achieved by man in teaching apes to speak. A chimpanzee is reported to have acquired a one-word vocabulary consisting of "mama," and an orang-utan managed a croaking "paper" and "cup" after considerable training.[78] In both cases the sounds were habitually made during inhalation rather than exhalation. Warden, Jenkins, and Warner conclude that "an ape has motor equipment suitable for speech production. At the worst it could speak intelligibly, though perhaps with a brogue. It can hear well enough to distinguish ordinary words. In learning ability it is superior to other animals, and while it is disinclined to utilize these capacities for the benefit of the experimenter there seems to be no valid reason for assuming that it can never be taught.... The chief problem is one of motivation." [79] The narrow constriction of the ape jaw, mentioned previously, would doubtless have some influence on the "brogue," but the relatively slight development of the "speech center" of the ape brain probably indicates neurological deficiency. At all events, man is the only Primate to use language for the communication of ideas and the only Primate to teach it to his children.

"Psychological" comparisons. A great many experiments have been performed to test the mental abilities of infra-human primates. As a whole these creatures seem to be the most "intelligent" of animals, but tests have not yet proved unequivocally that apes are smarter than monkeys, a finding which may be due to fault in the tests rather than lack of any real difference. For example, De Haan found that a male capuchin monkey when tested by methods used by Kohler on chimpanzees showed itself no less intelligent than the chimpanzee, and more so than the gorilla, gibbon, and orang-utan.[80] Kluver, on the basis of extensive experiments with monkeys, doubts that any great gulf in instrumental ability separates monkeys from apes.[81] Harlow finds that in responses to two-cup and four-cup delayed reaction problems, New World monkeys are in no way inferior to the rhesus and other Old World forms.[82]

The Pithecoids, at least, are unusually handy, among animals, in tool-making and tool-using. Warden reports that both Old World and New World monkeys not only show considerable ease of learning tool-using, but retain such habits with little loss over a period of two years or more.[83] Stacking boxes one on top of another to reach a desired goal, such as a banana suspended from the top of the cage, is easily mastered by chimpanzees. Yerkes' animals solved this problem quickly and without instruction. The orang, however, had to be shown for five days before it "caught on." A gorilla stacked four boxes unaided to reach food. Two Pithecus monkeys, despite patient instruction, never learned. An even easier method, for apes, of reaching a high goal seems to be "pole-jumping." The animals climb rapidly up a pole, balancing it the while, and jump upward off the end. Apes also show ready ability to reach a desired distant object by swinging to it from the end of a suspended rope. In another experiment a large disk was placed partly inside the cage so that food on the part outside the cage could be obtained only by rotating the disk. Chimpanzees showed no difficulty in solving this problem. Wolf [84] taught a group of chimpanzees to work for token rewards. They would work at pulling weights with ropes and be paid off in poker chips, which could then be inserted into a "chimpomat" which dispensed fresh grapes. Not only would the apes work diligently for this "money," but they learned to save it for the proper use in obtaining the primary reward of food.

Kohler [85] subjected his chimpanzees to a number of problem situations, involving the instrumental use of certain objects, which the apes solved successfully. For example, he hung food from the roof of the cage out of reach. On the floor was a box filled with heavy stones which had to be emptied and moved to a position under the food before the animal could reach its goal. This was done without instruction. Blankets, sweaters, and other objects inside the cage were readily used as tools for drawing in food from outside and the apes would also break branches off trees to use as rakes for drawing in food. Two pieces of bamboo were joined together like a fish rod to make a tool long enough to reach the food. The apes also were smart enough to use a short stick to pull in a long stick lying outside the cage, which in turn was used to reach food. An ape also on its own initiative emptied stones from a box so as to be able to drag it beneath a hanging stick which could thus be secured and used to obtain food outside the cage. Chimpanzees would also use a stick to push food out of an open tube, although they would usually withdraw the stick too quickly as if they expected to find food on the end of it. All of these accomplishments may appear to be excessively simple to us, but they indicate a high order of insight and problem-solving ability for any sub-human animal.

As respects "higher mental abilities" it appears that retentiveness in Primates is on the whole greater than in lower animals. Kohler's apes were able to find food which they had seen buried sixteen and one-half hours earlier and even a fortnight's delay did not prevent them from finding a stick with which food could be obtained. One of Yerkes' chimpanzees was able to find buried food after forty-eight hours and would carry on desultory searching (indicating memory of the fact that the food had been hidden, but not memory of its position) after a delay of seventy-two hours. A gorilla was less successful. Chimpanzees have also demonstrated that they could find food hidden in one of two or more places. In solving such problems apes and monkeys seem to respond most effectively to spatial ("position") cues. For example, Yerkes and Yerkes report that retention of complex spatial cues lasts three to four hours, whereas a problem based on color cues cannot be solved after a delay of even thirty minutes. Kohts also reported that her chimpanzee responded to non-spatial cues with great difficulty after even fifteen seconds of delay. Warden, Jenkins, and Warner summarize the evidence thus: "The data demonstrate that Primates (and apes in particular) can respond after periods of delay many times as long as those which mark limits for any other animal (except man). Furthermore, Primates can make successful delayed responses on the basis of spatial cues even though a fixed body position is not maintained." [86] Harlow has summarized on the basis of his own experiments the primates' abilities on delayed-reaction tests. The apes do best, followed in order of decreasing ability by baboons, Old World monkeys, New World monkeys, and lemurs. In summary, we may say that the Primates, and particularly the apes, are superior to all other animals in "memory" and in problem-solving ability which implies abstraction and imagination. [87]

Yet even the apes are far below man in many so-called higher mental abilities. We have mentioned Yerkes' finding of poor symbolic processes in chimpanzees. Another investigation has shown that appreciation of numbers and their relationships, as divorced from such ancillary factors as pattern, spatial and temporal modalities, is probably beyond the powers of subhuman Primates. De Haan [88] came to the same conclusion after trying to train a three-year-old "Java ape" to find a banana by turning over a box. The problem was as follows: the first time the monkey was rewarded after one turn-over of the box, the second time after two turn-overs, the third time after three; then the series was repeated. The monkey was unable to learn this simple problem, and therefore had no concept of numbers, in the opinion of the investigator. We must remember that counting requires symbols of one sort or another. That a normal human being would be able to handle such a problem with ease is apparently due to our ability and habituation to using words (vocal symbols) for counting.

Social behavior. The Primates normally live in groups and in general seem to be exceedingly sensitive to social influences. Apparently the social groups are larger in the smaller species than among the apes, and social positions within the group are usually arranged in more or less of a hierarchy of dominance, although this is not a "pecking order" as found, for example, among domestic fowl. Jealousy is common; acquisitiveness and aggressiveness for objects and possessions enliven life; gestures are commonly in use, as well as emotional vocalizations; the animals recognize signs of hostility and aggression, and do not hesitate to deceive one another with misleading postures and gestures. Exhibitionism is common, a trait which endears monkeys and chimpanzees to zoo and circus fans, and in nature the animals have been observed adorning themselves with flowers, leaves, and other objects. Their preferences for certain articles run through cycles reminiscent of human fads.

Among a number of types of human social behavior which seem to be foreshadowed among the Pithecoids, at least, the Yerkeses mention the following. [89] Playfullness seems to be characteristic, particularly among the young, in most species, and it is especially marked in chimpanzees. Activities resembling tag, wrestling, and mock-fighting have been observed among chimpanzees in their natural habitat. What might be called ownership has been reported for howler, baboon, chimpanzee, and gibbon. Howlers and gibbons have definite territories, "belonging" to the social group, from which intruders are rebuffed. The Hamadryas baboon males, if strong enough, seem to regard their females as private property from which rivals are driven, and with which they may do as they please, even killing them. Chimpanzees will appropriate objects and carry them around with them for days, resisting any attempts to take them away. Grooming of one animal by another is common among the Primates, and, in Yerkes' view may foreshadow the barbershop and the hairdresser among humans. At all events "flea picking" and "grooming," as practised by Primates, usually are a social occupation involving at least two animals, except among the Tarsioids. Among the lemurs the animal may occasionally lick its own fur and comb it with its procumbent lower incisors and scratch itself with a second digit of its hind foot on which there is a claw instead of a nail. Mutual grooming occurs also; the two animals use their mouths for the purpose and employ the hands only to hold each other's fur. Tarsioids lick themselves and scratch themselves with two hind toes; but do not indulge in mutual grooming. Among the Pithecoids, however, mutual grooming plays a large part and the work is done exclusively with the fingers. Animals spend hours going over each other, picking dandruff, dirt, and debris and usually conveying the booty to the mouth.[90] It is perhaps not without significance that the Pithecoids, who fondle and carry their children in close bodily contact, have developed grooming involving bodily interest and contact as a social function to a greater degree than other Primates.

Social life in nature. In addition to a large literature of anecdotes, travelers' tales, and short-time observations we have four rather complete and systematic studies on Primate social life in natural surroundings: Zuckerman's [91] report on the African baboon, Carpenter's [92] field study on howling monkeys in Panama, Carpenter's [93] more recent report on gibbons in Siam, and Nissen's [94] observations of chimpanzees in West Africa. In addition, Carpenter has made incomplete observations on macaques and orangs.

Baboons. These animals normally live in herds or bands which are in turn composed of polygynous families. The family consists of a male overlord, his females, nursing infants, and a variable number of juveniles. In addition there may be a few nearly mature bachelors not necessarily offspring of the overlord which are tolerated and which in some cases later establish families of their own. Organization of the herd or band itself is not clear; the primary group is the family and in this organization is based upon male dominance. The baboons apparently are very pugnacious and fights between males over females have been reported lasting for days. The female is usually passive in her submission to her overlord and may actually use "presenting" behavior to avoid punishment. The males pay little attention to infants, whose care devolves upon the mothers. In general, the dominance of the baboons upon which social grouping is dependent, is brutal, conflictual, and based upon physical force. Social power is in the hands of males who are able to exercise a physical despotism.

Howler monkeys. The studies of howlers on Barro Colorado Island, Panama, by Carpenter represent the most complete observations of monkey society in the wild state which we have to date; and these New World Primates enjoy a type of social life entirely different from that of their Old World cousins the baboons. While the latter have dog-like projecting muzzles equipped with heavy canine teeth, the howlers' dental equipment is modest so far as fighting potentiality goes. The hyoid bone in the throat of the howler, however, is enlarged so that the larynx is a powerful resonator capable of producing a vast volume of sound. And in conflict and competition the howler depends upon his voice rather than upon physical violence.

The howlers live in bands (called "clans" by Carpenter) which are geographically isolated from each other and each of which occupies a given stretch of forest. These bands range in size from 4 to 35 individuals with a median size of about 18. On the average each band contains 2.48 adult males, 7.10 adult females, 3.34 infants, and 4.9 juveniles. In contrast to the baboon set-up, the howler band is not composed of discrete families. It is a closed society which repels attempts of other band members to join up, and it defends its territory from encroachment with pugnacious-sounding screeches and howls, which are usually sufficient to obviate necessity for physical combat. Within the band itself a sort of promiscuity prevails. In a receptive period a female will copulate with several males one after another, and although she may refuse one male in preference to another, she displays no faithfulness to any particular one. Furthermore, males do not act possessive and there is none of the jealous fighting over sexual privileges which is characteristic of baboons. Each band moves through the trees of its territory during the day in a definite order of progression. Usually one or two males act as leaders and dominate the group in the sense of giving directions by a variety of grunts and barks. The nursing females bring up the rear of the band, which travels slowly, usually not more than 500 yards a day. When another band appears to be encroaching the males set up a series of fierce barking roars which serve to bluff off the intruders. In short, the howler society is a peaceful one with no permanent family groupings, little jealousy, and with dominant individuals maintaining their positions and functions vocally, rather than through physical force.[95]

Gibbons. The gibbons observed by Carpenter in Siam live only in families. There is no larger social unit. The family ranges in size from two to six individuals, with the modal number being four, an adult pair and two young. Thus the gibbon appears to be essentially monogamous, for, of twenty-one family groups studied, only two contained more than one adult male, and only one family contained two adult females. An occasional solitary male was observed, but this is most unusual and probably represents a temporary condition of widowhood or bachelorhood. The "married" gibbons are very coöperative with each other, and in contrast to many other Primate types, the female does not seem to be dominated by the male. The mates engage in sex activity at all times of the menstrual cycle and also during pregnancy, a feature which may account for their monogamous tendencies in contrast to those species in which the female is sexually coöperative only during certain phases of the cycle. The mated pair usually shows a good deal of antagonism to other married pairs and replies to interference with physical violence. The male is protective toward the young and plays with them and grooms them, until they begin to grow up. Then, however, he becomes cool, if not antagonistic, and the young adult male offspring is forced out of the family to set up one for himself. Since there are comparatively few children in any family group at a time, the opportunities for socialization of a broad type are limited. Each family has its own private section of the forest which is defended vocally and by actual fighting. "Visiting" among families is not encouraged, except in the case of courting youngsters looking for mates. Carpenter distinguished nine different types of vocalizations which are used in family control and correlated with stimulus situations. Gestures and facial expressions also serve for control purposes. Most vocalization occurs during the early part of the morning when the groups are starting out on their daily foraging rounds. In summary, the gibbon seems to be the most fanatical "family man" among the infra-human Primates yet reported. In fact, all social life takes place in small family groups which are typically monogamous and in which husband and wife seem to be equal partners.

Chimpanzees. Because of their tractable dispositions in captivity,[96] chimpanzees are the best known of the great apes, but only one systematic, although incomplete, field study of their life in the wild has been published. It would appear that chimpanzees live in bands ranging from 4 to 14 with an average of 8.5 individuals. These bands usually contain several adult males and several adult females, so that it would seem to be a case of "group marriage" rather than either monogamy or polygyny. Nissen is unable to give any data as to the permanency of these groups. It seems that the largest male acts as a sort of leader, and that the group moves about in a nomadic fashion without any definite territorial prerogatives. A great variety of vocalizations are used and a good deal of bickering seems to take place, although little actual physical fighting, as in the baboon band. On the whole the chimpanzee dominance seems to be of a friendly sort. Males engage in grotesque dances in front of females they are trying to "court" or seduce, as well as stomping on the ground and thumping on trees. All members of the group are coöperative in protecting and assisting other members, although communism does not seem to be so striking as among the howlers. A good part of the energy of these animals is involved in social play of one sort or another. Nests of leaves and branches are built each night for sleeping, and young animals share the nests of their mothers.

Other species. Carpenter has observed *macaques* in their native habitat in various regions. He reports [97] that they live in troops in which the number of females always exceeds the number of males. For example, a typical grouping consists of six adult males, thirty-two adult females (twenty-five of which had infants) and ten juveniles—a total of seventy-three animals. In all cases the males dominate the other individuals of the group, but not in the brutal way of the baboon males. Surplus males usually live together in bachelor groups.

Carpenter has also reported less extensive observations of *orang-utans*.[98] The group he observed consisted of two adult females with young infants and a large adult male. The male was often widely separated from the females, but kept contact by means of loud calls seldom heard in captivity.

Summary of Primate social life in nature. Carpenter [99] has summarized the general characteristics of infra-human social patterning in so far as it has been observed under natural conditions as follows. (1) There is a marked variability from genus to genus both in total size and patterning of groups. (2) Organized groups usually contain more adult females than males, with the exception of the groups of gibbons. (3) Bachelor groups for adult males occur in some species. (4) Each species seems to have its own average size of group. (5) Primate groups are semiclosed, and the groups have a high degree of constancy from season to season and from year to year. New groups are formed by budding off of older ones. (6) Each primate group in nature tends to possess its exclusive territory from which members of other groups are excluded, but federations between groups seem to be rare, probably because of the lack of ability

of the animals to use abstract symbols. (7) Within all groups there is
competition among individuals, which results in establishing positions of
dominance and subordination. (8) The lack of definite seasonal breeding
seasons and the consequent continuous, if sometimes intermittent, sexual
activity tends to reinforce the social bonds within the group. Primate
females are receptive for a relatively longer time during their estrus cycle.
However, other types of activities, such as mutual grooming, play, and
feeding, also reinforce the social bonds between the members of the
group. (9) Communication is used to organize the group and the activities
of the members within it. The following forms of communication have
been noted: gross overt motions and gestures; stereotyped gestures of a
more symbolic type; vocalizations (cries). However, Carpenter points
out that "the repertory of gestures and vocalizations of a species (of
sub-human Primates) is rather definitely fixed by hereditary determinants." [100]

PRIMATE ADAPTATIONS

We have reviewed briefly and in a comparative way the structural
and functional characteristics of the Primates so as to be able to understand man's place in nature, and, more particularly, his potentialities and
limitations as seen in the perspective of the zoölogical group to which he
belongs. One thus sees that there is a broad, general pattern common to
the Primates as a whole; but, on the other hand, it will not have escaped
notice that many differences exist between various groups within the
Primate order itself. Thus one may speak not only of a general Primate
pattern, but of Primate patterns. For a proper understanding of man the
latter are at least as important as the general, overall characteristics of
the order.

The evolution of the Primates is known in some detail and it is now
understood that in the course of their history the Primates have developed
several distinct types of adaptation, which are still reflected to some
degree among the living representatives of the order. [101]

1. The earliest, primitive Primates were apparently small, furry
animals, pronograde in posture and locomotion, and rather generalized as
to habitat. Some apparently lived in trees, others partly on the ground,
but highly specialized adaptation to arboreal conditions was not characteristic. The Lemuroids still reflect this type of adaptation to some extent,
although many species are at present specialized to given environments.

2. The second major type of adaptation made by some Primates was
brachiation—specialization for tree life by swinging from the forelimbs.
This was a specialization in the truest sense of the word, for a truly
brachiating animal is fitted only for life in the trees—not in brush, or

half in the trees and half on the ground. The orang-utan at the present time is an animal highly specialized for this type of arboreal life, and structurally it is practically helpless in a terrestrial situation. Relatively large body size is characteristic of all Primate brachiators. Life in the trees, even in the primitive stage, involves enhancement of the visual over the olfactory senses, development of muscular and nervous coördination involved in the "senses" of balance and timing, and so forth, but the brachiating specialization required structural ability to rotate the arm at the shoulder, grasping function of the hands (and, although not necessarily, the feet), and adjustive changes in trunk and viscera adaptive to an upright, hanging, or crouching posture.

3. The third general physical adaptive combination which has been "tried out" by the Primates is complete terrestrial life. So far as we know this has taken two different forms among the "first" order of mammals. (a) Some of the Primates have completely emancipated themselves from arboreal life and spend all their time on the ground—but they have made a quadrupedal (four-footed) adaptation. The hamadryas baboons of South Africa are good examples, as are the so-called barbary apes of North Africa and Gibraltar (the only indigenous Primates, aside from man, at present current in Europe). To mention only two features of these ground-dwelling monkeys, they have had to sacrifice freedom of the hands (which they must use for support) and have had to develop relatively large snouts, as if to compensate for their inability to make manual explorations and manipulations. The ground-dwelling monkeys, nevertheless, have both eyes in the frontal plane (and stereoscopic vision) and various other features of the more developed Primates. However, they are structurally specialized to certain, limited terrestrial environments. (b) The real innovation in terrestrial adaptation was made by the predecessors of man. These animals came down out of the trees, as it were, but preserved the upright posture which, at least in part, had already been attained as a result of the brachiating specialization. But, instead of support and locomotion in the "hung" position—dangling from arms grasping branches overhead—these functions were performed in a standing position, and the feet and hind limbs became specialized for support and locomotion in a completely bipedal mode. For the first time the forelimbs were completely freed from these functions and, as we have seen, various other mutations were selected out concomitantly—enlargement of the brain, and particularly the frontal areas; complete opposability and flexibility of the fingers and thumb; reduction of the facial skeleton and musculature leaving the relatively prominent nose and chin; comparative reduction of the length and circumference of the arms relative to the legs; lumbar curve in the small of the back; reduction of

the canine teeth relative to the other teeth; comparative reduction in size of teeth and jaws; non-opposability of great toe set in line with other toes; foot with transverse and antero-posterior arches; wider and more basin-like pelvis (blades face one another in upper portions); relatively large size of infant at birth; greater growth period, and so on. This adaptation was a *generalized* one enabling the animal to survive—with culture—in almost any earthly environment.

Thus we see that man shares a number of basic structural and functional features with all the Primates, but that he is the product of a type of adaptive change which none of the other living species succeeded in accomplishing. If we search for the evolutionary backgrounds of man's present ascendancy we can only conclude that the adaptive changes which led to the successful bipedal terrestrial mode of life seem to have provided the "groundwork," both actually and figuratively speaking, for the present abilities and future potentialities of the species.

NOTES TO CHAPTERS 2 AND 3

1. Zuckerman, 1933, p. 16.
2. Linnaeus used the term *Primate* for the "highest" order of the mammals. He included men, monkeys, lemurs, and bats. As at present defined, the bats are omitted. Linné, 1735.
3. Darwin, 1859, 1871; Huxley, 1894.
4. McDermott, 1939; Yerkes and Yerkes, 1929, pp. 1-26.
5. Zuckerman, 1933, p. 63, quoting Woollard, 1927, pp. 1-17.
6. Smith, G. Elliot, 1926.
7. Zuckerman, 1933, p. 107, citing Painter, 1924, 1925.
8. See Yerkes and Yerkes, 1929, for detailed discussion of the apes; also Hooton, 1931, 1942.
9. Figures in this and the following sections, unless otherwise specified, are from those compiled by Schultz, 1936.
10. Schultz, 1936, gives 60 kg., but in a later publication he gives the average adult male weight at 45 kg. and average adult female weight as 40 kg.: Schultz, 1940. These figures agree with those of Grether and the Yerkeses, 1940, except that the latter give a figure of 50 kg. as the average for the adult male chimpanzee.
11. Yerkes and Yerkes, 1929, p. 552.
12. Hooton, 1931, p. 43.
13. Schultz, 1936, p. 449.
14. Schultz, 1936.
15. Tilney, 1928.
16. Poliak, 1932.
17. Fulton and Keller, 1932.
18. Zuckerman, 1933, p. 145.
19. *Ibid.*, p. 138.
20. Schultz, 1936, pp. 263-265; Virchow, 1929.
21. Carpenter, 1940, pp. 59-60.
22. Black, 1925. The standard compilation of data in physical anthropology is Martin, 1928; see also Hooton, 1931; 1946.
23. These and other percentages comparing the proportional size of the skeleton in man and other Primates are those given by Schultz, 1936.

24. Carpenter, 1940, pp. 67-68.
25. *Ibid.*, p. 75.
26. Jones, F. Wood, 1926, pp. 67-69.
27. Gesell and Halverson, 1936.
28. Smith, G. Elliot, 1927.
29. Benson, 1941, p. 221.
30. Zuckerman, 1933, pp. 58-59.
31. *Ibid.*, pp. 51-53, 59; Nuttall, 1904, p. 214.
32. Calmette, 1924.
33. The discoverer of this fact was apparently V. L. Kellogg; *see also* Ewing.
34. Cameron, 1929.
35. Hamlett, 1939; Goodman and Wislocki, 1935. In both these species bleeding is usually not apparent externally, but only in vaginal lavages.
36. Hartman, 1932.
37. Aulmann, 1932.
38. Elder and Yerkes, 1936; Tomilin, 1936.
39. Carpenter, 1940, pp. 130-131.
40. Noback, 1939.
41. Zuckerman, 1930-1931.
42. Zuckerman, 1932, pp. 40-47.
43. Yerkes, 1939a.
44. Mortimer, 1940.
45. Extensive descriptions of reproductive and sex activity will be found in Yerkes and Yerkes, 1929; Zuckerman, 1932; Hamilton, 1914; Bingham, 1928.
46. Yerkes, 1933; Tomilin and Yerkes, 1935.
47. Elder and Yerkes, 1936.
48. Yerkes and Tomilin, 1935.
49. Schultz, 1936, p. 268, except for adult weight of chimpanzee, from Schultz, 1940, and Grether and Yerkes, 1940.
50. Schultz, 1936, p. 267.
51. From Schultz and from Zuckerman, 1933.
52. Grether and Yerkes, 1940.
53. Yerkes and Yerkes, 1929, p. 568.
54. Zuckerman, 1933, pp. 26-27. Italics mine.
55. Schultz, 1931.
56. Schultz, 1936.
57. An excellent bibliography and discussion on this and other "psychological" features of primates is to be found in Warden, Jenkins, and Warner, 1936, pp. 363-420, 526-535.
58. Grether, 1939a.
59. Grether, 1939b.
60. Spense, 1934.
61. Kohts, 1928.
62. Kohler, 1925.
63. Kohts, 1928.
64. Elder, 1934a, 1934b.
65. Shepard, 1910.
66. Thorndike, 1901.
67. Cunningham, 1921.
68. Kohts, 1923; Yerkes and Learned, 1925; Furness, 1916.
69. Yerkes and Yerkes, 1929, pp. 301-309.
70. Yerkes and Nissen, 1939.
71. Carpenter, 1934.
72. Yerkes and Yerkes, 1929, p. 534.
73. Bauman, 1923, 1929.

74. Straus, 1934.
75. Cunningham, 1921.
76. Kellogg and Kellogg, 1933.
77. Yerkes and Learned, 1925; Kroeber, 1928.
78. Furness, 1916.
79. Warden, Jenkins, and Warner, 1936, p. 393.
80. Quoted by Zuckerman, 1933, pp. 119-129.
81. Kluver, 1933.
82. Harlow and Bromer, 1939.
83. Warden, 1940.
84. Wolfe, 1936.
85. Kohler, 1925.
86. Warden, Jenkins, and Warner, 1936, p. 416. Quotation by permission of the publisher, The Ronald Press.
87. See Harlow, 1932.
88. De Haan.
89. Yerkes and Yerkes, 1935.
90. Yerkes, 1933; Zuckerman, 1933, pp. 71-73.
91. Zuckerman, 1932.
92. Carpenter, 1934.
93. Carpenter, 1940.
94. Nissen, 1931.
95. On dominance among Primates, see Maslow, 1936-1937.
96. Yerkes, 1939b.
97. Carpenter, 1942b.
98. Carpenter, 1942a, p. 186.
99. Carpenter, 1942a.
100. *Ibid.*, p. 204.
101. For more detailed studies of the evolution of the Primates, see Montagu, 1945, pp. 46-64 (a relatively "popular" account); Gregory, 1916; Romer, 1941; Hooton, 1946.

CHAPTER 4

The Fossil Predecessors of Modern Man

THE EXTINCT SPECIES OF MAN

THE PRESENT species of man represents a branch of the Primate tree towering high above and spreading its shadow far beyond the other branches which have evolved from this trunk. The fundamentals of man's structure and behavior are derived from the Primate base, but these generally Primate features have burst into an efflorescence which outstrips even the wildest grotesqueries of any of the other branches of the Primate stem. Yet, the present type of man did not spring suddenly to his present heights from a generalized Primate level. At least, so far as our present knowledge allows us to say, nature made a number of abortive efforts before she achieved the paragon of simian ability which we know as man today. And it is of course possible that the present species will one day become extinct to be succeeded by yet another, or by none at all. No sudden changes in the physical features of the species are anticipated for the near future.

The story of human evolution as it is known from geological and paleontological evidence is as yet far from complete. It suffers not only from the absence of many pages, but of whole sections. Nevertheless, despite obscurity in some details, we may say that the synopsis of the story at least is in hand and fairly clear to the qualified reader. Yet, before examining the bones of our predecessors, it is necessary to form some acquaintance with the system of geological time-reckoning covering the period in question. For human-like creatures have been living upon the earth a very long time in terms of a single human life, or even in terms of the Christian era. Considered from the point of view of the age of the earth, however, or even of the length of time that living beings have occupied it, man as we know him is a comparative late comer who has joined the family of animals and dominated it, somewhat like an impetuous bully, relatively recently. But man did not, like the senti- mentalized "Baby Dear," "fly out of the nowhere into the here." The species appeared as the end product of a long period of evolutionary development. Most of our information is supplied by the evidence of geology and paleontology and it is therefore necessary to have an idea of the general outline of geological time.

HOW PREHISTORIC TIME IS CALCULATED

The age of the earth is now usually estimated, on the basis of a study of the rate of decomposition of certain radioactive substances, to be between a billion and a billion-and-one-half years. The subsequent history of the earth has been unraveled, in outline at least, by geologists and paleontologists studying the stratified rock formations and the gradually changing character of the fossilized organic forms often enclosed therein. The total thickness of the sedimentary deposits is said to be over fifty miles, but in many parts of the world they have been partly eroded, and often they are bent, tilted, or even completely tipped over so that the original order of deposition is not superficially apparent. When rearranged in their proper chronological order they appear in stratified form as in the accompanying simplified table (which should be read chronologically from bottom to top). Names have been given to the systems of rocks and to the periods of evolutionary development of living forms associated with the rocks.

From an examination of this table it is apparent that definite evidence of man, as distinguished from apes, appears only at the close of the Pliocene epoch, roughly 1,000,000 years ago and that the Primate order itself differentiated from the mammalian class as late as the Eocene, some 59,000,000 years ago. Since evidence of man first appears at the close of the Pliocene, it is during the succeeding period, the Pleistocene, or Age of Glaciers, that we are to look for his prehistoric development. During this time all known "fossil men" appeared.

The glacial period. For reasons which are not entirely clear to science, the earth was subjected to a series of cold cycles during the Pleistocene period, resulting in the advance of ice sheets over much of Northern Europe and North America. In Europe the ice sheet extended to approximately the fiftieth parallel, or roughly the latitude of London, Prague, and Kharkov. In North America it came somewhat farther south, reaching to about the fortieth parallel. In both hemispheres the advance was variable and certain areas, for example, parts of southwestern Wisconsin, western Newfoundland, and the Yukon Basin in North America were apparently never visited by the ice. In the Southern Hemisphere the glacial periods were signalized by lowering of the snow line on mountains an average of about 3,500 feet, while the lower altitudes were characterized by "pluvial periods" of heavy rain which correlated in time with the glaciations farther north. The impounding of large amounts of water

SIMPLIFIED GEOLOGICAL TABLE WITH LIFE FORMS

Rock System or Period		Life Period and Forms
4. Quaternary	Psychozoic "Age of Mind"	*Holocene or Recent* (Began about 25,000-15,000 years ago) *Homo sapiens*
		Pleistocene ("Age of Glaciers") (Began about 1,000,000 years ago) Skeletal remains of early man
3. Tertiary We are now getting closer to modern times and may begin to mention rough approximations of periods in terms of years	Cenozoic Began 58,000,000 years ago	*Pliocene* (15,000,000 years) Modern-type apes Probably hominids by end of period as shown by archaeological evidence of Eoliths (crude stone implements)
		Miocene (20,000,000 years) Primates: ancestral gibbons; generalized chimpanzee-gorillas Probably before end of this period some anthropoids, man's ancestors, had descended from trees and assumed upright posture.
		Oligocene (10,000,000 years) Primates: ancestors of Old World monkeys; early apes in Egypt
		Eocene (duration 13,000,000 years) Development of mammalian orders Primates: lemuroids and tarsioids only
2. Secondary	Mesozoic "Age of Reptiles"	*Cretaceous:* specialized reptiles; mammals first split into monotremes, marsupials, and placentals *Jurassic:* reptiles at highest development, modern fishes, earliest bird (archaeopteryx) *Triassic:* small mammals, probably insectivorous and marsupial
1. Primary	Paleozoic "Ancient Life"	*Permian:* early land reptiles *Carboniferous:* first insects, first true amphibians, early reptiles *Devonian:* lung fishes, bony fishes, possibly first amphibians *Silurian:* sharks: dogfish with cartilagenous skeletons *Ordovician:* vertebrate fishes *Cambrian:* invertebrates only
	Eozoic "Dawn Life"	Simple plants, radiolaria

in the continental ice sheets resulted in an average lowering of the ocean level which amounted to between 400 and 600 feet, with the result that "land bridges" appeared, connecting certain areas now separated by water. For example, Europe was connected with North Africa during at least part of the Pleistocene by land bridges across what are now the Straits of Gibraltar and the Straits of Sicily (between Sicily and Tunis). Siberia communicated with North America across the present Bering Strait. These land bridges are of importance because they explain in part certain similarities and dissimilarities of flora and fauna between the areas so connected. On the other hand, there is no evidence of large land bridges connecting the Western and Eastern Hemispheres across either the Atlantic or Pacific Oceans during the last million years or of large oceanic islands, which fact seems to invalidate the theory of a lost Atlantis or a sunken continent of Mu in which man and civilization mysteriously originated long ago.

Study by geologists of gravel and mud deposits left by the glaciers, together with their contained evidences of life, has shown that the Pleistocene period was not one long stretch of unmitigated cold, but that several pulsations occurred; several periods of cold and of glacial advance alternated with periods during which the ice retreated and the climate turned appreciably warmer.

The divisions of the glacial period. In Switzerland, where these matters were first studied, four glacial advances can be distinguished, and this condition is true, with some minor differences, in most of glaciated Europe. For the sake of simplicity, then, we shall consider only the principal pulsations in Europe as shown in the accompanying table. The four main glacial periods of Europe have been named Günz, Mindel, Riss, and Würm, respectively. The retreat of the ice following the final, or Würm, climax was characterized by three hesitations, or minor advances, called, respectively, the Buhl, Gschnitz, and Daun pauses. In North America, five or six advances of the glaciers have been distinguished and named in chronological order as follows: Jerseyan, Kansan, Illinoian, Iowan, and Wisconsin.

The dates (in terms of the Christian terminology) given in the accompanying table are only rough estimates on which there is not yet complete agreement even among experts. These dates, however, perhaps represent in a general way the present trend of geological opinion, and give us an approximately correct time scale on which to measure the speed or slowness of man's evolution, which is our principal need at present. It should also be remembered that glacial dates vary with location in the glaciated area. Retreats, for example, began later, the farther north the locality.

TABLE OF GLACIAL PERIODS

	Final land rise in Baltic	4,000 B.C.
	Daun retreat, began	6,500 B.C.
	Daun pause, began Ancylus Lake	7,500 B.C.
	Gschnitz retreat, began Yoldia Lake	8,500 B.C.
	Gschnitz pause, began	13,500 B.C.
	Buhl retreat, began	18,500 B.C.
	Buhl pause	18,500 B.C.
	Würm or Achen retreat, began	25,000 B.C.
4th Glacial	Würm advance, began	75,000 B.C.
3rd Interglacial	Riss retreat, began	125,000 B.C.
3rd Glacial	Riss advance, began	250,000 B.C.
2nd Interglacial	Mindel retreat, began	450,000 B.C.
2nd Glacial	Mindel advance, began	500,000 B.C.
1st Interglacial	Günz retreat, began	600,000 B.C.
1st Glacial	Günz advance, began	1,000,000 years ago

THE PREDECESSORS OF MODERN MAN

A. PREDECESSORS OF APES AND HOMINIDS

It is believed by most experts that the Primate order, including monkeys, man, and the apes, evolved out of the order of Insectivores and that this differentiation took place during the Eocene period. During this period evolution continued still further with the differentiation of primitive Lemuroids and Tarsioids. Probably the Catarrhine branch itself had appeared before the end of the period. We recall that the Catarrhine branch is represented at present by the Old World monkeys, the great apes, and man. About the beginning of the Oligocene the generalized Catarrhine monkeys apparently separated into two branches, one of which continued along the line of evolution which eventuated in the present Old World monkeys and the other of which gradually developed into the Simian and Hominid types. During the Oligocene, however, the distinction between ape and human branches had not yet developed.

Parapithecus. The earliest ancestral anthropoid ape so far discovered is Parapithecus, the lower jaw and teeth of which were recovered from lower Oligocene deposits in the dry lake bed of the Fayum, Egypt. The size of the parts indicates an animal about half the size of the modern gibbon, the smallest of the great apes, and the form of the teeth suggests a mixed diet of insects, fruit, bird's eggs, and small reptiles, although this inference is based as much on inference from living forms as on the teeth themselves. Paleontological authorities are convinced that Parapithecus stands in or near the line of descent leading to the anthropoid apes and to man. Of particular interest is the fact that this fossil is the earliest to display the dental formula characteristic of apes and men: [1]

$$I\frac{2}{2} \quad C\frac{1}{1} \quad PM\frac{2}{2} \quad M\frac{3}{3}$$

Propliopithecus. Probably the nearest representative of the common ancestor of man and apes of which we at present have evidence was Propliopithecus, also recovered from the lower Oligocene of the Fayum although from a slightly later deposit than Parapithecus. Here again only the lower jaw is present and is about three-fourths the size of the modern gibbon's jaw. But there is little doubt that Propliopithecus was a small ape of a gibbonoid type, and not a monkey. This creature possessed not only the ape-man dental formula, but also the five-cusped pattern on the grinding surfaces of the molar teeth, which is also characteristic of modern apes.

Miocene apes. The large apes developed during the Miocene period from the small and primitive anthropoids of the preceding Oligocene, and their jaw-bones and teeth have been recovered from Northern India, Egypt, Kenya, and several localities in Europe. By the middle Miocene definite ancestors of the four modern great apes had already evolved. *Paleosimia*, an Indian middle Miocene fossil, is probably an ancestor of the orang-utan. *Dryopithecus* is a Miocene genus represented by at least six species, some of which seem to be directly ancestral to the gorilla and chimpanzee and all of which show features which ally them, even though remotely, to man. *Sivapithecus indicus* is an upper Miocene fossil more or less intermediate between the Paleosimia and the Dryopithecus types. Most authorities agree that man is derived from a primitive Dryopithecus [2] or Sivapithecus stock, and that the divergence of the human line did not take place until these types had reached large apelike size. This most probably was during the Miocene period.

B. ORIGIN OF THE HUMAN BRANCH

We have already indicated the time when, according to present evidence, it seems most likely that proto-humans developed. This was sometime during the Miocene period with a continued development during the succeeding Pliocene, although complete skeletal evidence is by no means available. An Indian Pliocene genus, *Ramapithecus*, may represent one of these generalized human predecessors living during the Pliocene, as is suggested by its teeth which are more manlike than apelike.

The place of origin of the Hominids is either Asia or Africa. Points in favor of Africa are: it has the most manlike of living apes (chimpanzee, gorilla), the earliest fossil type (Parapithecus), and the most manlike Simian fossils (Australopithecus and related types, to be discussed below). Asia, on the other hand, may claim: more species of fossil apes, two of the earliest and certainly the two most primitive types of the human family (Pithecanthropus, Sinanthropus), and two living ape types (orang-utan and gibbon). Most experts incline to Asia as the birthplace of mankind, but the question is still open.

Characteristics. The apes and men have followed two divergent lines of evolution. The tendency in the case of the ape line has been toward more specialized hereditary adaptation to particular arboreal conditions.[3] With man on the other hand the evolutionary tendency has been toward the production of a more generalized organism, less closely bound by adaptations to particular environmental conditions, particularly those attending a tree-dwelling existence. Although we have no complete skeletons of Miocene or Pliocene precursors of man, we may deduce from a comparison of the known later forms of both men and apes something of the physical characteristics of these early ancestors. The following are postulated features: (1) Arms and legs of approximately equal length. In apes the arms are longer for swinging from tree branches (brachiation); in men the legs are longer for ground walking. (2) Life was probably spent partly in the trees and partly on the ground. The descent from the trees which ultimately was accomplished by the human branch was probably not yet complete. (3) Dietary habits were probably omnivorous. While other Primates are inclined to prefer vegetarianism, or the eating of insects (as is the case with Tarsier and lorises), man eats both plant and meat food. (4) A partially stabilized foot, permitting at least sporadic ground walking had probably developed. The prehensile foot of the ape is adapted to arboreal life, while ground walking requires a less flexible and more stable support. (5) Size was probably comparable to that of modern man or the chimpanzee; body was doubtless hairy; teeth and jaws were doubtless protruding and apelike; the molar teeth had five cusps (modern men have four); the external tail had disappeared; and the brain case was undoubtedly ridged and craggy.

Common characteristics of the great apes and man. Before proceeding further we may mention a number of bodily characteristics which the existing great apes and man possess in common and which serve to distinguish them from the other members of the Catarrhine division (Old World monkeys).

1. Absence of external tail
2. Smaller number of presacral vertebrae, on the average
3. Wider pelvis

4. Wider chest; sternum shorter and flatter
5. Five-cusped molar teeth (in early forms of man; in modern man, one cusp has been lost)
6. Frontal sinus (chimpanzee, gorilla, man)
7. Absence of ischial callosities

C. FOSSIL PALEANTHROPIC TYPES

We now propose to review the outstanding characteristics of the principal fossil hominids known to the present time. All genera and species previous to the appearance of *Homo sapiens* are known as paleanthropic types, while the various races of the present (sapiens) species are termed neoanthropic types. These are merely convenient terms for distinguishing early from more recent types of men.

The Australopithecine apes (South African fossil apes). Before examining specimens of true hominids it is necessary to accord brief mention to these fossils. *Australopithecus africanus* was found at Taungs in Bechuanaland in 1924; the skeleton was that of a child with its permanent dentition just erupting. Two apparently related types were found and described by Dr. Robert Broom more recently: *Plesianthropus transvaalensis*, found at Sterkfontein in 1936; and *Paranthropus robustus*, found at Komdraai, near Sterkfontein (Transvaal), in 1938. Australopithecus was found in deposits which were probably laid down during middle Pleistocene times, while the latter two are identified with upper Pleistocene strata. The relatively late geological age rules out the possibility that these particular forms could have been ancestral to man, although it is conceivable that the ancestors of these South African apes were developing through Pliocene times parallel to the development of the hominid ancestors.

They seem to be superapes which evolved in the relatively unforested area of South Africa and survived into Pleistocene times only to become extinct later. In this sense they represent an example of what *might* have happened to the truly human stem. There is little doubt that they are descendants in some way of the *Dryopithecus-Sivapithecus* group, which seems to possess the characteristics expected in the common ancestors of the higher apes and man. In general these types are more manlike than existing great apes in that their incisor and canine teeth are smaller, the spaces between them (diastemata) reduced, the chin is slightly better developed, the forehead fuller, and the frontal sinuses larger. On the other hand the molar teeth are, on the whole, larger than in modern man, whereas the cranial capacities fall somewhat short of even the smallest hominid brain case (estimated adult capacity of *Australopithecus*, 600 c.c.; *Plesianthropus*, female, 440 c.c.; *Paranthropus*, male, 600-650 c.c.).

Readers unfamiliar with paleontology and anatomy may be surprised to find that so many of the types described below are based upon comparatively meager skeletal remains, such as a jaw or a few bones. Only a thorough course in anatomy or physical anthropology would convince the most skeptical of the validity of reconstructions based upon such evidence, and for the present we must content ourselves with the assurance that the following summaries represent the prevalent opinion of experts in these fields. A further surprise may be registered with respect to the scarcity of the remains of fossil human types. We can only remind ourselves that it is a fortunate combination of circumstances that bones hundreds of thousands of years old are preserved at all, and that it is a matter of luck that they are discovered by modern investigators. Ancient man, of course, did not lay his bones away properly labeled and protected for the benefit of modern anthropologists.

The Oldest Hominid Fossils

We shall now examine the hominid fossils, beginning with those which seem least removed from subhuman ancestors in structure and mentality.

MEGANTHROPUS PALEOJAVANICUS (Ancient Java Ape Man).
  Discovery: 1941 by G. H. R. von Königswald in Central Java.
  Geological Age: Probably lower Pleistocene.
  Remains: Fragments of a jaw.
  General Characteristics: Many human features, but size is greater than that of any other form of man, and is close to that of the large male gorilla.

GIGANPITHECUS BLACKI (Chinese Giant Ape).
  This type has been recognized on the basis of three giant manlike molar teeth retrieved by von Königswald from Chinese apothecary shops in Hong Kong between 1934 and 1939, and subsequently studied by Weidenreich. It was named in honor of Dr. Davidson Black, who first recognized the Peking type of fossil man (see below). No geological dating.

It is possible that these two giant types are related and that they stood in ancestral relationship to the Pithecanthropus-Sinanthropus group of Java and China.

PITHECANTHROPUS ERECTUS (Java Ape Man, Trinil Man).
  Discovery by Dr. Eugene Dubois of Holland, 1891-1892, in bed of Solo River, near Trinil, Java. Second adult specimen discovered by von Königswald, Central Java, 1937; a third, juvenile skull, 1938; a fourth, also 1938.
  Geological Age: First or second interglacial periods (some disagreement) while Java was part of Asiatic mainland. Associated with extinct elephant Stegodon.
  Remains: Original discovery included top of the skull, left thigh-bone, three molar teeth, part of jaw bone, scattered over a distance of forty-six feet.

Representative parts of two other skulls and fragments of a fourth found recently.

General Characteristics: (1) From left femur 455 mm. long and bearing the linea aspera on the back, it is calculated that the ape man stood 5 feet 8 inches tall and weighed about 154 pounds. (2) Skull: external index, 71.2; endocranial index (of brain), 80; this indicates that much of the length of the skull was due to heavy development of bone, particularly over the eyes. Capacity, 940 c.c. (largest gorilla 650 c.c.). Parietal and frontal association areas of the brain showed some development, indicating probability of speech, memory, and culture. (3) Teeth more manlike than apelike. (4) No chin, heavy jaws. (5) Heavy brow ridges. (6) Low vaulted skull.

The third specimen reported by von Königswald in 1938 shows resemblances to Sinanthropus and indicates that Pithecanthropus and Sinanthropus may be closely related.

HOMO MODJOKERTENSIS (Another Pithecanthropus type).

Geological Age: Lower Pleistocene, possibly older than Pithecanthropus (some disagreement).

Remains: Fairly complete cranium, but without facial bones or teeth. Obviously a child, but of indeterminate age because teeth are missing. Probably about two years of age.

General Characteristics: Cranial capacity 650 c.c. which is about two-thirds that of modern infant one year old.

SINANTHROPUS PEKINENSIS (Peking Man).

Discovery: In 1926 two human teeth were found at Choukoutien, thirty-seven miles southwest of Peking in cave deposits of early Pleistocene age. In 1927 another tooth was found. On the basis of this single tooth (a fossilized lower molar), the late Davidson Black, Professor of Anatomy in Peking Union Medical College, established a new genus and species of hominid, named *Sinanthropus pekinensis*. Fossils are found in filled-in fissures and caves at base of low limestone hills, which were open caves in Pleistocene times. Further excavations carried on after 1927 by Cenozoic Research Laboratory of Geological Survey of China in collaboration with Peking Union Medical College, recovered a number of loose teeth and two lower jaws with receding chins. A nearly complete brain case was found in 1929 by W. C. Pei, a Chinese paleontologist. A second skull and several fragmentary jaw-bones and teeth were subsequently recovered. Three more skulls and some fragments were announced in 1936 by F. Weidenreich, Black's successor at Peking. Crude stone implements of chert were found with the bones. Over one hundred loose teeth, several loose jaws, and a variety of miscellaneous bones have also been found.

Geological Age: Latest opinion would place Sinanthropus in the period in North China corresponding to the Mindel (second) glaciation in Europe. Certainly it is at the latest middle Pleistocene in age.

Remains: To date Sinanthropus is represented by the skeletal parts of about forty individuals, including male and female adult and juvenile specimens. No individual is known from an entire skeleton, and many are represented by teeth only. Remains consist chiefly of fragments of skulls and lower jaws; a single clavicle is known; also the fragments of seven thigh-bones and one arm-bone. Skulls usually occur in groups isolated from long bones, indicating possible victims of head-hunting. The basal portions of the skulls are often crushed. Remains of hearths occur and in one place a pile of seeds of a fruit (hackberry) later used by American Indians for flavoring food.

General Characteristics: (1) Medium stature, upright posture, as shown by limb bones which do not differ greatly in proportions from those of modern man; (2) low vaulted dolichocephalic skull; (3) narrow forehead, but wider than that of Pithecanthropus; (4) heavy supra-orbital torus; (5) narrow parietal region; (6) thick-walled brain case; (7) average skull capacity about 1,000 c.c., with range from 900 to 1,200 c.c.; (8) nasal bones broad and flat; (9) cheek-bones broad and flat; (10) teeth resemble those of apes more than those of recent man; larger than Neanderthal teeth; wrinkled crowns, "shovel incisors" (characteristic of modern American Indians and some other Mongoloids).

EOANTHROPUS DAWSONII (Piltdown Man).

Discovery: By Mr. Charles Dawson, a lawyer, in Sussex, England, 1911-1912, in a shallow bed of alluvial gravel at Piltdown. Cranial fragments were found first, then within a few feet of them the right half of a lower jaw containing two molar teeth. A considerable controversy has raged over the question of whether or not the skull and jaw belong to the same creature, although the best authority now inclines to the belief that they do. In 1915, two miles from Piltdown, two other fragments of frontal and parietal region of closely similar cranium were found.

Geological Age: Gravels in which the remains were found are generally thought to be early Pleistocene. Since they represent an alluvial deposit, however, there has been some doubt as to whether the human remains are contemporaneous with the geological deposit.

Remains: Original find at Piltdown: left temporal bone, left parietal with a considerable portion of the frontal, a large piece of the right parietal, posterior part of the occipital, nasal bones; all of these cranial fragments are not substantially different from *Homo sapiens*, except for the thickness of the bones of the brain case. In addition, however, were found: most of the right half of the lower jaw with two molar teeth. The jaw very closely resembles that of a chimpanzee. The lower molar teeth, however, although primitive and with five cusps, have higher crowns than the teeth of the chimpanzee. Somewhat later in the same site a canine tooth and also the nasal bones apparently of the same skull were found.

General Characteristics (assuming skull and jaw belong together): (1) Mesocephalic skull of quite modern appearance: well developed frontal region; poorly developed supra-orbital ridges; capacity 1,240 c.c.; (2) apelike jaw; no chin prominence; apelike simian shelf (not present in either Neanderthal or Heidelberg types); (3) canine tooth large and projecting above level of other teeth (apelike); incisor teeth probably large and apelike; (4) pronounced prognathism of apelike jaw and modern-type skull. Cultural remains included: a number of eoliths, one paleolithic worked flint and a large bone implement.

The Neanderthal Species and Related Forms

The Neanderthaloid group of fossils are the most numerous and most widely distributed of any of the known types of paleanthropic men.

Over thirty skeletons or parts of skeletons usually classified as Neanderthal or closely related in type have been recovered from various localities in Europe, Africa, Asia, and Indonesia. In addition to the true Neanderthaloid, a number of related species are included in this group: *Homo soloensis, H. rhodesiensis, H. heidelbergensis.* While each of these species shows some features peculiar to itself, the group as a whole is characterized by the following common features: (1) a flattened, gorilloid skull vault; (2) strong supra-orbital torus; (3) extremely sloping forehead; (4) maximum skull breadth just above the ear holes; (5) protruding "bun-like" occiput, with heavy occipital torus; (6) extremely long and broad face; (7) excessively large subnasal portion of the face; (8) canine fossa (a distinctively sapiens feature) lacking; (9) molar teeth with fused roots and enlarged pulp cavities; (10) dental borders even and canines not interlocking.

Homo Heidelbergensis (Heidelberg Man).

Discovery: In 1907 in sand quarry at Mauer, near Heidelberg, imbedded in river sand at depth of over seventy-nine feet.

Geological Age: Certainly second interglacial period, if not earlier.

Remains: A single jaw with teeth, the only specimen of its type so far discovered.

General Characteristics: (1) Very heavy and large; (2) no chin; (3) teeth and dental arch definitely human and not larger than in some modern types; ramus (lateral ascending portion of jaw) very wide with shallow notch; (4) teeth, human: canines not enlarged as in apes; third molars slightly smaller than others, as in man; molar crowns larger, but of modern type. Heidelberg Man was probably a proto-Neanderthal type.

Homo Neanderthalensis.

Discovery: In 1856 workmen digging in limestone cave in the Neanderthal, near Düsseldorf, Germany, discovered top of a skull, several arm- and leg-bones and pieces of a shoulder girdle and cranium. Dr. William King named it *Homo neanderthalensis* in 1864, but for some years most opinion followed Thomas Huxley in regarding it as an aberrant, apelike form of *Homo sapiens.* The famous German anatomist, Rudolph Virchow, asserted that it was a pathological specimen of *sapiens,* while others inclined to the view that the skull was that of an idiot. In 1848, the first known Neanderthal skull had been found in Forbes' quarry at the base of the Rock of Gibraltar, but it was not until 1906 that Professor Sollas of Oxford, after careful study, recognized it as a female Neanderthal. Since these original discoveries, abundant skeletal remains of the Neanderthal people have been recovered in Germany, Belgium, France, Channel Islands, Spain, Italy, Yugoslavia, the Crimea, Asiatic Russia(?), Tangier, and Palestine. Remains have been accompanied by fossilized bones of extinct animals and by artifacts which unquestionably prove both the antiquity of the Neanderthal people and the development of their culture (Mousterian). The most complete skeleton of Neanderthal type so far found is that named for the cave of La Chapelle-aux-Saints, in the Corréze, France. This was found in 1908 and was apparently a case of deliberate burial.

Geological Age: Neanderthal men lived in Europe apparently during the whole of the third (Riss-Würm) interglacial period and continued to occupy this region until the closing phases of the Würm (fourth) glaciation.
Remains: Practically all skeletal parts of Neanderthal man have been recovered, as well as specimens of different ages and stages of maturation. The Neanderthal is our best-known fossil type. Some of the principal finds follow:
Spy (Belgium): two partial skeletons found in cavern in 1886; include fairly well-preserved crania, jaws, and many of the limb bones. Geological associations clear and of Würm period.
Krapina (Croatia, Yugoslavia): fragments of a dozen or more Neanderthal skeletons including several children found in a rock shelter 1891. Some of the long bones were intentionally crushed and charred, perhaps indicating cannibalism.
La Chapelle-aux-Saints: skull, long bones, parts of shoulder girdle, pelvis, vertebral column, portions of hands and feet (1908).
Le Moustier (1908): boy about fifteen years old; shows adolescent characteristics of the type; in addition to bones, teeth well preserved.
La Ferrassie (1910-1911): an adult man and adult woman. In female, hands and feet well preserved.
La Quina: adult female (1911); skeleton of child not more than eight years of age (1916).
Weimar-Ehringsdorf-Steinheim (Germany): lower tooth near Weimar, 1892; two lower jaws near Ehringsdorf (1914-1916), the one that of an elderly individual, other of a child; cranial portion of young adult skull at Ehringsdorf (1925); nearly complete skull at Steinheim (1933). All of these specimens are definitely third interglacial.
Rome: nearly complete skull (1929); second skull (1935); third at Monte Circeo near Rome (1938) in midst of oval of stones indicating ceremonial burial and with post-mortem mutilation of the occipital base, possibly for removal of the brains.

General characteristics of Neanderthal type may be summarized as follows:

1. Short stature. La Chapelle-aux-Saints, 5 feet 2 inches; Neanderthal, 5 feet 4 inches; female La Ferrassie, 4 feet 9 inches.

2. Long bones: heavy, thick in shaft, large joints, marked muscle insertions; femura (thigh-bones) bowed forward as in apes and lack pilaster along the back which is conspicuous in modern thigh-bones. Upper surfaces of articular heads of tibiae (shin-bones) are inclined backwards, indicating a "bent knee" posture. "Squatting facets" on femur and tibia. Tibia oval in cross-section (prismatic in modern man). The thigh-bone of Pithecanthropus is actually more "modern" than those of Neanderthal.

3. Skull: brain case elongated and low; supra-orbital ridges immense, but divided; forehead low and retreating; occiput protuberant and bun-shaped; face long and prognathous; orbits large; nose short and broad;

mandible (lower jaw) powerful; rudimentary chin. Skull capacity well within or above modern average: 1,100 (Steinheim) to over 1,600 (La Chapelle-aux-Saints). Cheek-bones slope obliquely backwards; subnasal space long; lower border of nasal aperture sharp and nasal spine sharp; canine fossa lacking; mastoid processes small (large in man, a feature associated with head balanced on end of spinal column); marked occipital torus; attachments for muscles at back of neck extend high up; foramen magnum set far back—all of these features indicating that head hung forward.

4. Teeth: palate broad and U-shaped (paraboloid in modern man); taurodont molar teeth (large pulp cavities); teeth large; first and second lower molars frequently show fifth cusp; canines do not interlock; bite of incisors even; teeth always free from cavities.

5. Jaws: condyles large; articulate with shallow glenoid fossa (an apelike feature); very slight chin prominence; jaws protruding; ample space for tongue movement, but some of the muscles must have been inferior judging by the size of their insertions.

6. Vertebral column: lumbar curve feeble and sacrum straight instead of being anteriorly curved as in modern man (apelike features).

7. Arms: forearm short relative to upper arm (manlike feature).

8. Brain: right-handedness in La Chapelle specimen (left side of brain larger than right); crude and simple convolutions; frontal lobes 36 per cent of cerebral surface (apes 32, modern man 43); speech area well developed, also sensory, visual, auditory areas.

9. Ribs: round or prismatic (flat in modern man).

10. Foot structure: heel-bone short; probably weight borne on outside of foot; otherwise a human, not an apelike, foot.

Although Neanderthal man shows some anthropoid characteristics, in many ways he was as human as modern man. The point to bear in mind is that the Neanderthal population of Western Europe was not the ancestral type of *Homo sapiens*, although some interbreeding may have taken place after sapiens appeared on the scene.

HOMO SOLOENSIS (Solo Man).

Discovery: By W. F. F. Oppenoorth of the Geological Survey of Java in 1931 and following years, near Ngandong, a village near the Solo River, only six miles from Trinil, the Pithecanthropus site.

Geological Age: Probably comparable to the Riss-Würm (third) interglacial period of Europe.

Remains: Represented to date by eleven skulls and skull fragments and two tibiae (shin-bones). In all the skulls the basal region is missing, suggesting, as in the case of Peking man, that they may have been opened for removal of the brains, or were hacked away in head-hunting. No facial bones, jaws, or teeth.

General Characteristics: (1) Average capacity of skull about 1,200 c.c., (2) heavy supra-orbital torus, low retreating forehead; (3) occipital torus very heavy, indicating heavy neck muscles; (4) mastoid region of sapiens type. In many ways Solo man looks like a descendant of Pithecanthropus and possibly like an ancestor of the modern Australoid race. At the present time he is assigned to the general Neanderthal group, although he differs from the European Neanderthaloids in many respects. Bone and antler tools and some stone balls of andesite associated with skulls.

HOMO RHODESIENSIS (Rhodesian Man; Broken Hill Man).

Discovery: Found during mining operations at Broken Hill, Northern Rhodesia in 1921, at extreme end of long cave.

Geological Age: Uncertain due to disturbed condition of deposits.

Remains: Nearly complete skull, lacking lower jaw; sacrum, fragments of pelvis, a few leg bones.

General Characteristics: Many experts consider this type not as a Neanderthaloid, but as an aberrant sapiens type. (1) Low cranial vault; (2) supra-orbital torus immense and forms a solid "shelf" above the eyes; (3) face enormous in all measurements, with larger subnasal space than in any other human skull; (4) teeth have caries, the only fossil human teeth which do; (5) occipital torus and attachments for neck muscles very large; (6) tall stature shown by leg bones, which also indicate that the leg was fully extended, rather than being partially bent as in Neanderthal man; (7) cranial capacity about 1,300 c.c. A few crude stone implements associated.

All of the above finds indicate that the generalized Neanderthal type was widely distributed and that several "races" developed within the generalized type, as is also true of modern man. To quote Weidenreich:

If we admit that mankind of today, uniform regarding its general character but differing in special appearance, has developed from various regional stocks starting even from an earlier stage than that represented by the Prehominids, and if we assume, furthermore, that development was not going on simultaneously everywhere but was accelerated in one place and retarded in another, perhaps as a consequence of local influences, then all the discrepancies between the morphologic and chronologic sequence of the known types of fossil man can be understood. The old theory, claiming that man evolved exclusively from one center whence he spread over the Old World each time afresh after having entered a new phase of evolution, no longer tallies with the paleontological finds. For *Pithecanthropus* and *Homo soloensis*, both inhabitants of the same region, represent undoubtedly subsequent stages of one and the same local Javanese branch of early man and prove thereby, at least so far as Java is concerned, that Java man was tracing his own way in the direction of recent man independent of what may have happened to similar stages in other parts of the world.... The terms which are generally used to designate different human types involve the idea that each one represents a more or less divergent genus without generic connections. In order to avoid this incorrect interpretation, the time has come, as I think, to eliminate all those names which may lead to some misunderstanding in this regard. Instead of *Pithecanthropus erectus* we should speak of *Homo erectus javanesis. Sinanthropus pekinensis* should be replaced by *Homo erectus pekinensis* or *sinensis* and *Homo soloensis* by *Homo neanderthalensis soloensis*, etc.[4]

Transitional Neanderthal-Sapiens Types

Although the Neanderthal people do not appear to be ancestral to the modern type of man, is there any evidence that these two types may have interbred? A number of specimens have appeared which *suggest*—we do not say *prove*—this possibility.

GALILEE SKULL: Discovered in 1925 in a cave near the sea of Galilee. Pure Neanderthal type. Remains consist chiefly of frontal bone and right cheekbone. Because of geographical location may be partially ancestral to Mount Carmel types (below).

MOUNT CARMEL SKELETONS OF PALESTINE (Tabun and Skhul Men).
   Discovery: In 1931 and following years Dr. T. D. McCown (now of University of California) discovered the representative skeletal remains of at least twelve individuals, ten from a cave called Mughâret-es-Skhul and two from the cave called Mughâret-et-Tabun. In addition fragments of about twenty-eight additional individuals were recovered. The material has been published by McCown and the outstanding British authority on fossil man, Sir Arthur Keith.[5]
   Geological Age: The skeletal remains were found imbedded in breccia which is definitely of the latter part of the Riss-Würm (third) interglacial period. Directly associated were large quantities of artifacts of the Levalloiso-Mousterian type, which is also the culture associated with Neanderthal men in Europe and elsewhere.
   Remains: Forty individuals represented, twelve sufficiently complete to permit reconstruction. Both sexes, several ages, and practically all parts of the skeleton are represented, so that the finds as a whole constitute one of the richest discoveries of ancient man ever made.
   General Characteristics: The main interest in these skeletons centers about the fact that they present a range of physical form which varies from Neanderthal to modern man. In general the Tabun skeletal material is most purely Neanderthal in type, whereas the Skhul skeletons more closely resemble modern man. The range of traits is exhibited between individuals, that is, individuals may be arranged in a series beginning with those most closely resembling the pure Neanderthal type and leading up to those most like modern man. The variability is also to be seen in single individuals, that is, a single individual will show a combination of Neanderthal and of sapiens physical features. The result is that in these specimens we have a group which as a whole shows a mingling of paleanthropic and neanthropic physical features. At present there is disagreement among authorities as to the explanation. There are two possibilities: (1) the Mount Carmel people may represent a stage in the evolution of Neanderthal man into *Homo sapiens,* or, (2) they may be the result of a crossing or hybridization between Neanderthal and proto-sapiens groups. McCown and Keith hold to the first view, partly because no pure sapiens types of equal antiquity have been discovered in Palestine as yet. Most other authorities, however, regard the Mount Carmel people as hybrids. The outstanding feature of these people

in the skull is their possession of heavy and projecting supra-orbital ridges and a large heavy face (Neanderthaloid features) in combination with a high and large brain case typical of modern man.

BRÜNN-PREDMOST-BRÜX-COMBE CAPELLE: All of these finds are late Pleistocene in geological age and Upper Paleolithic in culture. The Brünn, Predmost, and Brüx finds, consisting of numerous skeletons, were all found in Czechoslovakia, while the Combe Capelle specimen was discovered in the Dordogne in France. All of these show a dolichocephalic skull, low vault, prominent supra-orbital ridges, and poorly developed chin (Neanderthal characteristics) which are thought by some to indicate mixture between sapiens and Neanderthal stock.

PODKOUMOK (Caucasus) and CHWALYNAK (Volga River, Russia): Two skulls, one from each of these localities, are also considered by some authorities to show mixture of Neanderthaloid and sapiens traits. If true, their easterly position is important.

UZBEKISTAN SKULL from Central Asia, at first thought to be definitely Neanderthal, is now considered to be a transitional type as well.

Regarding these Asiatic transitional types, we may quote Weidenreich: [6]

The Uzbekistan Skull, the Mount Carmel Skulls and possibly the Podkumok Skull represent forms which fit in between the Neanderthalian (Mousterian) stage of human evolution and that of modern man (*Homo sapiens*). The Uzbekistan Skull has been recovered from Central Asia, the Mount Carmel Skulls from Palestine and the Podkumok Skull from a river bank between the Black and Caspian Seas north of the Caucasus. These localities suggest that intermediate types may be found all over Western and Central Asia. There and not in Europe the transformation of the Neanderthalian into modern man may have taken place. The gap which separates the European Neanderthalian from *Homo sapiens* and which led to the deduction that the former has become extinct without leaving behind any descendants, seems to exist only in Central Europe. Toward the East intermediate forms emerge which bear witness to the continuation of the human line of evolution.

D. EARLY NEANTHROPIC TYPES

We do not have the space here to discuss all of the many finds of early *Homo sapiens*, but only certain highly significant ones. In the foregoing section we have seen that Neanderthal man held sway in Europe and in many other parts of the Old World during the third interglacial period and during most of the fourth glaciation itself, a period of occupation amounting to about 100,000 years. Shortly after the climax of the Würm (fourth) glaciation Neanderthal man suddenly becomes scarce in European sites, soon disappears altogether and is replaced almost without transition by men of the sapiens type. We do not know where the sapiens, or modern, type of man first evolved, although a few finds indicate that proto-sapiens types may be at least as old as the Neanderthal type. At all events, modern men were not common in Europe until about 25,000 years ago at the earliest, when they started to replace the Neanderthals. This replacement may have followed two courses: (1) the modern men may have driven out and exterminated their predecessors by force, guile, and the use of superior culture. This seems actually to have been the case in most of Europe. (2) The modern men may have interbred with and partially absorbed the grosser Neanderthals. This may have happened, as we have seen, in Palestine and farther East, and Dr. Carleton S. Coon has presented a strong case for its occurrence in parts of Europe.[7]

Middle Pleistocene Neanthropic Types

SWANSCOMBE MAN: Remains consisting of a parietal and occipital bone of a single individual, found in 1936 in the Thames Valley, England. Geological age is third interglacial, cultural remains associated with the bones are of Acheulean type. The bones indicate a high vaulted brain case of modern type (lacking the heavy brow ridges and occipital ridges of paleanthropic types). In this connection, we recall the "modern" aspect of the brain case of the geologically older Piltdown Man, also from Southern England.

GALLEY HILL MAN: Found in 1888, in Thames Valley, also of Riss-Würm geological age and accompanied by Acheulean culture. Skeletal remains show following features of the type: modern type brain case, cephalic index, 69, protruding occiput, sloping forehead, which is also very broad; no prognathism; chin of medium prominence; stature short, about 160 cm. Primitive features include: brow ridges, relatively small, but continuous; small mastoids; third molars large. This must have been a generalized form of ancestral white man, in Coon's opinion, who came into Europe with the retreat of one glacier and went out with the advance of the next. Coon regards the Galley Hill man as "the logical ancestor of the Mediterranean race and of all the subraces related to it."

KANAM MAN. Found by Leakey in East Africa, this specimen consists of a single mandible (lower jaw). Although Leakey considers it early Pleistocene, it probably is somewhat later. The jaw is of human type, showing some paleanthropic features.

KANJERA MAN: Four fragmentary skull caps found in East Africa. Extremely dolichocephalic with indices under 70. Smooth skulls, modern in type. Age probably Middle or Late Pleistocene.

Late Pleistocene Types in Europe

These early types of sapiens give us some hints that the modern type like ourselves was evolving at the same time that the Neanderthal type was flourishing in Europe and therefore did not suddenly appear without antecedents. Culturally these modern-type men, when they appeared in strength in Europe about 25,000 years ago, were much superior to their predecessors, and are identified with the Aurignacian culture. Aside from transitional types, showing some features thought to indicate mixture with Neanderthals, modern man of late Pleistocene time in Europe is represented in two so-called races, the Grimaldi and the Cro-Magnon. These "races" may actually have been merely variations within the general European population of the time. We mention only two outstanding "types."

GRIMALDI.

Discovery: 1901 in Grotte des Enfants on the Mediterranean coast near Monaco. This cave and neighboring ones had previously yielded remains of Cro-Magnon man.

Geological Age: Late Pleistocene. Culture Aurignacian.

Remains: Practically complete skeletons of a mature woman and of an adolescent boy about fourteen years old. Purposely buried together, suggesting that they may have been mother and son.

General Characteristics: These people were definitely *Homo sapiens* in type but interest centers about the fact that they show a number of features found in the modern Negro races: (1) dolichocephaly; (2) chins slightly developed; (3) pronounced alveolar prognathism; (4) nasal bones flattened and the nasal border of Negroid type; (5) relatively long legs and great length of forearm and shin in comparison to upper arm and thigh. In spite of these features we must be hesitant to regard these two skeletons as representative of an early Negroid group until more evidence is available.

CRO-MAGNON.

Discovery: First recognition of the type was given by the French anthropologists Quatrefages and Hamy to five skeletons found in the rock shelter of Cro-Magnon at Les Eyzies in the Dordogne, France, in 1868. Numerous other skeletons of this type have been found since in various parts of Europe.

Characteristics of the Type: (1) Men are tall, often over six feet; (2) cranium is high, capacious, smooth, and dolichocephalic; (3) face is short and broad (disharmonic skull); (4) forehead is vertical, chin prominent, and there is no protrusion of the jaw (orthognathous); (5) forearm and shin are relatively long.

Aberrant Types: Skeletons found at Chancelade, near Perigueux, France, in 1888 and at Obercassel in Germany in 1914, are like the Cro-Magnon type in general, although short of stature (about 5 feet) and with somewhat more massive skulls. The Chancelade skulls are quite similar to those of modern Eskimo.

Apparently the Cro-Magnon type did not die out in Europe but was absorbed into later mixtures. Numerous Cro-Magnon features are recognizable in certain population groups of modern France and the Iberian Peninsula.

Late Pleistocene Types in Indonesia and Australia

A discovery of later geological age from Java, considered in connection with its possible affiliations with the earlier Pithecanthropus and Solo types from the same region, may have an important bearing upon the origin and migration of the modern Australian race. We refer to the Wadjak.

HOMO WADJAKENSIS (Wadjak Man).
Discovery: 1889 by Dubois, the discoverer of Pithecanthropus, near the surface of an ancient alluvial deposit.
Geological Age: Late Pleistocene.
Remains: Two incomplete skulls.
General Characteristics: (1) Brains were very large, 1,550 and 1,650 c.c.; (2) brow ridges heavy, as in Australians; (3) jaws and teeth heavy and chin weak, but present; (4) nasal root depressed under an overhanging glabella; with nasal root narrow and opening wide, as in Australians.

KEILOR SKULL.
Discovery: 1940 in a sandpit about ten miles northwest of Melbourne, Australia.
Geological Age: Probably post-Pleistocene, according to Weidenreich,[8] although original report assigns it to third interglacial period.
Remains: Skull (which was broken into three pieces by the pick of the workman who made the discovery), one fossilized limb bone, several other fragments of bone. Possibly a quartzite flake artifact.
General Characteristics: According to Weidenreich, practically a duplicate of the Wadjak type, perhaps slightly more evolved toward the modern Australian type.

A number of other finds from Australia itself may be regarded as possible progenitors of the modern Australoids.

TALGAI SKULL.
Discovery: In Queensland, northern Australia, in 1884, but first described in detail by S. A. Smith in 1918.
Geological Age: Late Pleistocene.
Remains: Crushed skull of a boy about fourteen or fifteen years of age.
General Characteristics: Distinctly Australoid in type, but surpasses modern Australoids in size of palate and teeth, especially the canines. Also more prognathous. Dolichocephalic skull, capacity estimated at about 1,300 c.c., which is about the average for modern male Australians.

COHUNA SKULL.
Discovery: In Victoria, Australia, near Murray River, in 1925.
Geological Age: Geological and paleontological evidence not clear. Indication of antiquity in partial mineralization of the bones.
Remains: Adult male skull and parts of several skeletons.
General Characteristics: Primitive Australoid. Teeth and palate extremely large, but brain case like modern Australoids.

Late Pleistocene Types in Africa

In considering the antiquity of man in Africa we call to mind the possible Neanderthaloid affinities of Rhodesian man as well as the presence of middle Pleistocene men of sapiens type in East Africa at Kanam and

Kanjera. Several geologically later specimens have been uncovered in South Africa, all of Negroid or proto-Bushman stock.

BOSKOPF; T'ZITZIKAMA; FISH HOEK: All of these finds are of late Pleistocene age from South Africa. Generally speaking the skulls show similarities to those of the modern Bushmen of South Africa, although the Pleistocene men were of normal or taller than normal stature. It is conceivable that the modern Bushmen represent a degeneration from this earlier type, together with some mixture with a Mongoloid strain.

SPRINGBOK-OLDOWAY. The Springbok finds, from the Transvaal, and the Oldoway skull from Kenya, East Africa, are subject to controversy. Physically, however, they are in some respects proto-Negroid.

An apparently tall, slender Negroid skeleton, called the Asselar man, was found in a Late Pleistocene (?) river deposit in 1927 about 260 miles north of Timbuctu in the Sahara desert, thus adding to the evidence that the Negroid type had been differentiated by the beginning of the recent geological period in Africa.

Pleistocene Man in America

Although human artifacts of late Pleistocene age have a wide distribution in America, indisputable evidence of Pleistocene human skeletal remains has not been produced. The best cases to date are two finds published by Professor A. E. Jenks of the University of Minnesota during the 1930's. These, the Minnesota Lady and the Browns Valley Man, seem to have been recovered from late Pleistocene deposits perhaps 15,000 to 20,000 years old. They differ in no important respects from modern North American Indians of the same general region. There seems to be no doubt that man entered the Western Hemisphere before the close of the Pleistocene, and if these finds are acceptable, it is evident that the Mongoloid variety of mankind had already differentiated before the close of the Glacial Period. We thus see that there is evidence that the major modern varieties of mankind were already differentiated at least 15,000 to 20,000 years ago, for we have examined the Pleistocene proto-white men of Europe, proto-Negroids of Africa, and proto-Australoids of Indonesia and Australia.

THE EVOLUTIONARY HISTORY OF MANKIND

In the foregoing section has been presented an outline of the various types of fossil man, classified and named, according to the commonly accepted "classical" framework, into various genera and species. According to this traditional view the course of human evolution may be likened to a tree producing constantly diverging branches and twigs.

The various fossil types are thus considered to represent, for the most part, branches rather than the main trunk. All but one of these branches have withered, leaving the present species as the sole surviving branch, graced by a number of divergent twigs which we call races.

Recently a different view has been suggested, particularly by Weidenreich [9] and Dobzhansky.[10] In brief, this newer analysis postulates that man has been a single genus and a single species since the time of his divergence from ape and proto-human forebears, and that the various "genera" and "species" of fossil man which we have considered in the foregoing section are actually to be considered merely as races of a single species. This view of the matter would simplify certain questions which are now implied in the traditional classifications and explanations. We may briefly summarize certain points of the argument.

Biologists and geneticists point out that, on the whole, distinct species are "groups of populations which are reproductively isolated to the extent that the exchange of genes between them is absent or so slow that the genetic differences are not diminished or swamped." [11] Races, on the other hand, are "populations differing in the incidence of certain genes, but actually exchanging or potentially able to exchange genes across whatever boundaries (usually geographic) separate them." [12] In other words, species are not normally interfertile or do not interbreed, because of evolved differences in their respective genetic systems. Races, on the other hand, are either actually or potentially interfertile, but, so long as they remain distinct from each other in physical characteristics, are isolated by geographical or other nongenetic influences which prevent actual mingling of their genes. Thus so long as two groups show evidence of interfertility, even though they appear to be considerably different in appearance, it is safer to regard them as races rather than as distinct species.

A certain amount of evidence appears in the fossil record which suggests the possibility that the various Pleistocene types of men owe their physical differences to geographical isolation of a racial type, rather than to genetic isolation of a species type. Thus Weidenreich considers the various individuals of the Pekin and Java types to show sufficient similarity to be considered members of the same species. The Pekin and Java types can thus be considered two closely related horizontal or contemporaneous races, existing as early as the second glacial period.

What "races" were living in Europe or other parts of the world at this time is not clear. If Piltdown is accepted, it would seem that a "smooth-skulled" type or race had appeared in Europe even earlier than the Pekin-Java types in Asia. We see that the "smooth-skulled" type appears in later fossils, such as Swanscombe and Galley Hill (and possibly as early as the second interglacial period in the person of Heidelberg man, on the evidence of the jaw only). During the third interglacial period a "craggy-skulled" race, in the form of the numerous and well distributed Neanderthaloid specimens, was clearly inhabiting Europe, the Mediterranean region, possibly Africa (Rhodesian variety), and Central Asia (Uzbekistan). That the Neanderthaloids and "smooth-skulled" types were not separate species, but merely races originally geographically isolated, is suggested by the various fossil specimens, mentioned above (transitional Neanderthal-sapiens types), which seem to show intermixture between the two. It is thus possible to think of all the early types as racial variations of a single species, perhaps, which developed distinguishing features at various times and places as a result of geographical isolation and adaptation, but which did not lose their basic genetic unity.

Thus we are able to speak of "vertical races" developing through time, at least in certain parts of the world, and surviving in modern man. For example, it seems plausible to trace a series beginning with the Java Ape Men, through Solo, Wadjak, and Cohuna to the modern Australian natives. Pekin man may be linked through an unknown Neanderthaloid form to the modern Mongoloids. Rhodesian Man may have given rise to certain African forms, and the Neanderthaloids, mixing with their "smooth-skulled" contemporaries, may be the ancestors of some modern European types.

Although it cannot be said that this scheme is proven at present, it has the virtue of conforming to modern evolutionary and biological theory, and at the same time relieves the anthropologist of the necessity of postulating separate evolutionary developments and extinctions for a considerable variety of what were formerly believed to be radically different forms of hominids. At all events, there is so far nothing in the evidence which would refute this theory, in the light of the modern knowledge of genetics. This point of view also has a considerable bearing on our consideration of modern racial types. For, if it is entirely possible from the biological and genetic points of view, to consider forms so superficially unlike as the Neanderthal and sapiens types as racial or subspecies variations within a single species, the considerably fewer divergences between modern racial types sink into relative insignficance.

NOTES TO CHAPTER 4

1. Gregory, 1922.
2. Some authorities regard Dryopithecus as already specialized.
3. The mountain gorilla, however, is less arboreal than any other infra-human primate except the baboon.
4. Weidenreich, 1940.
5. McCown and Keith, 1939.

6. Weidenreich, 1945b, p. 161.
7. Coon, 1939.
8. Weidenreich, 1945a.
9. Weidenreich, 1943.
10. Dobzhansky, 1944.
11. *Ibid.*, p. 252.
12. *Ibid.*, p. 252.

For a recent, although not final, discussion of the giant early men of Java and China, see Weidenreich, 1945.

The reader is referred to Hooton, 1946, Part IV, for a more detailed, yet readable, discussion of fossil men.

As this book goes to press report has been made of the finding of so-called Tepexpan man, apparently in Pleistocene deposits in the Valley of Mexico. No reliable statement of the physical characteristics is yet available. (*Science*, May 9, 1947).

CHAPTER 5

The Hereditary Varieties of Modern Man

Of the various evolutionary experiments of the Pleistocene, now extinct, only one species of man survives, *Homo sapiens*. But this species has been on the scene for at least the past 25,000 years and in the interval has developed certain biological subgroups. No one who has seen some of the varieties of man has to be convinced that there is "something different" about a Negro, for instance, as compared with a Mongoloid, or that even the whites do not enjoy exact uniformity. For the student of man and of human culture it is essential to have at least a sound elementary idea of the physical differences within the human species and to be acquainted with their significance, if any, in cultural life. In short, there *are* hereditary variations among men and upon the basis of inherited and presumed genetic differences it is possible to sort out or classify certain subgroups. Do these hereditary subdivisions make any difference to culture?

It has been customary to describe these subgroups as *races*. Unfortunately this word has been so loosely employed during the past one hundred years or so, not only by political and other doctrinaire montebanks, but also by earnest scholars, that it now has a rather ambiguous meaning. In contemporary scientific literature, it has come to have two different types of referents. On the one hand, physical anthropologists and other zoölogists use *race* to designate subgroups within a species which are characterized and differentiated by hereditarily controlled physical features. On the other hand, the term is often employed by sociological and cultural students to describe certain types of culturally defined attitudes and other social relations between groups.[1] The latter is the usage of the "sociologists of race" who quite properly point out that in many situations "race" is merely a state of mind in which physical features and biological factors play a relatively insignificant rôle, if any.[2] In fact a whole branch of sociology dealing with these matters has grown up, usually labeled "race relations" in college catalogues.

In between and around these two groups of truth-seekers, the term

Note: References for this chapter will be found following Chapter 6.

"race" is often used by publicists and axe-grinders to refer to almost any concept which a writer or speaker wishes to employ in an argument whose purpose is to make invidious comparisons between two or more groups of people. For example, the defense of slavery started a series of fatuous "race" discussions during the past century in our own country, and we have recently seen the Nazis carry the misapplications of the term to the ultimate level of prevarication and obfuscation in our own time. Such perversions have led some serious modern writers to demand that the term be dropped from scientific usage entirely, in the hope of robbing fools and scoundrels of the aura of erudition which surrounds them when they misuse it.

However, our only alternatives are either to deny entirely that groups of men can be distinguished on the basis of hereditary physical features, or to invent a new vocabulary relating to these matters. The denial of racial differences is, as we shall see, manifestly contrary to fact. On the other hand, a new terminology runs much the same risk of perversion as the old, and further suffers from a tendency to confuse students who may be inclined (as I hope) to carry their inquiries further than the pages of this book into current scientific literature where the term *race* and its derivatives have not as yet been discarded in scientific discussions of the subspecies varieties of mankind.

In this chapter we are primarily concerned with the biological sub-groups of the species—we are dealing with taxonomies determined on the basis of biological characteristics. When it is necessary to use the terms *race* or *racial* in the strictly biological, or zoölogical sense, they will be employed without special markings; when used to refer to cultural patterns and social relations based upon or imputed to hereditary physical differences between human groups, the term "race" and its derivatives will be used in quotation marks.

PROCESSES OF HEREDITY AND GENETICS [3]

Most readers are probably familiar with the arguments about heredity and environment and are aware in a general way that the physical characteristics of the individual are supposed to be the result, in some way, of the interplay of these two factors. However, regardless of the influence of environment, the truth of the matter is that all individuals are provided with certain limited potentialities by "heredity." Although the environment may stimulate the manifestation of some of these potentialities and inhibit others, the limitations are there nonetheless. No human egg ever develops into a horse, regardless of its environment, and no modern ape egg ever develops into a man.

Phenotypes and genotypes. A human being, as any other organism, may be considered from two points of view by those interested in his heredity. The aspect which is most familiar to all is the physical form and function of the individual's body—the way he is built and operates. These bodily characteristics reflect the individual's heredity in a certain way and, taken together, they are called the *phenotype* of the individual or group to which he belongs biologically. The phenotype is the combination of bodily structures and functions displayed by the organism considered as a whole. However, it is frequently observed that children may display phenotypical features markedly different from either of their parents. It is impossible to understand in any systematic fashion what has happened or may happen as the result of breeding different races, different family lines, and different populations together merely on the basis of a naïve belief in "heredity" in the simple sense that implies merely that physical features are derived from our ancestors. The second aspect of an individual which we may investigate if interested in his heredity consists of the contents and organization of his germ plasm. Beginning with the classic experiments on peas conducted by the Austrian monk Gregor Mendel, which he published in 1867, we have gradually learned that the physical characteristics of organisms are determined by their genetic constitutions. The phenotype is often only a partial reflection of the genetic constitution, which is sometimes called the *genotype*. Only by having some knowledge of genetic principles can we grasp the problems which are involved in human heredity.

A good part of what we know about this subject has been obtained by painstaking study of certain lower animals which reproduce rapidly, with generations close together, and which are amenable to controlled breeding. Man is not a particularly good subject for direct study of genetics. Inasmuch as he has produced only about sixty generations since the birth of the Christ, and since he does not permit breeding experiments upon himself on a systematic scale, he is somewhat handicapped in studying his own heredity. We are therefore compelled at present to infer a good deal from genetic studies in other species and from a study of human phenotypes. It should be stated emphatically, however, that there is abundant direct evidence to show beyond any doubt that in man the processes of heredity and genetics conform to the same principles as in other species. It is only that we lack details regarding the precise genetic mechanisms involved in the inheritance of certain human physical features.

It is neither necessary nor possible to review the entire science of genetics here, but we must endeavor to set out a few basic principles which will aid us in understanding our own species.

Reproduction in the human species, as in all other bisexually reproducing organisms, is started by the penetration of an *egg* cell, produced by a female, by a *sperm* cell, produced by a male. The two cells first fuse, producing a fertilized egg or *zygote*, which then proceeds to expand by subdivision: the fertilized egg splits into two cells, which grow to full size and split in turn, and so on, until in the course of nine months in man the body of the fetus has grown within the uterus of the mother to the point where it is ready to be brought forth and to begin its life in the outside world. After birth it normally continues to increase in size, that is, to "grow," through cell divisions until it reaches maturity. Obviously the various cells combine into special structures and assume special functions. How is this process explained? What is it that determines the form and shape and other characteristics of the individual? How is it that certain cells specialize for one type of structure and function, while other cells follow other paths?

Genetic materials. The genetic potentialities of the individual are established at the moment the egg is fertilized by the sperm. In the nucleus of the human egg are 24 minute filaments called *chromosomes* and in the head of the sperm there are also 24 analogous chromosomes. When the egg is penetrated by the sperm these two sets of chromosomes are matched up into 24 pairs, or 48 chromosomes in all, in the newly conceived human being. The hereditary determinants of the new individual are carried in these chromosomes, which may be seen under the microscope, and it is to be understood that half of the 48 are contributed by the mother and half by the father. With a proper microscopic technique it is possible to see that each chromosome in fact consists of a series of ultra-minute globules or disks of gelatine-like substance arranged in series, like beads on a string. These are the *genes* which are apparently the ultimate factors in heredity. Each gene has a definite function in the physical development of the individual; each controls or regulates, either alone or in combination with other genes, its particular part or feature of the body, as it were. The exact mechanism of this control has not been established, but most authorities agree that the gene substance exercises a chemical action of some sort (perhaps that of an enzyme) on the development of the cells so that each one normally assumes its proper structure and function in the body.

Each fertilized egg, then, starts out with a particular combination of 48 paired chromosomes, each composed of a string or chain of genes. As the egg proceeds to develop into a baby through subdivision and growth of its cell, its chromosomes also divide, and each new cell which develops in the process of growth is provided with exactly the same combination of chromosomes and their constituent genes as was present in the original conception. Thus every living cell of our bodies contains our original genetic combination.

Genetic organization. Although each individual cell has 48 chromosomes, these are of only 25 types, which have been designated by geneticists by the letters A through Y. Thus, in conception, the A type chromosome from the father is paired with the A type contributed by the mother, and so on through the types, until we reach the X type. In human beings the eggs contain only X type chromosomes to contribute to the twenty-fourth pair, but a given sperm may contain either an X type chromosome or a Y type (in which case it contains no X type). The X type is a fairly large chromosome, whereas the Y type is small. If both sperm and egg contain X chromosomes, the twenty-fourth pair will be XX, and the individual will develop into a female, but if the sperm contains a Y type, it is paired with the egg's type, making the twenty-fourth pair XY, and the individual will develop into a male. The chances are even either way.

Each chromosome, as we have said, consists of a number of genes arranged in a serial order which is characteristic of its type, just as all rosaries, for example, consist of certain kinds of beads always strung together in the same order. Thus any A chromosome, for example, consists of certain types of genes arranged in a fixed order. When the two A chromosomes, for example, are paired at conception, so likewise, it is believed, are their constituent genes paired together and the two genes of a given pair have the same function. We may thus think of gene A1 from the father being matched or paired with gene A1 from the mother, and so forth. The cell is thus said to be double or *diploid*, both as to its chromosomes and its genes.

On the basis of a great deal of experimental work, which we cannot describe, it has been found that the genes in any given pair may be of two different types, which are described respectively as dominant and recessive. The physical features which they produce are likewise spoken of as dominants and recessives. These two types of genes are distinguished on the basis of their respective influence on the physical development of the individual. Thus, if the influence of two paired genes differs, the two effects are not mingled, as a general rule, but one gene "dominates" the other. For example, in a pair containing only one recessive gene (Aa), the recessive trait is said to be blocked by the influence of the dominant gene and the physical traits will appear the same as if both genes were dominant (AA). It is only when two recessive genes for a given trait are paired together (aa) that the recessive trait will be manifested.

Independent segregation of genes. We recall that, although every individual is provided with 48 chromosomes, nevertheless each individual passes on only 24 chromosomes to his offspring. Why is this, and how does the division take place?

It is obvious that if both father and mother contributed 48 chromosomes to their child, the latter would have 96, and that if he and his wife later each contributed 96 to their child, the third generation would have 192 chromosomes, and so on. The chromosome situation would shortly get out of hand. Instead of this, each parent contributes only half of his or her chromosomes, one of each type (A through X or Y). This so-called *reduction division* takes place in the germ cells of both mother and father at the time when the eggs and sperms are formed. We remember that each parent has 48 chromosomes, or 24 pairs, half derived from the mother and half from the father, in each case. Now, in the reduction division the 24 chromosomes which are to go into the sperm or the egg, as the case may be, are selected entirely by chance, although one is taken from each pair.

At the time of the reduction division in the germ cells, the two members of each pair of chromosomes elongate and the two chains of genes are stretched out side by side. In this process an exchange of genes between the two chromosomes may take place, a process called *crossing over*. In some cases whole sections of one chromosome are exchanged for similar sections of the other. Certain genes seemed to be *linked together* and are always exchanged in links, others may be exchanged separately and quite by chance.

Since the genes of the parents are thus shuffled about, it follows that their distribution to offspring on the whole follow the laws of mathematical probability. Naturally only one of every two mated or paired genes goes from each parent to the offspring. They are said to be segregated out from the pairings in which they existed in the respective parents. The chances of a given type of gene being paired with another type (for the same feature) can be computed statistically and predictions can be made on this basis. Each parent contributes to the child one chromosome of each of his pairs and, consequently, one gene of each of his pairs. The chromosomal pairs are independent in their distribution to the different germ cells.[4]

SUMMARY

We may sum this up in the three "Mendelian laws."[5]

1. Inherited characteristics are produced by genes (Mendel called them "factors"), which are transmitted unchanged, except by mutations, from one generation to another.
2. In each individual these genes are paired, and when the two genes of a pair are different in effect, one "dominates" the other.

3. In reproduction the members of each pair of genes segregate out so that just one of every two paired genes is transmitted from each parent to each offspring.

INHERITANCE OF CERTAIN TRAITS IN MAN

We may set out here a list of certain human traits of more or less "normal" type (as distinguished from lethal and degenerate traits) which are known to be inherited according to Mendelian principles in man. Multiple cumulative factors as well as modifying genetic factors are probably involved in most of them. The following table is an adaptation of that in Dr. David D. Whitney's book, *Family Treasures*.

TRAIT	DOMINANT	RECESSIVE
Allergies	Chilblains	Normal reaction
	General allergy	Normal
Body		
Head	Round	Long
Legs	Large circumference	Average
Stature	Short	Tall
	Obesity	Average weight
Cheek	Single dimple	Double dimple
Chin	Dimple	Absence of dimple
	Straight	Receding
Ears: lobe	Free	Attached, "soldered"
Eyes		
Color	Brown	Blue or gray
	Green	Blue or gray
	Hazel	Blue or gray
	Pigmented	Albino
Lids	Drooping	Normal
	Partial retraction	Full retraction
Eyelid fold	Epicanthic	Normal
Size of eye	Average	Small
Vision	Astigmatism	Normal
	Farsightedness	Normal
	Nearsightedness	Normal
Feet	Low arch	Average
Fingers	Six digits	Five digits
Extra digits	Crooked fifth	Straight fifth
Form	Non-tapering	Tapering
Joints	Normal	Loose and "double"
	One-jointed	Two-jointed fingers (normal)
Length	All short	All long
	Fifth short	Fifth average
Nails	Short	Long

TRAIT	DOMINANT	RECESSIVE
Hair		
Amount	Abundant	Scanty
	Baldness (males)	Normal
	Medium eyebrows	Scanty eyebrows
	Hair on middle segment of fingers	None
	Hairlessness	Normal hairiness
Arrangement	Cowlicks	None
	Clockwise crown	Counterclockwise crown
	Single crown	Double crown
	Frontal hair point	None
	High frontal hair-line	Low frontal hair-line
Color	Dark	Light
	Dark	Red
	Pigmented	Albino
	Ringed	Self color
	White forelock	Self color
Form	Curly	Straight
	Straight	Wavy
	Woolly	Straight
Length	Long eyelashes	Short eyelashes
Jaw	Long lower jaw	Short lower jaw
Lips	Cupid-bow upper lip	Absence of cupid bow
	Full upper lip	Thin upper lip
	Long upper lip	Short upper lip
Nose	Convex	Straight
	High bridge	Low bridge
	Straight	Concave
Skin	Dark	Light
	Freckles	No freckles
	Pigmented	Albino
Toes	Extra number	Five toes
	Second short	Second longer
	Webbed	Unwebbed
Tongue	Ability to roll tongue	Absence of ability

DISCUSSION

Hair form seems to be governed by two or more pairs of genes so that racial mixtures between whites and Negroes, for example, show different types of hair, rather than a picture of dominance and recessiveness. In the white race, however, woolly hair has appeared, apparently as a mutation, and seems to be governed by a single dominant gene carried in an autosome (not in one of the sex chromosomes).[6] Straight hair seems to show variable dominance over wavy hair; at least in Chinese-Filipino [7] and Chinese-Hawaiian [8] crosses. *Eye color* is affected by at least three basic genes concerned with pigment development, not to mention a number of other genes governing the distribution of the pigment. One of the three pairs of pigment-developing genes is called the albino pair of genes, and determines whether the eye will have any color at all: when both of the genes in this pair are recessive, the individual has the pink eyes of an albino. When a dominant is present in the "albino gene pair," but the other two pairs of color-producing genes are recessive, the eye will be blue, that is, pigment will develop on the rear side of the iris only. The other two pairs of color genes have to be dominant if dark melanin (coloring matter) is to be formed to produce what we call dark eyes.

Handedness is apparently controlled by a gene which operates in some way on the central nervous system. The gene for right-handedness is dominant to that for left-handedness. The *blood groups* are apparently governed by single genes. Multiple genes on the other hand control *stature*; [9] in fact each segment of the body is apparently controlled by independent genes or groups of genes, as shown by the occasional "disharmonies" (for example, short legs with a long trunk, and the like) which appear in crosses. It is believed that the genotype influences the endocrine glands, which in turn influence stature. Short parents tend to produce more variable progeny than tall parents, who, on the average, have tall children. Evidence seems to indicate, likewise, that size and proportions of the various features of the *head and face* are controlled by multiple genes. Whatever these genes are, they produce the effect of making round-headedness (brachycephaly) dominant over long-headedness (dolichocephaly). Multiple genes are also responsible for skin color.

Many of the known genes in the human constitution produce anomalies or pathological structures. In fact, they are known for this reason, because they can be more easily studied in genealogies. Among inherited anomalies of this sort are *white forelock*,[10] apparently inherited as a simple dominant; *opalescent dentyne* of the teeth, dominant; *hollow chest*,[11] governed by a simple dominant; *stubby* fingers,[12] conditioned by dominant genes which control hormones. Not a few of the other identified genes are sex-linked. For example, *red-green colorblindness* is apparently caused by a single recessive gene in the X chromosome and shows in males whenever they receive it, because they do not receive any dominant allele of this gene in their Y chromosome. *Hemophilia*, a deficient ability in the blood to form clots when exposed to the air, is due to the action of a single recessive X-borne gene, and almost invariably appears only in men. *Web-foot*,[13] manifested as a webbing of the skin between the toes, is apparently controlled by a single dominant Y-borne gene and consequently is inherited by all sons of affected males.

THE FORMATION OF SPECIES AND OTHER BIOLOGICAL SUBGROUPINGS

From a genetic point of view, then, a species is a group of organisms all of which possess the same kind and number of chromosomes, and in which each type of chromosome carries the same number of genes in the same order of series. It is this fact which renders all normal individuals of a species capable of interbreeding and also accounts for the fact that they look, and, in general, function more like one another than like members of other groups. In this sense mankind is one species, for all normal human beings regardless of race or stock are able to mate and to produce fertile offspring.

If the genes characteristic of a species remained absolutely stable, generation after generation, the species would never change, no sub-varieties would arise, and there would be no evolution. Actually, however, there is a process at work called *mutation* whereby spontaneous changes suddenly appear in certain genes of certain individuals. At present we have no satisfactory explanation of this process although we do know that mutations can be produced in the laboratory by both physical and chemical interference with the germ plasm of certain experimental organisms. Radioactivity and factors of nourishment have been invoked to account for the appearance of mutations in nature, but as yet we know little conclusively except the fact that genes capable of producing new hereditary effects in the organism do spontaneously appear. In certain species they appear with much more frequency than in others. Man seems to be one of the comparatively slow-mutating species.

Formation of varieties within the species. Once a mutation has appeared, it has to compete, one might say, with the genetic factor which it has displaced in certain individuals but which continues to exist in others. Offspring containing the mutation show bodily (or phenotypical) differences from other organisms with respect to the trait governed by the gene in question. The competition between the old and new models, so to speak, is called *selection*. Two principal types of selection may be noted. In *natural selection* adaptive traits which have the greatest survival value under current conditions are supposed to win out. The organism carrying the less adaptive trait is eliminated and its kind eventually ceases to reproduce. A special form of this Darwin called *sexual selection:* organisms carrying traits that enable them to obtain mates at the expense of other organisms lacking these traits, eventually eliminate the others through their monopolization of the reproductive possibilities. However, mutations also occur in traits which apparently have no great importance either in survival or in sexual selection. Blood types, for example, would seem to fall into this class of effects produced by mutations. *Artificial selection* always involves the interference of man, who arranges matters so that individuals possessing certain hereditary traits are enabled to survive and breed, whereas others are not allowed to reproduce their kind. Although we are most familiar with this process in the breeding of domesticated animals, we should not forget that we ourselves are domesticated organisms and that a certain amount of artificial, if unconscious, selection often takes place in human societies. For example, war may send men with the fewest hereditary defects to be killed without reproducing themselves. At all events, it is through selection of one kind or another that mutations may survive in the germ plasm and eventually come to constitute a part of the genetic material of a group of human beings. In this way hereditarily distinguishable groups may grow up within a species, new varieties and subvarieties may appear.

Supposing that a group within the species has developed, through the operation of mutation and selection, distinctive hereditary features with respect to certain traits. What can guarantee that such traits will remain stable within the group, that they will "breed true"? Breeding true to type is dependent upon a condition called *homozygosity*, or genetic purity. (The seeds, fertilized eggs, are called *zygotes*.) This means that the genetic material (genes) of the group are all essentially the same, that there are no great probabilities of unlike genes (for example dominants and recessives) being paired up because such genetic variability does not exist in the group. This is homozygosity. It is achieved by selection, but it is preserved by *isolation* and inbreeding. The group is not allowed to interbreed with other groups carrying other types of genes. For example, it seems likely that black skin originated in a brown-skinned population through certain genetic mutations which were selected for survival because of the adaptability of this condition under natural conditions in which the selection was taking place or possibly through sexual selection or on the basis of some other selective factor. During the process of selection, of course, a good many genes for brown skin remained in the population, but once they were eliminated, the black-skinned population had to remain isolated from breeding with brown-skinned or other non-black-skinned people, if it was to remain genetically pure. Fortuitous geographical isolation has actually occurred within historic times with respect to certain groups of human beings, and artificial isolation of a lesser degree is a common phenomenon in most large societies. For example, any measures to segregate Negroes and prevent their interbreeding with whites are attempts to apply genetic isolation by artificial (cultural) means. Genetic isolation of a group, of course, usually carries with it *inbreeding* within the group itself, for the obvious reason that outbreeding is rendered impossible by the isolation.

Genetic impurity of human races. It appears that the three large subspecies varieties of mankind must have originally differentiated via the mechanisms of mutation, selection, and isolation just discussed. Thus we have the white, black, and yellow races (named from the differences in skin color). However, man has been a notoriously restless animal from the first. Groups of men have been continually "on the move" since prehistoric times, always moving on over some new horizon, mixing with foreign populations, until the species has populated the globe. With such propensities, man has accordingly done little to preserve the "isolate effect" and the chances for homozygosity within the species or any of its constituent hereditary groups are correspondingly reduced. Furthermore, each advance in culture has usually brought with it increased contact between its possessors and other peoples, and has enhanced the opportunities for interbreeding. Thus, while it is possible that relatively homozygous isolated human groups may have existed in considerable numbers in the past, the chances of their continued genetic purity have progressively declined as time went on.

It is for these reasons that most authorities now agree that there are practically no pure races, subraces, or populations within the species at the present time. The heterozygosity is so great throughout the species that there are not only wide variations of type within any stock or substock, but also considerable overlapping of types. We have already seen the enormous number of possible genetic combinations which can be produced when an egg is fertilized by a sperm. It follows that even the slightest variety in the genes which may be brought together is capable of producing an extremely wide variety of physical traits. The result is that we now speak of statistical averages or trends, rather than of pure "races," when considering the subgroups of the species.

Each of the three major stocks, then—white, black, and yellow—may be thought of as possessing a characteristic statistical distribution of genes.

In many of the older studies of race, attention was directed solely to a study of gross physical characteristics, such as the cephalic index, the form of the hair, the color of the skin, and so forth, and subspecies groups were distinguished one from the other on the basis of the statistical distribution of such traits. With the rise of the science of modern genetics, however, increasing attention has been given to the genetic aspects of these matters. However, the man in the street still distinguishes races on the basis of their gross physical appearance, and phenotypical data still must be relied upon as primary data by scientific students of human varieties as well. However, these obvious physical criteria no longer enjoy the immutable and absolute status they once did. For one thing, a number of studies during the past thirty-five years have demonstrated that shape of the head and other such features may change under environmental influences, even without mixture or crossing between groups. Secondly, hybridization of groups has brought out a number of facts which can only be explained in genetic terms. Third, we now realize that many physical features are probably the product of very complicated genetic factors; for example, many genes, not single ones, are involved in skin color, stature, cephalic measurements, and so forth.

RACES OF MANKIND

Criteria of differentiation. It cannot be denied that hereditary groups, each differing from the other with respect to innate physical features, can be distinguished within the human species by the naked eye; and physical anthropologists have devoted a great deal of labor to the examination, measurement, and compilation of these features.

Although the standard picture in the public mind of a physical anthropologist at work is that of a bearded gentleman, garbed in a white smock or laboratory coat, applying a pair of cabalistic-looking calipers to the skull of his victim, it should be understood that there is actually no magic and nothing mysterious about his investigations, if scientifically pursued. Physical anthropologists, like other professional men, are not averse to being considered geniuses by the general public, but the enigmatic look on the face of one of these technicians while at work is usually merely the preoccupation common to conscientious men working with instruments, rather than the reflection of some inner light which has suddenly illuminated the esoteric incidents of his subject's personal or family history. Physical anthropology is not a branch of clinical medicine, and its practitioners are seldom in a position to tell you whether you should get married, have children, or continue to eat strawberries.

Any classification of the human species must be based upon observable or measurable bodily characteristics of a presumably inheritable type. Once this fact has been grasped, the impropriety of describing "racial" groups in linguistic or cultural terms is apparent.

All classifications are based upon a considerable number of bodily characteristics which can be measured or observed, and the classification is determined by considering *all* of these features together. Among the commonly used *measurements* are (1) the principal lengths and diameters of the body, including stature, shoulder height, sitting height, shoulder breadth, chest diameter, pelvic diameter, and so forth; (2) lengths of the appendages and their segments, including total arm length, upper- and lower-arm lengths, leg lengths, and so forth; (3) the principal diameters of the skull and face, including length, breadth, and height of the skull, length of the total and upper face, breadth of the face, length and breadth of the nose; (4) weight of the body, angles between various parts of the body, as the projection of the face, angle of the lower arm to the forearm, and so forth. Among the principal features determined by *observation*, usually by comparison with standard models or charts, are (1) the natural pigmentation of the head hair, body hair, iris of the eye, and skin; (2) form and distribution of the hair on the head, face, and body; (3) form and shape of the nasal profile, nasal septum, shell and lobe of the ear, chin, jaws and alveolar borders, cheek bones, membranous and integumental lips; (4) shape of the eye opening and the form of the lids, projection of the eyebrow ridges and certain other parts of the skull; (5) distribution of fat and muscle on the body and general body build.

The measurements can be compared one to another by means of *indices*, which are numerical figures epitomizing the proportions of one part of the body to another part. The anthropometric index about which laymen have perhaps heard most often is the *cephalic index*, so frequently used to distinguish major groups of men, one from the other. The cephalic index is an expression of the breadth of the head or skull in terms of a percentage of the length. $\left(\textit{Formula:}\ \dfrac{B \times 100.}{L} \right)$ Thus, if your cephalic index is 80, we know that the breadth of your skull is 80 per cent of its length. Similar expressions of proportion can be applied to other measurements of the skull, the nose, face, trunk, and so forth.

Head shape has been arbitrarily classified, on the basis of the cephalic index, into three categories as follows:

	Dry skull	Living head
Dolichocephalic or long-headed (D) ..	x -74.99	x -76.99
Mesocephalic or mid-headed (M)	75.00-79.99	77.00-81.99
Brachycephalic or round-headed (B) ..	80.00- x	82.00- x

The presence of muscle and other tissue on the sides of the head in life causes the index in the living to be raised two points above the equivalent proportions on the dry skull. Proportions between any other two measurements of the body may be similarly expressed in terms of indices.

In connection with these criteria of differentiation, a few points should be mentioned. 1. First is the fact that these measurements and observations all deal with anatomical features of the human body and are now fairly well standardized throughout the scientific world, in the same way that medical anatomy is standardized. Standard techniques and accurate instruments have been developed in order to limit the margin of error and guesswork. Even in observing the curliness and color of the hair, samples are used by the investigator, and skin and eye colors may be determined by comparison with standardized skin-color charts and artificial eyes, by color photography, and other techniques. Guesswork has been largely eliminated in determining the actual physical characteristics of a population, if these are studied with the available scientific techniques and instruments.

2. Secondly, it is apparent that the classification of prehistoric and unrecorded populations, whose only remains are their bones, is bound to be less accurate than that of the living. Only a portion of the bodily features of importance to classification are obtainable from the skeleton, for the characteristics of hair, pigmentation, and form of the soft parts rapidly disappear after death. As a result we are by no means certain concerning all the details of the racial types even of early Europe, which of all parts of the world has been most thoroughly studied, and we have no accurate information at present which would indicate where or when the subgroups of the species as we know them now originated. Genealogies are notoriously scanty and seldom contain data of anthropometric importance, and there is no human group whose measurements are fully known even for five generations.

3. In the third place, we wish to point out that the racial classifications recognized by science are in the first instance strictly anatomical. In the accepted classifications no functional criteria, either physiological or psychological, are used. The study of the physiological and psychological characteristics of the species subgroups is carried on only *after* these have been determined on the basis of purely structural characteristics of a presumably hereditary nature. Although it is conceivable theoretically that inherent functional criteria *might* be of significance for classification, the fact is that the best scientific investigations to date have not found such criteria reliable. It is of the utmost importance that the student grasp this fact before he ventures to take part in any discussion of the hereditary groups of the human species.

4. It should be clearly understood that most of the anthropometric categories used for grouping mankind—for example, the three categories of the cephalic index, mentioned above—are actually only arbitrary definitions established for the convenience of investigators, and that they therefore should be used with circumspection and judgment by those

qualified to do so. Thus, your skull may have an index of 76.99 (dolicho-cephalic). But this in itself does not mean that you are an "entirely different" type from some one with an index of 77.01, for example. So far as measurements and observations can be of help, they must be used in combinations, and the individual has to be studied *as a whole*. Further-more, we must not forget that these phenotypical data are often at best only crude approximations of the genetic constitution, which is the fundamentally important consideration in grouping individuals into races.

5. Finally, it is apparent that the features wherein one type of man differs from another are all characteristics of relative unimportance from the adaptive or survival point of view. For example, men are at no more disadvantage in the struggle for existence with long heads than with round heads, and there is no conclusive evidence that any of the other physical features commonly used for classification of mankind confer special advantages upon their possessors, with the possible exception of dark skin. Pure blonds are, of course, at a disadvantage in comparison with black- and brown-skinned people in sunny climates where they may suffer more from sunburn. Kinky hair has also been alleged to confer added protection from sunstroke by virtue of the fact that a mat of such locks contains numerous dead air spaces supposed to provide an insulating effect, but this supposed virtue has never been proven. There is also some evidence that dark-skinned peoples show more resistance to certain types of skin diseases than do light-skinned people.

We do not deny, of course, that distinctive features in size and pro-portions of the body may influence the cultural behavior and patterns of the group of people who possess them. For example, a short-statured group cannot wear the same size clothes as a tall group. Round headed men cannot wear the hard straw hats belonging to long-headed men. Short-legged persons are more comfortable on low chairs than tall persons. And so on. But these are adaptations which culture makes to the human organism, not adaptations which the organism makes to the *natural environment*. Few racial physical features seriously affect the respective races' abilities to adapt to the conditions of nature. It is the ability of our *species* in comparison with other species to make adapta-tions to nature which is of survival importance, rather than the differences among the races. All races of man seem to share the adaptive features of the species more or less equally.

Cautions for the amateur anthropometrist. Racial classifications of man at the present time are based essentially upon a sorting out of phenotypes. It is all very well to say that, in view of the heterozygosity of most human populations, this gives only a very incomplete idea of the hereditary subgroups of the species, but, until such time as we are able to secure more detailed information concerning human genotypes, it is about the best we can do. In order to render the observation of gross phenotypical characteristics more accurate and comparable, the techniques of anthropometry have beeen developed. These involve the use of several types of instruments, an accurate knowledge of certain aspects of anatomy, a great deal of painstaking work, and the ability and drudgery to treat the material, once gathered, statistically. In other words, in a laudable pursuit of accurate observation, anthropometry has inevitably been made into an elaborate ritual.

There is a general tendency for all ritualized behavior to become an end in itself, and anthropometry has not altogether escaped. Time is not so far past when a few anthropometrists seemed to be industriously bemused by a number of fairly patent fallacies, which they seemed not to recognize by reason of having their eyes too firmly glued to their calipers. This phase has passed for most professionals, but it may be well to mention one or two pitfalls of pure anthropometry for the benefit of laymen in the technique.

1. The mistake was often made of considering that the absolute measurements and indicial ratios of measurements were in themselves biological or hereditary traits. Actually, we have seen that there is little evidence that the length of the head or that the cephalic index, for instance, are biological in themselves. Certainly they are not manifestations of single genetic units, which are the truly significant biological traits. With respect to anthropometry it is well to bear in mind the dictum of "operationalism" to the effect that a measureable phenomenon is what you measure with a given type of instrument and a given technique. Head length is the distance from glabella to opisthocranion on the head as measured with a caliper of the standard type and not anything else, until proved so. At present the anthropometrist has little reason to attribute to any of his operations precise genetic or biological significance within the framework of generally accepted laws applicable to other species. He has no way of proving, for example, that head length as taken from glabella to opisthocranion is of any more general significance than that from nasion to inion, except that the first is a convenient measurement to take, is not subject to great personal error, and on "most" skulls glabella and opisthocranion are the two points farthest away from each other on the sagital line. Likewise, an index derived from two measurements is, strictly speaking, merely a ratio or comparison of the two measurements themselves. Therefore, to speak of the "inheritance of the cephalic index" is at best only a figure of speech, for we have no reason to believe that the cephalic index, *as such*, is a heritable characteristic. Such evidence as we have seems to indicate that heredity does not

deal in cephalic indices, but rather in certain characteristics of the skull which may or may not be significantly described statistically by the cephalic index as now computed. If it should turn out that the present measurements of length and breadth of the skull are insignificant genetically, the index derived from them would likewise be insignificant.

2. Measurements can and in many cases should be treated statistically, but the same cautions apply to anthropometric statistics which apply to all statistics. Not to go into technical details, statistics as properly employed in anthropology is not a science in itself, but a technique for manipulating numbers. One can make a game of shuffling numbers about and drawing out different combinations, just as one may amuse himself with a deck of cards. Since anthropometric data are expressed in numbers, there is always a temptation to play this game with less and less regard to the fact that the numbers themselves merely represent measurements taken on human bodies.

Dr. Carleton Coon, in his *Races of Europe*, has probably applied the method of statistically sorting and searching for the "original racial components" of mixed populations with more skill than any one else. But Dr. Coon sagely warns that although all statistical procedures "are useful, not one automatically answers any important questions." [14]

The point which it seems advisable to bear in mind is that anthropometry is a technique, and the study of human races is, at present, "work in progress."

The difference between type and population. It is customary to speak of races in terms of "types" and to imply that such types possess a certain biological immutability and purity. This attitude is one which is well adapted to cause the observer, then, to look with suspicion upon individuals or groups who do not conform to the type, imputing to such variants the possibility of "mixture," "tainting of the blood," and so forth.

It is well for the amateur in these matters to understand just what physical anthropologists do in studying the racial characteristics of peoples. They do not start with "types," but rather with *individuals of a population*. Such individuals are measured and observed in accordance with the standard anthropometric techniques and arranged in a *statistical series*, which in its simplest form is merely an orderly array of the various measurements arranged so that both the variations and the central tendencies can be conveniently studied. We have already seen that, on genetic principles, it is extremely unlikely that any one individual should be exactly like any other individual, anywhere. Thus there is almost certain to be some *variation* in any population. However, if one takes the measurements and observations obtained from a series of individuals supposedly representative of a given population, one may obtain *averages* or other types of statistical constants which express the central tendency as well as the range of variation. The average, then, is frequently used as the *type*. This distinction between average (mean) type and actual individuals composing a population must be borne in mind. For example, the statures of the series of individuals who make up a series may run from 155 cm. to 180 cm., with the average or mean coming out at 164

PHYSICAL CHARACTERISTICS OF THE THREE RACES OF MANKIND

Trait	White or Caucasian	Black or Negroid	Yellow or Mongoloid
Head form	Long to broad and short; medium high to very high	Predominantly long; height low to medium	Predominantly broad; height medium
Prognathism (projection of jaws)	None	Marked	Medium to slight
Face	Narrow to medium broad; tends to be high	Medium broad to narrow; tends to be medium high	Medium broad to very broad; medium high; cheek bones (malars) tend to be high and flat
Nose	Bridge high; form narrow to medium broad	Bridge low; form medium broad to very broad	Bridge low to medium; form medium broad
Chin	Usually projecting	Slight	Medium
Stature	Medium to tall	Tall to very short	Medium short to medium tall
Skin color	Pale reddish white to olive-brown	Brown, yellow-brown to brown-black	Saffron to yellow-brown; some reddish brown
Hair, head:			
Color	Light blond to dark brown	Brown-black	Brown to brown-black
Texture	Fine to medium	Coarse	Coarse
Form	Straight to wavy	Light curl to woolly or frizzly	Straight
Hair, body	Moderate to profuse	Slight	Sparse
Hair, beard	Moderate to heavy	Slight to moderate	None to slight
Eye			
Color	Light blue to dark brown	Brown to brown-black	Brown to brown-black
Form of lids..	Lateral fold occasionally	Vertical fold common	Medial epicanthic fold common
Lips	Very thin to medium; small eversion	Thick; much eversion	Medium thickness and eversion of membranous lips; often heavy integumental lips

cm. It is possible that no single individual in the series actually has a stature of 164 cm., and it is obvious that certain others do not. Even where some other type of statistical statement is used, such as the mode (the most frequently occurring value in the series) or the median (the central value in the series), the range of variations "on either side" of this "typical" value may be considerable.

In the following pages are set forth the specifications of a number of racial and subracial types. Let us remember that these are just that—average or ideal types—rather than descriptions of actual populations. Such classifications have a certain usefulness, but they have led to great confusion in the past, when it has been assumed that they are supposed to represent large groups of real people rather than averages or tendencies. Until we understand more of the genetics of race in mankind, the present type of tabulation should be regarded merely as a sort of rough guide to phenotypical variations within the species.[15]

SUBRACES AND OTHER NARROWER CLASSIFICATIONS

Because of the fact that each of the so-called major races obviously consists of individuals showing wide variations of physical type around a central statistical tendency, numerous efforts have been made to classify or sort out groups within the races. These narrower, but still extensive, groups are usually called subraces. In some cases, for example the Mediterranean subrace, breeds can be distinguished within the major race. Still smaller groups called hereditary strains can sometimes be distinguished within the breeds. The following outline will serve to illustrate certain differential characteristics of the races which are generally recognized among living men. With the increased intermixture of modern times most of these races are gradually losing their distinctiveness.[16]

HUMAN SUBRACES

I. White Race
   Subraces
   A. Australoid: natives of Australia
      1. Brow ridges: huge
      2. Foreheads: low and receding
      3. Cephalic index: dolichocephalic; small cranial capacity (c. 1200 c.c.)
      4. Chin: feeble
      5. Palate: large; teeth large
      6. Nose: broad, fleshy tip; deep depression at root
      7. Face: short and broad
      8. Skin color: red-brown to dark chocolate brown
      9. Hair form: wavy; dark brown to black

10. Hair distribution: abundant
11. Stature: medium; trunk short, legs long with thin shanks
12. Remarks: archaic white type modified in slightly Negroid direction by mixture with preceding Tasmanians (?)

B. Ainu: northern Japan
1. Hair: wavy; dark brown to black; more luxuriant than any other group of mankind
2. Skin color: dirty white
3. Cephalic index: dolichocephalic; moderate cranial capacity
4. Brow ridges: large, but not enormous
5. Prognathism: small
6. Palate and teeth: large
7. Nose: root depressed, broad and fleshy; moderately high bridge
8. Ears: long, well-developed lobes
9. Remarks: Probably closest to *sapiens* cave men of late Pleistocene Europe. Related to the Australoids, but no suspicion of Negrito admixture. Probably outlying remnant of an ancient population which at one time extended across Siberia into Europe

C. Mediterranean
1. Distribution: most of Mediterranean basin, northward as far as British Isles, southward across Sahara, eastward to India and beyond
2. General characteristics: dark brunet white ... dark hair and eyes ... dolichocephalic ... slightly wavy to loosely curled hair ... scanty distribution ... little prognathism ... high-bridged narrow nose with thin tip ... slender body build
3. Breeds
   a. *Classic Mediterranean:* ancient and modern Egyptians, many Arabs, Berbers, Italians, Spaniards
      (1) Stature: short to medium
      (2) Build: slender
      (3) Skull: smooth; brow ridges small, if any; dolichocephalic
      (4) Forehead: mediumly high; rounded; moderate slope
      (5) Cheek bones: flat
      (6) Nose: straight, narrow, medium height
      (7) Chin: pointed, only moderately prominent
      (8) Skin color: light brown to brunet
      (9) Hair: deeply waved, sometimes curly
      (10) Face: long and oval
   b. *Crude Mediterranean:* many Sicilians and southern Italians
      (1) Skull: more rugged and angular; brow ridges larger; dolichocephalic
      (2) Face: short and squarish; protruding cheek-bones and jaw angles
      (3) Chin: less prominent; squarer, often cleft
      (4) Hair: more abundant
   c. *Atlanto-Mediterranean*
      (1) Stature: taller
      (2) Build: heavier
      (3) Face: long, heavy bilateral chin

(4) Skin color: very white to ruddy tinge
(5) Hair and eye color: black or dark brown
(6) Skull: dolichocephalic to medium

D. Iranian Plateau: Persia, Mesopotamia, northwestern India
1. Pigmentation, stature, and body build: same range as medium varieties of Mediterranean substock
2. Skull: very large; extremely dolichocephalic; high sloping forehead
3. Brow ridges: heavy
4. Nose: projects strongly; high, broad, hooked; nasal tip depressed and thin to medium in thickness
5. Cheek bones: prominent
6. Hair: beard and body hair luxuriant
7. Face: long, strong chin, marked jaw angles
8. Remarks: probably most convex and hooked noses, so common in Near East, derive from mixtures with this type

E. Nordic
1. A depigmented offshoot from the basic long-headed Mediterranean stock. Distinctive features as follows:
2. Hair color: ash or gold brown
3. Eye color: blue or gray
4. Skin color: pink or ruddy
5. Stature: moderate to tall
6. Body build: robust
7. Skull: mesocephalic to dolichocephalic; strong chins; fairly heavy brow ridges
8. Face: longish; narrow; straight in profile; cheek-bones flat
9. Nose: straight, high-bridged, narrow
10. Beard and body hair: moderate to abundant

F. Alpine
1. Skull: brachycephalic; basic round-headed differentiation in white stock
2. Pigmentation: medium brown to hazel eyes; brown hair; brunet skin in light tones
3. Body build: short, broad, and rotund; neck thick and short
4. Hair form: slightly wavy to straight; heavier than Mediterranean
5. Hair distribution: abundant
6. Face: wide; square jaws; well developed chin both pointed and bilateral; lips of moderate thickness; palate broad and short
7. Nose: short, broad, fleshy in tip and bridge; medium height; usually straight bridge
8. Remarks: developed in western slopes of central Asiatic Plateau, near Hindu Kush and Pamirs, this basic stock diffused westward somewhat later than the Nordic. Alpine shows some Ainu affinities, differ in round head: lesser hairiness; greater refinement of facial features; broader, squatter body build.

II. Negroid Race
   Subraces

A. Pygmy Negritos: Found now only in marginal areas of the tropics: Congo forests of Africa; Malay Peninsula on Asiatic mainland; Andaman Islands in Bay of Bengal; remote interiors of New Guinea and Philippines. They preceded the Australoids in Australia and were the first inhabitants of New Guinea

1. General characteristics: extremely small stature and general body size...red-brown to medium brown skin color...black hair... dark brown eyes
2. Two general types
   a. "Adult" type...dolichocephalic...general body build like that of full-sized adult male, but reduced in size...bulbous forehead with central shield-like eminence with point directed downward ...jaws protuberant...upper lip very long and convex...chin long, but retreating...well-developed beard, fairly abundant body hair...sometimes slightly reddish in color
   b. "Infantile" type...brachycephalic...face very broad and short ...body proportions infantile: narrow shoulders, small chest, relatively broad hips, pot belly...little development of beard and body hair...jaws less projecting...skin color usually darker than in adult type
3. Remarks: Hooton thinks that adult type of Negrito is oldest. Both types are found in Africa, Malaya, and in the Islands.

B. Forest Negroes
   1. Stature: medium (156 to 167 cm.)
   2. Body build: heavy shoulders and torsos, long arms, long well-muscled legs
   3. Hair distribution: scanty
   4. Pigmentation: dark hair and eyes; skin often black
   5. Skull: dolichocephalic
   6. Prognathism: very pronounced; chin retreating
   7. Nose: broad; thick lip
   8. Lips: very thick and puffy
   9. Remarks: probably differentiated from "adult" Negrito type

C. Nilotic Negroes: upper Nile, Eastern Sudan
   1. Stature: very tall...long legs...short torso...narrow shoulders
   2. Skull: dolichocephalic...forehead higher than Forest Negro
   3. Face: broad and short...straight in profile...nose medium
   4. Chin better developed than in Forest Negro
   5. Lips: thinner
   6. Remarks: May be result of mixture with tall white stock of East Africa on the Forest Negro type.

D. Oceanic Negroes: New Guinea and neighboring islands
   1. General distinctions as compared with Forest Negroes:
      a. Hair frizzly, rather than spirally kinked
      b. Skin color more variable
      c. Most are long headed, but some brachycephaly occurs
      d. Forehead more sloping, brow ridges larger
      e. Face less prognathous
      f. Lips less thick and everted
   2. Subtypes
      a. "Melanesian": low, broad, Negroid nose...little body hair

    b. "Papuan" type: nose is broad, high-bridged, convex in profile, with depressed tip...heavy brow ridges...more body hair...body hair fairly plentiful, beard fairly well developed...lips thin

  3. Remarks: These two Negroid types may be result of mixture of two separate pigmy Negrito subraces with the Australoid subraces.

III. Mongoloid Race. Wherever it originated the Mongoloid race seems to have been the latest to diffuse over the globe, as shown by historical, distributional, and stratigraphic evidence.

Subraces

A. Classic Mongol: Mongolia, Northern China, Central Asia
  1. Stature: average about 5 feet 4 inches (163); taller in north
  2. Skull: brachycephalic, index about 86; narrower in north
  3. Face: very broad; square jaws, laterally projecting malars (cheek-bones) covered with fatty layer
  4. Skin yellow or yellowish brown
  5. Eye form: slit-like opening, slanting, total "Mongoloid fold"
  6. Nose: medium width; medium-height bridge; small root
  7. Hair: straight, black, coarse
  8. Body build: squat, broad shoulders, long trunk, short legs; taller and leaner in north

B. Arctic Mongol: Northeastern Asia and Arctic fringe of North America
  1. Stature: short
  2. Skull: medium to narrow
  3. Face: very broad, very long; jutting cheek-bones
  4. Skin: darkish yellow to brownish
  5. Eye form: Mongoloid fold less frequent than in Classic Mongol
  6. Nose: tends to be narrow

C. American Mongol: Spotty distribution among American Indians of both continents; now dominant among aboriginal populations, but apparently preceded by migrations of non-Mongoloid mixtures. Typically found in living populations of Pueblo Indians of Southwest, for example.

    A number of varieties and subtypes are found among American Indians. Partly they are explained by mixture with earlier, possibly non-Mongoloid types; partly they are local strains developed through mutations and isolation.

D. Indonesian Mongol: Japan, Thailand, Burma, Malay Peninsula, Dutch East Indies, Philippines, Indo-China, etc. Predominantly Mongoloid, but probably with admixtures of Mediterranean White, Ainu, and possibly Negrito.
  1. Stature: medium to short
  2. Skull: medium to broad
  3. Face: broad, projecting cheek-bones; short chin
  4. Skin: dark yellow-brown to red-brown
  5. Eye form: occasional Mongoloid fold
  6. Nose: medium to broad, low root, concave profile
  7. Hair: straight, black, sometimes slightly wavy

The foregoing classifications of mankind would not find agreement everywhere. Some authorities would add other groups, others might merge one or two of our groups. The subraces as here distinguished seem to represent hereditary divisions of the major stocks which have attained relative stability and (presumably) homozygosity, either through isolation or inbreeding. It is understood that the "type" in each case is actually a statistical abstraction. With respect to individuals within the race, there is no a priori reason why any individual should be identical with the type in all details, and consequently there is no reason why even any two individuals in the groups (other than identical twins) should resemble each other exactly. If we place individuals in a given racial classification it is because they resemble each other and the "type" more than they resemble individuals whom we place in some other category.

CHAPTER 6

Hereditary Varieties of Modern Man (*Continued*)

EVEN THOUGH they grant that racial types are statistical averages showing a considerable range of variability, many persons still believe that the physical type is nevertheless comparatively fixed or unchangeable, provided it is not subjected to intermixture with other types, that is, that environmental influences can do nothing to change the averages and ranges of a race. Considerable evidence has been accumulated within recent years to refute this belief. Racial types do change concurrent with environmental or situational changes.

The first important evidence in this matter was contributed by F. Boas [17] who studied hair color, stature and weight, head length and head breadth, face breadth, in foreign-born Bohemians, Slovaks, Hungarians, Poles, Hebrews, Sicilians, Neapolitans, and Scotsmen. He also studied their children, those born abroad and those born in the United States. He discovered important differences, particularly in skull measurements and indices, between those born abroad and those born in America, differences which increased with the length of time the parents had spent in this country. The cephalic index, for example, seemed to change from both extremes toward what appears to be a central tendency. For instance the cephalic index (of persons twenty years of age or older) for Sicilians born abroad was 77.8, for those born in the United States, 80.9; on the other hand, Hebrews born abroad averaged 83.3, whereas those born in this country averaged 81.0. In other words, the long heads became rounder-headed and the round heads became longer-headed. Fishberg, in an earlier, pioneer study had shown that American-born Jews tend to differ from Jews measured in Europe with respect, at least, to stature and, probably, head dimensions. [17]

An even more careful study of the same type of problem was made by H. L. Shapiro on Japanese immigrants to Hawaii. [18] He compared three groups: (*a*) Japanese born in Japan and still resident there; (*b*) Japanese-born who had migrated to Hawaii since 1884 from the same localities and the same families in Japan as the members of the (*a*) group; and (*c*) persons born in Hawaii of these immigrants of pure Japanese parentage. Forty-three measurements, twenty-one indices, and forty-one observations were taken on each of the 2,594 individuals involved. In general he found that the immigrants were larger in 72.4 per cent of the male and 67.9 of the female measurements of the body over their stay-at-home compatriots in Japan, and that the Hawaiian-born Japanese were even larger (in 55.2 per cent of the male and 46.4 per cent of the female measurements) than the immigrants.

Remember that in neither of these studies was there any question of race mixture. Shapiro's findings suggest two conclusions: (1) a (probably unconscious) physical selection had taken place in Japan which led the larger (and possibly more vigorous) Japanese to migrate, leaving their runtier, less enterprising (?), relatives and neighbors at home; (2) change in environment (including nutrition, living conditions, and so forth) released genetic tendencies in the group, which had previously been inhibited in the Japanese environment. According to the latter hypothesis, then, the fact that the children of Japanese immigrants are taller, for example, than their relatives who remain in Japan would indicate that the genes for taller stature exist in the Japanese in Japan, but that environmental conditions there do not permit their full expression.

A number of other studies have tended to confirm the finding that environment has an influence on the physical characteristics of a group. Mills [19] showed that Panama-born North American children were lighter in weight and slightly shorter in stature than immigrants to Panama of comparable ages. According to Appleton,[20] Chinese children born in Hawaii exhibited more rapid and steady growth than Chinese measured in China. Shapiro [21] also compared immigrant and Hawaiian-born Chinese: they differed significantly from each other in stature and other ways not ascribable entirely to differences in average age.

In addition to Shapiro's study, several others have been made on migrant Japanese. It was noted in 1911 that seven-to-sixteen-year-old Japanese children in twenty California schools were larger than children of the same ages in Japan.[22] Another study in 1921 showed that children born of Japanese parents in California were two inches taller and 30 pounds heavier than children born in Japan.[23] Spier [24] found that Japanese children in Seattle exceeded those in Japan in stature, width of head, cephalic index, and, on the average, in head length. A study of American-born Japanese boys and girls in 1933 showed that they exceeded the average measurements made by the Japanese Ministry of Education in height, weight, chest circumference, and relative length of the leg.[25] Other similar studies are reported by Ito.[26]

A careful and fairly large-scale study of the same problem in respect to Mexicans has been made by Goldstein.[27] He examined Mexican parents and their offspring born in Mexico and the United States, respectively.

His material shows many significant differences between adult American-born Mexicans and their immigrant parents of the same sex. Likewise, he showed that American-born Mexican immigrants differed in about the same ways from individuals of their same ages, born and raised in Mexico.

Lasker [28] measured 284 adult Chinese in the United States and compared them with average measurements for Chinese in China from the localities from which their ancestors came. He says, in summary,

Chinese born and raised in the United States differ in certain specific respects from those of Chinese immigrants born in China. These differences consist in an increase in stature and in all measurements highly correlated with stature: notably all measurements of the trunk and limbs other than chest depth.

Taking into account other studies, Lasker concludes that

The typical Oriental youth born and brought up in the United States or Hawaii, when compared with immigrants from the region from which his ancestors have come, differs in ways which may be ascribed to an "environmental growth factor." He is taller with longer arms and legs, relatively slenderer hands and feet and flatter chest. His head is likely to be shorter but broader and his nose to be relatively narrower. He has more body hair. Such changes are exemplified in Chinese in America and seem to signify a process caused by changed dietary or other factors attendant upon the migration of peoples.

The inevitable conclusion, in the light of all these facts, seems to be that *racial types in the physical or phenotypical sense, at least, are plastic and subject to environment influences,* which are capable of altering the type even in the absence of genetic mixture or mutation.

Other studies seem to point in the same direction, although in these the question of mixture of strains (not major races) cannot be entirely ruled out. In Europe, records have been kept for years of the stature of army conscripts. (One published record goes back to 1741.) For example, it is reported that the average stature of Norwegian men examined by the army has increased from 168-169 cm. in 1741 to about 174-175 now.[29] Italian recruits from the Piedmont born in 1807-1828 were 3.5 cm. shorter than those born in 1895-1916.[30] Military data collected on recruits in Ukrania show that over a ten-year period stature has increased one-half inch, weight 10.5 pounds, and chest circumference 0.6 inches, on the average.[31] The same trend is shown among civilian populations in various parts of Europe, Japan, and the United States.[32]

This trend has been dramatically demonstrated in studies of college and university students in the United States, each generation of which is generally taller than the last. Bowles' study of fathers and sons at Harvard and of mothers and daughters at Wellesley, Smith, Vassar, and Mount Holyoke has attracted perhaps the most attention. His material shows that not only is the younger generation taller and heavier than its parents, but also differently proportioned. The greatest increase in length in both sexes has appeared in the lower abdominal segment; hips are also narrower and buttocks more protruding in both sexes.[33] Among students entering Yale those over 6 feet tall formed 23 per cent of the class in 1941 as compared with only 5 per cent in 1891.[34] The same trend toward taller stature has been shown for various other institutions of learning.[35]

We may sum this up in the words of Shapiro.[36]

It is evident, therefore, that the former conception of the human organism rigidly held to fixed standards of development by the germ plasm must be modified. Instead we must conceive of a genetic control which is flexible enough to permit the organism a considerable range in its development. This does not mean that the human organism may be modified in any direction or to any extent.... It may perhaps best be expressed by saying that a given genotype or genetic combination has an orbit of plasticity within which it may develop normally. The extent of the orbit, however, is unknown.

RACE MIXTURE

Although it is doubtful that many educated persons still hold to the old myth that there are several species of existent man whose interbreeding is biologically impossible, some still accept the view that crossing of the races is somehow "contrary to nature." For those untutored in the scientific findings regarding hybridization, miscegenation often conjures up sundry imaginary horrors ranging from the production of monstrosities to feeble-mindedness. Remember that at this point we are *not* concerned with the *social or cultural results* of interbreeding, but only with the biological effects. Travelers and residents of colonial areas frequently assert that the half-breed inherits all the inferior qualities and none of the good points of his parental groups. The evidence, when closely analyzed, however, seems to indicate that such observations are based on the imputation of sociological characteristics to biological factors. The "half-breed" is frequently accorded an ambiguous social position somewhere midway between his parental races and is not permitted opportunity to display such desirable qualities as he possesses. Let us briefly examine some of the evidence of the biological results of cross-breeding.

We recall that hereditary physical features are controlled by genetic factors which operate on Mendelian principles. Many of the physical features of man, however, seem to be controlled by a combination of several pairs of genes, rather than merely by one pair. For example, it appears that the mulatto nose is the product of a number of minute factors, each of which operates on Mendelian principles. In physical appearance, then, it is a blend or mosaic.[37]

In an inbreeding population genetic segregation and recombination serve eventually to bring the pure dominant and pure recessive features out into the open. On the whole, it is believed that the more highly evolved traits dominate over the lesser evolved and that the normal or "healthy" traits dominate over the abnormal and "unhealthy." Inbreeding, then, serves to expose the underlying weaknesses of the group so that they may be selected out and to bring the dominants to a homozygous condition. In this sense, inbreeding of a group tends to strengthen it genetically. But once homozygosity has been achieved, no genetic "improvement" or change can take place in an inbred group except by mutation, and we have already seen that mutations are apparently extremely slow in appearing among humans.

What is the genetic effect of *outbreeding*, this much maligned process which in humans is so often stigmatized as miscegenation, race mixture, and "tainting the purity of the blood"?

On genetic principles the expected results of outbreeding may be summarized as follows. (1) The introduction of new genes increases the range of variations and hereditary potentialities. It is as if the "deck" were increased by the addition of some new cards. (2) In the first few generations, at least, following the cross there is to be expected a general glossing over of the imperfections of both groups, because the majority of the recessive features will be masked by pairing with dominants. (3) The majority of the apparently dominant features will thus, merely on the basis of chance, be heterozygous. (4) So far as physical form and function can be observed, this new heterozygosity will usually result in a phenomenon known as *hybrid vigor* or heterosis. The offspring of the cross will tend to be larger in size, more active, more fertile, and with improved vitality and longevity. (5) It must be remembered, however, that outbreeding does not in itself eliminate recessive genes. They may be masked in appearance for generations, but when they appear they must be eliminated, if the group is to enjoy the full benefit conferred by the addition of the new range of dominants to its genetic possessions.

It must be remembered that these principles apply to crossing between any genetic groups of the species, not only to so-called major races. These are the biological reasons in our society for the social requirement that we marry outside our group of "blood relatives." The modern era in Europe and America has seen the breaking down of former local isolation with a resulting mixture between local strains. Likewise an unprecedentedly rapid mixture between formerly isolated groups of whites has been occurring, especially in America. It is not unlikely, therefore, that at least a part of the previously mentioned increase in stature and weight among Europeans and Americans during the past few generations is to be attributed to hybrid vigor.

Let us now consider briefly some studies indicating what actually has happened when various groups, previously isolated, have interbred with each other. Although this sort of thing is often spoken of as "race mixture" we must bear in mind that we have no evidence that any of the interbreeding groups was actually homogeneous genetically before the interbreeding in question took place. Our purpose is merely to acquaint the reader with the fact that studies have been made of such breeding and to acquaint him with certain gross results of such inter-mingling of formerly relatively isolated groups.

Prehistoric hybrids. We know little enough about the races, to say nothing of their mixtures, in prehistoric times, but some evidence has come to light which seems to indicate that in the Mediterranean region, and perhaps in Europe, the youngest of the now extinct species of man (*Homo neanderthalensis*) and the modern species of man (*Homo sapiens*) may have interbred during the period when the modern type of man was replacing the Neanderthal population of Europe and the Mediter-ranean region. The most convincing evidence comes from two caves near the foot of Mount Carmel in Palestine, where, as previously mentioned (p. 88), from the cave named Mugharet-es-Skhul the bones of several individuals were excavated who appear to have been a mixture between Neanderthal and sapiens types, with the sapiens features predominating.[38] It is noteworthy that these "hybrids" had larger skulls than most modern men and were tall in stature, ranging from 173 to 179 cm. This mixture, if such it was, took place during the third interglacial period. Other evidence of possible sapiens-Neanderthal crossing has come from skeletons excavated in Oran (North Africa) and dating from the upper Paleolithic (probably last glaciation).[39] Again there is no evidence of stunting or degeneration, but on the contrary the skeletons showing hybrid char-acteristics must have belonged to individuals of more than average size and vigor. In fact, Coon is convinced that the upper Paleolithic popula-tion in Europe, previously considered purely sapiens, was in fact a mixture of various strains.

During the Middle Pleistocene, if not at other times as well, a mixture took place between early white dolichocephals and one or more non-*sapiens* hominid species, including Homo *neanderthalensis*. The result of this mixture was the development of a reasonably stable hybrid race, which was characterized by an excess of size, both of brain case and of bodily bulk. . . . Modern white men must include both individuals and racial entities which respectively possess and lack this non-*sapiens* strain, since all branches of white stock did not mix with it. . . . Modern European races which possess the former element show no signs of intellectual inferiority, or of any other discernible mental differences.[40]

Not all human paleontologists admit that this prehistoric miscegenation actually took place, but those who do are agreed that no dire results came of it. On the contrary, the result seems to have shown something very much like hybrid vigor.

We may now turn to some modern instances, in which there is no doubt that race crossing has taken place, and see what the outcome was.

White-Negro mixtures. One of the most careful published studies of Negro-white mixture is that of C. B. Day [41] based on fifty mixed families, whose genealogies were sufficiently known to establish the degree of mixture. The results of such mixtures may be partially summarized as follows. Woolly hair crossed with wavy or straight hair of whites is dominant, but when the white blood amounts to three-eighths the hair is frizzly, and when the white blood is increased to more than one-half the hair becomes first curly, then deeply wavy. When white blood is more than three-fourths, the hair may be moderately wavy or straight. The length of hair in women increases with the proportion of white blood. The red-brown, golden-brown, and flat brown tints in the hair increase with the proportion of white blood, but red hair sometimes occurs in persons with as little as three-eighths white blood. When the mixture contains more than one-half white blood, light brown and reddish brown hair are common. Pure ash blonds appear only among those with one-fourth Negro blood or less. Skin color is variable in mixtures; apparently pure dominants and pure recessives as well as mixed tones appear. Pink-white skin color sometimes shows up in half-Negroes. Mixed bloods often have very large dark freckles; the skin tans more easily and shows a tendency to darken with age. The skin about the eyes, the sacral area in the small of the back, and the external genitals tend to remain dark. The color of the iris of the eye tends to be lighter than in pure Negroes, but homogeneous dark brown irises occur with as much as three-eighths white admixture. Flecks and patches of yellow-brown tend to persist in the sclera even in near whites. Mixed eyes show up when a blond white stock is involved in the mixture and the iris is often zoned. Blue and gray eyes appear in half-whites. White admixture tends to raise the root and bridge of the nose, which, however, remains broad in mixtures, with a thick short tip and flaring nostrils. As the white element is increased the nose becomes longer and thinner at the tip, and the flare of the wings is decreased. The convex septum (in profile) is a persistent feature. Some Negroid features usually remain even in quadroon noses. Lip thickness and eversion tend to diminish with increasing white blood, but the lip seam persists. Beard and body hair of mixtures is thicker than in Negroes. The larger white types of ear appear to be dominant to the small Negro ear.

Mrs. Day's material indicates that segregation and dominance seem to operate within each group of stated blood composition, that is, in each case some appear to lean to the Negroid side, others to the white, with a middle group showing blended features. For this reason it is impossible to determine the degree of mixture from inspection alone. It is also apparent that most of the features discussed are not controlled by simple genetic factors, but rather by a complex of factors. As Hooton has pointed out, however, the material indicates a tendency toward gene linkages, irrespective of blood proportions. For example, finely cut, straight noses seem to be linked with straight faces, thin lips, dark skin, and woolly hair. This particular combination seems to be a dominant set. Light yellowish skin color seems to be linked with finer, curlier hair, prognathism, flat broad nose, and thin lips as a recessive set.[42]

Other studies of mixed bloods by Herskovits [43] and Davenport and Steggerda [44] show them to be on the whole intermediate between the ancestral races. These studies, however, lacked the precision of genealogical background available in the Day investigation, so that they shed less light on the specific results of crossing. No evidence of physical inferiority in mixtures has been brought forth in any of these studies, other than small percentages of "disharmony" in limb proportions [45] and jaws and teeth.[46] However, disharmonies of this sort are very common in many white Americans as a result of mixture of subraces and family lines, and there is no evidence that they lay a significant burden upon the cultural abilities of their possessors.

Before leaving the question of white-Negroid mixture, it should be noted that some of the vigorous peoples of modern times are apparently old mixtures of the two major races. For example, there is little doubt that the Hamitic-speaking herdsmen of the East African plateau region are mixed bloods. They are apparently descendants of nomadic conquerors, and at all events they have maintained the conqueror's rôle and upperclass privileges in most East African tribes.[47] Likewise, it seems undeniable that many inhabitants of India, including members of the upper classes, possess Negro as well as white blood; and probably this mixture has characterized southern India, at least, for some 1,500 years or more. Finally we note that one of the most progressive nations of South America at the present time, Brazil, recognizes no bar to intermarriage between whites and Negroes and seems to be suffering no decline in vigor or aptitude for civilization as a result of the mixed race which it is developing.[48]

Mongoloid-white mixture. A study has been made of marriages involving thirteen German and thirty-two French women to Chinese men, and the seventy-one children which had issued from these matings while the parents were still in their thirties.[49] The materials suggest that yellowish skin is dominant over pale white and pink skin; dark hair is dominant over blond, although it may be age-linked (hair tends to assume the darker shade as the individual grows older); straight, coarse hair is dominant over other types, and is also age-linked; dark eyes are dominant, although blue eyes may show up in the backcrosses to the European group; the slanting eye is dominant over straight eyes, and the internal epicanthic fold is dominant over lack of fold; round-headedness is dominant over other forms. Other facial features show a sort of mosaic: root and bridge of the nose tends to be higher in hybrids than in Mongoloids, but the wings and nostrils tend to be wider than in Europeans; the lips are thicker than in the European ancestors, but the chins are longer and more projecting than in the Chinese.

The intermediate or mosaic effect in many features is also brought out in Boas' pioneer study of half-breed Indians, but his material shows the hybrids to be taller and more fertile than the parental stocks.[50] Analogous evidence of hybrid vigor seems to be indicated in Boas' data on mixed and unmixed Siouan Indians.[51] Neither of these studies was genetically controlled, but the impression prevails that many Indian features, particularly pigmentation, are dominant to white features. The study of American Indians made under Dixon's direction [52] indicates that mixed-blood Indian women in the United States are definitely more fertile than pure-blood Indian women. For example the percentage of sterile marriages was 10.7 for full-blood women, 6.7 for mixed-bloods, and the average number of children in full-blood marriages was 4.5 as compared with 5.1 for mixed bloods. Although this increased fertility may be in part due to sociological factors, it indicates once again that mixing of races, at least, has no deleterious effect upon breeding capacity and vitality.

Williams [53] studied a group of 880 mestizo men and 694 mestizo women in Yucatan, products of more than 350 years, or twelve generations, of mixture between Spanish and Indians. In the absence of clear-cut genealogies, he divided the total series into five groups on the basis of physical characteristics, grading from the pure Maya type to the pure European type. No hybrid vigor was evident after so many generations of crossing, but Williams found that stature increases with assumed increments of white blood. The more Indian types have squarer shoulders and relatively longer arms, whereas the whiter groups have smaller chests. The head length increases with admixture of white and the value of the cephalic index tends to diminish. Wavy hair increases with assumed white blood and blood group O decreases. No significant differences in susceptibility to illness were shown between the mixed bloods and the pure stocks.

Hottentot-white mixture. One of the most interesting mixed groups are the so-called Rehoboth Bastards of South Africa. They are the product of Boer men who took Hottentot wives and who were consequently ostracized from South African Dutch society. About 1870 they founded the town and district of Rehoboth. Because of isolation and struggles with the surrounding groups, Rehoboth became a semiindependent society or community. European names were preserved, but marriages were allowed only between hybrids, and genealogies were preserved in many families for several generations. A study of this group was published in 1913 by the German anthropologist, Eugen Fischer.[54] The Hottentots themselves appear to be a mixture between a Bushman element and Bantu Negro, with some mixed brunet white. The Bushmen themselves in turn appear to be mixed Negroid and Mongoloid. Thus the original Hottentot element in the Rehoboth mixture had something of each major race in it. The European element was also a mixture of Dutch, German, French Huguenot, and other strains.

Some of the results may be summarized as follows. In stature the "Bastards" are taller than the average for either Hottentots or Europeans. Steatopygia—projection of the buttocks, characteristic of Bushmen women—appears in the mixed women at about the fourteenth year and reaches full development about the thirtieth year. Mixed women continue fat, whereas Hottentot women get thin with old age. Head form is closer to the Hottentot (dolichocephalic) than to the European. Elongation of the face is greater than in either parent group, and the root of the nose tends to be broad, flat, and low, although the bridge is variable in height. Projection of the teeth region (alveolar prognathism) continues in the mixtures, while the lip thickness varies with blood proportions. Lip seam persists even in about one-fourth of the near-Europeans. The chin is better developed than in Hottentots, skin color is lighter, while hair form and color seem in general to follow blood proportions. The mixtures look more like Europeans while young, but as they grow older the Hottentot features become more obvious. The mixed bloods are extremely fertile, with average offspring per women of 7.4, and they show no defects in health or constitution. It is interesting to note that the culture of this group is also a mixture of Hottentot and Boer elements, with the European traits predominating. Also two social classes have grown up and a "race" problem has developed: the upper class is more European in blood, and looks down upon the more Hottentot lower class.

Indonesian-white mixture. The native population of the island of Kisar in the Timor Archipelago is of mixed Mongoloid and white stock of the type usually classified as Indonesian-Malay, with some admixture of Oceanic Negroid. Rodenwalt has reported [55] on a mixed group now several generations old as a result of crosses between native women and soldiers of the Dutch East India Company, beginning about 1750. No hybrid vigor is evidenced, possibly because the mixture is of long standing, but the mixed group is healthy and fertile, with an average of 7.3 children per marriage. The hybrids are intermediate between natives and Dutch, with a tendency to age-linked juvenile blondness.

Polynesian-white crosses. Most American readers are familiar, through the writings of Nordhoff and Hall, with the saga of the mutineers of *The Bounty*. Before the novelists had popularized this story, Dr. H. L. Shapiro of the American Museum of Natural History had published the result of his investigations of their offspring in Norfolk Island, and in 1934 he studied the Pitcairn descendants. It will be remembered that in 1790 nine English mutineers reached Pitcairn Island in the Pacific, accompanied by possibly twelve Tahitian women and six to ten Tahitian men. In a few years all of the men had died or killed each other off, except John Adams who was left with the women and their hybrid offspring. Adams "got religion" and converted the whole brood, and the colony was lost until 1808. Between the latter date and 1856 three Englishmen joined the group, and in 1856 the whole population, by this time numbering 187, was moved to Norfolk Island, 900 miles southeast of Australia. Two years later two families returned to Pitcairn and five years after this another group of twenty-seven went back to Pitcairn. Shapiro studied both the Norfolk and Pitcairn groups.[56]

The Polynesians may be a stabilized mixture of white, Mongoloid, with some slight Negroid elements. Their mixture with whites in Pitcairn and Norfolk affords an excellent opportunity to study not only race mixture but also the effects of inbreeding since, because of their isolation, the members of the group were forced to inbreed to a considerable degree. In physical type the present-day hybrids show a blending of ancestral stocks with the English type predominating in the blend. Since the Polynesian ancestors carried a white element, this is not unexpected. Considerable evidence of hybrid vigor is apparent, especially in the first and second generations after the cross. Women born between 1815 and 1839 on Pitcairn produced an average of 11.4 children apiece, one of the highest rates on record. Fertility has, however, declined from this peak. Stature also exceeds that of either ancestral group, and was especially apparent in the 1820's. No evidence of physical or mental degeneration is apparent, with the exception that many hybrids are afflicted with very bad teeth, probably due to the lime-deficient soil of the volcanic island. Health and longevity are excellent. In general, we may conclude that hybridization of these stocks produces no degeneracy but, on the contrary, a good deal of hybrid vigor, at least in the earlier generations.

Mixed marriages involving whites and Polynesians have also been studied in Hawaii.[57] The hybrids here are intermediate in position between whites and Polynesians; there is little evidence of hybrid vigor, but no sign of degeneracy, and much evidence of increased fertility and longevity.

PHYSICAL EFFECTS OF RACE MIXTURE

We have reviewed the bulk of the scientific studies dealing with the physical aspects of race mixture and have come across no cases of monstrosity, infertility, degeneracy, or other horrible effects which are sometimes alleged to result from miscegenation. We seem to be justified in summarizing the findings *from a biological point of view* as follows:

1. Race-crossing in itself often results in increased fertility, and in any case in no impairment of vitality and longevity.
2. Hybrid vigor, exhibited in increased size and vitality, is often the product of race mixture, especially in the first few generations, and particularly when the original races involved are physically allied.
3. Mendelian inheritance operates in man, as in other animals, although in some respects it is difficult to study in man. The evidence seems to indicate that almost every factor used in the phenotypical classification of races is controlled by a considerable number of genetic factors. The result is that hybrids on the whole tend to show a mosaic or blend of their ancestral features and to stand midway between the two as regards physical features.
4. No evidence of biological deterioration appears as a result of race mixture itself.
5. Inbreeding may serve to manifest recessive genetic factors carried by the ancestry.
6. "Race" problems could be solved by the biological amalgamation of the races involved, without any reason to suppose that cultural development would suffer thereby.

When we say that biological amalgamation is capable of solving "race" problems, without doing biological harm to the resulting population, we do not mean to say that such a procedure is practicable in all social situations at the present time. In those societies where "race" prejudice, social discrimination, and invidious distribution of privileges have become part of the culture, the solution of the "race" problem by amalgamation is almost impossible on social grounds. Any attempt to introduce this solution in such situations until attitudes are changed would probably produce social disorders with serious consequences, especially for the minority group.

Nevertheless, there would be no "race" problem if there were no recognizable "races." The only way to obliterate the physical marks of racial difference is by amalgamation. Physical stigmata of racial difference cannot be eliminated by education or by any cultural device short of murder. Education, broadly defined, on the other hand, is capable of reducing attitudes of hostility and deprecation which attach social significance to these racial stigmata.

Instances in which cultural efflorescence have followed mingling of peoples and their diverse cultures are so numerous as to indicate that, if such mixture is not a prerequisite for the flowering of civilizations, it is at least not a hindrance. In Greece,

The significant thing is that in those regions where there was the greatest amount of race mixture, namely in Attica, Ionia, and in a very small corner of northeastern Peloponnesus, there was the highest development of Greek genius. In the outlying regions where there was the least contact with the older culture, namely, northern and western Greece and most of the Peloponnesus, there was no intellectual development at all.[58]

CONSTITUTIONAL BODY TYPES

One aspect of human physique which is obvious to even untrained eyes is body build, which shows variations seemingly cutting across race and subrace lines. In all races there are fat individuals and thin, muscular and flaccid, and so on. Several attempts have been made to study this phenomenon scientifically, of which the two best known are probably those of Kretschmer and Sheldon.[59]

Kretschmer,[60] a German psychiatrist, classified constitutional types into three categories: aesthenic (thin, stringy), athletic (well-muscled, in-between type), and pyknic (tendency to fat). He sorted individuals into these types largely on the basis of inspection and rough-and-ready measurements, and his primary interest was in what he considered to be a correlation between body type and tendencies to certain types of psychosis. Thus he claimed, for example, that the aesthenic (or leptosomic) type showed a definite tendency toward schizoid psychoses (dementia praecox, and so forth), whereas the pyknic and athletic types were especially susceptible to cycloid psychoses (manic-depressive, mood swings, and so forth). Normal personalities he classified into cyclothemes and schizothemes. Although these views attracted a good deal of attention, neither his classifications of physique nor the alleged correlations stood the test of later investigation.[61] One reason, perhaps, was the fact that the Kretschmerian technique for studying and classifying body types lacked refinement or precision.

In an effort to correct this defect and to reopen the question of personality correlations on the basis of a more refined classification of body types, Sheldon and his collaborators [62] at Harvard developed a procedure which is called *somatotyping*. Although this can be practised on the basis of the traditional anthropometric measurements and photographs, a new technique was devised, which, it is claimed, eliminates a good deal of labor and provides more satisfactory results for the purpose at hand. In essence the technique consists of photographing the subject through a screen which is divided into squares of standard dimension. The subject is photographed in three poses: from straight in front, from the side, and from straight behind, and always at precisely the same distance from the camera. The resulting photograph is covered by a grid from which all significant measurements may be taken with a ruler, and the photographs may be superimposed upon each other in order to compare the outlines of the body, the relative distribution of muscle and fat, and so on, when comparing one subject with another.

In place of the simple Kretschmerian scheme of three categories, Sheldon's method types individuals in a somewhat more sophisticated manner by the use of components. The three basic components of body type, according to this scheme, are (1) endomorphy, (2) mesomorphy, and (3) ectomorphy. Endomorphy is characterized by the relative predominance of soft roundness, the digestive viscera are massive and relatively tend to dominate the bodily economy. Since the digestive viscera are derived principally from the endodermal embryonic layer, this component is called *endo*morphy. Mesomorphy is characterized by a relative predominance of muscle, bone, and connective tissue; the body tends to be heavy, hard and rectangular in outline; the skin is made thick by a heavy underlying layer of connective tissue. This type is dominated by tissues which first develop in the mesodermal layer of the embryo. Ectomorphy is characterized by linearity and fragility; such a body has the greatest surface area and sensory exposure to the outside world in proportion to mass of body weight, and relatively the largest brain and central nervous system. These tissues are derived from the ectodermal layer of the embryo. These three basic components are respectively reminiscent of Kretschmer's pyknic, athletic, and aesthenic types: a fundamental difference, however, is that Kretschmer regarded his types as basic categories, whereas Sheldon considers them to be components.

Each of the five major regions of the body (head, thorax, arms, abdomen, legs) are "typed" in terms of the Sheldon components, on a scale of 1 to 7. A value of 1 indicates the minimum manifestation of a component and 7 indicates the maximum manifestation. The manifestations in the five regions of the body are then averaged and a three-digit formula is produced describing the somatype of the individual. Thus 711 signifies that the individual has maximum endomorphy and a minimum manifestation of the other two components; 171 indicates maximum mesomorphy; 117, maximum ectomorphy. Extreme types of this sort are relatively rare, and in the original study, covering some 4,000 college men, 76 somatypes were distinguished.

In addition to the three basic components, the somatyping procedure takes into account four "second order variables." (1) Dysplasia is a condition of disharmony between the different regions of the same physique, for example, one region of the body may be ectomorphic, another mesomorphic, or the like. (2) Gynandromorphy is a tendency toward bisexuality. (3) Texture refers to fineness and coarseness of structure. (4) Hirsutism refers to the amount of body hair.

Sheldon and others have attempted to carry this approach over from the study of physique into that of motivation and temperament. Thus they distinguish three types of temperament, each of which, in theory, is associated with a given somatypical component. (1) Viscerotonia is the temperamental reflection of endomorphy; (2) somatotonia "goes with" mesomorphy; and (3) cerebrotonia is associated with ectomorphy. Again one is reminded of Kretschmer's pyknic, athletic, and aesthenic personality types. The basic hypothesis is that "personality is a product of the play of a complex pattern of environmental pressures upon a living organism that carries on an innately determined constitutional patterning" (p. 234). As of the present writing, this hypothesis has not been fully "proved."

The personality types may be more fully described as follows: The "viscerotonic personality," according to Sheldon, tends toward general relaxation of the body. This is a "comfortable person." He radiates well-being, participates easily in social gatherings, makes people feel at home, has a warm interest in many people and a tolerance of their personalities; he expresses his feelings easily and communicates his joys and sorrows to others. He likes comfortable furniture and surroundings, and food is of great importance to him. He has a good digestion and is able to dispose of large quantities of roughage.

The somatotonic person is supposed to be active, energetic, addicted to exercise, and relatively immune to fatigue. He walks assertively, talks noisily, and behaves aggressively. He carries himself in an upright posture and reaches maturity early. He is concerned with present affairs, meets problems with activity rather than withdrawal or contemplation. While the viscerotonic type extraverts his emotions, the somatotonic type extraverts action.

The cerebrotonic type, finally, is said to be introverted. He inhibits the expression of his feelings. His history often shows a series of functional complaints such as allergies, chronic fatigue, insomnia, and so forth. He is often sensitive to noise, feels disinterested or awkward at social gatherings, shrinks from crowds, and meets his troubles by seeking solitude.

It should be borne in mind that these are "ideal" types of personality categories. Even if they should prove to be correct, we should not expect to find many individuals who manifest such personality types in unmixed form, just as we do not commonly find an unmixed body type. Whether or not any useful correlation can be found between body types and personality types, even according to this relatively sophisticated method of classification, is a matter for future investigation. The student, at this stage of the work, certainly has no reason to feel that he is doomed to a certain type of "personality" because he seems to have a physique which is predominantly of one type or another. There are too many unexplained exceptions to such a simple scheme—too many introverted fat men, and too many extroverted "human bean poles."

It is obvious, however, that important problems are presented in these and similar studies of human physique, which, if they could be solved, would greatly aid our understanding of human behavior. Two fundamental questions may be mentioned. (1) Do the same endocrine factors which seem to regulate the development of body structure and function likewise control "personality" and "temperament," and, if so, what are the details? (2) If this should prove not to be true, is it possible that individuals with certain physical traits tend to develop predictable correlated "personality" traits because the "personality" manifestation is *conditioned* to a large extent by the individual's body type? Does an individual develop a certain "personality" type, at least in part, because he has to "live with" a certain type of body? At present we can only hope that future work will answer these and other questions.

In the meantime the evidence does indicate the distribution of a variety of constitutional physical types cutting across racial lines. These constitutional types seem to be inherited, although the genetic details are not clearly understood at present. *Congenital body types do exist. Whether or not any reliable correlation exists between such body types and behavior organization, personality, temperament, and other psychological phenomena is at present unproven scientifically.*

Differences in body type, however, are not insignificant for culture. While it may not be true that persons with one body type are able to learn customs better than others, it does seem reasonable that certain body types are constitutionally better able to perform certain customs than others, just as the bodily features of age and sex determine in some degree the performance capacities of individuals. In this sense the culture of a society may reflect the distribution of such constitutional tendencies. In fact, body type serves as the basis for selection and grouping within many societies. In our own society, policemen and professional athletes, for example, tend to be chosen from the "athletic" or "mesomorphic" types. Persons running toward the "pyknic" or "endomorphic" type tend to choose the more sedentary occupations. The seemingly high rate of "aesthenics" or "ectomorphs" among university professors may not be so much due to temperamental tendency, as to the fact that in our culture, university teaching is one of the most rewarding occupations open to men of small muscles and low animal vitality. Most of them would make poor blacksmiths or steel workers, for example. This is merely to say that a culture usually takes advantage, as it were, of the physical differences among the members of its society. Differences in mental capacities are also recognized in the patterning of culture, but our present evidence does not indicate that mental and physical types are necessarily correlated.

Constitutional type and disease. Although it was asserted some pages back that an anthropometrist is not in a position to treat your ailments after measuring your body, there is increasing evidence that properly trained medical men in clinical practice are finding reliable correlations between certain constitutional types and susceptibility to certain types of diseases. At the present time this appears to be the most immediately "practical" aspect of constitutional studies, and seems to rest upon much firmer evidence than alleged correlations between intelligence or temperament and body type. The leader in this research has been Dr. George Draper.[63] He and his assistants have used conventional anthropometric techniques, observation, and the photographic technique of Sheldon for determining body type. Convincing statistical evidence has been accumulated of a tendency for individuals of certain body types to contract diabetus mellitus, gall-bladder ailments, peptic ulcer, and infantile paralysis, for example. Two types of diabetics occur; a somewhat thin, small-boned type with heavy development of Sheldon's second component of "muscular solidity," which tends to develop the severe, insulin-sensitive type of diabetes; and a heavy-boned, fat type, with heavy development of Sheldon's first component of soft roundness, which tends to develop the mild, insulin-resistant sort of diabetes. Sufferers from peptic ulcer, according to Draper's findings, tend to belong to the "linear division of mankind"—those possessing heavy development of Sheldon's third component, the type the public identifies as the "hatchet-faced dyspeptic." Gall-bladder patients, on the other hand, tend to be of the stocky, fat types (high endomorphy, in Sheldon's terminology) with heavy, square jaws, in contrast to the more delicate, longer, "lantern" jaws of the ulcer group. Children who have contracted infantile paralysis show a significantly higher incidence of the following morphological features than do those who did not contract the disease: larger size in the years before and after puberty; greater number of irregular pigment spots on the skin; large central incisor teeth with wide spaces between them; tendency for eyelashes to remain long with increased age, instead of shortening; tendency for hyperextensibility of the joints ("double-jointedness" and the like) to persist beyond childhood; the persistence of infantile low-bridged noses and internal ("Mongoloid") epicanthic eye-folds; small genitalia in boys, compared to their body size; rounded molding of muscular outline in boys. These traits are considered suggestive of faulty or retarded development in a general constitutional sense.

It should be pointed out that Draper and associates do not regard such findings as the above as indicating that there necessarily exists a causal relationship between certain morphological characteristics of a constitutional type and certain disease entities. The body type and other inherited features in question are to be considered parts of the whole man: they may be indicative of certain inherent lack of immunity, they may be connected with structural deficiencies which open the way for disease, they may expose the individual to psychological stresses which attack the barriers to disease, and so on.

It should also be remembered that such correlations as exist between constitutional type of characteristics and disease are to be thought of as tendencies or statistical trends which may not appear in a given individual. Many a thin, cadaverous-looking individual has never had any trouble with ulcers, there are numerous well-padded persons who have no complaints about their gall-bladders, and some sufferers from infantile paralysis exhibit few or none of the constitutional traits found above.

"PSYCHOLOGICAL" DIFFERENCES BETWEEN HEREDITARY VARIETIES OF MANKIND

A notion which shows unusual persistence among laymen is the doctrine of racial difference in psychology, or, more precisely, the idea that the races differ in innate intellectual capacity and therefore in their respective cultural abilities. This idea often can be reduced to a syllogism as follows, although it is seldom so formally expressed: "Physical groups within the human species differ because of hereditary (genetic) differences. Intellectual abilities are based upon hereditary differences. Therefore, the physically distinguishable groups within the species (races, and so forth) differ in hereditary intellectual abilities." The logical faults in such a syllogism we do not need to discuss, for the syllogism in this precise form may be a straw man which we ourselves have erected. However, the notion itself is common, that races and other hereditary subvarieties of the species are alleged to be capable of ranking in intellectual abilities, and that this ranking may be referred to hereditary factors. This is a notion which dies slowly among laymen,[64] although it runs directly counter to the conclusions of the scientific experts in this field, which we may state as follows:

No conclusive evidence of significant inherited racial or other subspecies varieties in intellectual capacities has been demonstrated scientifically, and, therefore, the study of man proceeds on the assumption that the *average* intellectual capacities of men which are of significance are those of the species as compared with other species, rather than those of any normal hereditary subgroup of the species as compared with other normal hereditary subgroups.

Let us very briefly review the evidence in favor of both views so that we can appreciate why the scientists take a view which is so contrary to that commonly expressed by the man in the street. We may begin with the "evidence" usually put forward by the latter and his spokesmen.

Differential evolution of the races. First we have the notion that the races of mankind represent different stages of evolutionary development. Negroes, for example, are alleged to be more "apelike" because they are, in comparison with whites, more prognathous and darker colored. What about the fact that whites are more hairy than Negroes, an equally "apelike" characteristic? Straight hair is characteristic of apes; on this scale the Mongoloids would be most "apelike" and the Negroes least "apelike." The fact of the matter is that if we add up the physical characteristics of the major races of mankind, we have to conclude that "apelike" features are about equally distributed among them. Therefore, the races differ in hereditary physical attributes, yes, but not in such a way that they can be ranked on an evolutionary scale. Therefore, any discussion of supposed intellectual capacities linked with alleged evolutionary physical features becomes scientifically impertinent.[65]

Physiological differences between the races have been adduced to indicate differential cultural abilities. Such features as basal metabolism, for example, have now been shown to be associated with a great many factors other than with heredity.[66] Whites who go to the tropics, after a period of habituation, approximate the basal metabolism rate of the natives. Therefore, no racial factor seems to be involved.

Cultural accomplishment. A third type of argument has been based upon the imputed differences in cultural accomplishment of the various races. It is not infrequently alleged, for example, that the Negroes are inferior to the other races in innate abilities, because they have never independently achieved the "level" of white culture at its best. In later chapters we shall see that culture, in one fundamental aspect, is a matter of *adaptation* to the situation in which its practitioners find themselves. In other words, the achievements of a culture should be judged on the basis of *compatibility with the components of its situation*. With respect to technical achievements, for example, we cannot blame a culture for failure to develop a technical form dependent upon materials non-existent in its environment. It is thus no reflection upon the civilizations of Mesopotamia, as compared to those of Egypt, that they created edifices of brick, rather than of stone, in view of the fact that their environment did not provide readily available supplies of stone for building purposes.[67] The same is true of the pre-Columbian civilizations of the Peruvian coast as compared with those of the *sierra* (mountain region). The real test of a people is whether or not they are able to adjust to the problem posed by the situation in which they find themselves. And there is no conclusive evidence to date which indicates inferiority on the part of any one race or other species subgroup in this respect.

Psychological tests. During the last thirty years literally hundreds of psychological tests of all the types which could be concocted by scientists have been administered to the various racial groups, and the results to date, to be frank, have been highly inconclusive. It is not necessary to review all of these attempts in detail.[68] We shall content ourselves with mentioning very briefly the tests and the conclusions derived therefrom in general.

In the first place, it should be understood that *no test has yet been invented which unequivocally measures innate as distinguished from acquired capacity. All psychological tests so far devised measure accomplishment under stated conditions.* This is no fault of the psychologists who have devised the tests, and is no reflection upon intelligence tests administered in our own culture to persons of the same average background. But the fact remains that *the intelligence test, as so far developed, measures intelligence in terms of cultural patterns with which the subject has to be familiar.* In short, they show what the subject is able to do with the cultural facilities at his disposal. This fact should in itself make us wary of basing our opinions of comparative racial intelligence upon "intelligence" tests as so far devised. As Klineberg says, "There have been many attempts to devise such 'culture-free' tests, but it appears unlikely that they will ever be successful." [69] He points out that, even if specific content is equally familiar to all groups, it would still be impossible to equate the tests for motivation, attitude toward tester, attitude toward competition, and customary attitude regarding speed of getting things done.

In general, tests on subjects of English, Scottish, German, Jewish, Chinese, and Japanese origin have shown results near the North American norm. On the other hand, 24 tests of American Negroes have given a median IQ of 84 (North American white norm is 100); 11 tests on American Indian, a median of 78; Mexicans, 85; and Italians, 85. [70]

Although some have hastened to interpret these results as indicating innate racial deficiency in the groups involved, soberer consideration seems to indicate that the results reflect differences in cultural and environmental opportunities rather than in innate abilities per se. For example, on the basis of tests given to the Army recruits of the First World War, Negroes from Ohio and Indiana turned out to be superior in both tests to Whites from Kentucky and Mississippi. "The most probable interpretation of this finding is that when American Negroes live under relatively favorable environmental [cultural] conditions their test scores are correspondingly high, and when whites live under relatively poor conditions their test scores are correspondingly low. It is apparently not 'race' but environment [culture] which is the crucial variable." [71] One of the most important cultural differentiations between Negroes and whites in North America is education. In 1935-1936, for example, the average per capita expenditure for all public-school pupils in the country was $74. In the Southern states the average expenditure for Negro children was $17.04 and for white children in the same states $49.30. [72] "In the light of the known relationship between good schooling and performance on tests of intelligence, it is hardly surprising that Southern whites obtain lower scores than those from the North or that Southern Negroes usually make such a poor showing." [73]

It is sometimes claimed that the superiority of Negroes in the North over Negroes and (sometimes) whites in the South is due to "selective migration" which draws off the superior Negro elements to the North. An investigation of this matter was made in 1935 which seems to disprove "selective migration" as a significant factor. "Those Negro children who migrated from the South to the North gave no evidence of being superior in 'intelligence' (as measured by tests) when they first came to the North; rather, they became superior under the influence of the better schooling and wider opportunities for learning provided them in the new environment." [74]

The present position. In view of all these facts, the only reasonable conclusion is that there is no scientific evidence to show either racial inferiority or superiority on the part of any of the major races of mankind. The inconclusive attempts to correlate constitutional type and personality have already been mentioned. In short, in the present state of our knowledge, the concept of biologically determined psychological differences between hereditary varieties of mankind is scientifically useless. We achieve the best results in interpreting and predicting culture by proceeding, for the present, on the assumption that all normal hereditary varieties and subgroups of the species (excluding, of course, obviously mentally deficient and diseased groups) are fundamentally equal in cultural ability. In other words, the ability factor may be considered to be relatively constant, and we may proceed to the consideration of more significant variables in our consideration of cultural phenomena.

NOTES TO CHAPTERS 5 AND 6

1. Berry, 1940.
2. The two concepts are neatly and amiably contrasted in articles by Krogman, 1943, and Redfield, 1943.
3. The reader interested in a more thorough review of genetics is referred to the standard textbooks; for example: Jennings, 1930, 1935; Dobzhanksy, 1941; Hogben, 1932; Burlingame, 1940. See also, Jennings, 1941.
4. See Jennings, 1941, for a simple exposition of the known types of inheritance.
5. So-called because originally discovered by the Austrian monk, Gregor Mendel, who first published his conclusions, based on the heredity of peas, in 1867.
6. Schokking, 1934.
7. Gates, 1929, pp. 315-317.
8. Dunn, 1923.
9. Davenport, 1917.
10. Fitch, 1937.
11. Snyder and Curtis, 1934.
12. Pendergast, 1936.
13. Schofield, 1921; for further examples of genetically identified traits of the sort mentioned in this section, see Burlingame, 1940, Chapter II; Scheinfeld, 1939.
14. Coon, 1939, pp. 250-251. Quotation by permission of the publisher, The Macmillan Co.
15. Cf. Krogman, 1945, p. 50; Howells, 1944, p. 222; Hooton, 1931, pp. 394-597; Hooton, 1939, pp. 60-192.
16. Cf. Hooton, 1939; Howells, 1944; for Europe, Coon, 1939.
17. Boas, 1911; Fishberg, 1905.
18. Shapiro, 1939.
19. Mills, 1942.
20. Appleton, 1927, 1928.
21. Shapiro, 1931.
22. Iyenaga and Sato, quoted by Lasker, 1945.
23. Kanjaki, quoted by Tsai, 1935.
24. Spier, 1929.
25. Suski, 1933.
26. Ito, 1942.
27. Goldstein, 1943.

28. Lasker, 1945.
29. Kiil, 1939. He also believes that earlier sexual maturity has been established.
30. Costango, 1939.
31. *Amer. Journ. Phys. Anthrop.*, 27:480, 1940.
32. See material tabulated in Bowles, 1932.
33. Bowles, 1932.
34. Huntington, 1945, p. 55.
35. See, for example, Newcomer, 1921; Gordon, 1930; Jackson, 1931; Barker and Stone, 1936; Deegan, 1941.
36. Shapiro, 1945, pp. 23-24.
37. See Hooton, 1939, for a semi-popular discussion.
38. McCown and Keith, 1939, Vol. 2. The authors take the view in this, their final publication, that these skeletons are evidence of the splitting of the two types, rather than fusion. They hold that the sapiens and the Neanderthal types were emerging at this point as separate species. This appears unlikely, as Howells among others has pointed out, because, as we have seen previously in discussing genetics, the formation of new species from a single ancestral type usually requires isolation of the emerging types. The view set forth in the text represents the opinion of the majority of experts at present. See Coon, 1939, Howells, 1944, pp. 201-203.
39. Coon, 1939, pp. 39-44.
40. Coon, 1939, p. 51. Quotation by permission of the publisher, The Macmillan Co.
41. Day, 1932.
42. Hooton, 1939, Chapter 5.
43. Herskovits, 1930.
44. Davenport and Steggerda, 1929.
45. *Ibid.*, 1929, p. 471.
46. Fleming, 1939.
47. Cf. Thurnwald, 1935.
48. Pierson, 1939.
49. Yun-Juei Tao, 1935.
50. Boas, 1894.
51. Sullivan, 1920.
52. Dixon, 1915.
53. Williams, 1931.
54. Fischer, 1913.
55. Rodenwalt, 1927.
56. Shapiro, 1929 (Norfolk Island); Shapiro, 1936, pp. 217-257 (Pitcairn).
57. Dunn and Tozzer, 1928; Wissler, 1930; Adams, 1937.
58. McClure, 1936, p. 28.
59. See Weiss, 1927; K. Young, 1940, pp. 316-324. Viola also established three types of body build: microsplanchnic (thin), macrosplanchnic or megalosplanchnic (fat, stocky), and normosplanchnic (harmoniously developed constitution). These types were applied in studies by Naccarati to compare intelligence and other psychological characteristics with body build, but to aid in these studies, Naccarati also developed a morphological index (M.I.), which is the ratio of height to weight. See Naccarati, 1921, Naccarati and Garrett, 1924.
60. Kretschmer, 1925.
61. See for example, Mohr and Gundlach, p. 157, a study made on prisoners at Joliet, Illinois: "Although there is no incompatibility between our results relative to physique and performance and those of Kretschmer relative to physique and temperament, an interpretation of the facts at hand does not require the retention of the concept of 'type.'" Klineberg, Asch, and Block, 1934, conclude that physical-mental types cannot be substantiated.
62. Sheldon, Stevens, and Tucker, 1940.

63. Draper, Dupertius, and Caughey, 1944; Draper, 1930.
64. Horwitz, 1944.
65. Howells, 1944, Chapter 18.
66. T. Carpenter, 1941; Wilson, 1945.
67. Lowie, 1941.
68. Klineberg, 1935a, 1945; Garth, 1931.
69. Klineberg, 1945, p. 73.
70. Klineberg, 1941, p. 255.
71. Klineberg, 1945, p. 70.
72. *Ibid.*, p. 71.
73. *Ibid.*, p. 71.
74. *Ibid.*, pp. 71-72. Quotation by permission of the publishers, The Columbia University Press.

CHAPTER 7

The Functional Aspects of Sex and Age

MALE AND FEMALE

ALTHOUGH no one disputes the fact that male and female human beings are distinct in the structure of certain of their organs, in general anatomical form, and in various physiological functions usually unmentionable in mixed society, there has been a tendency during this century to minimize such physical differences between the sexes in order to promote the "equality" of women, particularly in political matters. We can have no quarrel with any movement whose purpose is the elimination of invidious comparisons and of unfair distribution of privileges, especially if the latter has no basis in the functional potentialities of the sexes. But we should be in error in our efforts to understand the dynamics of culture were we to attempt to ignore such constitutional characteristics of the two sexes as do or may have a fundamental influence in the development and maintenance of cultural forms and functions. Furthermore, the recent evidence all but disproves the old myth that the female is in all respects "the weaker sex."

The fact of the matter is, however, that the female of the species *does* differ from the male, both in structure and in function. Culturally speaking, there is a certain range of customs more appropriate to females than to males, and vice versa. To ignore this circumstance is to ignore one of the most important "facts of life." No one insists that a man eighty years of age is capable of performing athletic culture patterns of a man of twenty-five. Yet there are propagandists of the feminist point of view who would have us believe that women can and should perform all masculine patterns customarily, with no loss of efficiency, with no impairment of health, and with full benefit to their offspring. If age is one of the facts of life, which imposes certain limits and perhaps confers certain advantages for the performance of specific cultural patterns, so also is sex. Our purpose here is to examine some of the constitutional differences between the two sexes to which cultural adjustment is made.

Few feminists at the present time assume so extreme a position as that just stated. The crux of the whole matter is the fact that in times past and in various cultures women have been denied the fulfilment of their potentialities as human females. The same has been—and, in fact, still is—true of not a few members of the male sex. But in so far as sex differences may properly influence social status and function, any serious and fair-minded student of culture will be heartily in favor of an equal distribution of cultural privileges, *constitutional sex differences considered*.

Although male-producing sperms (Y-bearing) are produced in equal ratio to female-producing sperms (X-bearing), it appears that the Y-bearing type has some advantages, so far as fertilization is concerned, over the X-bearing. At any rate, the evidence indicates that more Y-bearing sperms reach their destination and consequently more males are *conceived*. Estimates vary from 120 to 150 male conceptions to 100 female.[1] If no other factors were involved than the mere ratio at conception, it is likely that the males in every human population the world over would greatly outnumber the females. Such is patently not the case, and we must mention certain probable explanations.

Differential survival of males and females following conception. Although more males than females are conceived, the males show less ability to survive during practically every period of their subsequent existence. As regards the intrauterine period, studies of fetuses aborted, miscarried, and still-born show that from the second month of intrauterine life (when sex of embryo can first be determined), male mortality before birth far outstrips female mortality.[2] The same seems to be true not only of human beings, but also of other animals studied.[3] It is now believed by experts that the ratio of males at birth is closely connected with the general condition of the mother during pregnancy. Thus the more unfavorable the mother's condition, the less likelihood that she will bring forth a male child, or stated conversely, the more likelihood that she will lose the male child before it can be brought to live birth at full term. This view is supported by several facts of sociological interest, from which the relationship with cultural factors may be readily discerned. First, young mothers (who may be expected to be healthier mothers) bring forth a considerably higher ratio of boys than do older mothers. Second, the male ratio is higher in first births than in subsequent ones. Third, in our own country among those levels of society where maternal care and conditions are the worst, the ratio of males at birth is lower than in the higher-income groups. For example, among Negro mothers on the poverty level, about an equal number of boys are born alive compared with girls, whereas in the middle- and upper-income groups of both whites and Negroes the ratio in some cases is as high as 110:100.[4]

Two phenomena possibly correlated with these facts should be mentioned here. First, it is often asked why the extensive polygyny (practice of one man having several wives) actually practised in a number of so-called primitive tribes does not represent a gross cultural maladjustment. This question is usually based on an assumed equality of numbers of the two sexes in such societies, and the explanation usually given is that in primitive societies the life of the man is so much more hazardous than that of the woman that the ratio is reduced and polygyny becomes practicable without injustice to either sex. To this explanation must now be added the probability that, in many such societies, the conditions of prenatal care are such that the ratio of males to females is undoubtedly reduced from the start. A second matter which has been a mystery for years is the fact that during and immediately following modern wars, an abnormal excess of male babies is born, as if to compensate for the loss of males during the conflict. In the light of the foregoing principles of the differential prenatal survival of male and female, this mystery can probably be explained as follows: (1) during a war younger persons marry and younger mothers give birth, thus raising the male ratio; (2) there is a large increase in first births, among which the male ratio is higher; (3) with many married men in the services, their wives have a vacation from pregnancies, so that they are in better condition for later child-bearing.[5]

It thus appears that males are "weaker" from the point of view of survival from the moment of conception, as if nature valued them less than females. If one considers the matter from the standpoint of the survival of the species, it is obvious that male survival, in one sense at least, is less essential than that of the female. Whereas the normal woman, during her fertile period of life, produces only one fertilizable egg per month, on the average, and is able to bring forth a child only once every ten months (the extreme physiological limit), a normal man produces millions of viable sperms in each sex act, and is physiologically capable of fertilizing scores of women during the same ten months that his female counterpart is producing a single offspring. For the survival of the species, therefore, it is clear that fewer males are "needed." We shall see later that it is one of the peculiarities of the human form of life, however, that cultural patterns never permit the full utilization of the male "fecundity potential." This universal cultural restriction likewise is based upon scientifically discoverable factors which will be explained in due course.

At *birth and during infancy* the male death rate also exceeds that of the female. Among infants dying at birth or within the first day, male deaths exceed female deaths by about 33 per cent in our society. The ratio in 1943 was 9.9 for females and 13.1 for males.[6] During the first year an average of 48.2 males die for every 37.5 females (these figures are for the United States registration area for 1943),[7] and during the first three days following birth the male death rate is 50 per cent higher. Almost all common causes of infant death (with a few exceptions, for example, whooping cough) are more fatal to boys than to girls, and most of the congenital defects and weaknesses are more fatal for boys than for girls.[8] After the first year, the weakest of the males seem to be weeded out, and the excess of male deaths over female deaths drops from about 27 per cent to about 12 per cent, remaining at that figure until maturity.[9]

Also in *maturity and on into old age* male death rates run consistently higher than rates for females. At present the male excess for all ages averages about 25 per cent, and an excess of male deaths is characteristic of all racial groups in our population. Males exceed females in all the major causes of death except cancer, diabetes mellitus, exophthalmic goiter, and gall-stones.[10] Although differences in life activity and other environmental factors can hardly explain the excess in male mortality in the prenatal and infancy periods, it is probable that cultural and other environmental factors do play a part in maturity. For example, the male excess is lower among Negroes and whites on the lower economic levels, where women do not have such an "easy time of it" as in the higher-income groups.

Generally speaking, most experts are now agreed, however, that male resistance to death is below that of the female from the moment of conception onward. In maturity, however, the facts seem to indicate that females are more subject to disease and malfunction.

This is to say that, in our society at least, females are more often "reported sick" than males. Although adult males are on the average healthier—or at least complain less of their ailments—while alive, they do not survive their illnesses as well as females and consequently die off at a higher rate. It must be remembered, however, that available statistics on illness are for the most part from our own society and may reflect psychological attitudes as much as physical sickness. What are regarded as adequate reasons for visiting a doctor, going to bed, going to a hospital, and so on, are determined to a large extent by cultural factors. In our society it is regarded as "unmanly" for a man to complain of his ailments whereas no such criticism is leveled against a woman. It is, in short, possible that males have many more illnesses than appear in the statistics in comparison with females. Nevertheless, the higher death rates of males cannot be denied.

Although we have few reliable statistical data for other societies, there is good reason to believe that this differential survival tendency of the two sexes is characteristic of the species as a whole, except where special conditions are interposed. Added to this is the fact that in most cultures the occupations of males are probably more hazardous than those of females.[11] We may thus speak of a natural species tendency working toward the survival of an excess of females in maturity and old age which poses several conditions for cultural adjustment, among which we may mention the following. (1) If a society through its culture does not interfere with this "natural" sex ratio among adults, it is required to make cultural provision for the following statuses: spinsterhood or widowhood, either temporary or permanent, for the excess women—or polygyny (plural wives). (2) Cultural interference with the sex ratio may eliminate either of these necessities. A common form of cultural interference among so-called "primitive" peoples is female infanticide (killing of female babies). (3) The greater chance of survival of the mother is one additional factor, among others, which tends to make her the cornerstone of the family institution and adds to her importance in the rearing and education of children.

In the United States at the present time, although the ratio at birth is 105.5 males to females, the average expectancy of life at birth for white males in 1942 was only 63.65 years, compared with 68.6 years for females.[12] In 1944, the excess of females aged twenty-one years and over in the general white population was 331,000,[13] and the numerical chances of the average woman's obtaining a husband were declining from year to year.[14] Among Negroes, the proportionate excess of marriageable females was five times as great: 233,000.

Differential rates of growth. Although it is granted that mature members of the two sexes are obviously different in body form and function after puberty, it is often assumed that, until that process sets in, there are no essential differences other than those imposed by cultural training between boys and girls of the same chronological age. As a matter of fact, however, boys and girls develop at different rates and the evidence indicates that the female on the average not only reaches maturity earlier than the male, but that at most periods from birth to maturity, she develops at a faster rate than the boy. In other words, the girl in most stages is *biologically more mature* than the boy of the same chronological age. In the first place the average girl baby is ahead of the boy baby at birth, if we may judge from the rate of ossification or hardening of the bones of the fetus. Thus, ossification of the rubbery cartilaginous bones of the fetus begins with the heel-bone (calcaneum), an event which takes place between the eighteenth and twentieth week of intrauterine life in females, and between the twenty-second and twenty-ninth week in males. This is followed by the ankle-bone (talus):

twenty-second to twenty-ninth week in females, twenty-fourth to thirty-second week in males; next comes the hardening of one of the instep-bones (outer edge of the cuboid): thirtieth week to shortly after birth in females, thirty-eighth to several weeks after birth in males; then the thigh-bone (femur): twenty-fifth to thirtieth week in females, thirtieth to fortieth week in males; and the shin-bone (tibia): twenty-eighth week to birth in females, thirty-fifth week to shortly after birth in males.[15] Furthermore, the fontanelle, or soft open spot in the top of the skull, is larger at birth in male babies.

Boys, however, are larger at birth than girls; they average about 4 per cent heavier and up to one-half inch longer; their heads are slightly larger on the average, about one-fifth inch greater in circumference. Thus, although greater size is an inherent characteristic of the male from birth, he continues to develop at a slower rate than the female.[16]

Likewise, the girl is ahead on the average in the appearance of the permanent teeth.[17]

As regards comparative height and weight,[18] boys exceed girls on the average up to and including the tenth year. From the eleventh through the fifteenth year boys lag behind girls in height, and from the eleventh through the sixteenth years they are behind in weight, in comparison with girls of the same chronological age. Girls reach their "full growth" in the twenty-first year, whereas men continue to grow through the twenty-fourth year. Thus, although males on the average are constitutionally larger than females, even this advantage is wiped out between the tenth and seventeenth years, because of greater rapidity of growth toward maturity on the part of the females.

These differences in rate of growth and maturation between males and females are once again constitutional factors of the species to which attention must be given when considering questions of cultural adjustment. Thus, for example, there would appear to be a physiological basis for the fact that in the majority of human societies, women marry earlier than men. It would likewise appear that exactly equal patterning of education and training for boys and girls of the same chronological age would represent a cultural incompatibility.

Differences in functional and activity potential during growth and development. Basal metabolism tests show that the male from a period shortly after birth for the rest of his life produces and burns up more fuel than the female. Although cultural training in active sports and occupations may increase the need for greater energy output, it seems to be clear that from childhood the male organism is functionally constituted for a more active type of life than is the female. And, whatever may be the differences in cultural training and opportunities, a good deal of evidence has been accumulated to indicate that the _male_, even in infancy, actually _is_ more active,[19] in those activities which call for gross muscular movements and high output of energy. On the other hand small girls show better coördination in fine movements of the hands, they are better able to dress and undress themselves, and take a greater interest in clothes,[20] possibly also because in color discrimination and perception they are superior to boys their own age.[21] Girls also get the start on boys in talkativeness. "Nearly all investigators have found that, on the average, girl babies begin to talk a little earlier than do boys, that their vocabularies at any age are a little larger, and that they use longer sentences."[22]

The evidence of so-called intelligence tests is inconclusive so far as specific inherent sex-differentiated abilities among growing children are concerned. Girls get slightly better marks in school and show slightly higher marks on intelligence tests up to the age of puberty, but their superiority in these respects is not as great as their biological advancement over boys. Their showing may be influenced, however, by the fact that our educational system is based on the assumption that boys and girls of the same chronological age are equal. On the other hand, apparent constitutional differences in emotional activity between growing boys and girls have been noted. It is reported that boys are more aggressive, whereas shyness and "nervous disturbances" are more common to girls.[23] This has been tentatively explained on the basis of the difference in the male and female sex hormones respectively secreted in the two sexes.[24]

Adult differences of functional significance. By the time the average boy and girl reach maturity they show significant differences in structure and function, differences which can be overlooked in considering cultural adjustment only at the cost of confusion and lost efficiency. Such differences exist in all races of the human species, but are most marked in the members of the white stock. Thus in attempting to "sex" the bones of the pelvis, for example, anthropologists report that it is impossible to distinguish the two sexes, on the basis of the pelvic bones alone, in about 25 per cent of the cases of members of the colored stocks. Among small Negroids, the female type tends to converge on the male, and among squat Mongoloids, the male type tends to converge on the female. Nevertheless, with few exceptions, the male and female organisms, taken as wholes, are easily distinguishable within the various racial subdivisions. We shall mention only those differences of actual or possible cultural significance.

First, the male is on the average larger in both height and weight, not to mention various other measurements. Taking the species as a whole, the average female stature is only 93 per cent that of the male. Weight differences are less constant, due to factors of nutrition, mode of life, and age, but where such factors are equal for the two sexes, the adult male on the average outweighs the adult female of the same strain.

Considering the skeleton alone, trained anthropologists are often able to determine the sex from the examination of a few bones. Especially significant are the pelvis, skull, and long bones. The most pronounced sexual differences occur in the pelvis (the assemblange of bones at the lower end of the trunk), which is not surprising since the pelvis, among other functions, serves as the framework for the organs of sex and reproduction. The transverse diameter of the pelvis in women is usually proportionately greater than in men of the same biological group. (This measurement is commonly referred to as "width of the hips.") And it is often the only absolute measurement of the body in which women exceed men. In general, the male pelvis is narrower and higher than the female. In the female, the pelvis is broader (which serves the purpose of providing ampler support for the womb), its inlet and forward opening are wider (for the passage of the fetus in birth), and the surface markings of the bones are less pronounced (indicating that the muscles attached are smaller).

When other things, such as race and age following maturity, are taken into account, all the male bones tend to be larger and rougher than those of the female. The roughness of the long bones of the arms and legs represent the ridges to which the heavier male muscles are attached. The skull of the male is larger and craggier. In European whites, the capacity of the female skull averages a little over 89 per cent of that of the male (1,300 c.c. compared with 1,450 c.c.), which does not mean that women have less "brain power," but reflects the general overall smaller size of the female body as a whole. The jaws of the male are larger, as is the face as a whole. The brow ridges tend to be heavier in males (although this is a less marked characteristic of Mongoloids), the neck muscles are thicker and the ridges for their insertion on the skull correspondingly greater, the mastoid processes (behind the ear) are larger, and so forth.

Taking the body as a whole, most readers are familiar with male and female differences. The male is more heavily muscled than the female and the contour of the male muscles, except in abnormally fat men, is more clearly outlined, whereas the normal female is covered with a layer of fat below the skin; the male contours tend to be angular, those of the female rounded. The body hair of the male is heavier as a rule and differently distributed. Head hair of the male tends to grow shorter and in many races tends to fall out with age; in males the pubic hair (especially in whites) forms a triangle with its apex upward, whereas in females it forms a triangle with the base upward. Beard and face hair is always heavier in males.

In general outline, the male is distinguished by relatively and absolutely broader shoulders, and relatively narrower hips. The angle formed at the elbow between the upper and lower arms when the arm hangs straight downward, palm to the front, is more pronounced in women, as if to allow clearance past their wider hips. Due to being set in the proportionately wider pelvis, the thigh-bones of women converge more sharply toward each other at the knees, producing a somewhat knock-kneed impression, which is heightened by the typically heavier deposits of fat on the hips and buttocks. The chest of the man is usually broader and more capacious, but, of course, in females the breasts are developed, with prominent nipples and areolae.

These structural differences are apparently produced and controlled by the sex hormones secreted by the sex glands. These hormones are of two types, "male" (androgen) and "female" (estrogen), and both types are produced by the two sexes, but in different proportions. Thus a man secretes two to two-and-a-half times as much male hormone as the woman does, while the woman averages eight to ten times as much output of the female hormone as the man.[25] These hormones, secreted into the blood, have an effect upon all the other ductless and duct glands and hence upon the development and functioning of the male and female bodies, respectively. The output of sex hormones in women fluctuates much more violently than with men with the result that the "general endocrine balance" of women is less stable than in men, a fact that may account for women's traditional "emotionalism" and "flightiness" (which, to be sure, have been exaggerated on occasion by men). If it is true, as reported,[26] that hormone production in both men and women is highest in the spring, there may be something to "that certain feeling" which is popularly supposed to reach its height at that time of year.

In view of the different proportions of internal secretions, it is not surprising to find differences of metabolism between men and women—differences in the consumption of fuel and output of energy. Of interest to the student of culture is the fact that the woman is inherently more adaptable to changes in temperature than the man, due to her ability to reduce her metabolism in hot and to increase it in cold conditions.[27] Resistance to cold on the part of the woman is also enhanced by the layer of insulating fat under her skin. In hot conditions above 81 degrees Fahrenheit the average woman does not begin to sweat until the temperature is two degrees warmer than the point at which the man begins to sweat.

These characteristics are of obvious interest in considering cultural differences between the sexes with respect to clothing and types of activity.

On the other hand, the man seems to be inherently better able to adjust to rapid changes in activity. Because of the fact that his body chemistry is more stable, his level of blood sugar is relatively constant and capable of supplying sudden demands for energy. And he is able to run up a larger oxygen debt because of the fact that he has more oxygen stored in his system. This is probably correlated with the fact that male blood on the average contains a higher proportion of red blood cells, in which oxygen is stored.

For all of these reasons the physiological diet requirements of the two sexes vary. For example, men are said to require from 16 to 25 per cent more calories (energy food) than women, depending upon activity and occupation, whereas during pregnancy and nursing, women require extra amounts of proteins, calcium, iron, and vitamins A and C.[28]

Finally, and of great importance for social life, are the differences between the sexes in reproductive function. In normal women menstruation occurs on a cycle which varies in individual cases from once every three weeks to once every five weeks. Although the disadvantageous effects of this process upon the woman have been exaggerated in some cultures, all evidence does indicate that endocrine balance, energy output, and general ability to perform work efficiently likewise follow cyclic phases correlated with the menstrual cycle. No man has to contend with such bodily cycles. Likewise, pregnancy lays a competitive disadvantage upon the woman which cannot be denied, especially during the last four or five months. Giving birth itself is an incapacitating ordeal, even for the most "primitive" women, and a function exclusively female which cannot be ignored in any society. The care of infants, on the other hand, *could* theoretically be removed from among the obligations of women through the use of elaborate cultural equipment and organization, but, since man is a mammal, the tendency of the species is to place this "burden" likewise upon the female.

In the sex act itself there are certain obvious differences between the capabilities of the two sexes which are almost universally reflected in cultural patterns of one sort or another. For one thing, a woman may have intercourse without desire, whereas this is impossible for the man. Hence, only women can be raped, and only women are capable of heterosexual prostitution. Furthermore, since pregnancy is apt to result from sex activity, the consequences of such activity are more serious for girls than for men. It is therefore the general rule in most cultures the world over to lay down differential patterns for the sex activities of men and women. Such regulations are often assailed as the "double standard," but although in certain cases they may unjustly discriminate against women, their general occurrence seems to be based upon inescapable differences between the sexes in the sexual function itself, not to mention various other considerations which may be elaborated in certain societies.

Sexual division of labor and male dominance. The foregoing rapid review of the constitutional and structural differences between the sexes should indicate the biological basis for the universal division of labor of some sort between the sexes. The specific tasks and modes of behavior assigned to women are by no means the same the world over, as we shall see, but some type of difference in social activity is universally recognized. This may be granted, but it is often asked, What excuse is there for the men taking over the dominant positions, the most important jobs? Why do men usually control the systems of authority, at least formally? And so forth.

One might as well ask, Why don't men muscle women out of their insufferable monopoly of bearing and nursing children? Obviously they are physiologically incapable of doing so. Likewise, it would seem that women are physiologically incapable of competing directly with men in certain activities which require strength and endurance, or which may be controlled through exercise of these qualities. They are also unable to compete on the same terms for positions which require a more or less uniform output of activity, month in and month out, year after year. The average woman simply does not have the muscular strength of the average man,[29] the skeletal frame (broad shoulders, narrow hips, straight legs, heavier bones) to exert her strength competitively, nor the staying power to compete with men. Also, the competitive disabilities imposed on women by their menstrual and child-bearing cycles inevitably give men a chance to "take control" during the periods when they are temporarily incapacitated.

This ability of men to control a culture system has in some cases resulted in the assignment of women to functions for which men are actually better equipped, but which they consider undesirable. Thus in not a few societies women are required to serve as burden bearers or agricultural laborers. In some cases men are so occupied with other activities that the assignment of these tasks to women represents a fair division of labor under the circumstances. But it cannot be denied that, in the last analysis, men on the average have the physical power to dominate or control the division of labor. In other groups, however, for example in certain categories of our own society, we have the spectacle of men laboring strenuously throughout the day, while their women, after performing a few light household tasks, are free to spend the bulk of their time resting or engaging in recreation or "social" activities, in many cases having evaded their reproductive functions.

Although it lies within the hands of males to dominate situations by physical force, there are few societies in which women do not exert influence. The general difference is that the positions of men in most cultural systems more frequently carry with them the prerogative of control over women, than do the formal positions of women with respect to control over the activities of men. Also, as a general rule, activities which are regarded as privileges are more often formally assigned to male positions than to female positions. The influence which women exert, therefore, tends to be of an "indirect" rather than a direct type, since they tend to lack the formal prerogatives, culturally defined. It is not surprising, therefore, that we should expect to find that the "social personalities" of women tend to differ from those of men in the same culture.

Cultural definitions given to women's functions are also subject to various other factors, which will have to be analyzed in more detail at a later point. The object of our inquiry in this chapter has been to point out certain constitutional differences between the male and female organisms which may be thought of as providing one of the biological bases for the development of cultural patterns.

It should be noted that male dominance seems, on the whole, to be a characteristic of the primate order.[30]

THE FACTOR OF AGE

Among the differential physical factors which the culture of any society has to reckon with are the age distinctions within the population. Just as the performance abilities of the organisms composing a society are determined to some extent by the physical differences between the male and the female human being, so also are checks and limits imposed by the age of the organism. Wissler, in summing up this matter, says "this brief survey shows that age differences have an important place in all culture levels. They are probably recognized, formalized, and institutionalized because their biological realities force such recognition. . . . In short, every culture assigns the individual tasks selected according to the formal standards of age capacity. This is reflected in the universality of age classification." [31]

Span of life: possible and actual. It appears that the inherent span of life for the species as a whole is about 100 years,[32] although relatively few individuals reach it and a very few surpass it. Apparently individual longevity is controlled to some extent by hereditary factors: long life seems to run in families. However, most persons have their "natural" or inherent life span cut short by environmental factors which weaken or wear out the organism "before its time." The most important of such environmental influences are in all societies cultural, and most authorities agree that the *average length of life* everywhere can be increased by cultural means. In fact, this has been demonstrated in all modern Western cultures. Thus the median age of the population of the United States has been increased by about 10 years since 1850,[33] and Dublin says, "it should be possible to extend the average length of life to a maximum of about 75 years".[34] However, when all is said and done, both the lethal and the life-preserving influences in most persons' lives, once their hereditary tendencies are discounted, are provided by the culture. The increase in the average length of life in modern civilized societies has been largely the result of those culture complexes which we know as scientific medicine, modern nutrition, personal and community hygiene, and sanitation. Many a society is not so fortunate as to possess these cultural patterns. On the other hand, any cultural patterns which overtax the organism, provide it with faulty nutrition, expose it to accident or to attack by natural or human enemies, and so forth, tend to lower the age at which the average person dies. As a general rule, the patterns of all cultures up to the present seem to have been more lethal than life-preserving for the bulk of the population, in the sense that the average man dies earlier than his uninhibited constitutional ability to live would permit. Although this may sound like an unfavorable indictment of cultural life, we must bear two points in mind: (1) without culture the organism would not, in usual circumstances, survive at all; (2) the actual span of life in a given society is involved in the system of values incorporated in its cultural system. Thus in some cultures it is considered better to die young as a hero than to live long as a coward. In not a few societies the available patterns which must be followed for mere subsistence are such as to weaken the organism by overwork, expose it to lethal attack, or infect it with pathological organisms: in short, the individual has no choice. Thus, a considerable number of Eskimo men are killed every year in the hazards of hunting just as a large number of miners in our own society succumb either to occupational diseases like silicosis or to mine accidents. In neither case, we may presume, does the individual seek death, but he follows a hazardous occupation mainly because he does not know any other way to make a living. Although women in most societies seem to have the ability to live longer than men, their death rate is unnecessarily high in many groups because of poorly adjusted cultural patterns of child-bearing, which permit births too closely spaced and accouchements lethally hazardous by reason of the fact that the culture lacks means of preventing child-bed infections, and so forth.

Data from non-literate societies are far from complete, but they are sufficient for us to state categorically that average expectancy of life is much longer in the literate societies. Simmons estimates that the number of persons reaching 65 seldom exceeds 3 per cent in "primitive" societies.[35] This is not a necessary result of the fact that the latter are non-literate, but is to be attributed to the previously mentioned cultural complexes involved in life preservation. Thus in non-literate societies the proportion of persons in the higher age groups is smaller, whereas the proportional numbers of the young and middle groups are correspondingly larger than in "modern" societies such as our own. Because of increased average length of life and reduction of the birth-rate our own society has been steadily "ageing" during the past 100 years, so that at present more than one-fourth of the population is 45 years of age or older (compared with only 17.7 per cent in 1900, for example).

Because of the differences in abilities to perform customs at different ages, the distribution of age within the society is of considerable importance to every culture. Activity patterns which may be performed with ease by persons in their twenties, for example, are often grossly inappropriate for oldsters in their sixties. Therefore a culture or cultural complex, the performance of whose patterns requires youth, is maladjusted to a considerable degree if its society contains a high proportion of older people without appropriate patterns of performance. This type of cultural maladjustment has actually occurred in various areas of modern industrial life in which manufacturing techniques requiring speed and precision become unperformable by the older worker who is consequently thrown on the "industrial scrap heap."

Age and abilities. The skeleton and other parts of the organism show a series of progressive changes with age from which it is possible to tell within a range of a few years from the characteristic markings on the bones the age at which a skeleton's owner died. However, of more importance from the cultural point of view are the abilities generally characteristic of the various age groups. Recent studies of ageing indicate that there are no clear-cut age-ability classifications in most abilities, other than the reproductive functions, but rather they reveal the rise and decline of a series of curves of ability throughout the life span. In speed of motor performance, for example, there is a gradual rise of capacity in childhood and youth, followed by a slow decline of the same functions in maturity.[36] The young adult shows greater strength, swiftness, precision of movement, and steadiness of motor control than is generally true of old persons. The organism seems to reach the height of its physical powers about age 25 for males following which it suffers a slow decline, often by almost imperceptible stages, until by age 60 the average decrement for motor abilities is about 40 per cent, and by the eighties these abilities have been reduced between 50 and 60 per cent,[37] or by more than half.

Not only muscular and motor abilities decline with age after the twenty-fifth year, but also the organs of sensation and perception gradually lose their acuity. For example, the sense of pain gradually declines, so that aged people are often able to endure chest pains and abdominal disturbances without the agonizing symptoms of younger persons. Sensation in the lower limbs was shown in one study to decline from 100 per cent in the second decade to an average of 53 per cent in the seventh decade;[38] in another study, however, only to 71 per cent for the age group 50 to 79 inclusive. This decline in sensitivity has been attributed to changes in the posterior columns of the spinal cord.[39] Sight, as is well known, also shows increasing infirmities in the average person with advancing age, a decline which usually sets in gradually after the thirtieth year.[40] Hearing likewise shows a definite falling off in acuity, especially in the higher frequencies.[41]

It is not clear that basic learning ability for patterns within the aged capacities necessarily declines with old age, but the fact is that on the average older persons tend to form new habits with more slowness and difficulty than do young persons. This is probably due in part to lack of motivation and in part due to interference of previously established habits.

In females the life span is divided into three easily distinguishable periods by changes in reproductive function. First is the period of childhood, which is brought to an end by the onset of menstruation and the secondary sexual changes which usher in adulthood. Old age, in turn, begins with the menopause and cessation of menstrual and reproductive functions. In males the onset of puberty is less dramatically signaled and the reproductive functions usually decline gradually into old age rather than being brought to a definite end as in women. We have seen previously that the age of puberty seems to decline with increased nutrition and improved living conditions, and we must bear in mind that the abilities of any age group are everywhere enhanced by régimes or care which promote the health and welfare of the organism.

Although many abilities of the organism tend to decline with increasing age after maturity, we must not forget that age has its advantages which may be capitalized in the culture. Thus, the older person often compensates in steadiness and persistence for what he lacks in speed and strength. Likewise, the older person has experience which the youth lacks, and in non-literate societies the old are the only repositories of tradition and wisdom.

Age groups. Because of differences in structure and ability, persons tend to group together in any society because of similarity in interests, in activities, and in point of view. As Wissler says, "no matter what the social pattern, there will be a spontaneous grouping by age." [42] Most cultures accord some recognition to this tendency and provide special patterns for the various age classes, although the formal institutionalization of age classes is carried further in some cultures than in others.[43] The Andamanese recognized twenty-three age grades for men, the Incas ten age statuses. Almost everywhere distinction is made in some way between the age grades of infant, child, adolescent or young adult, adult, and old person. And passage from one age status to the next is frequently signalized ceremonially in the so-called *"rites de passage."* [44] With a very few exceptions, such as those groups in India where "child marriage" is practised, the first marriage itself is a passage rite which implies arrival at physiological maturity. In most of the world's societies marriage takes place as a general rule during the second or during the first half of the third decade of life.

In summary, then, age constitutes one of the organic factors with which any culture must be prepared to deal.

NOTES TO CHAPTER 7

1. Scheinfeld, 1944, p. 31.
2. U. S. Bureau of Vital Statistics.
3. Crew, 1927; Little, 1923; Whitney, 1939. Although ratios of conceptions and births are not completely adequate for non-human Primates, the fact is that in nature "organized groups of Primates usually contain more adult females than males. The gibbon ... is an exception." See Carpenter, 1942, p. 187.
4. Scheinfeld, 1944, pp. 33-35.
5. *Ibid.*, p. 35.
6. Vital Statistics—Special Reports, Vol. 21, No. 12, "Infant Deaths from Selected Causes by Age, Sex, and Race, U. S., 1943." Washington: Bureau of the Census, p. 187.
7. Statistical Abstract of the United States, 1944-1945, Washington: Government Printing Office, 1945, p. 81.
8. See reference cited in Note 6, p. 191.
9. *Ibid.*
10. Deaths and Death Rates for Selected Causes, etc., Special Reports, U. S. Bur. of the Census, Vital Statistics, 15 (21): 217, April 15, 1942.
11. In some cultural situations, however, this factor may be offset by the greater hazards of childbirth.
12. Longevity of American People at Peak in 1942, *Statist. Bull.*, Metrop. Life Ins. Co., 25 (4), April 1944.
13. Scheinfeld, 1944, p. 193.
14. Greenbaum, 1945.
15. Pryor, 1923.

16. Francis and Werle, 1939-1940.
17. Scammon, 1923.
18. From Holt and McIntosh, 1940.
19. Gesell and others, 1940; Thompson, 1936.
20. *Ibid.*
21. Staples, 1932.
22. Goodenough, 1934, p. 253.
23. Johnson and Terman, 1940.
24. Scheinfeld, 1944, pp. 96-100; Miles, 1935.
25. Scheinfeld, 1944, p. 153.
26. Darby and Childs, 1941; Scheinfeld, 1944, p. 153.
27. Hardy and Dubois, 1940; Hardy, Milhorst, and DuBois, 1941.
28. Roberts, Lydia J., 1944.
29. This is shown, not only by anatomy, but also by performance records. For example, women's world records in sports requiring strength, agility, and endurance fall far below those of men. In most cases the women's world records fall within the competence of a merely mediocre male athlete. See Scheinfeld, 1944, pp. 275-281.
30. Carpenter, 1944, p. 195, summarizing observations on howlers, spider monkeys, macaques, gibbons, orang-utans, chimpanzees, and gorillas, says: "There are few exceptions to the generalization that in societies of monkeys and apes the adult male or males of the natural group, in most situations, are dominant over the females and young. One exception may be that of the gibbon family from which I obtained the impression that males and females are about equally dominant."
31. Wissler, 1942, p. 83.
32. Dublin, 1942, p. 92.
33. Gillin and Gillin, 1942, p. 258.
34. Dublin, 1942, p. 92.
35. Simmons, 1945, p. 18.
36. Miles, 1942, p. 758.
37. *Ibid.*
38. Pearson, 1928.
39. Corbin and Gardner, 1937.
40. Price, 1931.
41. Montgomery, 1940.
42. Wissler, 1942, p. 85.
43. See Simmons, 1945.
44. Van Gennep, 1909.

CHAPTER 8

The Adaptive Imperatives of the Organism

A SUPERFICIAL view of man in comparison with the other animals is not highly complimentary to our species. The human animal is bereft of useful natural covering affording protection from the climate; organs of defense and attack are weakly developed; the two-legged locomotion of the animal is slow in comparison with the potentialities offered by quadrupedal locomotion; the upright stance, whatever its advantages, exposes the ventral surface to frontal attack and prejudices the visceral structures to breakdown; the hands and arms are finely coördinated, but generally too spindly to support the animal for any length of time; aesthetically there is a good deal to be desired of the flat chest, knobby knees, vestigial small toes, bulging cranium. In short, man is not outstanding either for brute strength, animal agility, or beauty. But we should not be misled. Aristotle put the matter fairly well some 2,300 years ago. Said he:

Much in error, then, are they who say that the construction of man is not only faulty, but inferior to that of other animals; seeing that he is, as they point out, barefooted, naked and without a weapon of which to avail himself. For other animals have each but one mode of defense, and this they can never change; so that they must perform all the offices of life and even, so to speak, sleep with sandals on, never laying aside whatever serves as protection to their bodies, nor changing such single weapon as they may chance to possess. But to man numerous modes of defense are open, and these, moreover, he may change at will, as also he may adopt such weapon as he pleases and at such times as suit him. For the hand is talon, hoof, and horn, at will. So too it is spear, and sword, and whatever other weapon or instrument you please; for all these can it be from its power of grasping and holding them all.

BIOLOGICAL FACTORS IN HUMAN BEHAVIOR

We have seen that man is an animal and, zoölogically speaking, one of the great apes, a subgroup of the Primate order of mammals. From these facts follow several conditions of human behavior. (1) The fact that man is an animal requires that he must nourish himself upon plant or animal substance, after the manner of all animals, rather than upon chemical elements and simpler compounds, after the manner of plants. (2) Sexual reproduction is required for the perpetuation of the species. (3) Infants are nourished by milk glands of the female or by artificial substitutes. (4) All the innate, physiological drives common to the higher Primates may be expected to be found in man, and the basic physiological needs of such animals also affect ourselves. (5) The fundamental processes of the learning of behavior may be expected to be the same in man as in his relatives of the animal kingdom.

Among the peculiarities of the human animal are the details of the reproductive process which seem to pose a number of inescapable conditions upon culture. Among these details are the fact that the upright posture and large skull of the infant are apparently responsible in part for the hazards of child-bearing, the fact that the infant is brought forth in a relatively more immature state than in most other animals, the fact that the infant is completely helpless for a relatively prolonged period after birth, and the fact that the act of childbirth tends to incapacitate the mother for active life for a relatively longer period than in most other higher animals. There is thus a basic species necessity for some type of family organization, at least, and other types of social organization prove evolutionarily desirable under the circumstances.

STRUCTURAL FACTORS IN HUMAN BEHAVIOR

The most important anatomical features of man, from the point of view of his behavior, seem to be the following: (1) The *hand* is completely flexible, and the thumb is fully opposable to all the other fingers. The hand and fingers are highly sensitive to touch, and the hand is relieved from the duty of supporting the body. The combination of these features renders the human hand the most adaptable of all manipulating and exploring organs of its type in nature. (2) The *upright posture* is conditioned upon the stabilized, arched *foot*, the stable extension of the lower limbs on the trunk, the *lumbar curve* in the small of the back, and the firm attachment of the pelvic girdle to the vertebral column by means of the fused sacral vertebrae. (3) The upright posture and the freeing of the hands for exploration are correlated with the *reduction of the olfactory areas of the nose*, the *straightening* (orthognathism) *of the face*, the position of the eyes in the frontal plane with *stereoscopic vision*, the *reduction in size of the jaws* and teeth. Thus the use of the nose and snout for direct exploratory contact with the environment has been reduced, while the bulk of the *exploratory function has been transferred to the eyes and hands*. (4) Reduction of the facial architecture has been accompanied by a *great increase in the size of the brain* and its bony case from an average capacity of 500 c.c. in the largest of the great apes to an average of 1,450 c.c. for modern males of the white race. Certain of the earlier evolutionary types of man, as we have seen—notably the Neanderthal type—achieved even greater average skull capacity. In modern man the increase of the size of the brain case has been accompanied by a decrease in its external relief functionally required in earlier forms for the attachment of heavy muscles operating the jaws and supporting the forward-hanging bulk of the skull. In modern man the skull has been balanced on the end of the vertebral column and the size of the neck muscles reduced. Unquestionably the increase in the cortical area of the brain over that of other animals is the greatest single evolutionary development in man, and makes possible the high level and flexibility of learning characteristic of the species. (5) The reduction of the hairy covering and of the thickness of the skin itself together with the mammalian trait of constant blood temperature sets the stage for the cultural necessity of protection against the environment, when outside conditions require it. (6) The ability to speak and to perform symbolic processes, predicated upon uniquely human neural structures, permits man to transmit his learned adaptations to his fellows and to his descendants.

PSYCHOLOGICAL PECULIARITIES OF THE SPECIES

The outstanding fact about man in the psychological realm is that he inherits through the germ plasm very few patterned, goal-directed activities (instincts, and the like), but that on the contrary he is required and able to learn goal-directed activities of a wider range and intricacy than any other animal.

SUBVARIETIES OF THE SPECIES

We have seen that the members of the species may be classified into three major *races* and a number of subraces and other hereditary groups. These classifications are made solely on the basis of differences in inherited physical traits, but, even so, the races thus distinguished are not clear-cut, for there is much overlapping in physical type. We have seen that there is no scientific evidence to date which would enable us to rank the races from an evolutionary point of view, nor are the distinctive physical characteristics of the various racial types of any important significance adaptively. Finally there is no evidence of significant average functional or psychological superiority or inferiority in any one race. Individuals differ in capacity in all races, but there is nothing to show that one racial group has a proportionately higher incidence of either innately superior or innately inferior individuals than any other. We thus rule race as such out of consideration as a possible causal or determinative factor in the development of culture.

Individual differences in constitutional type may be grouped into a number of classes, and all types seem to appear in all races. Although attempts have been made to associate temperament and personality with constitutional type, the evidence to date is inconclusive. In any case, such correlations, if and when established, would be a matter of individual differences within populations rather than differences between races. However, it may be admitted that in many cultures special cultural patterns are provided for certain constitutional types and that the functional abilities of the various constitutional types may form the basis for social grouping within a society, as when policemen, for example, are required to be of the athletic type.

Finally, we have seen that the factors of age and sex set limits to performance abilities and form the basis for functioning categories within any society. Such differences in functional capacity tend to require the development of cultural patterns fitted to the performance abilities of age and sex categories.

THE PHYSICAL AND CULTURAL ASPECTS OF HUMAN LIFE

Having reviewed certain facts regarding man as an animal we have only begun the understanding of the creature and his accomplishments. Even if we continued the examination of man the animal in considerably more detail we would still have—man the animal. But we would be a long way from insight or scientific understanding of his behavior or his works. The physical, zoölogical aspects of this beast interest us because they provide the raw material, that which man has to work with, so to speak. The resources and potentialities offered by the human body are extensive and malleable; and they should not be ignored, for in the last analysis all that man does and produces has to be done and produced with this animal body. But the organism is not by itself a phenomenon which would attract the excited notice of a Man from Mars who saw *homo* simply as one animal among thousands of species on the earth. It is man's culture and customs and material products of customs which would claim such a stranger's attention, and if he did not appear to be interested, we may be sure that men, being what they are, would see to it that he was before long.

Therefore, the two branches of the study of man—cultural and physical anthropology—are functionally interlocked: we cannot fully understand culture without some knowledge of the significant aspects of man as an organism; and, on the other hand, we cannot explain the behavior of the organism without an understanding of the significant principles of culture. It is this fact which distinguishes the study of man from that of all other species, for man is the only animal into whose mode of life culture enters to any significant degree, if at all. A strictly biological approach is sufficient to provide us with most of what it is needful to know for a scientific understanding of animals other than man; for once one recognizes the species, knows its biological character- istics and its natural conditions, one can with reasonable certainty predict the behavior of individual members and groups of the non-human species whenever one encounters them. This is true even of man's closest relatives, as we have seen in reviewing the habitats and habits of the larger infra- human Primates. We do not have to explain any sudden architectural innovations in the nests of our familiar wasps. We do not have to fear that ducks will suddenly appear above the hunters' blind some fine autumn clad in armor-plate of their own devising. Nor is it probable that we shall live to see the robins outside our window gradually develop a pattern of boring holes in trees like woodpeckers. And when any of our animal friends do seem to change their habits—as when the fish stop biting or the song-birds are late in the spring—these alterations can be explained on straight biological-ecological principles.

But with man the case is different. One may be well acquainted with scores of human beings in his home town, and feel that he knows a good deal about "human nature." But it is very unlikely that such a person, without prior knowledge, will be able to predict, simply on the basis of his experience with members of the species, the customs of a tribe of people in Central Africa or the Amazon Valley. No, man is a different case. Something has been added to the biological characteristics which are so reliable for identifying and predicting activities of other species, and that "something," to speak very generally, is *culture*.

It is not uncommon to speak of physical anthropology as a branch of zoölogy, but this is only partly true. It is true that physical anthro- pologists study man as an animal, but the fact of the matter is that no one can study man *only* as an animal—at least, if he hopes to contribute anything to the understanding of human life in this world. To repeat, man is a very special kind of animal. A mere understanding of his organism and its evolutionary and zoölogical position in the world of nature does not explain his behavior and does not enable us to predict it. Thus no useful branch of anthropology can be merely a branch of zoölogy, in the sense that it carries on its investigations on the strictly biological level, seeing man merely as another species among thousands.

For this reason, the study of man creates what sometimes seems to be a dilemma, and it is this apparent dilemma which has done much to retard our understanding of human beings and their problems for very long periods—since long before the development of modern science. There has always been a tendency among the students of man to divide into two camps: on the one hand, those who view man simply as an organism reacting to environmental pressures, and those, on the other hand who have tended to concern themselves only with the "spiritual" or "higher" aspects of human existence. Neat dichotomies of this sort are always inviting—and very often misleading, for they tend to blind us to the *overall configuration* of human life.

It is the contention of this book that these two aspects of man must necessarily be considered together: they are part and parcel of the total problem in which we are interested. Man the animal, the cousin of monkeys and apes, the beast whose organism is governed by the same natural laws as are imposed upon other animals, cannot be surgically separated from man the thinker, the inventor, the manipulator, the dreamer, and the believer in something "beyond himself." What man does or imagines, he does with the organism which God, working through the laws of nature, provided him; and beyond the capacities of that organism, in the last analysis, man cannot go. The pliability and malleability of that organism (including brain and nervous system), on the other hand, permit man to extend his activities and his aspirations into realms of accomplishment totally beyond the reach of any other type of animal. Thus it is that man does things which are in the main quite "un-animal-like" and he yearns for and conceives of things which are so far removed from the world of other beasts that he sometimes seems to be completely "above" it, totally cut off, infinitely removed from the crass and instinct-bound arena of the subhuman species. Yet, from the scientific point of view, we can never ignore the organism. Whether we like it or not, man is an animal and among the animals he is a Primate. Recognizing this, together with the zoölogical peculiarities of the species, we are able to appreciate and to understand the better the distance which our species has been able to travel beyond the hereditarily bound limits of its zoölogical kin.

The present organic and functional characteristics of the human species, which have developed in the course of its evolutionary development, impose certain broad general adaptive imperatives upon human beings if they are to survive in the struggle for existence. In a word, the human mode of adaptation is in general characterized by life in groups and by behavior governed by patterns learned or acquired by the individual following birth.

A SPECIES WHICH DEMANDS CULTURE

The fact that man has been able in certain times and places to surpass all other animals is not to be explained by any single innate ability, such as a finely timed and coördinated instinct like that of the honey bee, but rather by the fact that he has a number of generalized abilities of wide potential range.

Thus to a large extent, man is a "social animal" because he is the kind of organism which he is. One does not have to posit a "social instinct" to understand the universal human tendency to live in groups. Considering man simply as an animal among animals, we see that social life is by all means the best adjustment for him, in fact the only possible adjustment for his survival in the majority of situations. Human social life has various features not enjoyed by other animals, even the so-called "social animals," but we must recognize that human social life, as a general mode of species adaptation, seems to be dictated by certain general biological characteristics of human animals, such as those we have mentioned above.

The outstanding distinctive feature of human social life among human beings is, of course, the fact that its form is not uniform throughout the species. Among other "social animals," such as certain bees, ants, and wasps, the individual behaviors, interaction, organization, and artifacts (if any) are in all significant aspects identical throughout the species, regardless of what particular society or social group we may observe. In the human species, on the contrary, the form and organization of social behavior and artifacts shows a great deal of variation from one social group or society to another. In other words, a Man from Mars would not be able to predict the behavior of a man simply by identifying him zoölogically as a member of the species *Homo sapiens*. He would also have to know what group or society the man belonged to, and the observer would likewise have to be familiar with the conventional system of behavior and artifacts common to the members of that group. This is as true for any terrestrial observer as for a Man from Mars—in order to understand human behavior we ourselves have to understand the conventional modes of action and thought common to the group in which the behavior is involved or in which it was learned.

Thus even in the matter of adaptation to the physical environment the different social groups of the human species may respond to similar survival problems in a variety of distinctive ways.

The general system of behaviors, both overt and covert, characteristic of the members of a given society is called the culture of that society. Man is the only animal which possesses or practises culture to a significant

degree. If we are able to understand the general principles of this
phenomenon, as well as understanding the biological characteristics of
the human species, we are a long way toward comprehending human
behavior both in the individual and in the group. Without a grasp of
culture, on the other hand, one cannot understand man in any reliable
and systematic fashion.

In the next part of the book we wish to deal with culture and to see
if it also cannot be reduced scientifically to some kind of regularity,
which at least will enable us to understand its various manifestations and
perhaps to predict or even to guide its changes. Since culture is composed
of customs, we are addressing ourselves to a "science of custom."

When we say that we seek a science of custom, we mean that we
wish to go somewhat farther than merely describing the customs of
mankind, interesting, amusing, or disgusting as they might be. To be
sure, we must describe customs and learn to recognize their salient
features; this is the first step in any science. But we also wish to *explain*
them, to understand how they are developed and how they are maintained, to specify how they are linked together and integrated into
functioning institutions and cultures. This is our aim, and the reader is
asked to coöperate actively, not merely passively. For any one who is
willing to read a book on man is in a sense an anthropologist, and the
mutual aid and coöperation of all anthropologists are required if we are to
consolidate a science of man which will give us a solid basis for understanding ourselves and other peoples better. This book is only a guide
to further investigation, and as we learn more, it may well be that the
guide will have to be amended or even completely discarded in favor of
another one.

It is only fair to say that many authorities are not very sanguine
about the possibility of establishing the study of culture on a scientific,
generalizing basis, as distinguished from the descriptive and historical.
For example, Professor Kroeber, one of the most distinguished older
American anthropologists, has this to say:

We are becoming increasingly aware of culture patterns. But we know
extremely little, in any systematic or coherent way, about how they function
and operate; and beyond that lies the problem of the why of their behavior,
which may ultimately lead us back into psychology, or into the complex and
obscure field in which psychobiological and sociocultural factors are enlaced.
(Kroeber, 1944, p. 19.)

The somewhat pessimistic tone of Professor's Kroeber's statement is
shared by not a few writers. We have no intention of declaring categorically that Professor Kroeber, who has been right so many occasions, is
in this instance wrong. But I do not believe that we need to approach

our subject in a discouraged frame of mind. There are not a few aspects of custom and culture which are known in a systematic and coherent way, and we shall try to set them down. Likewise we shall endeavor to disentangle certain of the complexities of the psychobiological field in which culture is to some extent rooted. If we do not have all the answers, we at least hope to stimulate some one else to find them. So, let us turn to culture.

MAN AND PRIMATES

Above are shown, from left to right, skull profiles of gorilla, Australian aborigine, and modern European. Below is a ruffed lemur, representative of the "lowest" suborder of the Primates. To the right we see a Capuchin monkey, belonging to the New World (Platyrrhine) division of the higher Primates (Pithecoids).

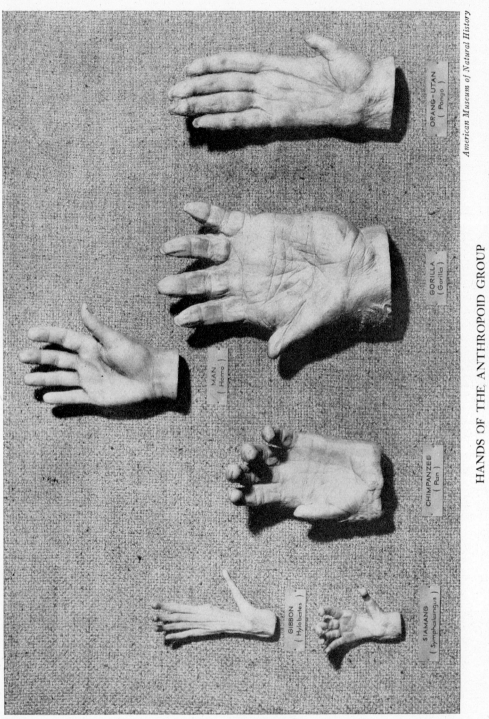

American Museum of Natural History

HANDS OF THE ANTHROPOID GROUP

In comparing the hand of man (upper specimen) with the hands of the anthropoid apes one notices the length of the human thumb relative to the fingers and its semi-rotated position which enables it to be brought easily into "opposition" to them.

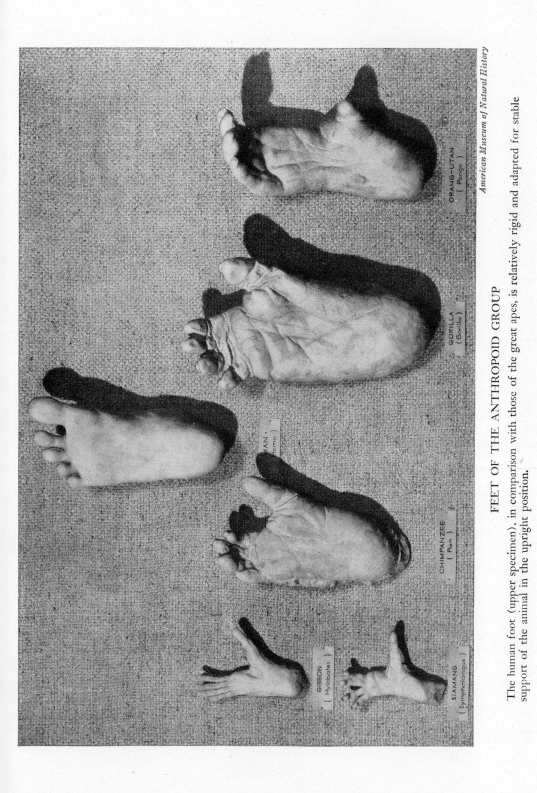

FEET OF THE ANTHROPOID GROUP

The human foot (upper specimen), in comparison with those of the great apes, is relatively rigid and adapted for stable support of the animal in the upright position.

ANTHROPOIDS

A young chimpanzee (upper left) and an adult gorilla (lower right).

ANTHROPOIDS

Above is a gibbon in characteristic swinging posture, below an orang-utan.

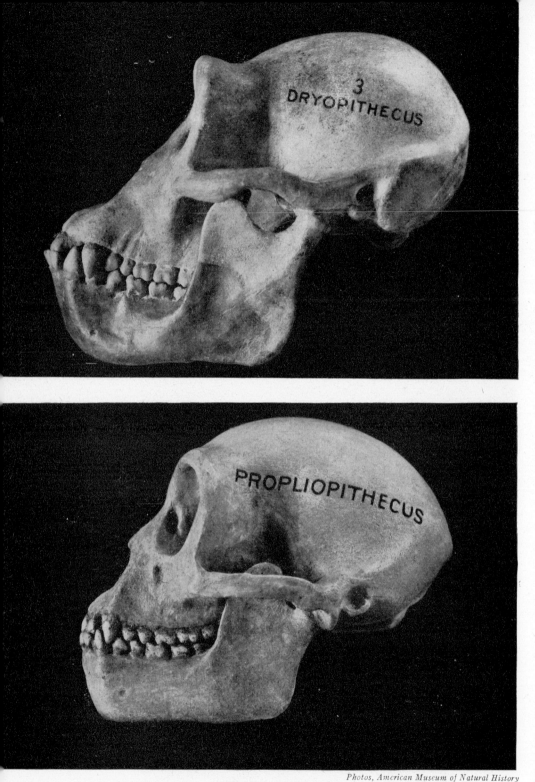

FORERUNNERS

Photos, American Museum of Natural History

These are restorations of the skulls of two of the early forerunners of modern apes and of man. Below we see Propliopithecus, found in the lower Oligocene of Egypt. Above is the restored skull of Dryopithecus, a Miocene predecessor of present-day apes and men.

Photos, American Museum of Natural History

THE ROBUST JAVA APE MAN

Above are fragments of Pithecanthropus robustus (IV) with Weidenreich's restoration of the skull. Note the thickness of the skull bones as compared with those of modern man (lower right). Below we see Dr. von Koenigswald with the restored skull. He is pointing to the "simian gap" between the teeth, a feature typical of the apes (as seen in the gorilla, lower left) but not of modern man (upper left).

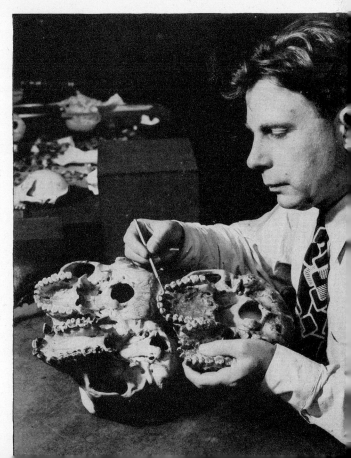

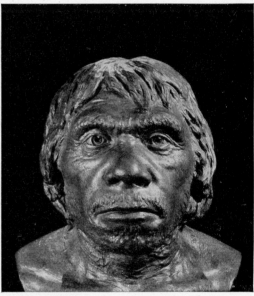

FOSSIL MEN

These are scientific attempts to show the appearance of fossil types in life. Below, Piltdown; middle, Neanderthal; upper, Cro-Magnon. (Restorations by Dr. J. H. McGregor.)

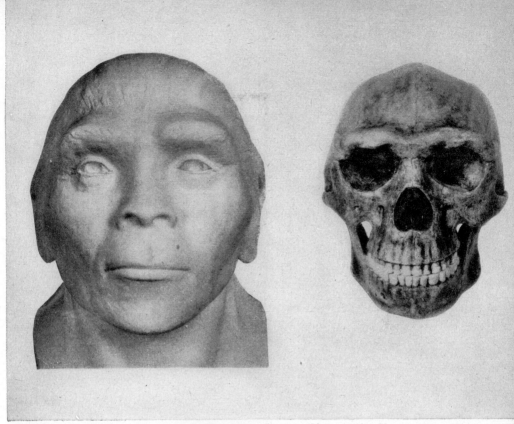

FOSSIL MEN

How did the early types look when alive? Here we have (lower picture) scientific restorations of the Java Ape Man (Pithecanthropus erectus), and in the upper picture a restoration of Peking woman together with skull. (Restorations [right] by Dr. J. H. McGregor and [above] Dr. Franz Weidenreich.)

NORDIC WHITE

Photos, Peabody Museum

ALPINE WHITE

RACIAL TYPES

MEDITERRANEAN WHITE

AUSTRALOID

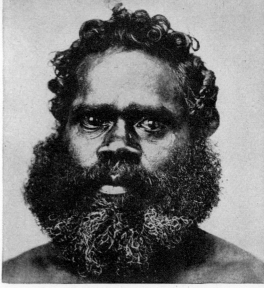

NEGROID (Gold Coast)

RACIAL TYPES

MONGOLOID (Chinese from Canton)

AVERAGE AMERICANS
OF THE 1890's

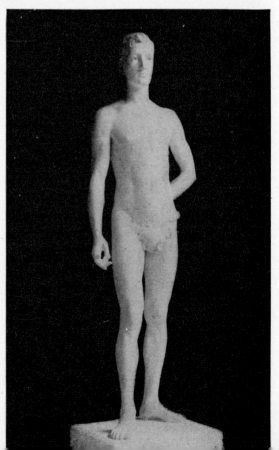

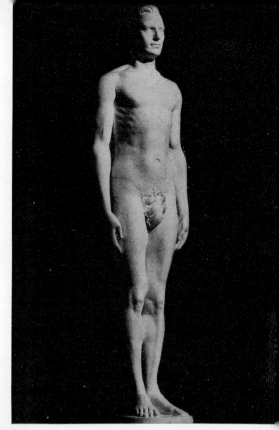

Photos, American Museum of Natural History

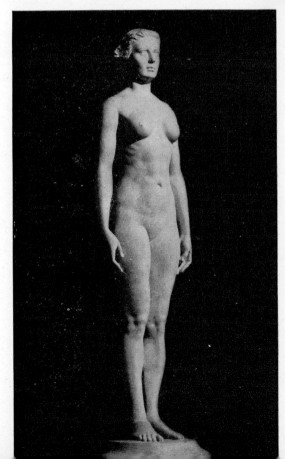

AVERAGE AMERICANS
OF THE 1930's

The statues have been made in each case from average figures of a large number of measurements of American men and women of early adult age. They show that over a period of 40 years "average Americans" had increased in size and had changed in certain bodily proportions, as discussed in the text.

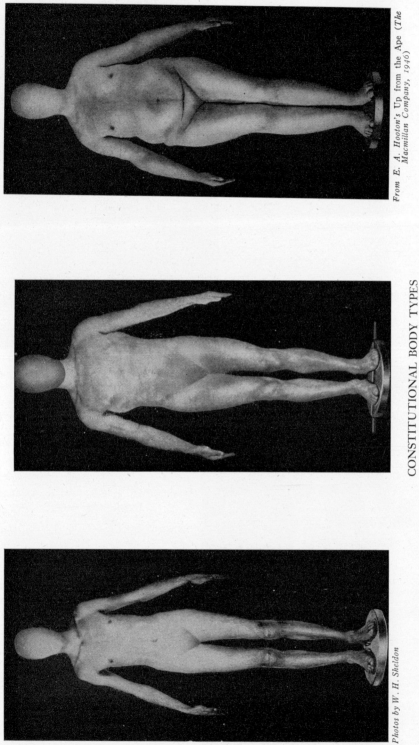

CONSTITUTIONAL BODY TYPES

Three different types of body build in modern man. According to the classification of W. H. Sheldon, each figure shows a high proportion of a given 'component' as follows: left, ectomorphy; center, mesomorphy; right, endomorphy.

CULTURAL CONTACTS

Direct contact (above). A North American in face-to-face relations with Peruvian coastal culture and its carriers at the market place in Monsefu, Peru. *Indirect contact* (below). The automobile tire is heralded in a Peruvian highland street which for centuries has known only the feet of men and horses.

Harry Conover

L. Green, from Gendreau, N. Y.

CONTRASTS IN
CULTURAL MEANINGS

Each culture defines "modesty," for example, in its own way and establishes a set of common understandings among the people who follow the culture. The relativity of such definitions of "proper" exposure of the body is illustrated by the contrast in costume between an American bathing girl of 1947 and a veiled woman of Cairo, Egypt.

Ewing Galloway, N. Y.

THE NEUTRALITY OF STATUS SYMBOLS

A skirt of shredded bark or grass is symbolic of woman's status in Samoa (upper picture) but is the standard costume for men among the Yagua Indians of eastern Peru (lower picture). These pictures also illustrate the differences between cultures in the definition of "proper" or approved exposure of the body, "right" use of personal decorations, and so on.

American Museum of Natural History

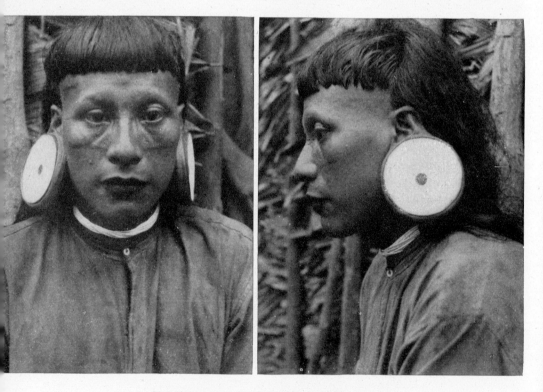

CULTURALLY APPROVED MUTILATIONS

The desire for prestige or for recognized social status may be a stronger motivation than feelings of pain and inconvenience. Some cultures prescribe certain permanent mutilations of the body as a means to desired status recognition. Above, a Mobali woman from the Belgian Congo with perforated upper lip in which is carried an ivory plate; below, a Koto man from eastern Peru, with wooden disks inserted in his enlarged ear lobes.

American Museum of Natural History

MUTILATIONS AND DEFORMATIONS

The "right" way to "improve" one's personal appearance depends upon the culture one follows. Above, a Secolla Indian man of eastern Peru wears a twig through his perforated nasal septum. In this culture men also wear their hair long and bound by filets, as shown, and they affect a cotton garment which, to a North American, looks like a dress. Below, a Mangbetu woman of the Belgian Congo, with artificially elongated skull, an effect enhanced by the conical coiffure.

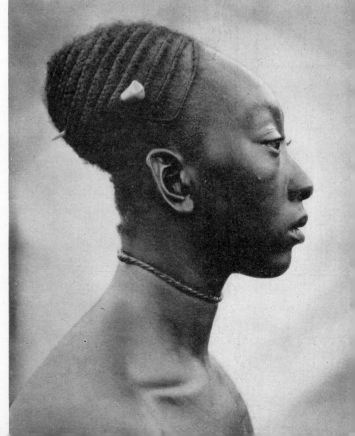

Photos, Richard Hudnut Dubarry Success School

CULTURAL
MODIFICATION
OF THE PHYSIQUE

In our own society elaborate patterns are available for bringing the individual's body type into conformity with the culturally approved ideal. In these "before" (above) and "after" (lower picture) exhibits we see the results claimed for such methods.

Photos, American Museum of Natural History

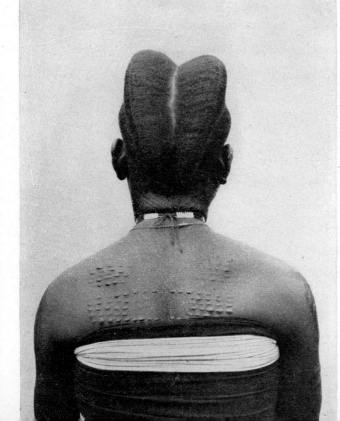

SCARIFICATION

One of the most painful customary responses to the desire for prestige and status is scarification, usually confined to dark skinned peoples. Here is seen an unusually good example of the results on face and body as displayed by a Budja woman from the Belgian Congo.

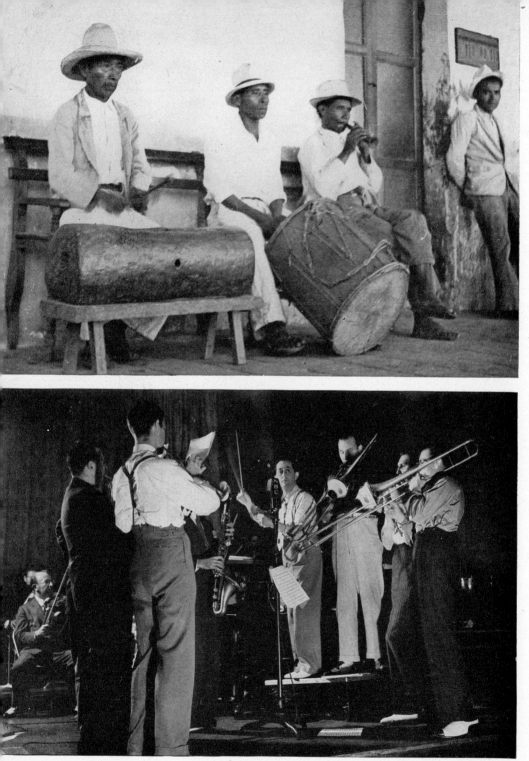

Ewing Galloway, N. Y.

CULTURE PATTERNS

Shown here are typical musical organizations from two different cultures: above, an Indian orchestra in Guatemala; below, a swing band in New York. Both are devoted to the production of music, both play for public dances. The reader is asked to specify the differences in patterning between the two cultures as illustrated in the pictures.

Department of Information, The Pennsylvania State College

CONFORMITY AND VARIATION

Above are six "queens" of an Indian fiesta in Guatemala, below are six members of a girls' tennis team in the United States. In each case the individual grooming, costume, and utensils conform to patterns common to the group. But a close inspection will also reveal that each individual woman exhibits some small variations from the group pattern.

ACCULTURATION

Although we are accustomed to believe that only "native" cultures are modified by contact with Europeans, acculturation often works both ways. In the upper picture we see a member of a group of European descent in the Peruvian highlands, which has taken over the poncho and other "Indian" items of dress. Below is an Indian man from the same general region in "native" costume, actually a modification of European 18th century lackeys' garb introduced by the Spaniards.

British Information Services

American Museum of Natural History

DIFFUSION

Results of the diffusion of European clothing patterns in Africa. The incongruous effects from a European point of view illustrate the fact that patterns are often diffused without their contexts and that they may be assigned new functions in the system of the receiving group.

British Information Services

Philip Gendreau, N. Y.

SYMBOLS OF STATUS

Above is a member of the ruling group of northern Nigeria dressed for ceremonial occasion; below a man of upper class status in North American society also dressed, according to the patterns of our culture, for a ceremonial occasion.

SOCIALIZATION

Among the Secolla Indians of eastern Peru, small boys are the baby-tenders and a tump-line sling over the forehead is the baby carriage. Among the Berbers of Algeria the girls look after the toddlers and carry them about in a shawl.

THE POWER OF ANIMALS

The domestication of animals was one of the first steps taken in certain cultures to increase the technological power available to man. Below is a tame trained elephant at work in Burma, the largest animal used for man's work in any society. Above are domesticated water buffalo with cart in Siam.

Ewing Galloway, N. Y.

Near East Relief

POWER TO MOVE BURDENS

The picture above shows the old and the new applications of non-human energy to transportation in the Peruvian mountains. In the foreground is a caravan of llamas, members of the camel family domesticated long ago by the Indians; in the background, a locomotive of the Central Railway of Peru. In the lower picture another species of the camel family bears man's burdens in the Near East.

CRUDE LAPP
HUT IN
SWEDEN

*Philadelphia
Commercial
Museum*

ALPINE FARM
HOUSE IN
SWITZERLAND

© *E. M. New-
man, from
Publishers
Photo Service*

SMALL FARM
HOUSE IN
NORTHERN
JAPAN

© *E. A. Salis-
bury, from
Ewing
Galloway,
N. Y.*

CULTURE AND ENVIRONMENT

These three differing examples of housing—all in cool temperate climates—
illustrate the fact that environment lays certain requirements upon culture
but does not usually determine the details of the patterns which are followed.

BEDOUIN
OF EASTERN
LEBANON

*Publishers
Photo Service*

SOUTH INDIAN
DECCAN
REGION

*Ewing
Galloway,
N. Y.*

ARAB
VILLAGE IN
NORTHERN
SYRIA

*Near East
Relief*

CULTURAL ADAPTATION TO DESERTS

Here are shown some of the varieties of pattern in housing and clothing
found among differing cultures in desert environments.

PHILIPPINE
ISLANDS

© E. M. New-
man, from
Publishers
Photo Service

WEST AFRICA

SAMOA

American
Museum of
Natural
History

COPING WITH THE TROPICS

Shown are three different native types of shelter in tropical regions.
In this and the foregoing two pages of pictures we see that the environment
dictates certain conditions of climate and makes available a limited range of
materials, but that man in different cultures has developed a variety of customary means of cultural adaptation.

PART II

Social Life and Custom

Introduction to Part II

No ONE can say precisely when hominid social life "began." But, from what we know of the human species and its predecessors this mode of existence must have appeared at practically the same time as did those features which distinguish manlike creatures from apes. Social life is thus an indirect product of biological evolution, although it is not in itself, strictly speaking, a biological phenomenon. This is merely to say that by the time that manlike creatures were evolved they had developed characteristics which made it impossible for them to survive without social life, at least for a period in each individual career. It is all very well for a species to be so constructed that its survival and reproduction depend upon association with its fellows at least for certain periods. Not a few other animals are so made as to require a social existence, also. But all the other "social animals" seem to be provided with inborn, gene-carried patterns of behavior which control their actions, once they find themselves in society. A social ant is not confronted by any problem of "what to do"; all the ant has to do is to grow up, to mature, and "nature," or his genes, tell him what to do at the various stages of his development: the worker cushee ant goes about his business of excavating the underground rooms of the nest, cutting tree leaves for the larvae, clearing the debris from the roadway to the source of supply, and so on, without, so far as we can determine, any personal perplexity about his next move, his social position, or the source of his next meal. His "instincts" take care of these matters for him. And his instincts are nicely adapted to the necessities for survival and reproduction, if not of all individuals, at least of the society. Social life on such a basis is entirely possible and, indeed, is very ancient among insects in comparison to man. Wheeler tells us that social life has evolved independently among ants at least twelve times and that ants were carrying on social existence as early as the Oligocene, some thirty-six to forty-six million years ago—at least thirty-five million years before anything which can be classed as even a fossil ancestor of modern man had appeared.

The human species and its hominid predecessors, however, were fortunate enough to develop characteristics which demanded social life, but not to develop the instinctual qualities of activity characteristic of the predominant behavioral aspects of the social configurations of other species.

Men, therefore, have to live together at least part of the time. But nature provides them with no precise *patterns* of activity. Needs there are, drives there are in the organism, but precise, adapted, goal-directed activities, except for a few relatively simple reflexes, are absent in the genetic materials and in the functioning organism. What to do? is the question which confronts the human species. And this is not so superficial as it sounds in modern parlance. It is not a matter simply of dissipating boredom; it is a question of stark survival, both for the individual and the species. For survival in all species is a matter, not only of structure, but also of behavior or activity.

The human answer to the need for adaptive behavior is culture, which is patterned activity, humanly invented and discovered, socially learned, socially shared, and socially transmitted from individual to individual and from generation to generation. Although culture serves, among other functions, that of biological survival and reproduction of the species, *it is a psychological phenomenon which develops only under social conditions.*

Therefore, viewing this matter of culture broadly, we see that there are two prerequisites for its development and characteristic functioning: (1) the physical characteristics of the human species, which have been reviewed in the previous part of this book, and (2) human social life.

In this part of the book we wish to expose certain of the functional characteristics of cultures, considered as systems of adjustment for human societies. It was anthropology which discovered the cultural concept, and one of the reasons for this discovery was the preoccupation of anthropology with "primitive" societies outside our own civilization. Much of what we know about culture in general has been derived from a comparison of the systems of social behavior in various parts of the world, under different conditions, and in varying degrees of complexity.

At the outset we must recognize that culture presupposes the organic features which characterize the human species. These matters have been dealt with in the foregoing pages. Furthermore, culture presupposes the basic characteristics of social life as it is found among human beings, and these features will be examined briefly in the next chapter. In short, we take the position that scientific concepts and knowledge of the organism and of society underlie our knowledge of culture. But these two factors, alone and in themselves, are not "sufficient causes" of culture; in other words, the postulates involving the organism-species and species-social life are not of sufficiently wide a character that one would be able to deduce culture in all its varieties and peculiarities from them alone. Further concepts and principles are required, a combination of still other approaches is needed, if we are to understand the phenomena of culture in a useful scientific way, if we are to arrive at valid generalizations regarding culture, rather than mere minute descriptions of local varieties.

From our knowledge of the species we have already deduced that cultural behavior or activity is learned, but we must acknowledge that learning, like any other process, conforms to certain principles. If culture is learned, it follows that the principles governing the processes of learning and of learned behavior must be examined and incorporated into our understanding of the functioning and dynamics of culture.

One of the striking characteristics of man is the fact that he seldom confronts nature as a naked organism, in the broad sense. He is practically always equipped with adaptable customs and adaptable artifacts, both of which are artificial creations in the sense that their specific forms are not given by heredity nor usually are they common to all the various groups of the species. Culture is thus a special form of adaptation to the environments faced by human beings, and we may examine its various manifestations in the light of the concept of adaptation.

However, man exhibits another peculiarity to which we must give attention. If he seldom exposes the raw organism to the environment, it is also characteristic that the environment which he faces is only in the minority of individual cases "nature in the raw." By this we mean to say that culture serves not only as adaptation to nature, but that the culture of a group usually succeeds in modifying the natural environment or in creating an environment which is itself in some degree artificial. In some social groups the individual passes his whole life in an environment whose every aspect is either completely artificial or strongly modified from its "natural" state. The modern city dweller of Western culture is a case in point.

We are therefore obliged to view culture, not only as response to the needs of the species vis-à-vis natural environments, but also as a creator of living conditions and consequently we must examine culture also as adaptation to such artificial or cultural conditions. When we speak of "environment" or "living conditions" we must bear in mind that these may be of a non-material character as well as of a material nature. Thus the symbolic conditions erected by a society are often just as demanding of adaptive behavior as are the forms given to sticks and stones.

Therefore, in the following chapters, we shall endeavor to review briefly the general principles of culture viewed in a dual aspect as adaptation and also as conditioning of life.

CHAPTER 9

The Elements of Culture and of Social Life

Basic features of culture. Taking human life as a whole the most important thing about human beings in general and about any one in particular is culture. This fact is not generally appreciated in all quarters as yet, but one of the purposes of this book is not only to demonstrate this fact, but also to show how a scientific knowledge of culture may be used for practical adjustments of individuals and groups. If we know the culture and its implications of a man or group of men we can predict a certain part of their behavior in given circumstances in the future and explain most of their actions in the past. This may appear to be too rash and too confident a statement to make about our fellow human beings, whom it is fashionable to regard as very mysterious and utterly un-fathomable creatures concerning whom no reliable science can ever be developed. But let us consider an everyday example. If you place a chair in front of your sister at a party in the living-room, can you predict what she will do with it? Of course. Provided she is a normal girl above the age of infancy, she will sit down in the chair; she will not straddle it, stand on her head on it, smash it up for firewood, or do any of a number of other things which she is physically capable of doing with it. The chair is a part of the cultural equipment of our society and she has learned to practise certain conventional customs in respect to it. If your sister or mine happens to be the kind of girl who is constitutionally or otherwise incapable of learning and practising the culture of our society, she will be removed to an institution for treatment of her condition or for segregation from the society of normal persons.

The scientific knowledge of culture is not, of course, a magic key to open the minds of men or to unlock the secrets of nations—not yet. It is a complicated matter and our knowledge of cultural science cannot be said to be entirely complete. But results *can* be obtained if one is willing to take the trouble to delve into the matter. We assume that those who read this are.

It is always well to begin with what the eye and other sense organs can perceive. In fact, all science is based on this type of knowledge—empirical knowledge. We can see culture about us at all times, in two of its aspects. First, we are aware of the *activities* of the members of our society and that these activities are more or less alike in given circumstances. Observe a middle-class family at dinner, for example. Manipulation of hands and mouth during the process of eating is much alike in all members present. These similar movements are customary actions or cultural activities. Then, another aspect of culture which is often obvious consists of tools or material objects which are used in conjunction with the cultural activities. For example, the members of our middle-class family do not eat with their fingers, but use knives, forks, and spoons, as well as a considerable number of other tools, utensils, and furnishings in the process of consuming their meal. These things we call the cultural *equipment*, and they also show a certain similarity. All table forks, for example, are much alike in shape and size. It is no accident that this is the case, for they are designed to be manipulated by means of certain conventional human actions, and it would be quite inconvenient if diners had to modify their behavior from meal to meal and from course to course in order to manage forks which might be anywhere in size from that of a hairpin to that of a pitchfork. No, many aspects of culture fit together, and are meant to fit together for the best interests of society and the individuals who compose it.

If a younger member of the family, say one, two, or three years old, is allowed to sit at the table we will usually see him acting somewhat awkwardly as he feeds himself. He does not handle his spoon in the "right" manner, he spills part of the food off the fork before it reaches his mouth, and he not infrequently misses his mouth entirely. All of this causes considerable exasperation for the older members of the family and sometimes embarrassment, if guests are present. Constant efforts are made to train the neophyte to act properly. From all this we begin to be aware of the fact that there must be something in addition to actions and artifacts (material equipment) in this matter of social eating. Although we cannot actually "see" it directly with any of our senses, we are forced to deduce that a *pattern* for eating exists and is known to the older members of the family group, although they may not be able to put it succinctly into words, and may deviate from it somewhat in their actions. Sonny Boy, the exasperating youngster, has a deal of trouble in conforming to it. But it is there, and his mother is doing her best to train Sonny Boy to act in conformity with it. Not only is there a pattern which seems to guide or govern the actions of the diners, but there seems to be a pattern behind the material equipment as well. The size of the table fork, number of tines, and proportion between handle and tines, for example, are fairly well standardized. There may be some slight deviation from this pattern in the collection of forks owned by our middle-class family, depending upon whether they were bought at Woolworth's or Tiffany's, but all the forks conform remarkably closely to the general pattern.

It is therefore apparent that three aspects of culture must be considered in everyday life. We might say that we can accordingly view culture on three levels for analytical purposes: (1) *the pattern level;* (2) *the activity level;* and, (3) *the artifactual (or material equipment) level.*

Cultural situations always involve at least the first two levels—pattern and activity—although we may sometimes observe cultural situations in which the artifactual component does not enter. For example, when you shake hands with a friend, you follow a conventional pattern and you perform conventional actions, but no cultural equipment is usually involved.

Patterns and activity, then, are to be found in practically all human situations from that of a simple evening meal to that of a conference for settling the problems of world peace. And it is only a rare situation in which cultural equipment or artifacts are not also involved. It is just as important to recognize this fact and to be able to think clearly about these aspects of culture as it is to disinguish between the color of people's skin and hair. In fact, culture is more crucial in planning the affairs of yourself or of the world than are the physical criteria of race.

We have not yet attempted to define culture, but before doing so, we should note explicitly two of its other features whatever the verbal definition may be. In our simple case of the family evening meal, we notice at once that the culture of this occasion is common to the members present. There is a certain uniformity in their actions, artifacts, and patterns. (1) Culture is always the possession of a social group of human beings. When we observe the struggles of the infant with the culture of his family group it dawns upon us that he was not born with this culture ready-made, as it were. He has to learn it. In short, (2) culture is learned, that is, it is acquired after birth through experience and instruction in a social group, rather than through the germ plasm. It is transmitted socially rather than biologically.

Preliminary definitions. Having proceeded this far, we are now in a position to try to formulate some preliminary definitions regarding culture. Verbal definitions are, of course, only approximations, but we may undertake to set down some words regarding this thing we wish to understand mainly as a device to aid us in sharpening our wits and opening our eyes, for our true and useful knowledge of culture, as of anything else, comes from dealing with the real article and thinking about it clearly.

Let us take the position that *culture consists of patterned and function-ally interrelated customs common to specifiable individual human beings composing specifiable social groups or categories.* Several of the words in this definition carry with them implications which should be made reasonably explicit before we go further.

A *custom* is the name which we apply to a habit which is socially learned, socially performed, and socially transmitted. A habit, in turn, is a learned reaction; more specifically, it is a tendency acquired through experience or training for the individual to respond in a predictable manner when confronted with a specific type of stimulation. The human organism is capable of two types of goal-directed activities—unlearned and learned. The baby's sucking and swallowing behavior exhibited shortly after birth is unlearned; likewise human infants do not have to learn to cry, to breathe, to eliminate. These unlearned tendencies to act in a predictable manner are apparently transmitted to the child through the germ plasm. But the number and range of such inborn tendencies to act are relatively few in human beings. The major part of all goal-directed activity of *Homo* has to be acquired after birth. This is accomplished by the learning process, which we shall discuss later. The result is a collection of habits which enable the individual to adjust more or less successfully to the situations with which he has to deal.

Not all habits, however, can properly be regarded as customs, for every individual develops some habits which are peculiar to himself alone, idiosyncratic, not shared by others of his social group. For example, one may have the habit of stepping on cracks in the sidewalk, tickling oneself behind the ear when speaking, or taking off one's right shoe before the left when retiring for the night. If these habits are not shared by one's social group, they are personal habits, not customs.

When we say that customs are socially learned, we mean that they are acquired by individuals "from" and with the aid of other members of the social group to which they belong. When we say that they are socially shared, we mean that others of the group also practise the customs with a certain degree of coördination. When we say that they are socially transmitted, we mean that the members of the group coöperate to some degree in training individuals in the acquisition of customs, which may be transmitted in this way to newcomers to the group, such as children of the group members, or immigrants, or to outsiders, as when mission-aries, for example, teach the customs of our religion to the "heathen" of Central Africa.

Since customs are, when considered on the level of the individual organism, habits, it follows that the psychological principles applying to habit formation, performance, and maintenance likewise apply in a fundamental way to customs.

Habits are empirically of two general types—overt and internalized. The overt types are usually observable by other persons without too much difficulty. They are manifested in the form of gross muscular movements, flushing, sweating, changes in pulse rate, and so forth. In some cases they must be observed indirectly by means of special instruments, for example, tubes in the mouth which collect and measure the flow of saliva. Internalized habits, on the other hand, are less obvious, they are never directly observable and must be inferred from observation of the overt habits or from other overt, empirically observable reactions. For instance the habits of "thought" and other "mental" processes must always be inferred from the speech and other "representational" actions of the individual. If all of this is true of habits, it follows that the same may be said of customs.

It thus appears that customs are a special class of habits, special because they have a social character rather than a purely individual one. Let us emphasize once again that all the types of human activity, whether muscular, glandular, or "mental," which may be modified or changed as a result of post-natal experience or training, are properly regarded as habits. It therefore follows that customs may be "mental" as well as "physical," or behavioral. Aristotelean logic, for example, is a complex of customs of "thinking" and it may be contrasted with other cultural complexes, such as Gallilean logic, symbolic logic, and so forth. Sex gender in nouns, a feature of most Indo-European languages, is a way of thinking about words and their referents, which may be contrasted with shape gender which (among others) characterizes Tlingit, a native language of the Northwest Coast. Ideas about the combination of features which constitutes a pretty girl are held in common by members of our own society; notions regarding God, "mental pictures" of the astronomical universe, concepts of democracy are all socially learned, socially practised or performed, and socially transmitted in our society. Each of these customs may be contrasted with apposite customs in other cultures. Thus we must realize that the term *custom* may include not only gross movements, but any learned reaction of which human beings are capable.

Behavioral customs, as distinguished from those which, for want of a better word we call mental customs, are, broadly speaking, of two general types: actional and representational. Both involve physical changes in some part of the human body which are observable either with the naked eye or other sense organs, or by means of special instruments. However, the two types of behavioral customs differ in function. The actional custom in its pure form is directed toward some goal or subgoal in the actual situation and its effect is to produce a change, however slight, in the physical or social aspects of the situation. The customs of eating, for instance, transfer food from some place into the human alimentary tract with the object of satisfying hunger or appetite. The customary pattern of chopping down a tree is directed at the tree itself and has the effect of altering the landscape, which in some cases is the primary goal.

Representational customs, on the other hand, although also overt and observable, always "stand for something else": they do not alter the actual situation directly, but they always have "meaning." Spoken language is a type of representational custom-complex found in all groups of human beings. The human activities involved in speaking (movements of throat, mouth, lips, and so forth) may be observed without too much trouble by the eye, and the sound effects may be perceived by the ear. But the activities and sound effects, considered only from the physical point of view, have little or no importance in themselves from a cultural point of view. It is what they represent which counts culturally. One may repeat the vilest curses and insults of the Tibetan language to an American who knows only English without eliciting a patterned reaction or any other significant change in the situation. On the other hand, if one speaks to some one who understands, the effect is not produced by the actions of the speaker directly, but is translated either into action patterns or into mental patterns on the part of the listener. The sounds themselves mean nothing if the listener does not know what they represent. So likewise with other types of representational customs such as gestures, facial expressions, writing, signaling, and most art activities, or their products.

Mental customs, finally, differ from those of the behavioral type mainly in the fact that they are not directly observable. In fact, the only path we have to knowledge of them is through inference from our observation of actional and representational customs. Mental customs are strictly internal so far as the activity involved in them is concerned, and they consist in such internal activities as thinking, fantasying, dreaming, imagining. Such phenomena are undoubtedly activities of the organism, even though science has not yet perfected any means for their direct physical observation. In the psychological literature it is customary to speak of them as "symbolic" activities. This term we wish to reserve, however, for a more general application. In other places the psychologists sometimes speak of this class of activity as "cortical," referring to the cortex of the brain. Inasmuch, however, as proof is not yet clear that the cortex is the only organ involved, and since the mechanisms of its function are not known in detail, we prefer to reject this term as well, in favor of the term *mental*, which by its very ambiguousness may serve our purposes better. "Mental" has been discredited when used in discourses which seek to oppose or divide human activities into two unrelated classes—mental and physical. In the present connection it should be remembered that no such dichotomy of human activity is intended. We recognize and accept the hypothesis that "mental" activity is a product of the physical organism. However, from the psychological point of view and from the cultural point of view on the social level, we also recognize that mental activities and customs are not observable to other people and therefore cannot directly serve as stimuli in cultural situations. They must always be made overt by means of representational activities of one sort or another. However, if mental activities may be learned, shared, and socially transmitted they may be considered customs. At various places in the subsequent discussion evidence will be offered which seems to indicate beyond doubt that this is the case. We must remember that the "inner world of custom"—the mental customs—of individuals is always learned, shared, and transmitted via the representational customs. Also, ideas, fantasies and other customs of this sort always emerge into action from this inner, covert world by means of the representational customs. Finally, we must recognize this inner sphere as the source of all customs. For, in the last analysis, it is only by mental perception or invention that new ideas and new usages are born. The inventor or discoverer must translate his mental innovation either by representations (for example, verbal description) or by actions (for example, demonstration) into the social realm, if others are to comprehend it and share it. The poem which A has invented may seem a very fine thing to him as he runs over it mentally, but it can be appreciated and socially shared by others of his group only if he writes it down for them to read, speaks it in their presence, or otherwise makes it known to them by representational customs.

Patterns. Customs are patterned. This means that, running through the individual variations in performance of a given custom, a trend toward uniformity may be observed. Because of individual differences in bodily structure, in experience, and in training, individuals may vary among themselves in their approximation to the pattern. In a similar sense we might speak of the pattern of a maple leaf which applies to the characteristics of all maple leaves and enables us to distinguish them from oak leaves. Yet, if we pick all the leaves off a maple tree and stack them on top of one another we soon see that each one differs from the other in minor details of size and outline. So also, observation of the actual practice of a given custom will show minor variations as between different individual performers, but at the same time general conformity to the pattern of the custom. The pattern, then, is actually an abstraction, which trained observers are able to recognize and analyze. The concept is a useful scientific tool, because it enables us to recognize the significant features of a custom without being thrown off the track by the variations.

Functional interrelations. The customs which constitute the culture of a given society or group are seldom, if ever, entirely independent of each other in function. If one looks into a kaleidoscope, one may describe in detail each of the pieces of colored glass which appear on the viewing field, but such a part-description by itself does not describe the total design which one sees and which is made up of these separate pieces of glass. If one gives the kaleidoscope a turn, one does not add or subtract any pieces of glass, but one of these elements may slip into a different position, whereupon the entire design assumes a new form. It is thus clear that the whole design is something different from the mere sum of its parts. Its character depends upon the individual qualities of the parts, upon the color, size, and texture of each piece of glass—but also upon the relations of the various pieces of glass one to another. An organized whole of this type is called a *configuration*, and an understanding of it depends upon a knowledge of the dynamic functional relationships of the elements which compose it.

The customs which compose a culture are likewise functionally interrelated one to another. One custom may "support" another one, to take one typical example of such interrelationship. For instance, in our society, a man does not ordinarily shake hands with a lady until he has been introduced to her; he does not put his arm around her until he has shaken hands; he does not marry her until he has put his arm around her, and so on. All of these customs are functionally linked together. In so far as the customs composing a culture are *consistent* with each other we say that the culture is *integrated*. Some cultures are more highly integrated than others, of course, and can be compared on this basis.

Taking the culture as a whole we speak of it as a configuration. And when comparing one culture with another we must compare not only the separate customs of each (the content of the cultures) but also the wholes as total organizations of custom. For example, both the German and the North American cultures possessed certain almost identical military customs, yet, without necessarily claiming that the North American culture was "better" than the German, it is obvious that the total configurations of the two cultures were different and distinct. The manual of arms may be practically identical in the two cultures, but the position and function of this complex of customs differs in the two cultures when we consider them as total organizations of custom.

Societies and social groups. We have seen that man is a social animal and we have discussed some of the species characteristics which explain the evolutionary appearance of this trait. Although individual human beings of course possess culture, they always derive it from a social group of some kind. Even a hermit who has decided to remove himself from all social groups, was born and reared in one, and in the process acquired certain customs which he carries with him into the wilderness. The hermits of the Libyan desert in early Christian times, for example, pondered the Infinite. Starting at least with conventional theological concepts, they read the Bible, and many of them wrote down their conclusions. In all of these activities they made use of customs acquired during their lives as social individuals.

A social group is not to be confused with a mere aggregation of human individuals, such as the inmates of the cells on the solitary confinement block of a penitentiary. The basic requirement of a social group is that it consists of at least two or more individuals and that they be able to stimulate each other and to respond to each other, in the basic psychological sense. The sociological term for this relationship is *social contact* and the opposite state is called *social isolation*. Anything which tends to impede the ability of the constituent individuals to stimulate and to respond mutually, may reduce a social group to a mere aggregation. It is obvious that an aggregation cannot possess a culture of its own because it is so constituted that the individuals involved are unable to teach or otherwise transmit customs to each other or to practise them in coördinated fashion.

It is to be understood that the contact necessary between individuals of a group may be either *direct* or *indirect*. In the direct type, the stimulation of one individual impinges directly on the receptors of another, as in face-to-face situations. In the indirect type interstimulation is carried on by means of third persons or by some instrumental agency, such as letters, publication, telegraph, signal drum, and so forth. Groups whose internal contacts are mainly of the direct type are usually called *primary groups*, while those which depend mainly upon indirect contact between the members are called *secondary groups*. In our own society the immediate household is usually a primary group, while such an organization as the Democratic party as a whole is a secondary group. The content and organization of culture usually show concomitant differences in primary as compared with secondary groups.

From what has gone before it is obvious that social groups may differ in size and character. The largest type of social group is a *society*, which may be defined as the largest body of human beings whose members share a common culture (including language) and consequently common objectives, interests, and feelings of interdependence. Most societies, even the smaller ones, are in turn composed of categories or subgroups of one kind or another. Universal social categories are those based on sex and age. These subgroups may, of course, develop *subcultures* and specialized customs within the framework of the society as a whole. Thus, among ourselves, we have the custom of wearing skirts, which is restricted to females as a subgroup, and the custom of smoking pipes, which is customarily confined to the male subgroup (even though there be certain eccentric females who attempt to copy the males). Only babies wear diapers and are permitted to take nourishment through rubber nipples, while only adolescents and adults are allowed to drive automobiles. In many a society, it is also possible to recognize subgroups and subcultures based on locality and region, such as the people of Brooklyn with their dialect and other customs, the region of the Deep South with its dialect and customs. Other subgroups may be based on interests generated or modified by the culture itself and may possess specialized customs oriented toward such interests. For example, in Polynesia the canoe-makers were often organized into something like guilds, just as electrical engineers, for example, may be considered a specialized group among ourselves.

Artifacts. It may have been noticed that we have not specifically included material equipment or artifacts in our definition of culture. The reason is that we consider culture itself to be fundamentally composed of learned reactions of human beings whereas material equipment is not a learned reaction. Rather it is either a product of such activities or an adjunct of them. The importance of the material equipment in all cultures is very great, and it is for this reason that in the first section of this chapter we have pointed out that the "artifactual level" must always be considered in dealing with cultural situations. Many a custom cannot be performed without an artifact—you cannot tip your hat, for example, if you do not have a material object which we call "hat" on your head. A Pueblo potter cannot make a water jar unless she has a supply of prepared clay at hand. And so on. Artifacts as adjuncts to customs play two rôles: through their stimulus value they may evoke performance of the custom, as when a stop sign on the street cues to the driver the custom of braking his car; and, because of certain qualities, artifacts may serve to enhance the natural response capabilities of the human animal. In the latter case, artifacts are usually called tools. The spear-thrower, for example, has the effect of lengthening the radius of the arm, thus enabling a man to cast a spear farther than he can without this tool. A set of brass knuckles increases the ruggedness of one's fist and permits one to deliver a more punishing blow than if unaided. However, neither as an adjunct nor as a product, does a piece of material equipment enjoy formal or functional independence. Neither the form nor the function of an artifact can be explained without a consideration of the application of human customs. The form of an artifact can only be explained in terms of the customs which were practised to produce it. The function of an artifact can only be explained in terms of the customs which involve its use. An artifact cannot be trained to respond, to receive stimuli; it cannot be motivated. It is clear, therefore, that the principles which can be used to explain customs will not apply to artifacts directly. In a consistent science of culture, artifacts must be regarded therefore as representing a type of condition under which certain customs operate, but not as customs themselves. Customs must be adapted to artifacts in the same way that they must be adapted to conditions of the natural environment, and the fact that artifacts are artifically created conditions produced by customary action is of supreme interest, but does not alter the basic principle involved.

In short, we may say that culture is always a "product" of the members of the species themselves; it is activity. Material equipment, on the other hand, is always the product of cultural activity, which mediates or stands between the organism and material equipment.

THE ADAPTIVE SERVICES OF CULTURE

Culture is to be thought of as a certain type of activity of the species: social, learned, patterned activity. On the basis of evolutionary theory we are led to believe that any type of activity of a species, whether innate or learned, must serve *some* adaptive function. Otherwise it would be eliminated in the struggle for existence.

For the species. Nature provides that each species adapts in some degree to the conditions under which it must carry on its existence. If the species is unable to do this it is inexorably eliminated sooner or later. There can be no doubt that culture, in general, is a form of adaptation developed by the human species. Most other animals adapt by means of selected factors of the germ plasm which in turn produce adaptive characteristics in the organism. These hereditary characteristics which enable other non-human species to withstand the "slings and arrows of outrageous fortune" are to be seen either in their structure or in their inborn behavior patterns, or both. The heavy fur coat and the protective white coloring of the arctic hare protects the animal from the climate and from its enemies. The instinctive, untrained search for nectar of the honey bee is a form of activity which enables this organism to survive in the environment for which it is specialized. We have seen, however, that on the whole man lacks either structural adaptations or inborn tendencies for behavior of a specialized, adaptive type. This is one of the prices he pays for being a generalized animal, not closely adapted to any particular environment, but able to travel and make himself at home in most parts of the globe. It is all very well to be unspecialized and fancy free, in a manner of speaking, but something must be substituted for the inherited adaptations of other species if man is to survive.

For the group. Culture is ordinarily associated in specific cases with social groups, social categories, or societies. By definition culture itself could not exist in the absence of groups, and the zoölogical evidence seems to indicate that neither the individual members nor the species as a whole could survive without group life. We must therefore recognize that culture, as a form of adaptive activity, serves not only the species as a whole, but also the group to which it belongs. It follows as a general principle that a cultural system or configuration should be of such a nature as to preserve a certain modicum of internal harmony between the members of the group; it should contain customs so organized together that the group is not torn and rent asunder by internal dissensions; it should provide customs which enable the group to survive in its relations with other groups or societies with which it is in contact; it should provide patterns for leadership and followership and other forms of internal organization tending to promote internal order and coördinated activity of the group.

It is not too much to say, then, that the group or society itself is held together by and owes its existence to the type and organization of cultural patterns which it practises. Indeed, this fact is evident on every hand, both in historical and modern times. It is now agreed, for example, that the fall and decline of the Roman Empire is to be attributed, regardless of other factors, at least in part to the "decay" of customs and their integration within its culture. And the internal dissensions of France in 1939 seemed to show gross cultural conflicts which had not a little to do with the defeat of that nation by Germany. When the culture "comes apart at the seams" the society or group is in imminent danger of losing its identity and its very existence. Social adjustment is quite as essential to man as physical adjustment.

For the individual. A human being without culture is an abnormality. The only such individuals known are a few children, abandoned at birth by their parents or otherwise isolated from human society for prolonged periods during early childhood, plus feeble-minded or mentally ill individuals who are unable to learn culture and must be cared for by other humans. Except for abandoned children who have been tended by wolves or other wild animals—and the number of authenticated cases is extremely small—none of the cultureless individuals would have survived

at all, except for the performance of cultural behavior on their behalf
by other human beings.

From this we may conclude that culture means survival itself for
the individual. The inborn, goal-directed activity patterns of the human
infant are so few and so poorly adapted to his necessities that without
care he starves or succumbs to the rigors of the climate, to mention no
other lethal influences. It is true that infants can suck without being
taught, but they lack the ability to find the nipple for themselves—it has
to be placed by some one else in the mouth before the sucking reflex will
start. Infants can cry out without training—much to the annoyance of
their nurses—but this trait serves only to call attention of others to their
needs, not to satisfy the same directly. Infants can urinate and defecate
without instruction, but are unable to dispose of the waste materials in
a way which avoids disease and irritation.

The culture, through the practised customs of its surrogates (mothers
and nurses), thus preserves the very life of the typical human being at
the start. As he grows older, our individual is able to learn self-preserving
patterns of the culture himself, if "normal"; but all his life he will be
dependent upon being able to practise the customs of his group, if he is
to survive. Thus we may say that the culture provides the ordinary human
being with the solution to the majority of the problems he will face in
life situations. He does not have to "figure out" how to survive every
time a dilemma arises; he only has to practise the appropriate custom
which, it is to be hoped, he has already learned. When we say that a
certain person "doesn't even know enough to come in out of the rain"
we mean that he has not learned the appropriate customs which would
protect him from environmental pressures. Other aspects of this matter
will be discussed in succeeding chapters.

We conclude that culture as learned social activity serves an adaptive
or survival function for the species, the group, and the individual.

EVIDENCE THAT CULTURE IS LEARNED

In our own society, however, we sometimes have difficulty in convincing ourselves that the customs which we practise are actually
acquired or learned. They seem so much a part of our nature that we
are sometimes inclined to regard them as inherited, in the biological sense.
This is to some extent due to confusion over the meaning of "learning."
We shall discuss the basic principles of learning and behavior as they
are concerned in culture in Chapter 11. We may mention other types of
evidence here.

There are three types of data which convince us that the customs of mankind are not inherited biologically, either by the species or by any subgroup within it. First, we have the investigations on new-born infants, already mentioned, which indicate the extreme paucity of inborn goal-directed activity patterns of any type. This material still leaves open a question, however. Some one may say, "O. K., human babies don't come into the world already equipped with adaptive behavior. But, how do you know that they may not develop inherited tendencies as they mature? Possibly the patterns carried in the germ plasm don't emerge until certain stages of development are reached, just as age-linked dark hair often does not appear until the child is half-grown." At this point we bring in our second type of evidence, consisting of various carefully controlled studies of identical twins who have been reared apart from each other and have grown up developing different custom patterns. In these cases the individuals were identical in inheritance and differed only in the type of experience and training accorded them. If they grew up to exhibit different culture patterns we can hardly assign the culture to heredity.

Finally, and perhaps most convincing for anthropological purposes, we have the evidence of the variability of human culture itself. We have already seen that all qualified experts agree that the species is one, biologically speaking. Yet the cultures practised by diverse groups within the species vary enormously among themselves. Likewise there is no uniformity or regularity in the types of culture to be found within a single race or other subgroup of the species. Many a full-blood Negro is culturally North American, whereas genetically he is practically identical with his relatives still practising cannibalism in West Africa. World War II convinced most Americans that soldiers of Japanese ancestry when brought up as Americans, can be culturally as American as any one else, and entirely different from their and our enemies under the influence of Tokyo. When we are acquainted with the great variety of cultures it is impossible to believe that culture is carried in the germ plasm. There are only two other alternatives: either it descends upon people in some mysterious, unknown fashion, or it is learned. The first hypothesis has no data to support it, while the second seems to fit the facts.

SUPER-INDIVIDUAL ASPECTS OF SOCIETY AND CULTURE

Although every society is composed of individuals and although the culture in each case has to be learned and performed by individuals, the society and the culture are not to be confused with the individual. The society normally extends beyond the life span of single individuals, and the culture covers areas of experience beyond the range of any one individual, whether in time or space or subject-matter. The individual, society, and culture are in some senses independent variables. An individual dies, but the society may go on with much the same potentialities for action as previously. On the other hand the society may remain the same, even with the identical membership of former days, while the details and emphasis of its culture change, and certain customs and artifacts are replaced.

From the point of view of performance and participation we might look for analogy to one of those enormous animated electric signs which hang above Times Square in New York. Each sign is composed of thousands of individual light bulbs of different colors and degrees of brightness, and as these lights go on and off in synchronized and patterned fashion, the sign is able to tell an animated "story," spell out whole series of messages, produce the effect of explosions, and so on. The individual bulbs are somewhat like the individual human beings in a human society. They differ among themselves in performance abilities and in the effects they produce—some are 40-watt bulbs, others are 100-watt; some are yellow, others are white; and so on. The 10,000 bulbs of a single sign are like the membership of a society. For they are organized, sorted out according to their abilities, and assigned certain places in the scheme of things. If right bulbs are in wrong places, the designs which the sign is supposed to produce will fail of performance, for we may think of these designs—the animated cartoon story, the advertising message, and other "effects"—as analogous to a culture. The individual units must be properly organized according to their performance abilities if the total effect is to be produced. However, if one bulb goes dead, the show does not stop. Another of similar type is inserted in its place and takes up the duties of its predecessor—the show goes on. Furthermore, in these advertising displays, the total display is changed from time to time (in order to keep the advertising message "fresh"). However, it is not usually necessary to discard the 10,000 bulbs of the collection. The individual units are reorganized into new combinations, fitted into new positions on the framework, and made to work together to produce the effects required by a new pattern.

Thus in a human society the group as a group may continue long after the individual has dropped by the wayside, and the group itself may come in the course of time to perform new patterns.

The analogy, of course, is only illustrative of certain features, because human beings, their societies, and cultures, differ in many important respects from electric signs. First, the electric bulbs are not sentient beings and their coöperation does not depend upon socio-psychological interaction, as is the case with human individuals. Second, the collection of individual bulbs does not reproduce itself, as does a human society. Third, the patterns of an electric sign are mechanically and electrically controlled, whereas those of a human society operate on the basis of sociopsychological principles. Finally, the patterns themselves are not invented by any bulb or group of bulbs working together, but are imposed from without and are actually invented in a human brain. In culture, the patterns themselves have to be evolved in the minds of some individual or individuals belonging to the society in question or, at least, to *some* human society. And the changes in pattern arise in the first instance from variant behavior on the part of individuals. The invention of a new pattern is beyond the abilities of any bulb in an electric sign, but it is usually within the potentialities of any normal member of a human society.

Nevertheless, in human society as in the mechanical sign, the total pattern of the culture is achieved by the coördinated, coöperative effort of many individuals and is usually beyond the scope and frequently beyond the ken of any one individual's assigned rôle.

CULTURAL ENVIRONMENTS

The adaptive function of a cultural configuration is of the first importance because, if it falls below a certain minimum of success, the society will perish or pay a heavy price in maladjustment. The culture thus serves as a shield for the group and the individual, a screen between them and raw nature, and a set of adaptive techniques for confronting environmental problems. However, shields and screens always have an inside as well as an outside surface. Thus, the protective and adaptive services of a culture always have the effect of creating an internal cultural environment—internal in the sense that it lies within the cultural boundaries.

The environment, as structured or formed by the cultural system, in turn poses problems of adjustment and adaptation on the part of human beings living within the system. And patterns for such adjustment are usually provided in the culture. Thus it is characteristic of cultures to provide patterns for human adaptation (1) to the objective environment, and (2) to an environment or series of environments as defined by the culture.

A relatively simple aspect of the matter is illustrated by the use of weather-tight houses in cold climes. The walls and roof of the house protect the inmates from the outside elements of nature, but the interior of the house is itself an artificial environment to which the occupants must learn to adjust and in which they must carry on many of their activities.

A less obvious type of cultural world is that created simply by the patterned configuration of the behaviors of other persons and their patterned relations to the individual or group in question. Thus the cultural environment of persons who live in a society of ranked social classes is different from those living in a relatively classless or egalitarian society, regardless of the material artifacts and techniques adapted to natural survival. The individual of, say, low class category must learn the patterns of behavior and attitude considered appropriate to this position in society, if he is to adapt, that is, if he is to stay out of trouble and avoid excess punishment.

Furthermore, the culture may structure the objective environments and situations psychologically through the development of mental customs and symbols. Thus, even a natural situation will "look" one way to the member of one society, and may appear quite different to the members of another society. No amount of objective demonstration will convince many persons in our own society that a graveyard at night is not filled with active and malicious, or at least prankish, ghosts and they insist on practising the cultural patterns intended as protection against these supposed features of the situation. Such persons having to pass near or enter a cemetery at night will cross themselves, repeat prayers, clutch amulets, and so on.

The imposition of form and meaning upon the natural or objective features of situations is accomplished by a feature of culture which we call the cultural projective system. These projective systems may be either realistic or unrealistic in the objective sense; but from the point of view of persons practising the culture both types are "real." If your culture has taught you that a feeling of malaise, listlessness, and depression is a symptom of having "lost your soul," we may expect you to seek the required magical means for recovering the lost soul, and you hire a medicine man. It does not matter to you that in our culture such a situation appears somewhat different to us.

Thus, training in a given cultural system will so condition the average man's perception that he will "look for" and "see" features in the environment and in certain situations which are in line with cultural expectations. This fact has been demonstrated repeatedly in psychological testing as well as other forms of observation.

To sum up, the culture provides solutions for many problems of survival in the natural world. At the same time a culture creates situations and poses new problems, which in turn need solution. The artificial and conventional environments of cultures are just as "real" to participants in the culture as are the features of the objective natural environment. Finally, cultures usually contain customs for the adjustment of individuals and groups to the cultural environment.

CULTURAL "CONTENT"

The average man in his everyday life is usually more concerned with the "content" of his culture than with matters pertaining to patterns, of which he is, in fact, often unaware as such. The "content" of a culture or of a cultural element consists of the customary activity and artifacts (if any) involved, plus the current notions of the purposes and goals which are supposed to be served. When we speak of cultural content we are concerned with questions of, What goes on? How is it done? Who does it? Why does he or do they believe that it is necessary or desirable to do this? What tools or other artifacts are used? Such matters are usually tangible and "real"; they can be described in terms of actional, representational, and mental customs and of the artifacts which are used with them. Cultural content always involves actual *energy*, directed, harnessed, or stored for purposes publicly known to the practitioners of the culture.

Many discussions of customs are concerned with content only. That is to say, they merely describe what is done, with what, where, under what conditions, by whom, and why. Later on we shall attempt to show that a final, basic analysis of culture requires likewise a consideration of the underlying patterns and their relationships. But for the present, in the following few chapters, we shall be concerned primarily with the content of culture, as defined.

However, even the novice in such matters is aware of the fact that cultural content may be viewed from at least two angles. First, one may describe the actual customary activities and artifacts involved and appraise the energy put forth to achieve certain aims. This might be called the detailed approach, the atomistic angle of investigation. But experience in such affairs always convinces the observer that the energy involved is *organized*. In other words, the customs are linked together in the interest of the desired result, the participants' behavior is directed or channelized toward certain goals, the artifacts are designed to fit into the over-all configuration of effort. Particularly does cultural activity involve the organization of the energies of individuals and groups, who, unless organized, would prove totally ineffective in achieving the goals or purposes sought.

It has been customary in anthropological studies of living cultures to describe the content of the culture studied under a more or less standard outline, conforming in some respects to what Wissler [1] called the "universal culture pattern" and what Murdock [2] has described as the "common denominators of culture." The largest extant collection of source data on the contents of cultures of the world is in the Cross Cultural Survey, housed in the Institute of Human Relations at Yale University. During the recent war this was combined with various "strategic indexes" compiled and organized under the auspices of the Navy Department, the Office of the Coördinator of Inter-American Affairs, and some other agencies. The result is an unparalleled collection of original source material, covering more than a thousand cultures, organized according to a systematic outline covering all general types of cultural manifestations known. This Outline of Cultural Materials [3] is probably the best guide yet developed for an understanding of cultural content. It should be familiar to all students of cultural anthropology and should be used in connection with all field investigations of culture and custom, even though the nature of a particular problem or of a particular culture may require the investigator to modify the basic outline in specific cases. The major categories of culture content covered in this scheme are the following: language, communication, exploitative activities, technology, implements, housing, food, drink and indulgence, dress, daily routine, labor, specialization, exchange, finance, transportation, travel, recreation, art, numbers and measures, lore and learning, reaction to nature, religion, ethics, property and contract, social stratification, family, kinship, social organization, government, social control, ingroup conflict, war; customs and institutions dealing with the following: the human organism, sex, reproduction, infancy, childhood, youth, marriage, adulthood, old age, sickness, death and socialization.

Murdock has also compiled a partial list of types of items which occur "in every culture known to history or ethnology." It should be understood that these *universal similarities do not imply identities* in specific content but rather refer to types of cultural content found everywhere. The list follows in alphabetical order.[4]

age-grading	decorative art	feasting
athletic sports	divination	folklore
bodily adornment	division of labor	food tabus
calendar	dream interpretation	funeral rites
cleanliness training	education	games
community organization	eschatology	gestures
cooking	ethics	gift giving
coöperative labor	ethnobotany	government
cosmology	etiquette	greetings
courtship	faith healing	hair styles
dancing	family	hospitality

housing
hygiene
incest tabus
inheritance rules
joking
kin-groups
kinship nomenclature
language
law
luck superstitions
magic
marriage
mealtimes
medicine

modesty concerning
    natural functions
mourning
music
mythology
numerals
obstetrics
penal sanctions
personal names
population policy
post-natal care
pregnancy usages
property rights

propitiation of super-
    natural beings
puberty customs
religious ritual
residence rules
sexual restrictions
soul concepts
status differentiation
surgery
tool making
trade
visiting
weaning
weather control

Thus it appears that all cultures conform to a single basic plan, even though they differ widely in detail. The single basic plan seems to be explained by the unity of the species—that is, man has the same basic wants everywhere and the same basic resources for satisfying them—and by the fact that, regardless of a wide range of specific variations, the general conditions of the planet with which culture has to deal show a pattern of fundamental similarities.[5]

In the following pages we shall attempt to deal with only certain aspects of cultural content and organization of culturally patterned energies and their performers.

NOTES TO CHAPTER 9

1. Wissler, 1923, Chapter 5.
2. Murdock, 1945.
3. Murdock, and others, 1945.
4. Murdock, 1945, p. 124.
5. In other words there are a limited number of possibilities in culture and social life. See Goldenweiser, 1913; Thurnwald, 1937; Gillin, 1944b; general discussion in Sorokin, 1941, pp. 669-714.

CHAPTER 10

Cultural Situations: The Principle of Compatibility

IN THE LAST chapter it was mentioned that, despite many differences in detail, a basic pattern seems to underly all cultures. As students of mankind we are interested in both the variations of culture and the similarities. If no similarities in culture could be found and no regularity could be discovered, we would be helpless in our attempts to explain and predict cultural phenomena. In this chapter let us direct attention to certain general and recurring problems which all cultures have to face. No culture exists and functions in a void: it is always faced with a situation. A cultural system is in one sense merely a set of patterns for dealing with a given situation in the interests of the population which it serves. But since the conditions of culture A may well be somewhat different from those of culture B, it follows that we should expect the patterns of the two to differ in details of content. Nonetheless, it appears that all situations in which cultures have to operate have certain general characteristics in common.

It would be sensible to speak of these matters in terms of "environment" alone were it not for the fact that many persons think of environment in terms merely of "natural factors" concerned with physiography and subsoil resources. Since other factors as well are usually involved in cultural adjustment, it seems more helpful to think of the problem in terms of "situations" in which we can distinguish different type of components. These are of a general nature in the sense that the general type of factors included in a given type of component usually occur in all cultural situations.

These general components of cultural situations may be described as: (1) the human component; (2) the environmental component; (3) the social component; (4) the not invariably present foreign cultural component. The adjustment of any cultural system requires at least a minimum adjustment to these features of its situation: they lay down the conditions under which the culture must operate. The principle governing such adjustment we call *compatibility*. We may say that a custom or a cultural system is compatible with its situation, or any component elements of it, to the degree that the performance of the custom or of

198

the system has the effect of maintaining the integrity and functional capacities of the social group practising the custom or culture. Compatibility, in short, deals with the *adaptive aspects* of a culture. The mere existence of the social group which the culture serves depends upon a basic compatibility between the culture and its situation. In this sense, all functioning cultures must show a certain minimum compatibility, ipso facto. Yet there may be many stages between "bare existence" and "perfect" adjustment and in this range lie many of the problems which beset certain societies.

Compatibility is one of two major principles governing cultural adjustment. The other, which will be dealt with in a later chapter, we may call *consistency*. The latter has to do with the internal organization of the constituent parts of a culture. Maladjustment may arise in cultural systems either from violations of compatibility or from violations of consistency.

Now let us illustrate briefly some of the factors which may be involved in the various situational components.

HUMAN COMPONENT

Biological human beings are, of course, an indispensable element in every cultural situation. It is the human beings who must translate into customary activity the patterns of the culture, and, since customs are learned reactions of human beings, culture, by definition, cannot exist in situations from which human beings are absent. However, the organic characteristics of the members of the human social group condition to some extent the culture which is practised by the group, and the customs must necessarily be adapted to the performance capacities of the group members.

Species characteristics (See Chapters 2-8). We have already discussed at some length the hereditary characteristics of the species as a whole and it is unnecessary to deal with them here other than to point out again that they are by all odds the most important organic factors involved in the development and performance of culture. The general characteristics of the species and its basic biological needs also account for the fundamental similarity which is to be found in all cultures. No culture can long exist which runs counter to the requirements and potentialities of the species as a whole.

Racial characteristics (See Chapter 5). We have previously discussed the various constellations of presumably genetically controlled physical features which may be identified within the species and have pointed out that the verdict of science holds that up to the present no significant differences have been discovered between the races and other species subgroups with regard to their respective capacity for learning or inventing culture. However, there is some evidence which would indicate that certain genetic groups are better adapted organically to certain environments than others. This seems to be clearest with respect to the advantage apparently enjoyed by Negroids over other races in the ability to adapt organically to wet tropical environments. This factor must be assessed in studying the form and function of customs in these regions. For example, adult Negroids seem to be singularly unsusceptible to heat stroke and sunstroke, while whites are peculiarly apt to fall victim to these ailments. Negroes also seem to have greater inherited resistance to malignant malaria than whites. The result is that the culture of white groups in the tropics must contain customs and artifacts compensating for their lack of organic resistance to the wet tropical environment. Sun helmets, spinal pads, restricted hours of labor in heavy sunlight, and anti-malarial régimes would seem to be cultural compensations of this type. As a matter of history, the whites on the whole have not shown much success in establishing permanent, stable settlements in the low wet tropics.[1]

Also we must recognize that certain customs are specially compatible with the characteristics of certain races or subraces. An example of this principle is to be seen in the distribution of tatooing and scarification as means of enhancing personal beauty, as it is conceived in various societies. Tatooing is almost invisible on black skins, so that we find this custom confined on the whole to non-Negroid peoples. Scarification (raising of decorative welts through the controlled formation of scar tissue in or under the epidermis), on the other hand, produces visible patterns on black skins and can be produced without the discoloration which it effects on lighter-colored skins. Likewise Negroids apparently grow heavier scar tissue. Therefore we usually find scarification confined to the cultures of Negroid peoples.[2] With respect to artificial deformation of the skull, which is practised on infants in some cultures as a means of conforming them to the cultural ideal of beauty, it happens that the flattening of the back of the skull (occipital deformation) is singularly difficult to accomplish among long-headed peoples whose babies have projecting occiputs, for the reason that the baby's head tends to roll onto one side, rather than staying in position with the back pressed firmly against a cradle board or other deforming instrument. Consequently, we find occipital deformation only rarely as a custom in dolicocephalic societies.[3] Although a wide range of hair-dressing styles is applicable to each of the various types of hair, there are certain types of coiffure which can be used only with straight hair (Mongoloid), others which are confined to kinky hair (Negroid), and others to fine-textured wavy hair (White).[4] The elaborate rolls and buns of the formal coiffure of Japanese women with their long, straight hair, are practically impossible for kinky-haired Negroid women, for example. Finally, to mention only one other example of this sort of thing, have you ever seen a Negroid or a Mongoloid wearing pince-nez eye glasses? Probably not, for such an artifact is ill adapted to the broad, comparatively low-bridged noses of these groups.

Characteristics of this type may condition the cultures of groups which possess them. Of more frequent importance, however, are physical or organic characteristics within a given group. We refer to organic characteristics which may be distributed within a particular society, but which are not necessarily distributed in the same proportions to a race as a whole. We remember that all but a few isolated societies show a good deal of phenotypical variation in physical form, and as a general rule, the larger the society, the greater is the variability of physical form likely to be.

Body size. The recent war has demonstrated how the distribution of body sizes in a population affects culture. For example, it was discovered in the early part of the war that the human quarters in a number of types of combat airplanes were too small to accommodate the body of the average air crewman, and rather elaborate studies in physical anthropology had to be carried out to determine the distribution of body sizes in the Air Force and to adapt aircraft designing to them. Likewise, since it was impossible to design ball turrets of large size on bombers, the number of small-bodied men available who possessed the other requisite qualifications as turret gunners had to be determined before this type of machine could be used in quantity.

In other words, there are certain customs which large individuals can perform which small persons cannot, and vice versa. The culture of the group may be influenced by the distribution of body sizes.

Body type and musculature. Although, as mentioned in Chapter 6, most attempts to demonstrate a one-to-one correlation between body type and personality type have so far proved inconclusive, the existence of fundamental differences in body type, fattiness, and musculature is recognized by all authorities. The different body types seem to exist within all races, although perhaps in varying proportions, and a good deal of evidence indicates that the types differ in their abilities to perform certain patterns of behavior.[5] For example, Seltzer has recently demonstrated that individuals high in the "masculine component" are less susceptible to fatigue from certain types of muscular work than others.[6]

These matters will have to be investigated in more detail before we can be precise in all instances, but we may assume on present evidence that a culture tends to show some positive relation between its customs and the distribution of various body types in its population.

A few examples may be mentioned from ethnogeography. The Nilotic Negroes, such as the Dinka and the Shilluk, possess a body build which is, on the average, very slender, with tremendously long legs, long arms, short body, and narrow shoulders. The habit of standing on one leg, rather like a crane, with the sole of the opposite foot planted against the inside of the knee joint seems to be customary among the men. Also, notably among the Dinka, a complex of customs has developed for stalking wild game on foot through the swamps of the Nile. Although it is conceivable that such customs would be possible for short, stubby-legged people, we cannot overlook the fact that the long, stilt-like legs of the men render such customs particularly well adapted to the "human component" in this situation.[7]

Organic abnormalities. The "abnormalities" with which we are here concerned are those which are atypical for healthy members of the species as a whole. In certain cases, of course, these conditions may be typical or universal for the group in question. For example, on the island of Granada in the Caribbean Sea (one of the Windward Islands), a whole community lives in more or less self-sustaining fashion, although a large proportion of the individuals are said to be feeble-minded, and a high percentage of albinism exists among them. In Durham, North Carolina, lives a comparatively large group of deaf mutes who have developed a sort of subculture of their own, differing in some respects from the general pattern of the community. For example, they have a church where all preaching is done in sign language.[8]

The famous San Blás Indians of Panama, although not feeble-minded, are characterized by an incidence of 0.69 albinism, which is at least 50 times greater than "normal" in human populations.[9] The unfitness of these albino Indians of the tribe for certain types of cultural activity may be gathered from the words of Lionel Wafer,[10] a buccaneer who first reported on them as they were in 1691:

> They see not well in the sun, poring in the clearest Day; their eyes being but weak, and running with Water if the Sun shine toward them; so that in the Day-time they dare not to go abroad, unless it be a cloudy Dark Day. Besides, they are but a weak People in Comparison of the Other, and not fit for Hunting or other laborious Exercise, nor do they delight in any such.

Perhaps because of these deficiencies, the males are prohibited from marrying.

Although organic pathologies attributable to microörganisms and parasites are always conveyed by the environment, the effects which they have on the functional abilities of a population seem to be linked to constitutional organic factors, such as resistances and immunities. In so far as the members of a group are incapacitated by such conditions we should expect either some degree of cultural adjustment or a loss of survival power in the group. For example, the prevalence and virulence of hookworm in certain communities of the United States is apparently partly to blame for the cultural "backwardness" of these groups, often described as laziness, shiftlessness, moral irresponsibility, and so forth: the parasites cause a decline of energy in the members of the group; in turn the culture compensates by substituting customs of "sloppy house-keeping," for instance, in place of the more efficient customs of other areas.[11] In the case of the natives of Buka and western Bougainville every one is said to be afflicted with malaria, for which there is no effective cultural defense or compensation. The result is that the society pays a fairly high price in miscarriages and still births attributable to malaria in the pregnant women.[12] Modern medicine is, of course, a type of cultural complex whose goal is the elimination of the necessity either for compensatory readjustment of other customs or for the payment of organic costs by society as a result of pathologies.

Societies differ organically in their resistance to certain diseases: a pathology which may require elaborate cultural defense or compensation in one population may require little cultural adaptation in another. Medical investigations among the Indian populations of Guatemala, for instance, indicate that the pathological effects of infection with syphilis, which are a serious problem in most white populations, appear much less frequently among infected Indians. Not only is the primary stage of the disease less virulent, but also the debilitating and crippling forms of tertiary syphilis, such as tabes, locomotor ataxia, and general paresis, appear seldom, as compared with whites.

The incidence of organically determined mental disease in a society is difficult to determine with accuracy, even in literate societies, so that we do not know whether significant differences in the presence of these ailments exist between human societies or not. It is probable that they do, and an abnormally high rate would be bound to have its repercussions in culture.

ENVIRONMENTAL COMPONENT

The environmental component of the situation includes all "natural" features except the human, the social, psychological, and artifactual components. It includes topography, physiography, flora, fauna (except humans), weather, geology, soil, natural resources, and so on and so forth. Taken together, these natural factors lay limitations upon the development of culture and provide a range within which specific customs and artifacts may be evolved. This, of course, is a very different thing from saying that the environment determines the culture in detail, as the "environmental determinists" would have us believe. A cold climate, for example, requires shelter of some sort if the group is to survive, but it does not determine whether people will develop the custom of sheltering themselves in igloos or in steam-heated brick houses. A given environment, in other words, usually permits a number of alternative cultural adaptations, rather than merely one. And by setting certain limits it may render impossible certain adaptations which are avilable in another environment. The prehistoric cultures of both the coastal region and the mountain region of Peru were well developed, although illiterate at the time of the Spanish conquest. It was no accident, however, that on the coast buildings were usually erected of adobe or wattle, whereas in the mountains the preference was for stone. Stone is very plentiful in the mountain regions of Peru, very scarce on the coast. On the other hand, the fact that both the coastal and mountain people of Peru were without systems of writing cannot be attributed to the environment one way or another, except in the sense that they were isolated from cultural centers where writing systems had been invented and were in use. Writing, having been imported into the region by the Spaniards, now flourishes in both the mountains and the coast under environmental conditions which have not significantly altered since prehistoric times. Diffusion and contact with foreign cultures may thus break the hold of environment.

The natural environment is not necessarily immutable. It may be changed in some respect by the application of cultural techniques. The introduction of the repeating rifle and the horse removed the buffalo herds as a significant item from the natural environment of the Great Plains, which in turn rendered the buffalo-hunting economy of the Indian tribes useless. The terracing and irrigation of precipitous and semi-arid hillsides in ancient Peru and in China have converted unfavorable environments into ones suitable for farming. Although no culture is as yet able effectively to control the climate (many have supernatural techniques for trying to do so), not a few cultures have techniques for producing an artificial (heated) climate indoors in the winter, and our own culture is able to produce artificial cool climates in summer with air-conditioning. The alteration of natural environmental features by cultural interference is so well known that there is no need to cite further examples. Nevertheless, all of these cultural alterations are actually adjustments to the natural environment, even though they modify it or partially remake it.

SOCIAL POTENTIALITIES IN CULTURAL SITUATIONS

"Social" and "cultural" have often been used loosely and interchangeably in the literature of social science. Although it is quite true that in real life no society exists without a culture and no culture functions without a society, nevertheless society and culture do not always remain in a one-to-one relationship with each other. The one may change without concomitant change in the other, or vice versa. If such happens, various "problems" usually arise, by virtue of the fact that the cultural system gets out of adjustment with the social potentialities of the group it is supposed to serve as a guide to customary behavior. The well-known examples of "cultural lag" illustrate this type of maladjustment. Witness, for example, the county organization in many of our states. The counties were originally laid out and organized so as to include a territory whose center could be reached by horseback or wagon in the days of slow communication and travel, when the population was sparse and widely scattered. Each small county was provided with courthouse, jail, judges, sheriff, and other officials. At the present time, with larger population and swift means of communication and travel such units and their employee organization are often a totally useless expense which adds not only to the tax burden but also to the slowness and red tape of administering justice and executing the laws.

The population to be served by a culture always exhibits certain social potentialities for interaction. The culture provides the actual patterning of this interaction. But such patterns may be far from compatible with the potentialities. What are some of these features which may characterize a group or society and to which the culture is called upon to adjust?

1. **Numerical size of the group** is a primary datum, because it sets limits to the kind and amount of social interactions which may take place between the individuals. Generally speaking, the smaller the group the greater is the opportunity for intimate and frequent contacts and interactions among all of the members. On the other hand, the smaller the group, the smaller is the opportunity for specialization of functions or elaboration of the complexity of the culture.

These general propositions are illustrated in college classrooms. It is a common experience that personal contacts between instructor and students and between the students themselves are usually reduced in a large class. When it comes to the assignment of work such as term reports, on the other hand, the variety of subjects which can be covered by a small class is necessarily more restricted than when the group is larger.

It is therefore obvious that the culture of a society consisting of, say, one hundred individuals cannot be the same, either in complexity or content, as that possible for a society of 140 million. In the small society the personal relationships can be more frequent and more intense; the number of subsidiary groups is necessarily smaller; the problem of the distribution of economic goods, other things equal, is simpler; the possibility of developing specializations of cultural activities is restricted; and the number of geniuses and other gifted individuals capable of producing cultural innovations is usually smaller.

Although the personal contacts between the members of a small society or group are more frequent and more informal, the variety of stimulations which the average individual receives is less than if he lives in a larger group and is exposed to a greater range of ideas and actions.

2. **Spatial distribution of population.** Another factor of primary social importance is the manner in which the population is distributed in space, because it affects the patterning which may be applied to the interactions between the members of the society. This matter is of course to some extent influenced by environment and by the cultural patterns themselves, but is nevertheless a basic datum to which the culture of the group must make adaptation. For example, if the population is thinly scattered over a wide area in a way which interferes with personal intercourse, a loosely integrated set of behavior patterns, values, and attitudes results, as on the western frontier of the United States, *or* cultural adjustments are made in the form of special customs and artifacts for travel and communication, such as has happened in the western United States of the present day.

The concentration of individuals close together, on the other hand, multiplies contacts, demands coöperative efforts in obtaining sustenance and preserving health, and frequently produces personal conflict and friction, as in the overcrowded areas of large cities. At any rate, the culture is required to adjust itself to this factor of spatial distribution: customs and artifacts are developed around it. If, for example, a society is scattered over a number of small islands, some means of over-water transportation or communication will have to be developed culturally if the society is to maintain its integrity. The exact cultural patterns involved are not determined by the necessity, but *some*thing has to be done culturally. Inter-island contact may be maintained by motor-driven water taxis as in modern Venice, or by canoes and swimming as in Manus.[13] Communication between relatively isolated groups may be maintained by telephone, telegraph, and wireless, as in our society, or by means of signal drums, as in certain tribes of eastern Bolivia, or by means of a pattern of periodic reunions or corroborees, as among the Australian tribes. Orderliness in large concentrations of population in cities may be maintained by raising buildings high into the air and channeling traffic along streets laid out in a rectangular grid, as on Manhattan Island, or by spreading relatively low buildings over a wide area interspersed with winding and curved streets, as in London. The spatial distribution of the people poses the problem; the cultural pattern provides the answer.

3. **Basic family associations.** One type of association or social contact is practically inescapable in any society. This is the contact which the infant has with its mother or nurse. To be sure, the mechanics of reproduction, the fact that man is a mammal, and the relative helplessness of the human infant are organically given, but these organic peculiarities of man conspire to set up a basic *social* situation with which every culture has to deal in one way or another. Mother (or a substitute) and child are inevitably drawn into a setup requiring social interaction on the part of both. For reasons which we do not have to elaborate here, the basic mother-child relationship tends likewise to be extended to other relatives or kin. Thus the child is usually placed in contact with its father or its mother's husband, with its siblings, and with the parents of its parents. *The family and the kin* are social groups which occur in every society and can scarcely be escaped by the average child in any part of the world. The customs which may be practised by the members of these basic social constellations are not provided in the germ plasm and in fact vary from one society to another. The universal existence of family and kinship constellations, however, is a basic factor of the social component of any cultural situation, and each culture must inevitably contain patterns of custom, adjusted to this circumstance.

4. **Sex and age differentiations.** A self-perpetuating society is obviously not homogeneous, but inevitably contains both males and females, infants, children, and adults (and usually, although not inevitably, aged individuals). The respective members of the different sex and age categories differ in their abilities to learn and perform customs, as we have shown in Chapter 7, and it must be admitted that these differences are fundamentally due to organic structure and function. But the fact that the various categories must live together in a society or group creates a social factor which we cannot overlook, and which cannot be ignored by culture. Among fishes, for example, sex and age categories also occur, but in many species no social significance arises, because the individuals disperse and go about their business without the necessity of coming to terms with each other in a coöperative community life. With fishes then, we may speak of sex and age differences as matters of exclusively organic interest. In man they account for social circumstances to which every culture is required to make some kind of adaptation.

5. **Individual differences.** In reviewing some of the facts of genetics we have seen that the chances of any two human beings, excluding identical twins, triplets, and so forth, being exactly alike either genetically or in appearance are practically nil. If we add to this the fact that each individual's experiences in life are unique in some respects, it is easy to see that no human group is homogeneous in all details. There are bound to be differences in physique and temperament among the members of any society. Some are relatively strong, others weak physically; some comparatively bright, others dull; some coöperative, others not; some larger than others; and so on, even when sex and age are equated. The range of these individual differences will usually be greater, the larger the population, but they are always present in any society. Again the culture is required to adapt to the circumstance if maladjustment is to be avoided. Customs must be developed which allow for some leeway in their performance if the entire population or any large segment is expected to practise them. For deviants who are unable or unwilling to perform the customs of the majority, the culture must provide either special customs to fit their abilities (for example, the special classes for backward and bright students, respectively, now being introduced into our school systems) or patterns for their suppression (police methods, jails, and so forth).

FOREIGN CULTURAL COMPONENT

A very few cultures, such as those of the Polar Eskimo and parts of Tibet, seem to have functioned for appreciable periods in complete isolation from other cultures, but such isolation is not typical of cultural situations. It is all but universal that outside or foreign cultural influences are to be found penetrating a cultural situation, at least to some degree. Ideas, usages, and artifacts from the outside are usually to be found in any cultural situation and they constitute one of the groups of factors to which some kind of adjustment must be made. They may be few in number and they may be presented at a relatively slow rate, as is the case, for example, with trade cloth and steel tools among the remoter tribes of the Amazon basin. Slow and steady diffusion from the outside may appear to be almost insignificant, but, nevertheless, constitutes a set of conditions to which the culture must adjust. On the other hand, outside cultural contacts may be of a shocking or traumatic character, as when a society is conquered by outsiders and suddenly has the outsiders' culture thrust upon it; a major recoil and reorientation of the conquered people's culture may be necessary to preserve its integrity. Again the situation may require constant and active reciprocal contact with outside cultures, and means must be found to maintain such contracts while still preserving the functional efficiency and integrity of the "home" culture and society. Our own culture, for example, is faced by this problem and has had some success in making the adjustment. To take another example, the Todas, who live in the Nilgiri hills of Southern India, maintained a distinctive cultural configuration of their own, although they shared the plateau area of their habitat with four other tribes each of which also maintained a distinctive culture—the Badagas, the Kotas, the Kurumbas, and the Irulas (the latter two in the surrounding hill country).[14] The culture of each of these societies was so adjusted that it was not self-sufficient in itself, but depended upon artifacts and services provided by the others. The Toda culture, as such, would obviously have been somewhat different if this situation had not prevailed.

The foreign cultural factors have become increasingly important in the cultural situations of most societies as the world has effectively grown smaller, so that travel and communication between societies have increased in frequency and volume. The problems presented by outside influences in the case of primitive cultures faced with the encroachments of modern civilization have often been serious and have been extensively discussed in a large literature of "acculturation." Likewise accommodation between cultural elements is a necessity in the modern world of civilization, for the various national and regional cultures of contemporary nation-states and areas are increasingly in contact with each other and constantly tending to penetrate across each other's boundaries.

Contact with outside culture almost always sets up a condition calling for change of some type. Whether the changes will be adjustive or not is by no means foreordained. Such contact may actually result in disintegration or destruction of the receiving culture, as in the case of the now extinct Tasmanians, or it may result in cultural accommodation and enrichment of all the several cultures involved. At all events, the introduction of outside elements into the situation is a condition which must be carefully studied and appraised.

Perhaps some of the foregoing matters may be more fully appreciated by the consideration of a concrete situation, that of the Old Order Amish of Pennsylvania. These people also illustrate certain features of cultural integration and consistency, but one of the principal problems of their culture is adaptation to a changing situation.

THE OLD ORDER AMISH OF PENNSYLVANIA [15]

The Old Order Amish of Pennsylvania constitute a non-conforming group which lives within the area of North American society and culture, but which up to the present has maintained a sharply distinguished subculture of its own.

There are about 3,500 Old Order Amish in Lancaster County, Pennsylvania, and they occupy an area about 25 miles long by 15 miles wide on the "Limestone Plain" of this region. But they are closely surrounded and infiltrated by other Americans practicing general North American culture, and the Amish are of the same European physical stock (mainly Swiss and German in origin) as the majority of their neighbors.

In attempting to understand the present culture of these people we are not required to deal with differences in the human component, as compared with that of their neighbors, nor with special peculiarities of the environmental component. These two components are for practical purposes identical in the situations of the Amish and the non-Amish of this region.

The fact that the Amish have a literate culture enables us to obtain the historical background of many of their cultural forms in more detail than is often possible in non-literate cultures, and we therefore are given some clues to the conditions under which the culture was originally established.

Historical Background. The sect known as the Swiss Brethren came into existence in the German-speaking part of Switzerland during the Zwinglian Reformation (of Lutheranism) shortly after 1520. Among the main tenets of their creed was insistence upon adult, rather than infant, baptism and a literal interpretation of the Bible by the communicants themselves without the interposition of an ecclesiastical hierarchy. The prevailing state churches, whether Roman Catholic or Lutheran, regarded the movement as heretical and hounded the Brethren from one region to another, often using ruthless methods of exterminating them. The Brethren were a non-resistant people who refused to bear arms, and, since at this time Swiss mercenary soldiers were widely employed in Europe, the Swiss government also interested itself in persecuting the non-resisters, with the result that the major part of the Brethren group moved to the Rhineland region of Germany. At the same time that the movement was spreading in the upper Rhineland a similar religious group known as the Anabaptists arose in the Netherlands. There, about 1536, a leader by the name of Menno Simons appeared, whose followers became known as Mennonites. The Swiss Brethren of the upper Rhineland and the Mennonites of the lower Rhineland gradually fused, until by the latter part of the seventeenth century they were more or less united. However, among the Swiss Brethren a leader named Jacob Ammann arose who finally in 1693 led a schism, and his more conservative followers came to be called the Amish. These people were mainly from Alsace and the upper Rhineland area. The Amish, then, are an offshoot of the general Mennonite movement. In the early part of the eighteenth century, persecution of the group in Europe decided them to move to the New World and they came to Pennsylvania because of the advertised religious tolerance of William Penn. The bulk of the ancestors of the present-day Amish seem to have come to Lancaster County between 1710 and 1750.

In Europe the people belonged to the peasantry, and were thus both rural and lower class in background. They were determined to break completely with the social order of their place and time and to found a way of life based on the organization of the early Christians as set forth literally in the New Testament. The basic tenet of the Amish culture is that nothing is to be accepted or approved merely because it happens to be custom or law, but that all practices and activities must be based on the "Bible standard." The Bible is interpreted literally and the fitness of all customs must pass the Bible test. It appears, therefore, that the original movement represented a revolt by lower class, under-privileged people against the culture of their day in Europe, which had proved too punishing and too devoid of satisfactions to be followed longer. The Bible held forth the promise of reward after death and the anticipation of this type of reward was sufficient motivation to lead to the establishment of certain new customs.

This much of the historical background enables us to understand in some measure how the Amish culture came to be established in the first place. Let us now consider its present content and organization, and the prospects of its continuance in Pennsylvania.

Distinctive Content of the Present Culture. The Amish * are an exclusively rural-dwelling group who live on their own farms in one of the better agricultural regions of southeastern Pennsylvania, the so-called Limestone Plain. They are highly successful farmers and, although the average farm is only about fifty acres in size, the value of the buildings and other improvements may amount to $25,000 or more per farm, and the average gross income ranges upward of $4,000 per farm in good years. The Amish are not conservative in the actual techniques of farming, except that they are prohibited from using tractors for field work; otherwise they have often been in advance of other farmers in the adoption of new methods of rotating crops, applying fertilizer, and developing commercial agricultural products.

Far from being ashamed of the opinion of outsiders, the Amish make a point of being a "peculiar people" who do not conform to the standards of the world. The biblical justification for this orientation is found in Titus, 2:11-14: "For the grace of God that bringeth salvation hath appeared to all men, Teaching us that, denying ungodliness and worldly lusts, we should live soberly, righteously, and godly, in this present world; Looking for that blessed hope, and the glorious appearing of the great God and our Saviour Jesus Christ; Who gave himself for us, that he might redeem us from all iniquity, and purify unto himself a *peculiar people*, zealous of good works." See also Romans, 12:2: "And be *not conformed* to this world." (Italics ours.) Derived from or justified by these basic principles a number of "peculiar" customs have developed.

a. Dress and ornament. All men wear their hair in a long bob with bangs over the forehead. Neither men nor women may part the hair anywhere except in the center. Unmarried men shave; married men wear a beard but may not grow a moustache. (A moustache is considered the mark of a military man.) No woman is permitted to cut or curl her hair and all comb their hair exactly alike except that unmarried girls are allowed to braid theirs and to wear it as a bun on the back of the head. Outer articles of clothing are exactly alike for all members of respective sex and age groups, and decidedly

* We shall use the word in this chapter to refer to Old Order Amish although two other, more liberal, Amish groups have split off. The latter are known as the Church Amish, for they hold their religious services in special buildings, whereas it is one of the peculiarities of the Old Order Amish that religious services are held only in private houses or in barns. Amish groups of the three different sects live in Pennsylvania, Ohio, Maryland, Illinois, and Iowa. The Old Order group with which we are here concerned lives in Lancaster County, southeastern Pennsylvania, and constitutes a recognized community or society.

quaint in comparison with current styles of outsiders, which by the Amish are considered marks of worldly ostentation.

Men and boys wear broadfall trousers with plain, home-made suspenders. Jackets worn for dress may have no lapels, no outside pockets, and no buttons —they are held together with hooks and eyes. (Work clothes may have buttons and even zippers, but these garments are considered strictly utilitarian.) Atop their bobbed hair, males wear broad, flat, black felt hats in winter and broad, flat, straw hats in summer. Women have no "styles," for all of the same age group must wear outer garments of identical pattern. None of these garments may be made of printed goods, and only solid colors are permitted. Full skirts and long-sleeved blouses are *de rigueur*. Married women wear aprons which match the color of their dresses, whereas unmarried girls wear white aprons. All females wear white devotional head coverings and identical home-made bonnets. "Store hats" are forbidden for women.

All of these peculiarities of dress are justified by biblical injunction, according to the interpretation of the Amish. Apparel must be substantial (Genesis, 3:7,21), modest (I Tim., 2:9,10: "In like manner also, that women adorn themselves in modest apparel, with shamefacedness and sobriety; not with braided hair, or gold, or pearls, or costly array; But (which becometh women professing godliness) with good works"; I Pet., 3:3,4: "Whose adorning let it not be that outward adorning or plaiting the hair, and of wearing of gold, or of putting on of apparel; But let it be the hidden man of the heart, in that which is not corruptible, even the ornament of a meek and quiet spirit, which is in the sight of God of great price"), and economical. There should be sex distinction in clothing (Deut. 22:5: "The woman shall not wear that which pertaineth unto a man, neither shall a man put on a woman's garment: for all that do so are abomination under the Lord thy God"). The wearing of jewelry and certain ornamental garments by women is believed to be interdicted by the terrible prophecy of Isaiah, 3:18-24: "In that day the Lord will take away the bravery of their tinkling ornaments about their feet, and their cauls, and their round tires like the moon, The chains, and the bracelets, and the mufflers, The bonnets, and the ornaments of the legs, and the headbands, and the tablets, and the earrings, the rings, and nose jewels, The changeable suits of apparel, and the mantles, and the wimples, and the crisping pins, The glasses, and the fine linen, and the hoods, and the veils. And it shall come to pass, that instead of sweet smell there shall be stink; and instead of a girdle a rent; and instead of well set hair baldness; and instead of a stomacher a girding of sackcloth; and burning instead of beauty." The requirement of the devotional head covering for women is based on I Cor., 11:5,6,13: "But every woman that prayeth or prophesieth with her head uncovered dishonoureth her head: for that is even all one as if she were shaven. For if the woman be not covered, let her also be shorn: but if it be a shame for a woman to be shorn or shaven, let her be covered. . . . Judge in yourselves: is it comely that a woman pray unto God uncovered?"

It is obvious that the customs and equipment concerned with dress serve at least two cultural functions: (1) they provide a constant and easily discriminated stimulus for both the group members and outsiders, which tends to evoke customs appropriate to this particular group, and (2) they tend to represent the symbolic patterns of "peculiarity" of this culture as based upon the Scriptures.

b. Other Distinctive Traits Associated with Material Equipment. Except in emergencies, the Amish are not allowed to drive or ride in automobiles, particularly not for amusement or pleasure. The means of conveyance in use is the *open black buggy* with a single horse for unmarried men, and the rectangular topped, single-horse *gray buggy-wagon* which somewhat resembles an old-fashioned horse-drawn milk wagon, for married men. Dash boards and whip sockets are forbidden. Likewise the ownership or personal use of auto trucks for carrying loads is forbidden; only *wagons and teams* may be owned or operated. If an emergency requires one of the "worldly" type of conveyances, it may be hired with a driver. Telephones are not allowed in the houses, nor electricity or any of the farm or household conveniences operated on electric power. On the other hand, gasoline engines for pumping water are permitted and all types of modern farm machinery are in use, except tractors for field work. Tractors may be used only for belt power.

Houses follow the general patterns of the region, except that they are large, often with twelve to sixteen rooms, and are arranged with interior folding doors so that they may be opened up for the house religious meetings which frequently involve an attendance of over two hundred persons. Rugs may be only of the "rag" variety, and ostentatious furnishings, as well as most modern household appliances (except sewing machines), are eschewed.

Most clothing, except some underclothing and work clothes for men, must be made at home by the women.

Pictures and photographs are forbidden. "Thou shalt not make unto thee any graven image, or any likeness of any thing that is in heaven above, or that is in the earth beneath, or that is in the water under the earth." (Exodus, 20:4.)

c. Value system. The principal values of the Amish culture may be summarized as follows: (1) Nonconformity is held to be obligatory in everything in which "worldly" standards conflict with the Bible. This is known as the principle of the "unequal yoke," based on II Cor., 6:14: "Be ye not *unequally yoked* together with unbelievers: for what fellowship hath righteousness with unrighteousness? and what communion hath light with darkness?" (Italics ours.) In effect this means that social contacts with outsiders, which might lead to cultural diffusion from the outside world, are held to the minimum. The tabus upon cars, telephones, worldly amusements, marriage to outsiders, higher education, living in cities, in towns, and the joining of any associations other than the church are all consistent with this value. (2) The Bible, literally interpreted, is believed to be the source of all values. This in part explains the resistance of the Amish to education beyond the eighth grade. (3) The bearing of arms, going to war, and litigation in courts of law are all to be avoided on the authority of Jesus' command, "Resist not evil." It is, of course, possible to see this as a result of the persecutions which the group suffered in Europe: when the culture was in formation, it was early discovered that physical and legal resistance was non-rewarding, and a tabu upon such actions became established as part of the culture. (4) Farming constitutes the strongest positive interest and value of the people. The only suitable occupation for an Amish is farming and it is the ambition of every man to own his own land. The Amish work longer hours than any of their neighbors, and due to the fact that they spend no money on amusements and relatively little on clothing, mechanical conveniences, etc., young men are usually able to acquire land relatively early in life. (5) Money is valued only for the purpose of acquiring land and the necessities of life.

It is to be noted that the high values placed upon farming as an activity and land as property are not derived from Scripture from which the other conscious values of the culture derive. Thus the total value system is not consistently unified in the strict sense of the word. Nevertheless, until recent times the two major systems of values have proved consistent with each other and mutually rewarding: the type of life required by the principle of non-conformity, etc., channeled the energies of the people into a single-minded devotion to agriculture which has produced success and rewards; on the other hand, devotion to rural life and unremitting labor on the farms has had the effect of isolating the people from the type of contacts and activities which might run counter to the religious values.

Objectives of the Culture. It would seem that Amish culture is dominated by two objectives, using this term in the sense discussed on p. 496, to refer to major goals of internal organization within the system. These two major objectives we might term (1) "the Christian way of life" (as defined in the cultural interpretation of the Bible) and (2) successful agriculture (in terms of abundant crops and agricultural products rather than in financial terms, which within the culture are more or less incidental). It should be recognized that the one objective is a "sacred" organization of cultural content, whereas the second is "secular." So far as our information goes neither the authority of the Bible nor the whole mental system of religious beliefs is functionally involved in the agricultural complexes, except in the prohibition of the use of field tractors. Planting, plowing, manuring, and all other techniques seem to be backed by a strictly secular (or "common sense") set of mental patterns.

Customs of Interaction and Organization. The Amish eschew all forms of "worldly" amusement and seek their relaxation in Sunday church meetings, in frequent visits between families, and in Sunday evening "sings" for young people. The effect of these customs is to maintain primary contact within the community. The Sunday evening sings are the mechanism of courtship: a young man sets out in the evening with his open buggy, picks up his young lady friend, and they drive (without chaperonage) to the house of some neighbor where the affair, consisting of hymn-singing around a table, takes place. Before marriage, the man is supposed to use a go-between to arrange the union with the girl's parents. Marriage with an outsider is forbidden. Weddings are elaborate affairs, and all social gatherings are characterized by the consumption of huge meals of home-cooked food. Marriage is said to be very stable, and divorces are unknown. The only permissible ground is adultery, of which no cases are reported. The younger son usually stays on the farm of his parents, and, when he takes over the management of the place, his father and mother retire from all except odd jobs. They live in an independent wing of the house, thus preserving close contact with the children, without imposing their presence upon the intimacy of the younger family. The family is patriarchal, and all decisions are supposed to be taken by the husband and father.

Smoking, drinking, card playing, and going to movies are prohibited. Amish are not allowed to read books for pleasure, but they are required to be literate, for every one must spend a certain amount of time "searching the Scriptures" for suitable texts. Thus the group approves elementary education in the three

Rs, but disapproves of consolidated schools and of all education above the eighth grade for its own members. The reasons for this are twofold: Once an individual has learned to read the Bible he is thought to need no further education, for the Bible is the source of all knowledge; likewise consolidated schools and higher education tend to bring the children into contact with "the world" and to take them away from their tasks about the farm, to which they should be inured at an early age. The result is that Amish children go to one-room "little red school houses" scattered about the countryside.

The literacy problem is complicated by the fact that the Amish are bilingual. They speak English and also a German Rhenish dialect, now much mixed with English words. The Bible and the hymns, however, are read in German; thus, the children become literate in English in school, but their parents teach them to read German at home.

Another reason for being able to "search the Scriptures" is the fact that church officials are chosen by lot. It is believed that the Holy Spirit speaks through the mouth of any true believer, but since any man may be chosen as a minister, bishop, or deacon, he should be acquainted with the Bible so that he can preach according to the accepted patterns, which require heavy quotation from Holy Writ. Since speaking from notes is forbidden, men must have memories well stocked with Bible texts.

The Amish territory is divided into eighteen church districts; each contains about one hundred adult persons and each is presided over by a bishop chosen by lot. Sunday meetings are held at the various houses in rotation. The bishop, ministers, and deacons form a sort of directing council of the district, but the whole membership decides matters of discipline, custom, and creed. The organization is on the congregational basis, with each district theoretically independent. In practice, decisions are expected to be unanimous.

Several mechanisms operate in a positive way to encourage compliance with the patterns of the culture. One is the custom of advice relationships. A man hardly ever takes a major step, such as buying a farm, getting a loan from a bank, and the like, without consulting some older man. Often the older men of his district congregation undertake to advise him as a group. Also a mutual aid system is in operation. The deacon of the district is responsible for collections for the poor fund and mutual aid fund, and a member who is the victim of misfortune is helped by the group without question, providing he is in good standing (has not broken the tabus). For this reason, no Amish were on relief or WPA during the depression. The advice relationship and mutual aid thus prove to be highly rewarding, particularly to the younger member of the society.

Mechanisms of Maintenance. The question which arises in the mind of any outsider is, How can this culture so different from that about it be maintained in the group? We do not have a full account of the patterns of socialization of the child, but even on the basis of the data at hand, and our general knowledge of cultural dynamics, we may make some reasonable suggestions.*

* It should not be inferred that the absence of certain data is in any sense a reflection upon the industry of the investigator, Walter M. Kollmorgen, whose period of field work was limited to some four months. In fact, a complete report upon all details of a culture of this sort, whose practitioners make a fetish of negating contacts with "outsiders," appears to be a task well nigh impossible from the point of view of a field ethnologist. The usual motivations which may be aroused by ethnolo-

1. Competing customs have little chance to be presented and tried out due to the operations of nonconformity and isolation. Members of the community are removed from contacts which would serve as stimuli or models for the learning of outside customs and outside cultural drives. The joining of associations, attendance at school beyond the eighth grade, living in cities and towns, working in industry—all such possibilities of contact are expressly forbidden because they are thought to be "contaminating."

2. Rewards for practising the group culture and refraining from outside "temptations" are very great. Through the advice relationship the individual is given group solidarity and aid in his projects. In time of trouble or when starting out on the purchase of a farm, etc., the community comes to the aid of the individual with money, gifts of tools and stock, and in other substantial ways. The desire for response is satisfied from infancy exclusively by members of this society who practise its culture, so that a strong motivation is acquired for imitating the members of the group in order to secure their approval and their attentions. In addition to such practical rewards, it must be remembered that a very strong acquired drive is inculcated in the members of the group, namely, the desire for salvation after death. And the members are taught that the reward of this drive is only obtainable by practice of the group customs. Finally, the culture is rewarding in the mundane business of farming, and a group member has only to look about him to see that the Amish on the whole are more successful agriculturists than non-believers. Thus a number of universal and acquired drives are operative in the culture to motivate the practice of the customs which, it is believed, bring satisfactions of the type desired.

3. The fear of punishment is also a powerful motivation. The members are taught to believe that transgression of the tabus violates the will of God and that its eventual aftermath is certain punishment in the fires of Hell after death. A more practical and immediate punishment is also provided by the group. A member who violates any one of the tabus is brought to account by the church officials and the district church group. If he does not publicly confess and "mend his ways," he is henceforward "shunned." "Shunning" means that other members of the group withdraw from all social intercourse with the wrong-doer: they will not speak to him, coöperate with him, or enter into any intimate relationships with him. It amounts to social ostracism, and is said to be considered extremely painful. This type of punishment is particularly severe in a culture of this type, practically all of whose patterns imply primary contacts between individuals: there are no customs in the culture which fit the individual either to lead a solitary life or to "make his way" among strangers, so that the average individual cut off from contact with his kind by "shunning" is left almost without cultural resources.

If outside contamination were not punished by the group itself, attempts to mingle with outsiders would be punishing at least at the start, anyway. In fact, at the present time there is a certain tendency on the part of outsiders to treat the Amish with hostility and ridicule on account of their "peculiarities." Thus the Amish individual who endeavors to enter into social relations with outsiders is apt to find the experience disagreeable in contrast to the

---

gists to secure the coöperation of the members of a society in the study of their culture seem to be eliminated in this case—desire for money, goods, praise, adulation, pride, pleasure, narcotics, etc.

warm atmosphere of self-righteous mutual understanding which he finds in his own group.

4. The cultural situation is so arranged that so long as isolation is maintained, the learning of all acquired drives labeled as "worldly" is inhibited. The process is not essentially different from that whereby the "regular" American culture inhibits the development of an acquired drive, say, for morphine. The average Amishman, once he has settled down, apparently no more desires to go to movies than the average North American in general desires to take morphine. If the "worldly" acquired drives can thus be prevented from developing, "worldly" customs for their satisfaction have no motivation on which to be built.

Compatibility and Consistency in Amish Culture. Although Amish culture apparently arose in Europe out of a conflict situation, its success depends upon cultural isolation. As a closed system of custom, it seems to work well and to perpetuate itself and its society.

On the whole, the culture seems to be remarkably compatible with the various components of its situation, with the exception of the social and outside cultural components. The technical procedures are adapted to the land and climate of the region; the customs are well adapted to the artifacts in use, and this compatibility has been the more maintained because new artifacts have not been hastily introduced. The culture seems to be fitted to the capabilities of the group, for long life and health are characteristic of the Amish. The psychological component is well managed within the isolated culture so that the customs are well learned, and conflicts, either within the individual or within the group, seem to be remarkably few. Within the group itself the culture is adapted to its social potentialities, except for the fact that at present no successful solution for increased population has been found. The traditional solution is more land for more farms, but the Amish are finding increased difficulty in acquiring the needed land. Since business or industry is ruled out of consideration for members, a cultural crisis is arising. Some cultural change or innovation will have to be introduced to solve the maladjustment between the patterns of the culture, the increasing population, and the limited supply of available land. We may observe that, so long as conditions of land procurement remain as they are, the only solution which would preserve the isolation of the group would be the introduction of cultural patterns of family limitation which would stabilize the population and eliminate the land hunger coincident with expansion in numbers. At present, large families are the rule.

The growth of population and area have also produced social factors which are incompatible with the transportation and communication techniques and which have caused the latter in turn to become incompatible to some extent with the artifacts used. The population is now spread out so that one frequently has to travel twenty-five or thirty miles to "go visiting," one of the universal patterns of the culture which maintains primary contacts and also provides relaxation. The pattern of using only horses and buggies is very costly in time and, in short, is not adapted to frequent visits over such distances. The telephone, which might offer a partial substitute, is likewise barred from general use. Thus, certain of the patterns which are adapted to and compatible with a small group of families located close together, are proving incompatible to an increased society spatially distributed over a wider area. Unless some changes are introduced in the patterns of travel and communication, the web of personal relationships upon which the society rests will tend to loosen and "come apart."

The outstanding incompatibilities of the Amish culture are, of course, with the foreign cultural component. This is not entirely accidental, for the Amish culture explicitly states as one of its major objectives the maintenance of "peculiar" customs. Now, two cultures may exist side by side without necessarily being in conflict with one another. It is possible for the system of Culture A to contain patterns which render it perfectly compatible with Culture B. It would appear that on the whole this has been true of the Amish culture until recently. Patterns of withdrawal and nonresistance enabled it to exist compatibly within the area of general North American rural culture. Recently the "outside cultural component" has developed some innovations which have changed the situation. We may mention only two which Kollmorgen analyzes in some detail. One is the developing movement for consolidated schools, supported by state laws and state and federal funds. This has been evaded by the Amish through establishing parochial one-room neighborhood schools, but this evasion of course doubles the cost of Amish education. Furthermore, it is entirely likely that before long the state law will require longer years of schooling for children, so that the Amish will be required to go to high schools or at least to remain in school beyond the fourteenth year. This would be inconsistent with the pattern of putting children to full-time work at age fifteen. Another change in the outside cultural component of the situation is the new program of agricultural coöperative and relief measures initiated by state and federal agencies during the 1930's. The Amish refuse to coöperate because they are forbidden to join associations of any kind outside their church, but such refusal places them at a competitive disadvantage in relation to non-Amish farmers, and is inconsistent with one of the major objectives of the culture, namely, successful agriculture.

Other incompatibilities with the changing outside cultural situation may be mentioned. The outsiders have hard-surfaced the country roads, so that buggy horses are "pounded to pieces" in the course of a year or eighteen months' use. Also not a few buggies and horses have been smashed up in serious accidents by speeding motorists on the highways. In short, the horse and buggy patterns are no more adapted to the new roads than they are to the new distances involved in the social factor. Likewise, the ban upon the use of motor trucks and field tractors places the Amish farmers under a heavy competitive burden as compared with others, for, without these inventions, more time and man power is required to do the same work.

So long as the Amish society and culture maintained isolation, it would seem from information available to us that the elements of the culture were remarkably consistent with one another. None of the major patterns of the culture seems to have run counter to one another and all goals and objectives appear to have been mutually consistent.

It might be noted that the two major objectives of the culture, "the true Christian life" and successful agriculture, are consistent with each other and support each other, but that the one does not penetrate the other. Religious patterns of action or representation do not appear in the agricultural customs and complexes (except for the prohibition of field tractors). The whole agricultural sector of the culture is secular and its mental systems are of the common-sense types. For example, the Amish scorn "book farming," for they believe that one learns the proper agricultural techniques only by practice, but they employ manure and commercial fertilizer, rotation of crops, planting of legumes to restore nitrogen to the soil, and so on. There are no religious rites or beliefs associated with this work.

This case illustrates that a consistent and well-knit cultural system is possible without the complete pervasion of religious beliefs into all aspects of the system. It is true, that, among the Amish, the religious beliefs have some influence on the fact that the people are almost exclusively agricultural, but the religious element is a negative one. The principle of the "unequal yoke" interdicts mingling with outsiders, and farming one's own land or that of other believers is the only practical road open for the avoidance of the unequal yoke. Yet this is a negative influence of the religious beliefs. The religion does not demand the practice of agriculture on biblical or other supernatural authority. It simply prohibits types of work which would require Amishmen to work with non-believers. Agriculture happens to fit this requirement under the circumstances, and was also established in the historical circumstances of the original founders of the culture.

Conclusions. If it is true that the integrity and continued existence of a cultural system are, as we have assumed, dependent upon the compatibility between a culture and its situation, one of three possibilities for the future lie before the Amish culture. (1) Recent changes in the cultural situation may be eliminated and the situation may be restored to its former condition to which the present culture is well adapted by isolating patterns. This possibility does not seem at all likely. The outside world "moves on": agricultural cooperatives, consolidated schools and higher education, paved roads and automobiles, are here to stay, and further innovations are probably on the way. (2) The Amish culture may fail to change in any significant adaptive particular. If this happens, it seems inevitable that the incompatibilities and resulting inconsistencies of the culture will bring about its disintegration, if the group continues to live in its present situation. At least two times in history the group has avoided incompatibilities with its situation by migrating to a new situation. This solution, however, is much more difficult and impractical at the present time. (3) Certain changes in patterns and organization of the culture are inevitable if the culture is to remain in its present situation. Customs of family limitation would solve some of the problems attendant upon spatial and numerical expansion of the society, but would probably run counter to biblical injunctions. What seems more likely is the development of certain impersonalized patterns of custom which would enable Amishmen to mingle with and interact with outsiders, while not identifying with them. Sol Tax [16] has reported upon a number of Indian communities of Western Guatemala which have developed this solution to the problem of maintaining their cultural integrity while mingling with and carrying on commercial relations with outsiders of different cultural type. On the whole this type of solution depends upon the development of strong acquired drives early in life, which can only be satisfied within the culture of the group and which are inconsistent with the acquired drives of outsiders.

If this proves impossible, we may expect to see a gradual infiltration of Amish culture by outside patterns. This process is generally known as "acculturation." The end result, if it runs its course, will be the substitution of Amish cultural elements and organization by those of general North American culture, and the eventual disappearance of Amish culture as a discrete system and of Amish society as a social unit.

Notes to Chapter 10

1. Price, 1939.
2. Dembo and Imbelloni, 1938, pp. 110-135.
3. *Ibid.*, pp. 228-337.
4. Damon and Russell, 1944.
5. Sheldon, Stevens, and Tucker, 1940.
6. Seltzer, 1945.
7. Seligman, 1932; Hofmayr, 1925.
8. Personal observations. Systematic study of these groups has not been made.
9. Harris, 1926.
10. Wafer, 1729.
11. Vance, 1935, pp. 411-431.
12. Blackwood, 1935, p. 14, for Buka; Shattuck, 1938, for Guatemala Indians.
13. Mead, 1928.
14. Rivers, 1906.
15. This summary of Old Order Amish culture is based primarily on Kollmorgen, 1942. For a discussion of various Separatist sects in Europe and an intensive study of one of them, the Dunkers, in America, see J. L. Gillin, 1906.
16. Tax, 1941.

CHAPTER 11

The Principles Underlying the Learning and Performance of Customs

ACQUAINTANCE WITH the hereditary processes and physical structure and function of the species is a necessary background for the understanding of human life, for in the last analysis, man cannot transcend the limitations imposed by his inherited capacities. But an analysis based on biological principles alone does not tell us the whole story of man nor provide us with operational tools whereby we may understand and predict his behavior in social life. We have seen that one of the reasons for this is the fact that little of man's behavior is laid down in patterned form in his germ plasm. We may say that the *capacity* to react and to learn patterns of reaction is provided by nature, and we must admit that nature has been generous in this respect, for man's capacities and potentialities are wide indeed. The patterns of reaction themselves, however, are not on the whole given in the germ plasm. Out of the great variety of potentialities the human individual must fashion for himself, or with the help of others of his own kind, the actual patterns which he employs.

It has already been intimated that it is one of the functions of the social group to aid the individual in this necessary process. The group or society, through its agents or surrogates, provides certain patterns of activity already planned out, as it were, and it trains the individual to practise these patterns. The whole system of patterns common to a society or social group is called the culture.

The science of anthropology may claim most of the credit for the discovery of the phenomena and concepts of culture, for the anthropologists in their incessant comparison of human societies throughout the world early came to the conclusion that the many and varied manifestations of human life could not be explained solely on the basis of biological principles. Yet in many of the earlier writings, culture was taken as something given; many pages were written describing cultures of the world's peoples, but the anthropological effort stopped at description. Few attempts were made to explain culture dynamically. Then

221

came a period in which it was fashionable to assert that culture was learned, and this statement was made repeatedly in anthropological and sociological works dealing with the subject, but the matter was left at that, as if the word "learned" settled everything. It was as if one should describe in great detail a wide variety of motors and state that they were "electrical" without giving any attention to the principles or peculiarities of electricity itself.

The investigation of learning processes is, of course, one of the specialties of the science of psychology, and it must be admitted that this science had been having its troubles with the problem during the time that anthropologists were discovering and describing culture. In recent years, however, psychology has made enormous strides in the understanding of learning processes and in explaining behavior, so that now the time has arrived when psychology and anthropology can join hands in the solution of cultural problems.

If we admit that culture is learned, we must then go to psychology for the basic principles of learning and behavior which have been tested by experimental procedures on man and other organisms. However, the principles of learning and behavior are always stated in terms of the *conditions* under which the organism operates or may operate. In the psychological laboratory it is of course possible to arrange and manipulate conditions to suit the convenience of the investigator and thus to test the crucial factors in behavior processes. It appears that basically the same general principles of learning apply to man as to all other organisms, although man shows considerably more aptitude for learning than any other animal. However, one of the peculiarities of man is the fact that the learning and performance of culture always takes place in social situations. This is to say that the *conditions* of human cultural learning always involve social factors and that these conditions are frequently artificially arranged by the operation of the already existing culture of the society. On the whole man does not learn and perform culture under conditions which might be described as "nature in the raw."

In the scientific division of labor, it devolves upon anthropologists and other social scientists to analyze the socio-cultural conditions under which the cultural learning and performance of human beings take place, for the psychological principles will not "work," that is, will not give us reliable explanations or predictions, unless they are applied with a full understanding of all crucial factors found in the situations in which cultural activity takes place. These conditions vary in detail from one society to another, and it is one of our obligations to combine the appropriate psychological principles with our knowledge of social life, by means of "transformation equations," into what prove to be reliable principles or generalizations regarding cultural life in all its manifestations.

In the following pages we shall review in a simplified manner certain general principles applying to learning and the performance of learned activity in general, and we shall suggest briefly how they may be applied to an understanding of the dynamics of human culture. As has just been said, this is not a traditional approach in cultural anthropology, but a relatively new development. The science of human relations is still in course of development, and the student may have the satisfaction of participating in its progress himself. It is to be understood that most of the principles set forth in this book, even though stated in didactic form, need to be tested further. We need an increasing refinement and precision in the science of man, and no student should be content with mere memorization of the accumulated data and traditional principles or "laws."

One of the advantages which the beginner in cultural anthropology enjoys is that he does not need an elaborate laboratory or expensive equipment in order to carry out his studies. But he does need a set of mental concepts: he must be able to think clearly and to identify the significant phenomena which he sees about him. He can apply the concepts we set out as well in his own neighborhood as in some tribe of savages, but he has to apply them sagely. To a large extent, the cultural anthropologist carries his tools "in his head" rather than in an instrument case. It is one of the objectives of this book to place these "tools" in the heads of students, rather than merely to compile an encyclopedia of facts collected by other observers.

FORMATION OF HABITS AND CUSTOMS

What is a habit? Customs are actually habits from the psychological point of view. A common way of putting this is to say that culture is "acquired behavior," but what exactly is meant? If you acquire a habit, where does it come from? Actually no learned action is acquired; the potential reaction exists in the repertory of the organism before the learning process begins. If you cannot stand on your head, no amount of teaching or experience will develop a head-standing habit.

A habit is a learned tendency in the organism to perform a given response from its innate repertory under given conditions. That which is acquired is a connection between a certain complex of conditions and the response. The firmer the habit is, the more likely that the organism will bring forth the response in question on any occasion when confronted with the conditions specified. Thus the organism acquires a tendency to act in a predictable manner.

What are the conditions under which habits are formed? One of the simplest formulations is that of Miller and Dollard. To form a habit, an organism has to *feel* something, it has to *want* something, it has to *do* something, and it has to *get* something. The more technical terms are *stimulus, drive, response,* and *reward,* and they refer in general to the conditions under which learning takes place.

It is apparent that this approach to learning is a pragmatic one. It is firmly rooted in empirical evidence, but this evidence is of a macroscopic or molar character, rather than of a microscopic type. In other words, modern learning theory does not depend upon a detailed knowledge of the workings of the nervous system, and in this respect differs from the older type of behaviorism which imputed certain still unverifiable events in the synapses as crucial in the learning process. Modern learning theory of course recognizes the importance of the nervous system and its function in mediating behavior, but it also recognizes that synaptic modifications as a result of learning have not been discovered by actual dissection with present techniques, nor are they necessary to predict an animal's reactions. As Hilgard and Marquis put it,

> In the present status of our knowledge, neural theory is not basic to conditioning theory. The known facts of neural function cannot be utilized to predict or to limit the results of behavioral studies. None of the several principles and facts ... can be deduced from present direct knowledge of the nervous system. Even the basic law that a response varies in magnitude with the intensity of stimulus would be equally true if the nerves were copper wires or pneumatic tubes. . . . This point of view of course does not preclude the possibility that on the basis of future work neurological prediction of behaviorial facts may be achieved.[1]

The processes of learning seem to be fundamentally the same throughout the animal kingdom and man learns in essentially the same way as other animals. Conditioned learning has been demonstrated experimentally with protozoa, worms, snails, crabs, fish, reptiles, pigeons, chickens, rats, sheep, dogs, monkeys, apes, and man, not to mention many other species.[2]

A common experiment used by psychologists to demonstrate in the laboratory the basic interplay of stimulus, drive, response, and reward in the learning process is the following. A hungry untrained rat (drive: hunger) is placed in a box at one end of which is a small cup and a lever (configuration of stimuli). If the animal presses the lever, a pellet of food drops into the cup and the rat may eat, but of course the rat does not "know" this when introduced into the box. When first placed in this dilemma the hungry rodent must learn by *trial and error.* Driven by hunger, he starts *random activity:* he runs about the box, sniffs, stands up on his hind legs, paws the walls, and so forth. None of these responses brings any reward, that is, they do not satisfy his hunger. Finally, however, he presses the lever, the food appears, and he eats, that is, he is rewarded for the response of bar-pressing. But the one pellet does not satisfy him and he again becomes active shortly after he has swallowed the pellet of food. The second time he wastes less time in unsuccessful trials and comes to the bar-pressing response without so many pre-liminaries. On each successive trial he goes more directly to the bar until he finally learns that bar-pressing is the one response, in this situation, that produces the reward. The preliminary, random, unsuccessful move-ments have dropped out and the habit of bar-pressing has become established.

Rats, of course, are excessively stupid animals as compared with *Homo*, but men acquire habits in the same fundamental way. Random trial-and-error learning has been the experience of all of us at some time or other. At one time the present writer, who has had ample experience in driving automobiles but little in repairing them, was nursing a station wagon along an abandoned road in Guatemala when the motor stopped dead. The writer, like the rat, was motivated by hunger and fatigue as well, for it had been a long day and he wished to get to his camp. In the fading light of a late afternoon he opened the hood and tried to get the motor started. He removed every wire in sight, put it back again, loosened the spark plugs, jiggled all the movable parts in view, screwed and unscrewed all the nuts and bolts he could move, emitted sundry curses, prayed, sat down and scratched himself, and so on. Finally he happened to place the correct wire on the correct connection, and the motor started. If this wasn't random trial-and-error behavior, suggest a better word. Unfortunately the car stopped again about a week later. It required only about half an hour to find the correct response this time. But after the second experience, the writer sat down, while the matter was still "fresh in his mind," and drew a diagram of the wiring so that he was able to identify the recalcitrant wire in the future, something which he, being a *Homo sapiens*, should have done on the first occasion. Probably every reader can call to mind a similar experience.

At this point it is worth mentioning that, although men learn by the same processes as rats, *men have some advantages* which rats do not have. (1) In addition to gross physical responses, men are able to make *mental responses*, that is, they are able to "figure out" situations to some extent "mentally." In this way, men are able to transfer a certain amount of the overt trials necessary for discovering a correct response to their cerebral cortexes. Likewise correct responses can be remembered mentally as well as merely kinaesthetically. In this type of response, language both spoken and silent is a great aid. We know that other animals do not possess true symbolic language and whatever other mental behavior they may be capable of does not seem to aid them greatly in solving problems. (2) All men except new-born babies possess some culture which can be used in new situations. Representational culture patterns are very useful in cutting out random responses and in conserving correct responses, once they are discovered. Thus, the business of making a diagram to indicate the proper wire to hook up eliminated random response on future occasions. (3) Men have available the presence of other members of their society as well as the culture of the society. The customs of the culture are themselves correct responses for their appropriate situations and certain members of the society are usually in a position to show the individual which is the correct response and which the wrong one. In this way a society through its culture cuts down or eliminates many trials for its members. As a last resort a stranded automobilist, even in Guatemala, can go somewhere (although it may be at a considerable distance) and get a garage mechanic who can show him how to start his car.

Let us now consider more specifically certain of the factors involved in learning.

Stimulus. Technically a stimulus is any pattern of energy which impinges upon the receptor organs of the organism with sufficient intensity to evoke a response. Stimuli may come from inside the body as well as outside it. Any one who has ever had a tooth- or a stomach-ache can appreciate this fact. Stimuli may be visual, tactile, auditory, gustatory, olfactory, visceral, muscular, in the joints, and so forth. Although for laboratory purposes situations can be arranged in which only a single stimulus at a time is involved, a human being in most situations of life is confronted by a *configuration of stimuli* at any given time. In such a configuration, as in any configuration, one or several of the various stimuli may be of special significance, but nevertheless, as the Gestalt psychologists have demonstrated experimentally, the structure or pattern of the whole stimulus situation is of importance. In other words we learn to respond to configurations as wholes as well as to individual items of stimulus value. The familiar optical illusions printed on the puzzle pages of newspapers demonstrate this fact clearly. Stimuli, considered either individually or in configuration, are said to have two aspects: (1) drive aspect and (2) cue aspect. In everyday language one may say that *the drive aspect of a stimulus tells you that you want something, the cue aspect tells you what to do about it.*

Stimuli must always be *adequate* if they are to play a part in behavior. The psychologists say that they must be of sufficient strength or intensity to cross the sensory threshold and they must fall within the sensitivity range of the species. Otherwise, they are incapable of eliciting a response. For example, ultra-violet light is "invisible" to human eyes, that is, it lies outside the sensitivity range of the human retina and therefore is an inadequate visual stimulus. A light pat on the skin will usually not evoke a withdrawing response because the intensity of the stimulus is insufficient to cross the sensory threshold of pain.

It should be pointed out that experience and training may induce the organism to "notice" stimuli which otherwise may be ignored and therefore may lack adequacy. This principle seems to explain the alleged "keener senses" of many primitive hunters and trackers. Tests have shown that primitives are actually no more sensitive neurologically or physiologically than civilized men, but that their training has often taught them to notice cue stimuli overlooked by others. The same is true of well-trained detectives, for example, in our society.

Drives. A completely satisfactory definition of drives has not been produced, but for present purposes we may regard a drive as *any condition in the organism which heightens its susceptibility to stimuli and impels response.* Drives are also called motives, motivators, instigators, wants, and desires, and we shall use these words in various contexts later in this book. It is probable that physiology will one day show us conclusively that certain internal stimuli, at least, are usually involved in the arousal of the primary drives which seem to rise of themselves as a result of deprivation (for example, sex, hunger). However this may be, it is clear from the point of view of the average human being that a drive may arise "by itself," as when one gets hungry in the absence of any exterior stimuli, and also that a drive may be aroused by appropriate stimuli, as when one gets hungry as a result of smelling food cooking.

For purposes of behavior science we recognize two types of drives: primary drives and secondary drives.

Primary drives. These are also called *basic drives*, and so forth. Evidence seems to indicate that most of them are inherent in all human beings, although in individual cases they may exist only in latent form. For example, there are few persons in our society who have ever experienced the stark gnawing of general hunger, as distinguished from appetite for some particular object of food.

Among the more important primary drives which are commonly recognized are those we call (1) primary physiological drives for (*a*) air, (*b*) nourishment, (*c*) water, (*d*) pain, (*e*) sex, (*f*) urination, (*g*) defecation, (*h*) cold, (*i*) heat, (*j*) fatigue. When any of these drives is raised the animal—perhaps man—goes into activity which continues until either the drive is in some degree lowered, or until the organism is exhausted and further response is at least temporarily suspended.

Since these drives motivate all men it is obvious that all human cultures must contain some customs for lowering them, for giving satisfaction.

It might be said that these drives are basic to all culture, for all societies and established social groups have developed certain customary ways of satisfying these drives at least to a minimum degree. Likewise all societies have developed customs which control or modify the primary drives to some extent. An important aspect of every culture is the control, as well as the satisfaction, of the primary drives through the development of time and space coördination of the habits based upon them.

For example, the pearl divers of Polynesia learn to hold their breath under water for two to three minutes (control of air hunger); four meals a day are the thing in England, three per day in America, two are considered sufficient among the Lepchas of Assam,[3] and one meal per day is *de rigueur* among the Vedda of Ceylon [4] (control of food hunger); habitual repression of thirst for twelve-hour periods is not uncommon among cowboys in our own country, while twenty-four hour abstinence is fairly common among some groups of Arabia and Central Asia (control of thirst); sex suppression until marriage is theoretically characteristic of our culture and all societies lay some restriction upon the sex drive; control of urination and defecation with respect to time and place of these functions is established during childhood in all societies, although the degree of control and the methods used vary widely; time and place for sleeping as well as training in endurance (suppression of fatigue) are also familiar and vary from group to group; apart from anesthetics, suppression of the unmitigated pain drive, while perhaps the most difficult type of drive control to establish, is characteristic of many primitive peoples. The actual cultural manifestations of drive activity and their variations and controls will constantly appear in our analyses of culture. It is sufficient at this point to emphasize the pervading influence of drives upon human learned activity and especially upon that most important class of learned activity which we call culture.

The foregoing primary drives seem to be clearly physiological in the sense that physiological processes may be identified as at work when the drives are aroused. There seems to be another class of primary drives which can also be recognized as universal in the species. Physiological evidence concerning their operation is not so clear as in the case of the so-called physiological drives and they are not so well understood. We may call them the (2) *primary psychic drives,* for want of a better term. One of these seems to be (a) the *drive for new experience;* we might also call it "restlessness," "desire to escape boredom," "the exploratory drive," "the activity drive," and so forth. This characteristic is apparently a primate trait. At least it seems to be present among most of the anthropoid Primates, who are a notoriously restless group of animals, constantly given to exploring their own bodies and their surroundings even when their physiological drives are satisfied. If we are correct in considering this a basic human drive, its effect is to expose the organism constantly to new and different stimuli, which is the first prerequisite for learning new habits and customs. It would explain in part the very wide variety of habit and custom patterns current among members of the human species. Many another type of animal learns only a very limited range of habits, not only because of structural and neural limitations, but also because, once its basic physiological drives are quieted, it is content to "take things easy," rather than constantly impelled to "poke its nose" into new situations and dilemmas, as seems to be the case with our species.

Another of the basic psychic drives may be called (*b*) *desire for response from others;* it might be designated "the social drive." It is basic in the sense that it seems to be universal to the members of the species (even though overridden or modified in some cases). We do not have conclusive evidence, however, that this drive is innate. It may well develop as a result of the infantile dependency which is the lot of all human beings by reason of the helpless condition in which the infant is brought into the world. Since all humans, however, owe their very lives to ministrative responses of others during a period of years, this drive becomes the property of all men.

A final primary psychic drive seems to be (*c*) *frustration drive* or *basic anger* or aggression. This has a physiological basis, the most prominent feature of which consists in a heavy discharge of adrenalin into the blood, and it is aroused when a goal-directed response or course of action is interrupted before reaching the goal. As with other drives, it motivates a variety of random responses until the correct drive-reducing response is found or unless the proper response is established by training. According to the observations of Watson and others, this drive is present in newborn infants (it is sometimes called "rage" in the literature). The uncontrolled flailing of the arms of an infuriated untrained man when attacking an opponent represents the random response to this drive, while the skilfully planted left hook of the trained boxer in a similar situation represents a trained, cultural response.

Secondary or acquired drives. While the basic drives are at the root of all we learn, it is characteristic of human activity that much of it is motivated by acquired drives, developed as a result of life experience in certain types of conditions. Actually, acquired drives are deeply ingrained habit complexes which in the ultimate analysis are of course based on the primary drives. But the acquired drives are elaborations of the primary drives which serve as a "facade" behind which the functions of the underlying drives are masked. They are also anchored to the conditions of life of a particular place and time. Thus, since culture and social life set many of these conditions for human beings, it follows that each culture has the effect of developing acquired drives, in some sense peculiar to itself, in the psychological systems of the members of the society to which it pertains.

Although the acquired or secondary drives current in a given society always have to be described in terms of the culture of that society, they fall into three major classes, taking all cultures in general: (1) anxieties; (2) appetites; and (3) frustrations.

An anxiety is a drive which is based upon *anticipation* of pain or other punishment. Pain seems to be the most motivating of all the primary drives, and human beings as a rule rapidly learn to identify situations in which it has been experienced in the past. The mere presentation of such a stimulus configuration or any significant part of it will lead one to anticipate pain. This anticipation of pain or punishment is called *anxiety* and it becomes motivating in itself, since it is an uncomfortable, punishing state of affairs. Under the drive of anxiety one will learn habits or customs which lower anxiety and worry, or which enable one to avoid it. So-called "normal" anxieties are those based upon reality, that is, the situations which arouse them actually do contain the potentialities of pain. Neurotic anxieties, on the other hand, are based upon an unrealistic apprehension of the situations which arouse them: they are involved in a number of types of mental illness.

Punishment, as distinguished from the primary drive of pain, is the condition of unrelieved drive tension. When any drive, whether primary or secondary, is aroused without any effective lowering, the situation is said to be punishing. The child who has burned his hand in a fireplace may become anxious whenever he sees a fire. A man who has been arrested by a policeman may become "uneasy" whenever he passes one on the street. Anxieties may be attached to any stimuli which occur in a setting anticipatory of pain or punishment. And it may be remarked that culturally induced anxieties and learned responses for reducing them play a large part in every society. "Social control," for example, could scarcely operate without them. Our "consciences" and the super-ego of Freudian theory function to a large extent on the basis of culturally conditioned anxiety drives. In our society, for example, most of us are much concerned by anxiety regarding our security in old age, and this uneasiness supposedly serves to motivate us to work hard and to save our money. It is obvious that we are not born with apprehension of a poverty-stricken dotage: we learn this form of anxiety and also the customs of industry and thrift which are supposed to enable us to avoid the punishing effects of penury. The acquired drive of security anxiety in our society apparently rests upon such primary drives as hunger, heat, cold, pain, and the like, but as a motivation it is none-theless distinguishable from the primary drives themselves. In fact, a given acquired drive often involves a blending of a number of different primary drives, as is the case in this instance. Anxiety regarding security in old age apparently does not exist at all in some societies, because the cultural patterns are so organized that old persons are never punished simply for being old: kinsmen, for example, may supply economic support.

The specific anxieties depend upon the specific cultural organization of each society, but we may mention a few of the more common of such anxieties: sexual anxiety, prestige anxiety, sickness anxiety, anxiety regard-ing the supernatural and the after life, and so forth. On the basis of these acquired drives the most elaborate customs may be built, and acquired drives may come to be every bit as motivating as the primary drives themselves. In fact, they may be more so, and the acquired drives may override the primary drives, as we shall see in Chapter 14. For instance, we may assume that an acquired drive for prestige motivates customs designed to enhance personal beauty as locally defined. Numerous cultures contain customs for satisfying this desire: tatooing, scarification, deforma-tion of various parts of the body are a few examples. A man's ambition among the Marquesas Islanders, for example, was to be tatooed from head to foot. The cultural procedures available were extremely painful, and required years to complete, but every one tried to go through with them anyway. It is clear that in such cases the punishment to be derived from unsatisfied secondary prestige drive was rated as greater than that received from the (primary) pain drive. The elaborate and prolonged religious rituals of many peoples seem to be motivated by anxiety re-garding the supernatural. Intricate forms of etiquette, complex habits of entertaining, and flamboyant styles of dressing may be developed on prestige anxiety, even in our own society. Everyday experience convinces us of the motivating, driving power of many of these acquired drives.

Appetites are also acquired drives, refinements, as it were, of certain basic drives, often in combination. In all societies people have to eat, but in each society certain types of food are preferred over others; every-where normal individuals desire sex gratification, but only for certain (culturally defined) types of sex objects; universally men must breathe air, but in some societies they prefer to have it scented, in others, laden with tobacco smoke, and so forth. These preferences are taught to the growing members of a society and become extremely powerful motivators. One has only to consider the complex organization of customs necessary to provide the "indispensable" cup of coffee to the American breakfast table to realize that the acquired drive or desire for coffee exerts a very pervading influence as a motivator of customs. Again, appetites may become more powerful than the primary drives themselves which underlie them. Cases are on record of individuals coming close to starvation rather than eat insects in the absence of their accustomed food. In our society an individual will "walk a mile" to satisfy the acquired desire for cigarettes, while the phrase, "I could not love thee half so much loved I not honor more," is an expression of the overriding influence of prestige drive on sex drive.

Acquired angers or frustrations are developed in connection with specific factors in a given situation which are defined by the culture as blocks or impediments to the attainment of legitimate goals. For instance, a foreign society may be regarded as the "traditional enemy" of our society, and we are conditioned to feel anger when the enemies or their works appear upon our horizon. Or the Devil and persons who are believed to follow his orders may be thought of as constantly interfering with our practise of the good life and so may arouse our ire. It is obvious that such angers are culturally induced, for they are not universal to all men. In some societies no traditional enemies are recognized, and many others have no concept of the Devil. In any case the acquired anger is a desire or want to do away with or to circumvent the supposed impediment or irritation.

Although acquired drives may serve as the basis for habit-building, they must be maintained by occasional primary drive reinforcement. Otherwise they tend to extinguish. If a child discovers through repeated experience that the mere presence of a burning fireplace in the room with him is not painful, his fear of fireplaces may eventually evaporate, because the anxiety is not reinforced by pain. If one discovers that eating oranges produces sores in the mouth, one loses one's appetite for oranges. A standard "cure" for the smoking habit is to paint the throat with silver nitrate which causes a feeling of nausea when one inhales, and supposedly robs the smoker of any feeling of satisfaction to such an extent that he loses his desire to smoke. Actually the desire (acquired drive) to smoke seems to be based on a number of primary and secondary drives, so that a "cure" of this sort is seldom permanently effective in itself.

In sum we may say that a primary drive is a want for a *general* type or category of satisfaction unmodified by culture whereas a secondary drive is always a want for a *particular type* of satisfaction created by a particular culture.

Cues. The drive value of a stimulus depends upon its strength; a jab with a knife is more motivating, produces more response, than a pin prick. The cue value of a stimulus, however, depends upon its distinctiveness. We may say that the drive aspect of a stimulus tells the person to respond, whereas the cue aspect tells him where to respond, when to respond, and which response to make. The drive aspect of a pin prick in the back impels movement, the cue aspect tells you to move forward, that is, away from the stimulus object and the pain which it arouses. The sign outside a candy store may arouse your appetite for chocolates and at the same time show you where it can be satisfied. Every stimulus has something of both drive and cue aspects, although the two may not be equally balanced. A tantalizing odor of roast beef may rouse your hunger drive, without indicating its source. On the other hand a plain sign, "Roast Beef," in a restaurant window may indicate clearly enough the direction to take for eating, but will arouse no hunger drive if you have just finished a hearty meal.

Although it is convenient to speak of stimuli as discrete units, in actual life, as previously stated, we almost invariably react to patterns or configurations of stimuli. The nerves inside our bodies are constantly receiving internal stimuli which serve to maintain muscular tonus and vegetative organic functions as well as more comprehensive behavior; when reacting to external stimulation the individual always finds himself in a situation which involves a large number of stimuli, one or more of which at the moment carry more drive and/or cue value than the others and which are hence most effective in producing the response. The dominant cue in such a situation may then cue not only a single stimulus but the whole configuration.[5] Noticing a cue can itself be a learned response and this is called "learning to pay attention." If we take this view of the whole organism receiving stimuli in a complex stimulus situation we rid ourselves of some of the limitations of the "reflex arc" type of earlier behavioristic analysis.

Drives and needs. It is noteworthy that there is no necessary one-to-one correlation between drives, considered in the psychological sense, and needs, taken in the usual biological meaning. It is true that primary drives, particularly those of the innate physiological type, seem in most cases to correspond to biological needs, but even in this respect it is not clear that the correspondence is perfect. For example, it is questionable as to whether or not there are innate drives or hungers for certain types of minerals and vitamins which are actually biologically necessary to a balanced diet. We have very little evidence to show that people feel such hungers, unless they have been trained to respond to certain cues and have developed acquired drives which are satisfied by the ingestation of these materials. There is, at least, no doubt that many societies actually exist whose cultures provide no such cue training or acquired drive development, and that the members of such groups are in fact badly nourished from a biological point of view.

Acquired drives, as already mentioned, in some cases may actually run counter to biological needs. When one undertakes to follow a life of celibacy, for example, under a drive, perhaps, of desire for sanctity, one is obviously committed to an anti-biological course of action, from the species point of view. Other acquired drives may and actually do, in certain societies, lead individuals to postpone the age of marriage, to reduce the numbers of their offspring artificially and so on. The drives which combine to motivate a war may actually produce reactions which have the effect of nearly eliminating the population of a society, as was the case with Paraguay in her wars of 1869-1870 with Argentina and Brazil.

We must conclude then, that while culture provides the mechanism whereby a society makes adaptation to its biological situation, there is nothing inevitable either in human nature or in the underlying psychological processes which guarantees that such adaptation be perfect, or even "good." Just as an individual may have "bad" habits which involve him in inefficiency, illness, or even death, so also a society may possess "bad" customs considered from the point of view of biological survival. If the customs do not maintain a minimum degree of survival value, the society itself will eventually disappear.

The important point for us to realize, however, is that, since customs are learned, they can be changed for the "better," if necessary. This is one of the reasons that we devote so much attention to the basic mechanisms of learning and performance, so that we shall be in a position to understand the proper measures in such cases.

Response. Cues and drives may be actively present, but the essence of a habit or a custom is the response, overt or covert, which is made by the organism. Unless the organism responds, there is no hope of forming a habit. A custom is no custom, unless members of a social group *do* something.

We say that the response is *elicited* from an organism when the latter is under drive and is stimulated. This implies, as already indicated, that the response must come from the innate *repertory of the organism*. In other words man cannot *learn* to perform acts of which he is structurally incapable. Thus we find no cultures in which the custom occurs of walking barefoot, suspended head downward from the ceiling. Regardless of the strength of drive and the orientating quality of stimuli, there are certain things that human beings just cannot do, by virtue of being human beings. Most of us can never learn to wag our tails no matter how hard we try because we have no external tails, and we can never learn to turn our heads about so that we gaze directly backwards, as can that talented animal the tarsier.

A precise knowledge of the outside limits of human response would be of considerable theoretical importance, because such limits would ipso facto constitute the outside limits of the *content* of human culture (although not the limits of its complexity, of course). In Chapters 12 and 13 we take the reader on a partial tour of these boundaries in order to suggest what may be discovered regarding this matter when it is subjected to more systematic investigation.

Even if we do not know the outside limits of human response potentialities, we do know that the variety within these limits is very great indeed. The human animal is in many cases capable of making a bewildering variety of responses for the satisfaction of a single drive. It is this fact which is at the root of the great variety that we find when examining the cultures and customs of mankind. It goes back once more to the fact that man is a very generalized animal.

Our present knowledge of human response capabilities is neither systematic nor complete as regards all details. But we do know that the animal is versatile. Even so, it is possible to recognize three classes or levels of learnable responses: (1) actional responses, (2) representational responses, and (3) mental responses. Since customs are merely social habits, it follows that we may recognize these three types of customs as well.

A response is *any* reaction which the organism is capable of producing under stimulation or drive. From the point of view of the outside observer, as we have said before, these responses may be either (1) overt, or (2) covert, or (3) a combination of both. At the cost of repetition, we may reaffirm that the overt responses are easiest to observe, and they consist of gross muscular, muscular-glandular (as in vomiting), and positional changes, circulatory changes (such as flushing and paling), and sound effects produced by the vocal or other internal organs of the body. Thus, on the whole, we may classify actional and representational responses as overt. In the case of the actional responses we are able to observe the gross muscular, glandular, positional, and circulatory changes which may be involved. In the case of representational responses, this is sometimes not true; for example, we cannot easily observe the muscular movements involved in speaking, although the sound waves thereby produced exert a direct stimulus upon our receptor organs. On the other hand, the quality of importance with respect to representational responses is not the ease with which we may observe them, but rather the manner in which they may serve as substitutes for other types of stimuli and response.

The mental responses are the least well understood of all. Nevertheless, it is granted that all normal men are capable of producing ideas, fantasies, mental pictures, concepts, dreams, and so forth. We call these reactions mental responses, because they seem to consist of "mental" activity which on the whole is symbolic of overt activity of one sort or another. One of the abilities of man consists in the fact that, instead of *doing* something (in the overt sense), he may "think" it. And, although the mechanisms are not completely understood by psychologists, it is agreed by most authorities that mental activity is capable of producing reward, as well as, although probably in a different way from, overt activity. Most of us have probably experienced the inner satisfaction resulting from a fantasy in which we flatten an opponent too large or powerful for us to overcome in overt action. According to the Freudian theory, which seems to explain such matters better than any other, many of our dreams are wish fulfilments of somewhat the same kind. The important point for cultural science, however, is that human beings are capable of producing *ideas* as a form of mental response. We are able to structure a situation mentally, carry out mental trial-and-error responses, and reach a solution mentally and covertly before engaging in any overt behavior whatever. Furthermore, there seems to be no doubt that mental responses of certain patterns can be learned. All of us have had the experience, for example, of having a popular tune "running through our heads." This is obviously a mental response, for there is nothing overt about our activity in such a case. It is equally obvious that the tune is not original with us, but that we have learned it.

We may transfer all of this to the cultural level and state that mental, representational, and actional customs characterize human social behavior or culture. The representational customs serve as mediators, as it were, between actional and mental activity, and it is only through representational customs that the mental activity of one individual can be communicated to another. These representational responses and customs may be verbal (speech), or they may be actional customs of any type which have the quality of standing for or representing something else—wigwag motions of the arms, gestures of the hands, "expressions" of the facial muscles, postures of the body, and so forth, may all have representational quality provided their referents are conventionally understood. Representational customs thus serve as second-order stimuli, and their sufficiency depends upon the training which the recipients have had concerning them. When we say that a representation is a second-order stimulus, we may illustrate our meaning as follows. When some one says to you, "You're a stinker," your prestige drive will probably be aroused. Yet you do not respond directly to the muscular movements in the throat of the person who utters this imprecation; you respond to the sound waves impinging upon your ear drums. Even so, the uneasiness or anger you feel is not directly due to the intensity or other physical characteristics of the stimulus itself, but rather because this particular combination of sounds carries with it the representation of an idea which the speaker presumably has formed in his "mind" and which is a conventional mental pattern in your culture, although not necessarily customarily applied to you as a stimulus. The words serve as a representation of the conventionally understood, and hence cultural, mental activity of the speaker.

It is obvious that the particular sounds produced in the utterance of words (representational customs) have no stimulus value unless there is mutual understanding, the result of common training, with respect to them. Any one can insult you in a foreign language until he drops from exhaustion, but if you and other members of your group do not understand his language, he evokes no response from you.

It is to be presumed that the reward value one receives for performing representational customs often depends on whether or not such customs or habits have the effect of stimulating either other persons or oneself to an actional response (custom) which directly lowers the drive in question. You may say to others, "That fellow is a traitor" and receive satisfaction from the action which the others take toward the object of your remarks. Or, you may say to yourself, "That man is a traitor, and I'm going to report him to the FBI." The representation which you make, in either case, serves as a stimulus to subsequent action which produces reward. Technically this type of reward is called *secondary reward*. In such a case a given response does not produce a reward immediately, but rather it serves as a stimulus or, together with other factors, "sets the stage" for a response which *does* produce reward. Such responses and such habits (when established) are said to have an *instrumental function:* they serve to "pave the way" to an eventual satisfaction. As we shall see in subsequent pages, much of man's cultural activity is of this instrumental nature.

The innately possible responses to a given set of stimuli usually are elicited in an order which is called the *initial or innate hierarchy.* The response most likely to occur is called the *dominant response.* In human infants, for example, crying seems to be the dominant response to many forms of painful stimulation, and it is therefore much easier to teach a baby to cry than to whistle in order to attract the attention of its mother. After weaning, the dominant drinking response of humans seems to be sucking between the lips, although the case of Kamala, the Wolf Child of India, indicates that lapping water with the tongue, while somewhat lower in the innate hierarchy, can be reinforced and learned, especially if one spends the first few years of one's life in the company of wolves.

Normal human beings beyond the early days of infancy, however, develop learned responses, which may be arranged in an order like the innate hierarchy. We speak of this as the *resultant or learned hierarchy* of response, or *habit family hierarchy*. This means that, at least by the time one has reached the stage of adulthood, and to a lesser extent long before, the normal human being has learned a number of responses to a given stimulus, and that the most likely first response to a given stimulus will depend upon the individual's past training. The dominant learned response may well be quite different from the dominant innate response. One's first impulse, as we say, after receiving a sharp slap on the face may be to cry out at the pain; yet in polite European society the young man thus injured by a young lady forces a nonchalant smile to his face and bows. The innate response to a deep wound is to cry out, then to assume a flexed position of the body. Yet among the Makusi Indians of British Guiana wounds are washed out clean and held for a time over the fire, or in trunk injuries the patient is laid on a framework over the fire. "Even the most horrible agony cannot force a murmur from their lips." [6]

One final principle must be mentioned in connection with response, namely, the principle of consistency. This simply states that if two habits have been formed to the same situation the performance of one must not interfere in any way with the performance of the other.

Reward or reinforcement. We have seen that, if an individual is to learn, he must be *stimulated* to make a response. How does the response get learned, so that it will be repeated when the individual is faced by the same dilemma on subsequent occasions? Why is it that the rat leaves off his aimless puttering about in his box and concentrates on pushing the bar whenever he is hungry? Why does even a witless professor connect up the proper wire in his balky station wagon after several trying experiences? The answer is that acts are learned if they are rewarded. In other words, nothing succeeds like success. The technical term for this is *reinforcement*, and the technical definition of reinforcement is "lowering of drive." Any act, therefore, which lowers the intensity of the drive dominant in the situation in question, is reinforced and thereby tends to be repeated under similar conditions of stimulation on later occasions. On the other hand, unsuccessful, unrewarded responses tend to drop out for lack of reinforcement. The process whereby unrewarded acts disappear from behavior is called *extinction*. For example, the searing pain of a burn on the flesh can be momentarily assuaged by immersing it in water; even more relief is possible by covering the burn with grease; while the most lasting reward ordinarily available in a household is obtained by covering the wound with tannic acid. It is not surprising that, where these choices of response are available, the tannic acid response becomes the dominant habit, because it is most heavily reinforced, while the water and grease responses tend to become extinguished. Thus the strength of a habit depends upon the amount of reinforcement which it receives. On the other hand, thrusting a burned hand into a salt-water solution, for example, brings no relief from pain, but actually accentuates the existing pain. Such a response, therefore, is readily extinguished for lack of reinforcement (combined with punishment).

A habit may be thought of as a bond connecting a specific response with specific stimulus or stimulus configuration. Three factors determine the strength of a habit: (1) number of rewarded training trials, least important of the three factors; (2) strength of drive during training; and, (3) amount of reward per trial during training. The larger the number of reinforced trials, the greater the strength of drive, and the greater the amount of reinforcement per trial, the stronger the habit will be. Strong habits are more resistant to extinction than weak ones. In the average human being many of his strongest habits and customs are almost in-eradicable, except by a complicated process of psychoanalysis. One reason for this is that they have been established by literally thousands of "rewarded training trials," often beginning in early infancy under conditions of high drive. Since these events often were well progressed before the individual's mental responses became "conscious," he is totally un-aware as to "how he got that way." For this reason certain of our customs seem to us to be part of original human nature. If these customs were alike in all societies, we might agree, but the fact that they are not, taken together with studies of early learning in infants, leads us to conclude that they are learned.

Adaptive aspects of learning. It is clear that the process of learning, as thus formulated, serves adaptive functions for man and other organisms. From the point of view of the survival of the individual and the species, the learning process may select out certain responses to environmental conditions which provide satisfaction for biological or biologically-based needs, while eliminating unadaptive responses. Man has developed artificial environments which we speak of as the cultural situations of social groups and, through the mechanism of acquired drives and responses, men learn to adapt to these artificial conditions along the same lines as to crude natural conditions.

This formulation of learning differs from certain of the older "associa-tionistic" theories, which emphasized mere temporal contiguity between stimulus and response as the determining factor in learning. According to such views, if a stimulus and a response occur together often enough, a habit is formed through mere association. Little attention was paid to drive and no place was given to the importance of reward.[7] The result was that a theory of learning based upon pure association provided no mechanism (reinforcement) for the selection of specific responses out of a welter of possibilities and also offered no explanation as to how a habit, once formed, could ever be stopped (extinction).

It is now realized that reward is the crucial element in learning habits and in their maintenance. It is only through reward that a habit is *reinforced or strengthened*. Reward, as we recall, is the effect of lowering drive or giving satisfaction. In other words, a response will not be learned as a habit unless it "pays off" in the form of satisfaction to the drive or drives under which the individual is operating. Furthermore, your individual will not continue to practise the habit unless in the future it proves to be rewarding; in fact he will not continue to practise it unless it proves to be *more* rewarding than any other possible habit which may come within his ken.

Finally we may mention that it has been discovered that reward is the more effective the closer it occurs in time to the completion of the response. *Delayed rewards* are not ineffective by any means, but *immediate rewards* are more effective. Thus when two responses (say, customs) are competing, the one which provides the more immediate reward will tend to win out over the response giving delayed reward, other things equal. "Having one's cake" often produces the effect of a delayed reward, whereas "eating it" provides direct reward. When customs appear to be changing it is always advisable to consider the reward values of the habits involved. Rewards may be distinguished in another way as well: they may be *direct* or *indirect*. A habit providing direct reward produces lowering of drive upon the completion of this habit alone, as for example when one drinks a glass of water to quench his thirst. Another type of habit must be successfully performed in conjunction with other habits if the full reward is to be provided. For example, when we have a cold we may learn to drink many glasses of water as part of the "cure." However, the drinking of water alone does not usually produce a remission of the feeling of malaise which characterizes the condition of having a cold. Water-drinking must be practised together with the taking of nose drops, staying in bed, and so on, and all of these practices together may not rid us of the cold until several days have passed.

Gradient of reward or reinforcement.[8] A good deal of human behavior is learned as a series of acts linked together and ending in a "goal response." Consider your tired middle-class American preparing for bed. The principal drive is fatigue. The sequence may be something like this. First, he washes; then he takes off his clothes and hangs them up; next he puts on his pajamas; next he arranges the pillow carefully;

then he gets into bed and tucks the covers about him; next he turns off the light and finally lies down relaxed and in a few minutes goes to sleep. The final act—lying down relaxed—is closest to the reinforcement (lowering of the fatigue drive). According to the gradient of reward theory, some reinforcement stretches backward toward the first response of the sequence, but in a diminishing amount. Thus the first item, washing, is somewhat rewarded as a preliminary to sleep, but not as much as removing the clothes. Even more rewarding is putting on pajamas, poking the pillow, arranging the covers, and turning off the light in the reverse of that order. We are not considering the independent reinforcements which incidentally attach to each of these acts, but only the spread of the final goal reinforcement of escape from fatigue. The gradient of reinforcement explains why the last item in a series of responses may under certain conditions crowd out the others, why, in other words, it may move forward in the series. Under conditions of extreme fatigue, for example, our middle-class American will skip over all but the final item of the series; he will throw himself directly on the bed in a relaxed position. "The gradient of reward has the function of forcing the subject toward the shortest of alternative paths to a goal and of tending to eliminate unnecessary responses from a sequence." [9] Much of the elaborate ritualism so commonly found in social life can be in part interpreted in terms of the gradient of reward, as can also some of the apparently useless overelaboration of all aspects of culture to which Linton has drawn attention.[10]

Anticipation. The tendency of the gradient of reinforcement to force out earlier members of a rewarded series of acts, if combined with generalization to similar situations, gives us the principle of anticipation. In other words, there is a tendency for responses near to the point of reward to move forward in the series, to become anticipatory. The puckering of the mouth when one sees a lemon is an example of anticipation; the puckering has moved forward in a series which originally consisted of seeing lemon, picking it up, biting into it, puckering the mouth, which was reinforced through mitigation of the bitter taste by reduction of the area of taste receptors in contact with the juice. If Mr. Smith has learned that a polite conversation with Mr. Brown usually ends in a quarrel in which he is forced either to defend himself or withdraw, the polite preliminaries will tend to drop out of the sequence, and Smith will tend to respond with defensive or withdrawing responses on the first sight of Brown.

Anticipation is the mechanism whereby various acquired drives develop and operate, especially anxieties, which are anticipatory of punishment.

The principle of anticipation plays so wide a rôle in human social life that we shall not discuss it further here, but shall refer to it again in discussing various aspects of culture.

Multiple drives. For the sake of simplicity we have on the whole been discussing habits each of which has the function of lowering a single drive. However, we should make it clear that a habit or a custom may be motivated by a combination of drives and may have the function of lowering several drives at once. In fact, this is one of the outstanding features of culture, that the customs may be so arranged as to "kill several birds with one stone." In our society, for instance, men perform the patterns of work to get money (an acquired drive), but many work patterns must also satisfy the desire for prestige (an acquired drive); if they do not have at least these double functions, many individuals will not practise them.

Extinction of habits. We have seen the crucial function of reward in the formation and maintenance of habits. It used to be thought that mere repetition of an act would make it habitual, would in some way "groove" it into the nervous system. It is now understood that repetition in the absence of reward actually results in the loss of the habit in the long run. This process is called extinction. A housewife, who has been rewarded by obtaining good quality meat at a certain market, establishes the habit of going to that market to trade; but, if something happens whereby the market repeatedly fails to supply her wants, she gradually loses the habit of trading there. Extinction usually extends over several trials, if no other factors interfere in the process, and the stronger the habit, the greater is the number of unrewarded repetitions required to extinguish it.

We should not confuse extinction with forgetting which occurs simply through failure to practise a given response (usually for lack of the appropriate stimulus).

Punishment and pain. A habit often dies out rather slowly under simple extinction. When habits or customs disappear rapidly the process is usually accelerated by the application of pain or punishment. Technically this process is not the same as extinction (lack of reward), but rather consists of raising the pain or anxiety drives. In order to lower these drives the organism is forced to adopt responses which are incompatible with the previously practised habit. Thus the pain- or anxiety-avoiding habit displaces the other one by incompatibility rather than by extinction. If our lady not only does not obtain sirloin steak of the flavor which she desires in the market, but also gets "ptomaine poisoning" from the meat she does buy, further purchasing expeditions to that market will be definitely ruled out at once, without her continuing any further merely unrewarded trials. In other words, if a habit not only is unrewarded, but its performance also raises a pain drive, anxiety will develop in the situation in which the former habit was practised, and another habit or habits (possibly avoidance habits) will develop. Our housewife may respond to punishment by simply avoiding the market where she obtained the putrid meat, or she may develop another response which consists in going to a different market further down the street. In this way punishment tends to eliminate a habit by forcing the organism to substitute a new response.

Punishment may also eliminate habits which are actually being practised with reinforcement by raising the level of anxiety above the level of the drive on which the original habit is operating. A small boy's raids on the cooky jar are motivated by an appetite for sweets and reinforced by the rewards of this illicit pilfering. The punishment of a hard spanking, however, may raise his fear of punishment above his desire for sweets. On the basis of this latter drive (anxiety) he learns an avoidance response when stimulated by the sight of the cooky jar, and this avoidance is reinforced by relief from fear.

Later we shall see that many of the so-called controls which exist in every society involve rewards, either primary or secondary. On the other hand, it is a commonplace in social science that social control everywhere rests in the last analysis upon "force", that is, direct raising of the pain drive. Thus every society raises in its members a number of anxieties (secondary drives) based upon occasional direct resort to pain. On the basis of these anxieties, numerous habits are developed in the bulk of the population which serve the dual purposes of reducing anxiety in the individual and of providing "socialized" culture patterns whereby numbers of people can interact together in orderly fashion. By returning your neighbor's watch rather than putting it in your pocket you reduce the gnawing fear of discovery and punishment which haunts the thief, and the habit of returning stolen property thereby is reinforced. We must remember, however, that secondary or acquired drives are learned on the basis of experience and must be reinforced from time to time by the primary, innate drives upon which they are based. Thus thieves must be caught and punished directly, if the anxieties upon which honest habits are built are not to be displaced.

The fact of extinction, however, emphasizes the importance of reward in human life, for it enables us to understand that mere repetition does not strengthen a habit, or even maintain it, and that non-rewarded repetitions progressively weaken a habit. Thus reward is fundamental to learning, and since so much of human behavior is learned and acted in society, we may say that *reward is fundamental to human social life*. We may anticipate later discussion to remark that no cultural system which fails to provide adequate rewards can long exist. This point is of importance in understanding culture change and culture contact.

Spontaneous recovery. The adaptive function of extinction is to force the individual, in the absence of reward for the old habit, to try a new response until one is made which is rewarding. However, if none of these is rewarded the old response may be tried again. This tendency for the effects of extinction to disappear with the passage of time during which no trials have taken place is called spontaneous recovery. A fisherman getting no catch with worm bait may try grubs; but after a period of no reward from grubs, he may go back to worms for a few tries. Part of the so-called erratic behavior in human beings is chargeable to spontaneous recovery.

Generalization. There is a tendency for habits learned in one situation to transfer to other similar situations, although the less similar the new situation, the less strength will the original habit have. This generalizing tendency is highly important in adaptation, for an individual is very rarely confronted a second time with an exact duplication of the stimulus situation in which he first learned a response. If generalization were not operative, one would have to go through the whole learning process hundreds of times every day, since no two situations are ever exactly the same. A child burned in one fireplace will tend to withdraw from all fireplaces; a boy who has learned obsequious compliance to the orders of his father may behave likewise in all situations where he is subject to authority; all Chinese may "look alike" and be treated like the Chinese laundryman with whom first contacts were had; when you enter an hotel in a new city you behave much as in the hotels where you have stayed previously. Finnegan put the matter extremely when he said "Pigs is pigs." Apparently many of the "stereotypes" which characterize American public opinion are generalizations of this sort. Customs involving categories of society—classes, castes, bosses, laborers, and the like—illustrate the process of generalization in social life. The *gradient of generalization* describes the rating which can be assigned to cues with respect to their similarity to each other. For example, a response to Negroes may have been learned originally to the stimulus of a fat, dark Negro "mammy." All other negro women can be rated on the basis of similarity to his specific woman. The more they resemble her, the greater the likelihood of their eliciting the original response. But as one proceeds to lighter-colored and medium-sized women, to still lighter and thinner women, to very light and very thin women, the similarity becomes progressively less. As the gradient of generalization falls off there is a a corresponding decrease in the likelihood that the original response will be elicited.

Differentiation or discrimination. As the gradient of generalization approaches zero the tendency for the original response to appear also approaches zero. Thus a child may generalize its responses to a large number of more or less mammy-like women, but will fail to respond similarly to a Chinese woman. One may respond more or less routinely to a wide variety of hotels, but feel no familiarity if he finds himself in a "flophouse." This is called differentiation or discrimination. Differentiation is again an adaptive process, dependent upon reward. It is the process whereby one learns to distinguish unlike situations one from the other and to develop correspondingly adaptive responses to each. It is based upon the innate ability of the organism to distinguish between cues. Thus in certain types of color-blindness red and green cues cannot be distinguished. Within the range of normal human abilities, however, discriminations can be and must be learned. Much of human socialization is concerned with teaching the child to distinguish edible from non-edible types of substances, relatives from non-relatives, good grammar from bad grammar, and so on and so forth. Differentiation is the process of setting limits to categories of stimulating situations, generalization is the process of developing categories or classes from unique stimuli. And in these processes all societies make greater or less use of symbols. Words, of course, symbolize similarities and differences. Uniforms on policemen, for example, tend to cut out numerous differential cues in the officers of the law and thus increase our tendency to generalize our responses to all of them. Badges of rank and distinction, on the other hand, serve to set off certain individuals and groups as distinctive stimuli to which we are expected to respond in distinctive ways.

PERSONALITY

To some students of individual personality our use of the term *habit* to refer to *all* types of learned reactions of human beings may sound strange, because they have been accustomed to employ the word only to refer to gross overt learned reactions. There is no point in quarreling over words. If we use the word *habit* in a broad sense we avoid difficulties arising from having to introduce other words and concepts to explain certain phenomena, and our terminology gains in consistency. It is understood that man is as capable of learning "mental" and "projective" habits as any other kind. "Custom," as we have already pointed out, is a socially shared habit.

Constellations of habits and customs. As a result of training and experience in early life most normal individuals develop constellations or functional configurations of habits which become deeply imbedded in their personality structure. These constellations consist of habits of all types—actional, representational, and mental—organized into a system of sorts. In so far as these are common to the members of a social group, we may regard them as aspects of culture.

Almost everywhere the growing child develops a constellation of reactions toward his parents, which, by generalization, is extended to others in authority and which may be "projected" symbolically into the realm of the supernatural,[11] and in other directions. For example, the training system of children among the people of Alor, in the southwest Pacific, is such that the individual gradually develops a system of attitudes and actions toward parents characterized by hostility, lack of confidence, lack of security, displaced aggression in the form of stealing food, and so on.[12] Discussion of the influence of custom on personality must be postponed to a later chapter, but it should be noted here that these "basic constellations" of personality which are repeated over and over again in persons of the same group are actually closely integrated sets of customs firmly learned and embedded in the person. In so far as a culture creates a "basic personality type" among the members of its society we are able to predict and to understand the behavior of these individuals; but such behavior always has to be understood in terms of the system of rewards and punishments which the culture sets up and to which the individual is subjected during the formative period of his life.

Consciousness. We owe to the investigations of Freud and his followers most of the systematic knowledge which we possess of the unconscious and subconscious processes of human beings. If Freud did not discover the fact that many of our motivations and actions are unconscious, he at least directed attention to this phase of human reactions and provided us with a rational scheme of interpretation. He pointed out that many of our reactions are based upon motives of which we are not clearly aware. Particularly with regard to mental activity, the organism often seems to seek to disguise the true motives and the true stimuli, usually as an escape from anxiety (an acquired drive, resulting from experience). Or again, aggression may be expressed symbolically, but in disguised form. These disguised mental activities are often apparent in dreams and fantasies, even though the individual is not fully aware of their meaning.

For example, as a result of parental neglect the individual may feel a lack of support, a sense of insecurity. Yet he may be punished for expressing this anxiety openly. It is even punishing to admit anxiety consciously to oneself, particularly when the outside world provides no patterns for relieving it. Consequently, it appears in disguised form in dreams, in which the individual may repeatedly dream of falling from high places, of slipping down the face of cliffs, of being deserted, or the like. Furthermore, the overt expression of aggression may be punished. In the patriarchal family of nineteenth-century Europe, for example, the male child's frustration drive toward his father was often apparently raised to a high point, but, due to the all-powerful authority of the father, the child was helpless in its attempts to lower its aggression overtly. The reactions to the drive were consequently "repressed" to the unconscious level, and would appear in dreams in various disguised forms.

Freud therefore posited three levels of mental or symbolic activity: the conscious, the subconscious, and the unconscious. We may say that on the conscious level, the mental reactions are capable of being translated into the representational reactions or words which are understandable by other persons in terms of the conditions of the outside world, cultural conditions included. On the subconscious and unconscious levels the linkage of mental activity with language has been lost, at least temporarily. In the subconscious the loss of linkage is due primarily to forgetting, that is, lack of practise or to the operation of unconscious drives not heavily punishing, and it can usually be reëstablished without great difficulty. For example, one may not be able to call up a person's name, although it is "on the tip of the tongue," partly because of lack of practise (meaning that one has not been heavily motivated to call the name) and partly because the person may arouse a certain mild anxiety, or some other drive. Mental activity which remains on the purely unconscious level, however, is deeply repressed and is often disguised because its expression in "rational" representational form has proved highly punishing in some way to the individual in the past. On the other hand, certain mental activities may remain unconscious because they were established in early childhood before language was acquired and there has since been no motivation to put them into words.

We shall refer to these matters later, but we wish to point out at this time that the same basic principles of stimulus, drive, reward, and punishment apparently apply not only to conscious but also to unconscious and subconscious activity. Furthermore, there is no inconsistency in speaking of *unconscious customs*, provided the activities involved are socially learned, are common to members of a social group, and in other respects conform to the criteria of customs in general. This is actually true in fact. For example, studies of dreams of the members of a social group usually show a similarity in organization and manifest content as well as forms or modes of symbolization, which may be contrasted with dreams from another group.[13] Such evidence seems to indicate beyond much doubt the performance of unconscious mental customs. Thus it is that culture molds not only the overt actions of the members of a society, but to a considerable extent, the unconscious life as well.

LEARNING AND CULTURE

The above principles have been well tested experimentally by the psychologists. The concrete examples of learning which we have given have been for the most part characteristic of what is called trial-and-error learning, in which the subject tries a number of random responses from its innate repertory until it happens to make a successful response, which is then rewarded, whereupon the first step in habit formation is completed. A number of other types of laboratory setups have been used for manipulating the conditions under which learning takes place, the technical details of which are of less interest to us—conditioned learning, instrumental reward learning, instrumental escape learning, and others. The same general principles apparently apply to all. The question which does interest us is, What does learning have to do with culture and human life in society? For human beings are not rats in cages and their behavior appears so complex that the applicability of these broad general principles may appear doubtful.

We have considered some of the evidence in the first part of this volume which leads us to the conclusion that human culture is learned behavior. From the point of view of learning theory we may mention the following points of significance which will bear upon later discussions. When we speak of culture "doing" something, it will be understood that actually cultural influences are brought to bear on individuals either by surrogates or agents (individuals), or by cultural products (artifacts).

1. Culture provides the *conditions* for learning. Upon birth a human baby enters a man-made environment which to some extent intervenes between him and the raw, "natural" environment. He is surrounded by artifacts whose number, uses, and form are characteristic of the culture of his society. He is surrounded by older human beings who have been trained in certain ways of thinking and of doing. The artifacts and the behavior of the humans who surround the infant provide a series of stimulus situations which are repeatedly presented to him as he grows to adulthood. These stimulus situations are, furthermore, in some respects unique to the society in which the infant is born. The infant is like the rat in the experimental box; he is confronted by ready-made stimulus situations, to which he must learn to make specific responses.

2. Culture systematically *elicits appropriate responses*. While a certain amount of an individual's behavior is learned by trial and error, nevertheless every society makes special efforts to elicit the responses which are considered appropriate to certain situations. The small child's

finger is taken out of his mouth; the baby is placed on the appropriate place for elimination; eating tools are put in its hand, and its arm is guided. When language has been established the child, and later the adult, is constantly directed to make certain appropriate responses. The particular responses desired vary from culture to culture, as does the amount and intensity of direction and elicitation, but in no society is the individual allowed to grow up discovering all of his culture by trial and error.

3. Culture, through its products or agents, provides reinforcements. Not only are the appropriate stimuli presented, and the proper responses elicited by the culture of one's society, but also a constant press of rewards and punishments operates to hasten the learning process, and to extinguish undesired habits.

Thus we may say, not only that culture *is* learned behavior; it is also a setup for *learning* behavior of very complex and specific types.

4. The culture of a society therefore *has certain self-perpetuating tendencies*, so long as the human population which manifests the culture does not die out. However, since culture is learned, and all learned behavior is subject to change correlated with changes in the stimulus and the response situations, it follows that culture also is subject to changes, which can be interpreted at least in part on the basis of the psychological principles which we have been discussing.

It should not be supposed that the psychological principles set forth in this chapter are in themselves sufficient to explain all of human cultural conduct. In later pages elaborations of these and other principles will be brought forward to establish a series of working postulates for the analysis of cultures. But the basic laws of learning and performance as here described are so fundamental to an understanding of cultural dynamics that a chapter has been devoted to their exposition in this place. It should be plain that these principles are not Behavioristic in the doctrinaire technical sense of the term. There is nothing inconsistent between them and Gestalt or Freudian psychological systems. As cultural anthropologists we have no interest in doctrinaire rivalries between psychological systems. Our concern is to use such conclusions from psychology as have been shown to be reliable and which can be incorporated into a consistent theory of culture.

NOTES TO CHAPTER 11

1. Hilgard and Marquis, 1940, p. 336.
2. *Ibid.*, pp. 29-32.
3. Gorer, 1938, p. 96.
4. Sarasin, 1893, Vol. 1, p. 408.
5. Marcel Proust in the first pages of his long novel, *Remembrance of Things Past,* gives a picture of the cue value of certain stimuli.

6. R. H. Schomburgk, 1837, p. 266.

7. E. L. Thorndike was the first to deal systematically with what is here called reinforcement; see, Thorndike, 1911, p. 244: "The greater the satisfaction or discomfort, the greater the strengthening or weakening of the bond." For a more recent statement by the same author, see, Thorndike, 1935. The principle of "substitution" in contiguity was developed by I. P. Pavlov, 1927, 1928, 1932. A somewhat different view, inevitable conditioning by substitution in simultaneous presentation of stimuli, is associated with E. R. Guthrie, 1935. For summaries of various theoretical views and experimental data on reinforcement, the reader is referred to Hilgard and Marquis, 1940, Chapter 4.

8. "Gradient of the effects of reward" is used by Miller and Dollard in essentially the same sense as C. L. Hull's original term "goal gradient"; Hull, 1932.

9. Miller and Dollard, 1941. Chapter 2.

10. Linton, 1936, p. 301.

11. Kardiner, 1945.

12. DuBois, 1944.

13. Kluckhohn, 1945, 105-106.

CHAPTER 12

Human Resources as the Raw Material of Culture

THE CONCEPT OF HUMAN RESOURCES

WE HAVE taken the position, which is shared by all authorities on the subject, that cultures and their constituent customs are learned by human beings, but we cannot let the matter stand with this simple statement if we wish to be in a position to analyze specific cultures and to assess changes in them effectively. On the basis of the general principles of learning and behavior we know that man can *learn* only what he can do, and that he does not do anything unless he *wants* something. Culture is therefore limited by the range of human capacity to make response and to be motivated by drives of certain types. This point is emphasized here because it is not uncommon to discuss culture on a higher and more abstract plane without first understanding its roots. We must make it plain that culture is actually a product of mankind and that it can contain nothing which man is incapable of producing. Thus it is that culture depends upon *human resources*, considered as basic human abilities. All cultures make a selection from among these human resources. All cultures apply human abilities to the natural resources of their situations; all cultures construct artifacts from material objects; all cultures construct mental (projective) systems attributed to the supernatural. But all of these products and activities come ultimately from the resources of the organism.

In order to make this point clearer we shall review in this and the following chapter some of the things which the people of various societies have learned to do, so that we may appreciate the basic resources of the species.

For lack of space and other considerations, we shall deal with basic human resources in a somewhat selective and partial fashion in these chapters. In considering the range of customary response, for example, we shall confine ourselves for the most part to "actional" customs, and not attempt to suggest here the range of possible human responses in "representational" and "mental" customs. These types of custom will be considered later. Also in discussing customary reactions based on fundamental drives, we shall consider only a certain group of these drives, leaving it to the reader to trace out the relation between custom and the drives of sex, elimination, response, anger, new experience, and so on.

The essential point is that anything a group of human beings can learn to do may become a part of their culture. If we look at the material in this way we may get a clearer view of the fact that culture is, after all, a product of the organism in society, and at the same time, by reviewing some of the reactions made among the various societies of mankind to basic drives, we are afforded an opportunity to see in a functional way the great variety of customs within the species.

Although the general idea that culture is limited by the response abilities of the human species has been stated, it has never been sufficiently documented to permit the setting up of precise corollaries or deductions of practical analytical or diagnostic value.[1] Likewise the variety of human customs has been a source of entertainment and amusement since the beginning of recorded history, but the diversity in the "ways of doing things" among human beings has never been systematically studied from the point of view of cultural dynamics as seen in the light of modern psychological findings concerning learned behavior.

In considering the range of response in the repertory of the human species we are interested in two aspects: limits of the range, and the variety within it. Once we knew accurately the outside limits of human performance, we should also know the limits of cultural activity (although not necessarily the limits of cultural complexity, of course), while more precise and organized knowledge of the learned or learnable responses of the species within the outside limits of the repertory would increase the soundness and value of science in all types of social and personal planning and readjustment which involve the cultural factor. Just as each language has historically made a selection, as it were, of a limited number of sounds among all those of which the human vocal apparatus is capable, so the general culture of each society, even our own, contains only a portion of the responses which the species is capable of developing into customs. Thus, when we are confronted with a custom that appears to be maladapted or inefficient, we should be able to consider the possible substitutes which we know, either from reliable reports of their practice in other societies or from experimental evidence, are part of the human stock or repertory. The response or performance potentialities of the species are the building blocks, we might say, from which cultures are constructed.

In dealing with the learned interactions, or "cultural" aspects of activity current in any social group or society, we recognize three levels of analysis. First is the pattern level, where, by abstraction or conceptualization, we may speak of a more or less integrated system of culture patterns which serve as the "plans" or "specifications," as it were, for learned social activities, and which, taken as a whole, we call the cultural system. Second, on the activity level, we find the actual customs or learned activities, overt and covert, common to the members of the group or to certain social categories within it. These activities conform, with greater or less deviation, to the patterns of the cultural system. Third, at the materialistic level, we find the artifacts, which are material products and material equipment of customs. They represent material results of the operation of customary activity on objects or substances of nature; and they may, in certain cases, serve as adjuncts to the performance of customs. In this chapter we are primarily concerned with customs themselves, which are to be regarded as socially learned, socially shared, and socially transmitted human activities.[2]

It is now generally recognized that every culture contains, among others, two outstanding types of customs: universals and specialties.[3] The universals are those customs which are common to the "run-of-the-mill" members of the societies where they are found. A universal is practised by all the normal adult members of a given society or group. Every culture also contains specialties, which are customs confined to certain selected groups or categories within the larger group or society. The bases of such social selection may vary, and certain of them may have nothing to do with innate ability to perform the specialties involved. For example, in our society each fraternal group practises specialties exclusive to itself, but the membership is chosen for social qualities, such as prestige status and congeniality, rather than for physical qualities involved in the performance of the specialties. On the other hand, it is true that many, if not all, societies tolerate or encourage the selection of some subgroups on the basis of innate abilities to perform specialized customs. Thus, for example, small men are selected as ball-turret gunners on heavy bombers, because large-bodied men literally cannot get into the cramped quarters of the ball-turret at all.[4] However, it is not entirely clear in all cases whether performability of the specialized customs is the determining factor. For example, we are usually surprised to find a short, thin man working as a blacksmith, but the fact that such individuals do in fact follow this trade seems to indicate that training can to a degree overcome what we think of as an innate physical handicap. The actual, rather than the traditional, physical requirements for many types of specialties will need to be carefully examined, if a successful adjustment is to be made for the thousands of wounded veterans of the war. This is a field for the fruitful joining of physical and cultural anthropology and psychology, which could have great practical value in job analysis, personal readjustment, and kindred problems.

In the following pages, however, we shall not emphasize customs confined only to specialties, and we shall avoid entirely performances of "freaks" or unusually talented individuals. Our object is to explore the range of customary responses which seemingly are or could be common to the members of societies in which they are found. All of the evidence of mental testing seems to indicate that learning ability is fairly equally distributed throughout the species; and, in the absence of counterevidence, we may assume for the present that a custom which has been learned by any one social group of "ordinary persons" could be learned by any other such group.

Let us now explore briefly the material available on some of these matters as it may be found in a cursory inspection of the ethnographic literature.

MUSCULAR RESPONSES

Some "unusual" muscles involved in customs. From the point of view of a North American, some of the most unusual muscular responses to become customary in any group are the exercises of the Indian cult of Yoga.[5] In the exercise of diaphragm-raising the practitioner stands with his feet a few inches apart, with trunk and knees bent a little forward, hands slightly over the knees. He exhales completely, then, raising the ribs in mock inhalation, he raises the diaphragm, causing a marked depression of the abdomen. Somewhat more difficult is voluntary vomiting. The exerciser drinks four or five glasses of water on an empty stomach, bends forward, spreads his legs, rests hands on knees, and then exhales deeply. Abdominal mucles are contracted backward and upward, then relaxed. This muscle contraction is repeated at the rate of seven or eight times per minute. With a little practice one vomits at will and cleanses the stomach of impurities. Another method of stomach-cleansing is to swallow a thick piece of cloth about twenty-two feet long and three inches wide. After the cloth is in the stomach, proceed to the diaphragm-raising exercise, interspersed with isolation and rolling of the recti-abdominis muscles. After about twenty minutes the cloth is pulled out by the free end that remains between the teeth.[6] In order to follow this procedure of cleansing the stomach, it is necessary to learn "the most important of the purifactory exercises . . . in which the two muscles, the recti-abdominis, are isolated: first together and then independently." After the diaphragm has been raised, while the practitioner is in the standing position, the portion of the abdomen above the pubic bone is dragged downward and forward by voluntary action of the abdominal muscles. If this is done, the two recti-abdominis muscles, long flat muscles extending vertically on either side along the ventral surfaces, will stand out, somewhat like cords, on either side of the upper abdomen. The next stage is a rolling manipulation, consisting of rapid contraction and relaxation of the two muscles in succession from right to left and left to right.[7] Having learned to do this, one is now able to learn not only stomach-cleansing, but also colon-washing. When the recti-abdominis muscles are isolated a partial vacuum is created in the colon, which enables water to be taken into the rectum, provided that one learns to open the anal sphincters voluntarily. For those who cannot establish voluntary control over the relaxation of the sphincters, a bamboo tube is used. A similar technique is used to wash the bladder. Apparently it is impossible to learn voluntarily to open the urethral sphincters, so that the Yoga practitioner inserts a lead, silver, or rubber tube as far as the bladder with the outer end in a bowl of water. By performing the isolation of the recti-abdominis, he draws up a half-glass of water into the bladder and retains it for about twenty minutes. Yeats-Brown also claims that followers of Yoga are trained to open the pyloric valve of the stomach voluntarily in order to pass large quantities of water rapidly through the alimentary track.[8]

Control over the anal sphincters may be established so that they may be alternately contracted and relaxed for several minutes in succession. This exercise may be combined with diaphragm-raising by relaxing the sphincters with each inhalation and contracting them with exhalation. Once complete voluntary control is established, the sphincters are opened while the abdomen is withdrawn for the diaphragm-raising exercise, so that the gases may be forced out of the lower colon. When the abdominal muscles are relaxed, the same process is repeated in order to take in fresh air from the outside.

Still another Yoga response strange to us is the tongue-rolling exercise, in which the tongue is voluntarily rolled backward and upward to cover the posterior nasal cavities leading into the pharynx at the base of the skull. This response is apparently almost beyond the range of normal human capabilities, although some learn it without surgery. The majority, however, cut the frenulum at the base of the tongue a little each week until the fibrous band is completely severed.[9]

We see from this material that it is apparently within the range of human capability to learn voluntary control over the diaphragm, several muscles of the ventral wall of the abdomen, certain of the smooth muscles of the stomach and alimentary track, the anal sphincters, and certain muscles of the tongue.

Although the skeletal architecture of the human foot is not adapted to opposability of the great toe, a considerable degree of lateral "spreading" and adduction is possible, providing voluntary control can be established over the muscles involved. Among civilized peoples wearing shoes, these muscles are almost entirely untrained. But reports of customs involving adduction of the great toe against the second toe as a grasping organ are so common in reference to primitive peoples as scarcely to require citation. For example, Man says of the Andaman Islanders that much use is made of the feet in holding and picking up light objects, and that the great toe is "opposable" (that is adductable).[10] The Maori of New Zealand "often used their toes to pick up any small article." [11] Métraux notes with respect to the Chorotí, Chulupi, and Matake of the Chaco region of South America that "the caraguata (Bromelia serra) plant is uprooted with a forked stick and the leaves are cut off with a wooden saw. The saw is held between the big and second toe and the leaf is rubbed against it." [12] From the Guiana region of Venezuela Simpson reports of the Carib Kamarakoto Indians that "women usually sew their dresses holding the cloth with the toes and pushing the needle toward themselves." [13] One of his illustrations shows a woman holding the crossbar of a small hand loom with the large and second toes of both feet. Covarrubias tells us how young girls of Bali are trained to take part in the sanghyang dedari dance of exorcism. At one point in the dance the girls, in a state of induced trance, climb on men's shoulders. Each girl maintains a standing position on the shoulders of her male partner by the grip of her "prehensile feet"; grasping the shoulders with the feet is a learned response taught to successive generations of girls.[14] The position is maintained for two or three hours at a time during the dance.

Sitting and walking postures may involve a wide variety of muscle, tendon, and joint responses, only a few of which are customary in any one culture. The painfulness of sitting on the heels in the kneeling position is familiar to Americans who have attempted to maintain this customary Japanese sitting posture for an extended period. Among the Maori the men usually sat in a cross-legged posture, while the women sat on the buttocks with the feet turned to one side in a position most uncomfortable for Europeans. The girls were taught to walk in an awkward-looking, loose-jointed manner, swaying from the hips, while the men practised a loose, shuffling walk. When working with anything on or close to the ground, the Maori customarily squatted on the heels, with the soles of the feet planted on the ground. Weeding of gardens was carried on in this position hour after hour, and even now, with the introduction of steel spades, the posture is used, and the muscular patterns of the arms are adapted to it, resulting in the spade customarily being thrust into the soil at a low rather than at a right angle. When camping out in wet weather, the Maori did not lie down, and learned even to sleep in the sitting posture, or at least to doze.[15]

With respect to arm responses, in Bali, for example, double-jointedness of the upper members is highly valued in dancers, with the result that the young candidate "exercises constantly to acquire suppleness of every muscle and control over each member."[16]

In the carrying of loads, a variety of muscle groups not employed in our own customs are put to use in certain other societies. Muscle groups in the neck may be trained for balancing heavy loads carried on top of the head, as is the custom among many Negro societies of Africa and among the Indians of Central America observed by myself and numerous others. This custom, by the way, has the virtue of leaving the arms free for work of other kinds. Muscles of the neck and of the chest may be trained to assist in carrying heavy loads resting against the back when a tumpline passing over the forehead is used. This custom is widespread among forest Indians in both North and South America and has been adapted by certain services of the United States Army. This writer has seen loads of up to 250 pounds carried several miles in this fashion.

In this brief review we have caught some glimpse of the variety and range of human muscular responses which can be elicited and learned as parts of culture. So far this intriguing subject has not been systematically studied. We do not know specifically what are the limits of muscular response which the members of a normal human society can learn. It seems improbable that the ordinary man can develop the versatility of Charles Warren, the "Yankee Dishrag," who could make dozens of muscles act separately. He could throw into energetic single action the biceps, the supinator longus, the radial extensors, the platysma myoides, and others. He could make his sartorius muscle show as a tight cord extending from the front of the iliac spine to the inner side of his knee. He could leave flaccid that part of the serratus magnus attached to the interior angle of the scapula while contracting the scapulae projected as in a luxation of the scapula. He was also able to contract the abdominal muscles so that the aorta could be felt with the fingers and could produce a bogus abdominal "tumor'" by driving the coils of the intestine within the grasp of his rectus and oblique abdominal muscles. He could dislocate nearly every joint in the body, easily contract at will both pillars of the faces, contract his chest to 34 inches and expand it to 41 inches. Warren was a plain looking man weighing 150 pounds and was the father of two children. The ordinary man probably lacks the innate ability to perform all these feats; yet his range of potential performance is undoubtedly wide, which is the point in which we are interested here.[17]

Efficiency of muscular customs. Physiologists tell us that in man the efficiency with which muscular work is performed is about 20 per cent.[18] Of the total energy which may be derived during muscular effort from the oxidation of stored fuel in the human body, only about one-fifth is converted into useful mechanical energy: the remainder is dissipated as heat. Generally speaking, then, it would appear that the most efficient cultures would be those involving only muscular habits which utilize that one-fifth most economically, that is, those which achieve the desired goals with the least expenditure of energy per unit of work performed. This again is a subject which has never been systematically investigated on a comparative basis, and it should be a worth-while research lead. But we must point out that its elucidation involves not only careful measurement of muscular patterns and metabolism, but also a precise study of the goals and motivations of muscular effort in the various societies of mankind, as well as a careful analysis of diets.

In our own society perhaps the most systematic work involving the relation of muscular responses and cultural patterns is that which has been carried on under the name of Motion Study, as a technique for increasing industrial efficiency.[19] Principles governing patterns of efficiency in the use of various parts of the body have been worked out, and they represent an effort of applied science to discover and introduce more efficient customary muscular patterns in certain industrial operations. For example, Barnes [20] states that the Principles of Motion Economy cover (1) the use of the human body, (2) arrangement of the work place, and (3) design of tools and equipment. The latter two aspects have to do with cultural equipment, but as regards muscular patterns it may be of interest to list Barnes' principles covering the "use of the human body" in bench work concerned with packaging, small mechanical assemblies, and so forth. (1) The two hands should begin as well as complete their cycles or part-cycles of work ("therbligs") at the same instant. (2) The two hands should not be idle at the same instant except during rest periods. (3) Motions of the arms should be made in opposite and symmetrical directions, and should be made simultaneously. (4) Hand motions should be confined to the lowest classification, (that is, use of the fewest muscles) with which it is possible to perform the work satisfactorily. (5) Momentum should be used to assist the workers wherever possible. (6) Continuous curved motions are preferable to straight-line motions involving sudden and sharp changes in direction. (7) Ballistic movements are easier and more efficient than fixation or controlled movements. "Fixation movements" are those which employ two groups of muscles, one of which is positive to the action, the other opposing and controlling it, as in non-Spencerian handwriting. "Ballistic" movement, on the other hand, is characterized by the contraction of one muscle group which starts the movement, then relaxes, as in swinging a pitch fork. The latter type of motion, if properly performed, is less tiring upon repetition, because fewer muscles are used and those in action are not kept continuously flexed throughout. Finally, (8) work should be arranged to permit rhythm of movement, as it is essential to the smooth and automatic performance of an operation. Although industrial engineers have found these principles to apply to the easing and increase in efficiency of work, they do not claim them to be all-inclusive. Says Barnes, "additional research which will enlarge our knowledge of the inherent capacities of the various members of the human body is greatly needed." [21] More efficient coördination of cultural equipment with muscular customs may also be achieved as illustrated, for example, by ruling out "one hand to hold" through the use of work-holding pigs and by positioning tools directly over the work where they may be reached with the least expenditure of energy and time. [22]

Another illustration is the investigation of Hoke on typewriting efficiency. [23] According to this study, the arrangement of the keys on the typewriter should be based on the inherent capacities of the fingers. Hoke says that the ability of the right hand compared with that of the left in typewriting is as 100 to 88.8. The first and second fingers of the right hand should carry the greatest load, and the fourth finger of the left hand the smallest. The present typewriter is poorly designed in view of these facts, because it places a load of 100 on the right hand and 131.25 on the left hand, overloading the left hand 47.7 per cent. This is an example of incompatibility, as between the human and artifactual components (see Chapter 10).

It is tempting to oversimplify the matter of muscle customs and to pass to the conclusion that cultures may be rated solely on the basis of the efficiency of such customs; that is the "best" culture is the one which has the most efficient muscle customs in the terms we have discussed. The comparison and evaluation of such customs, however, must also involve consideration of goals and motivations common to the society, as well as individual personality structures. It is perhaps more efficient to take morphine by hypodermic injection than by mouth, but the result achieved by either method is undesirable, on physiological grounds alone, if widespread throughout a society otherwise healthy. The efficiency patterns instilled in workers by industrial engineers become socially undesirable if they result in unfair exploitation of the workers by another group or in personal maladjustment.

Nevertheless, it is clear that customs involving muscular response may be combined in a great variety of ways for the achievement of goals considered socially and personally desirable and that our species is capable of many muscular customs which we have never thought of developing in our own culture. If we knew the human repertory more systematically, we should be in a position to make readjustments in various areas of customary activity where maladjustment or maladaptation of the existing customs creates social and personal problems.

NEEDS, DRIVES, AND RESPONSES

Another way to approach the question of human responses and their relation to culture is to consider them in connection with the motivations or drives common to the species. Perhaps any one who ventures into this field, especially an anthropologist, runs the risk of controversy, because psychologists themselves are not fully agreed upon terms and concepts. Nevertheless, if the valuable discoveries of experimental psychology are ever to be transferred from the rat laboratory to the level of cultural analysis, a start must be made sometime.

A considerable area of agreement seems to exist with respect to certain needs of the species for survival and health. Also, with regard to learned behavior, all authorities agree that the human organism, in common with all others, acts only when motivated by a drive of one sort or another, and that it maintains its learned reactions (habits, customs) only when such responses have the effect of lowering drive. In man there may be some drives which, when aroused, motivate unlearned activity which is nevertheless correct and goal-oriented (for example, "partial hungers").[24] But even in such cases the alleged hereditary response pattern may be modified by experience and training. Many another state of drive tension motivates only random activity until the individual happens to hit upon the correct rewarding response or is led to do so by teaching. In short, correct responses must in perhaps the majority of cases be learned by human beings. Since man is a generalized animal, more than one type of response may be satisfying to a given drive, and, therefore, learned responses may vary throughout the species.

It seems to be one of the functions of culture to provide patterns of response ready-made, and it is one of the functions of society, through its surrogates, to teach these patterns to newcomers, either by instruction or channelized experience. In this way the losses incident to random and trial-and-error behavior are reduced, and the functional efficiency of both the individual and of the society is enhanced.

Two general types of drives have been discussed in Chapter 11, namely basic or primary drives, and secondary or acquired drives.

It is clear that the concept of drive does not necessarily coincide with the concept of need. Thus, although there is no evidence of a species need for the inhalation of tobacco smoke, and various societies have existed for generations without it, it is well known that in our own society this acquired drive will motivate millions of individuals to exert effort to satisfy it, not to mention a whole set of other customs, which we call the tobacco complex and which are designed to satisfy this drive.

Customs are socially shared habits for the satisfaction of drives, but we are quite unable to say that all drives involved in human customs are based upon biological needs. On the contrary, it is evident that many acquired drives motivating the performance of customs are or may be opposed to biological needs in the primary sense. The satisfaction of an appetite for certain drugs often leads the individual to ill health and premature death. Customs of birth control associated, it may be, with an acquired desire for prestige, may result in the failure of the middle classes of our own society to reproduce themselves. Desire for prestige, sometimes combined with fear of discipline (anxiety) motivates soldiers to heroic but fatal deeds in battle.

Although the basic or primary drives may be overlaid and disguised by secondary drives, they apparently cannot be either suppressed completely or ignored in any society. Some kind of response must be made by every society to the pressure of the basic physiological drives. Also, each society must practise certain customs which are at least minimally satisfying to biological needs, or suffer the alternative of biological extinction. In those cases in which the customs are not fatal biologically, but still fall short of biological adequacy, we may expect the society to pay a cost or penalty in terms of illness, weakness, or other forms of physical inefficiency.

Let us now turn to a consideration of the range of customs which have been developed for the satisfaction of certain basic drives. We shall begin with a consideration of hunger.

HUNGER

Physiological psychology of hunger. In considering the relation of hunger and the other innate drives to the building of cultures we shall have to mention a few elementary facts from physiology, but such physiological considerations will be limited on the whole to data which appear to be of significance in habit and custom formation. It must be borne in mind that physiological knowledge of the needs and requirements of the human body is a relatively recent discovery in our own culture and that new findings in this field are constantly coming forth from research laboratories. Systematic field investigation based upon these findings in other societies has barely begun, so that we are at present far from being able to deal exhaustively with the nature of and reaction to physiological needs as they are manifested in the various cultures of mankind. The theoretical and practical importance of such an extension of knowledge is so great, however, that we shall discuss some of the data at hand for their suggestive value.

Physiological needs for nourishment. The physiological objectives of nourishment may be summarized under three heads. First, the fuel requirements of the body must be met to compensate for the constant oxidation and consequent loss of heat which mammalian living entails. The loss of energy in the form of heat varies from 2,000 to 4,000 calories per day for white adults, depending upon the type of activity in which the individual engages. As a rough average the fuel requirements of the white adult are estimated at about 3,000 calories per day.[25] In connection with hunger, we note that fuel in the form of food must be supplied to maintain the constant loss caused by oxidation. Carbohydrates (including starches and sugars) are the principal fuels used by the human body anywhere.

The second requirement is for protein, which seems to be necessary for the repair of body structures as well as for maintaining the normal colloidal composition of the blood.[26] Although the demands for protein are less heavy than those for carbohydrates, physiologists now believe that for an adult (in our society, at least) an average of 100 grams per day or 1.5 grams per kilogram of body weight is close to the minimum necessary for full health and vigor.[27]

Thirdly, the body requires a variety of minerals and vitamins in order to maintain full or adequate functioning. For example, the minimum daily requirement for adults for iron is 0.015 gram; for calcium, 0.45 gram; for phosphorus, 0.86 gram; for salt, 2 grams, and so forth.[28] Various bodily malfunctions result from deficiency of any of these substances. For example, the normal calcium content of the blood is about 10 milligrams per cent (10 milligrams to each 100 cubic centimeters of blood). If this concentration is seriously lowered, twitchings and convulsive movements appear, with full convulsions or collapse as the solution falls toward 5 milligrams per cent. On the other hand, if the concentration of calcium is increased above normal, the phosphate and nitrogen content of the blood is increased and the blood becomes so viscous that it will scarcely circulate. Calcium deficiency also results in long-range malformations and diseases of the bones and teeth, because the body draws upon the calcium stores in these structures to maintain homeostasis of the blood.[29] Lack of iodine, to mention another example, results in unbalance of the endocrine system with hypertrophy of the thyroid gland (that is, goiter) as one of the more familiar results. Marett has dealt extensively with the question of mineral deficiencies and has advanced a theory that the evolution of the species as well as certain cultural peculiarities of European history are to be correlated with mineral resources available at various times and places.[30]

Vitamin intake is likewise essential to the normal performance of many bodily functions, and for proper assimilation of other food substances. For example, vitamin D facilitates the absorption of calcium in the intestines and its storage in the trabeculae of the bones. Lack of vitamin A results in impaired vision and night blindness. Exposure of the retina to light produces a chemical change involving the bleaching of the visual purple. Before sensitivity can be restored, this pigment, which is structurally related to vitamin A, must be replaced. Vitamin A is also essential in maintaining the structural integrity of the epithelial cells, for without it these cells are replaced by stratified keratinized epithelium; in other words, lesions and deteriorated areas appear on the skin and mucous membranes. Vitamin A is formed from carotene, a substance associated with the green chlorophyll of plants, and is converted to the vitamin in the human liver.[31] Without going into details, we may mention that the minimum average daily requirements for vitamins in white adults are estimated as follows: vitamin A, 3,000 U.S.P. units; B$_1$, 200 International units; B$_2$ or G, 600 Sherman-Bourquin units; C, 400 International units; D, 135 U.S.P. units.[32] For further details the reader is referred to the standard works. It should be clear, however, that if requirements of this sort are physiologically necessary for the healthy functioning of the human animal, each society must inculcate customs which satisfy these needs, or pay the price of failure to do so in lost efficiency, lowered health, or eventual extinction.

Physiological needs and hunger drive. Many of the required substances may be stored in some form in the body, but an average daily intake of the quantities indicated seems to be required to maintain normal functioning and homeostasis. Deficiency within certain limits of any or all of these requirements is not always, nor very often, directly fatal to the individual or the population, but deficiency always results in some impairment of structure or function which must be compensated in one way or another. Thus, prolonged deficiency in energy-producing foods results progressively in loss of weight, emaciation, and decline in strength and ability to carry on activity. It is interesting to note that the internal economy of the body is such that the tissues of the brain and nervous system seem to be "starved" last of all, and that they may continue functioning long after the muscular and bony structures have deteriorated because of malnutrition.[33] Does this fact have any bearing upon the characteristic philosophical orientation of Hindu Indian culture, for example?

At all events, it appears that we may deduce from these facts of physiology the theorem that any culture that does not or cannot (perhaps because of environmental limitations) supply the nutritional requirements of its population will inevitably contain other patterns correlated with the nutritional patterns and compensating for them either in the form of decreased acivity or of activity of a restricted type.

In building customs, however, the members of human societies are motivated by psychological drives rather than by physiological needs. The complete physiology of the hunger drive is still obscure. Cannon pointed out that generalized hunger was made manifest to the organism by localized sensations of emptiness, dull and acute pain in the epigastrium, accompanied by periodic contractions of the stomach muscles which may progressively reach the stage of gastric spasm.[34] Recent evidence indicates, however, that the neural mechanisms of the stomach itself may not be the only factors, or even the crucial ones, at least in rats. Tsang concluded that hunger drive is present in rats even after the bulk of the stomach had been excised,[35] while Bash demonstrated that hunger drive persisted in rats after the stomach had been isolated from the central nervous system by the destruction of the vagi and splanchi nerves, concluding that "under certain conditions, after gastric sensations have been abolished, the hunger drive is maintained in undiminished strength by some biological process in which afferent neural impulses from the stomach play no part." [36] And in another paper he concludes that hunger must operate through a chemical reflex mechanism.[37] Young, on the other hand, is inclined to see no generalized hunger drive, but, rather, a complex of "partial hungers." [38] These he believes to be innate to the species (of rats, at least). In rats, he maintains, there is at present sound experimental evidence for the existence of at least ten independently variable partial hungers: those for protein fat, carbohydrate, water, oxygen, salt, phosphorus, sodium, calcium, and some factor in the vitamin B complex. "It is reasonable to assume," he concludes, "that if all partial hungers were satisfied, there would be no general hunger factor left over." And he points out in support of his view that experimental animals will continue eating some other food after they have been satiated on one food.[39] Also supporting this view, "it is well established that animals, including the human infant, if given a free choice among the components of an adequate diet, select proportions of fat, protein, carbohydrate, minerals, vitamins, and water which lead to normal growth and to the maintenance of health." [40] The implication seems to be that any animal, including man, will satisfy its dietary needs, "if given a chance."

For human beings in society, however, the opportunity for free selection may be limited by the environment or by the culture, or both. And, as a result of cultural training, members of a society may, and often do, learn to seek certain food objects and to avoid others, regardless of the requirements of a balanced diet.[41]

The ethnographic literature is by no means clear on the question of innate "partial hungers." The subject needs to be investigated further in the field, for there are not a few reports of cultures which have no patterns based on a desire for salt, for example. Osgood states that among the Tanaina, an Athabascan tribe of Alaska, "no salt is ever used." [42] Rochefort, an early reporter on the Island Carib, declares that those Indians regarded salt as contrary to health and, instead, peppered everything.[43] Stefansson reports that the Eskimo of his acquaintance regarded the taste for salt an acquired desire, similar to the desire for tobacco, and that, because they never taught their children to eat salt, Eskimo adults did not use it. Stefansson claims that he himself was able to "break himself" of the desire after several weeks on a fish and water diet.[44]

In her survey of the use of salt among North American Indian tribes, Hunter [45] found an apparent tendency for those tribes which aboriginally subsisted primarily on meat and fish to omit the use of salt as a condiment, whereas the predominantly horticultural peoples tended to add salt to their diet. Although there are a fair number of exceptions to these tendencies, Hunter explains the matter by the view that meat-eating peoples obtain sufficient salt in the blood and tissues of the animals they eat so that they have neither need nor desire for it as a condiment, whereas some peoples who are predominantly eaters of vegetable products obtain insufficient quantities of salt in their diet and feel a desire for its addition. Among the North American tribes who apparently did not use salt as a distinguishable article of diet and in whose cultures there were no customs based on a desire for salt are the following: the Penobscot, Menomini, Chippewa, Klamath, Kutchin, Tanaina, Coast Salish of Canada, Puget Sound Indians, Tahltan, Beaver Indians, Dog-Rib, Chipewyan, Tête de Boule, Beothuk, Karankawa, Lower Californians, Hupa, Achomawi, Ta'no'm, Wailaki; the Chichimec, Othomi, and Athabascan groups of Northern Mexico; the Crow, Blackfoot, Nez Percé, Mandan (?), Cherokee, Choctaw, Mohegan of Connecticut, and Iroquois.

The evidence is not clear as to innate "partial hungers," but the presence of diverse patterns based upon apparently acquired drives or appetites is quite apparent. Several of the authors speak of condiments which were used as "substitutes for salt." The Iroquois, for example, used maple syrup on their meat "instead of salt". Ashes were used by the Huron and other tribes to lend flavor to their food. Neither maple syrup nor ashes of ordinary non-salt-producing plants would supply the physiological need for salt, although ashes, of course, produce a sensation somewhat akin to salt in the mouth.

On the other hand, there are numerous reports from other peoples who show themselves ravenous for salt. If it is in fact true that salt-hunger is an innate drive (as distinguished from need) it may prove to be true, on investigation, that the dietary customs of certain cultures are so satisfying to the psysiological need that the drive is never raised to the point where it becomes motivating to the members of the society. More data are needed.

There is still another way of looking at responses based on hunger drive, namely, in terms of the differential satiety values of various articles of food. McLester [46] tells us that the satiety value of an article of diet may be measured in terms of (1) the length of time the food remains in the stomach in the process of digestion, and (2) the amount of gastric juice which it stimulates. Thus it is possible to achieve a sensation of "fulness" or satiety without necessarily having eaten a very nourishing meal. For example, the Bemba of Northern Rhodesia depend primarily upon a sort of mush made from millet meal, which they bolt down in large lumps without chewing. According to their view, one feels unsatisfied unless there is a sensation of tension and bloating in the abdomen after a meal. The bolting of coarse, unchewed mush produces this satisfying feeling apparently because it fulfils requirement No. 1 (above) for satiety value. Yet, according to Richards, the average calorie intake per man per day among the Bemba is only about 1,706, just over half of that considered necessary for a normal adult of moderate activity. [47]

On the other hand, meat possesses a high satiety value by virtue of fulfilling requirement No. 2; it stimulates a large gastric secretion in proportion to its bulk and hence it is said, in our culture, to "stick to the ribs." Fat and sugar both increase the satiety value of a food for the reason that they remain long in the stomach and are slow in digesting.

Thus the eating habits of the individual and of the society may in one way or another lower the hunger drive without supplying all the necessary requirements of the body for full health and efficiency. Whatever future research may show to be the precise physiological nature of the hunger drive or drives, it seems to be clear that men learn and develop customs based upon motivations which are lowered only by the introduction of *something* into the alimentary track.

Cultural responses to hunger and appetite drives. The natural human response to hunger is, of course, the introduction of something into the stomach. But eating customs usually consist of introducing certain substances into the alimentary tract (that is, making specific responses to specific categories of stimuli). For eating habits there seem to be two types of satisfaction or reinforcement, immediate and long-run. Immediate satisfaction is obtained by remission of the uneasiness, craving, stomach cramps, and other symptoms of hunger. But to be actually satisfying in the long run, it would seem that eating habits or customs, must also banish feelings of weakness, lassitude, and discomfort which are the ultimate aftermath of undernutrition. The establishment of eating customs and their maintenance, therefore, would seem to depend upon their ability to provide an immediate feeling of satiety, plus their action in reducing or preventing the rise of fatigue due to insufficient nourishment. It seems, however, that direct satisfaction of hunger or appetite is much more reinforcing than the effect of lowering fatigue drive, on the principle that delayed reinforcement is less effective than immediate reinforcement. It is possible that fatigue drive motivates customs involving energy intake, but it is doubtful that fatigue is directly or automatically motivating for customs involving certain mineral and vitamin intakes. Deficiencies in the latter eventually produce lassitude and fatigue, but their results are on the whole slow and cumulative in appearance and disappearance. Proper responses to mineral and vitamin deficiency are, therefore, not immediately rewarding in many cases. Hence the operation of fatigue drive as a psychological motivation in building physiologically proper mineral and vitamin habits and customs is usually quite indirect and must be mediated by intermediate, acquired motivations of one sort or another. The child, for example, may be motivated to drink his cod-liver oil by combining it with candy (which is directly rewarding to appetite), or by coddling, patting, or other immediate rewards.

Some species of leaf-eating caterpillars are said to be restricted in their diet to the under part of a leaf of a certain plant, while other species live on the upper surface of the same type of leaf.[48] In contrast to such species specialization, man as a species is extremely omnivorous. It seems that any substance which is mechanically capable of being swallowed (not too large, too rough, and so forth) and which does not immediately arouse pain drive (as do strong acids, lacerating substances, and certain quick-acting poisons) will, in suitable quantities, lower the hunger drive (or some acquired drive based on it), if introduced into the stomach. All such substances, in other words, which are not lethally or painfully poisonous may become cultural equipment associated with eating customs, for almost anything else can be reduced to the proper size and consistency for passage into the stomach.

Variety in food customs. To obtain some idea of how these principles actually affect culture, let us examine a few more or less extreme examples of customary foodstuffs, taken at random from the literature. The Vedda of Ceylon eat no less than five kinds of rotted wood, usually garnished with honey, bark, leaves, and fruits.[49] Among some of the Guiana tribes, green-heart seeds, which are woody in consistency, were grated, soaked, and "mixed with rotted wood, pounded previously and sifted" at those times of the year when cassava bread was scarce.[50] A number of cases are on record from the sixteenth and seventeenth centuries of peoples who had formed the habit of eating small pebbles after each meal,[51] and, to quote Gould and Pyle, "it has frequently been stated that the peasants of Styria are in the habit of taking from two to five grains of arsenious acid [arsenic] daily for the purpose of improving the health, avoiding infections, and raising the whole tone of the body. It is a well-substantiated fact that the quantities taken habitually are quite sufficient to produce immediate death ordinarily." [52]

Clay- and earth-eating is customary among various peoples, sometimes, at least, motivated by an actively felt desire or drive. Among the Issa-Japura tribes of Amazonia (mainly the Boro and Witoto), for instance, the desire for clay although regarded with disfavor in the culture, nevertheless is said to amount to an unconquerable craving, and if the clay cannot otherwise be obtained, it will be scraped from under the fireplace and eaten in secret. Possibly this is a response to a physiologic mineral need.[53] Schoolboys in Morocco eat potter's earth regularly before breakfast in the belief that they thereby learn their lessons better.[54] Dickens and Ford made a study of the widespread custom of clay-eating among the Negroes of Mississippi. The practice is also found among whites of this region, but is not so prevalent. By means of "hidden question" tests of statistical reliability, they found that 25 per cent of a random sample of 207 Negro school children had "eaten dirt" at least twice in a period of sixteen days. Clay soils only were used, free from sand, and of a reddish brown color. "Reasons given for eating dirt were: it is good for you; tastes good, rather sour, like a lemon; helps women who are pregnant; and tastes good if put in the chimney and smoked first." The notion that people crave dirt is common. They get to the place where they feel that they must have clay to eat. One hears, too, that dirt is carried long distances to people who can no longer get it themselves.[55] The authors conclude that "dirt eating is simply a culture trait like dipping snuff or smoking," although they think it may be related to an iron-deficient diet. More investigation is needed, because simply calling a practice a culture trait does not explain it.

Miss Hilda Hertz, formerly of Duke University, has, under the writer's direction, gathered some material on earth-eating among Negro informants in Durham, N.C. With her permission I quote a few passages from one of her informant's statements:

It tastes good, but only if you can find good dirt. Around here [Durham, N.C.] I haven't had any good dirt. Good dirt is red clay and comes in big, large lumps. . . . Laundry starch tastes much like good dirt, but is not quite so good. A good many people eat it instead of dirt. I learned to eat dirt when I was very small. My mother eats it, but not my father. His family does not eat dirt, but my mother's family does.

Of ten North Carolina Negro earth-eaters who comprised Miss Hertz's informants, six habitually ate laundry starch as a substitute when dirt was unobtainable or when in fear of disapproval. At least three of this group seem to have developed a starch appetite which displaced their former dirt appetite. To date, samples of the dirt eaten by Miss Hertz's subjects have not been chemically analyzed, so that we are unable to discuss the possibility that the practice of eating it is a response to an innate "partial hunger." This may well be a factor in the custom, but the evidence seems to indicate that the important factor is the presence of an acquired appetite (acquired drive) developed through training or experience. The fact that the subject's mother comes from a family of "dirt-eaters," whereas her father does not and has not himself acquired the custom is significant. Also it is significant that starch-eating may displace earth-eating, for it is apparent that the chemical composition of laundry starch has nothing in common with that of red clay and presumably would not satisfy the same physiological need. The similarity between the two substances seems to reside in the tactile sensation produced in the mouth, and one is led to believe that the craving, in such a case at least, is predominantly acquired rather than innate, although strictly physiological factors cannot be entirely ruled out.

Clay-eating was also a well-established trait among the ancient Peruvians. Here it may represent a trial-and-error cultural discovery based upon its medicinal value. Cobo reports also that "its powders, which are bland and loving, put on piles, are useful for drying them and consuming them, and mixed with vinegar and the sap of the *membrillo* (quince tree) are used to stop bloody stools." [56] Lawson and Moon [57] report that the modern Quechua Indians near Puno subsist mainly upon potatoes which are dipped before eating in an aqueous suspension of clay which they say "prevents souring of the stomach." They report that the clay is mostly kaolin, and remark that this substance is used pharmaceutically in modern medicine as a protective agent for gastric and intestinal mucosa and as a remedy for bacterial infection of the gut. The chemical composition of this edible clay of the Peruvian highlands is given by Paz Soldán as: silica, 54.4 per cent; aluminum, 23.4 per cent; peroxide of iron, 6 per cent; lime, 2.8 per cent; magnesia, 1.58 per cent; potassium, magnesium, traces; water, 10.5 per cent.[58]

Earth-eating in one form or another has been widely reported in the Amazonian and Guiana country.[59]

Judging by the number of societies which do so, it seems to be well established that members of the human species can be trained to tolerate and even to prefer putrefied food. It has been suggested that this may be a means of obtaining vitamins, as it is well known that the bacteria of putrefaction manufacture vitamin B_1, for example. So long as toxin-producing organisms are not present in the putrefaction, no harm is done to the consumer. We may cite a few examples of the customary consumption of putrefied food.

The primitive Vedda of Ceylon "have . . . a decided preference for their game 'high'— if so mild a term can describe the exceedingly advanced condition." [60] The Lepchas of Sikkim "prefer their meat high, but not maggoty." [61] Certain tribes of the Northwest Coast savored a form of systematically rotted fish, among them the Tanaina, who "preserve silver salmon for winter use by burying them during August in a hole dug in the ground five or six feet deep. . . . First, they put a layer of grass on the bottom of the hole, then a layer of silver salmon from which the viscera have been removed, then another layer of grass, then a layer of fish eggs, and again a layer of grass. . . . The fish become a little rotten but the eggs act as salt and the grass keeps them from freezing in a mass." [62] Referring to the North American Indians in general, an authoritative source says, "in many cases both animal and vegetable substances advanced toward putrefaction were preferred, as salmon eggs which were stored in sand, by the Alaskans, and immature corn in the ear which the Hurons are said to have soaked in water until it became putrid." [63] In Central America the Miskito and Sumu Indians of Nicaragua eat birds' eggs, "even when they are practically rotten." [64] These tribes also make two types of ensilage by burying green bananas or palm fruit, or sinking them in water. These products "have a very offensive odor, which may be smelled from a great distance," but nevertheless they serve as staple foods during parts of the year.[65] The Eskimo are perhaps better known for their relish of decayed food products. The Polar Eskimo eat decayed birds, feathers, flesh, and all, which have been cached and prepared for this purpose; [66] and Stefansson says that the August catch of fish among the Central group with which he lived is "out-right rotten" by the time it is eaten. He says that it is quite possible for white men to develop a desire for this mess and remarks of our society that "while it is good form to eat decayed milk products and decayed game, it is very bad form to eat decayed fish." [67] Among the Bemba of Africa "every item of a killed beast is devoured down to the ultimate entrail, in whatever state of decay. Small shreds of flesh are dried over the fire and lovingly stored in a corner of the owner's hut, whatever the smell." [68]

Although human groups may live on meat and/or fish alone, or on a combination of meat and dairy products, it appears that there are no societies which subsist upon a starch diet alone, which is apparently a response to the human requirement for protein.[69] The researches of certain societies as to the edibility of various animal species have resulted in eating customs involving animals of a considerable variety. Let us briefly consider only insects, vermin, and reptiles. The Issa-Japura Indians eat monkeys (sometimes with the hair), frogs, iguanas, and head lice. With respect to the latter, "a scurf comb is a most important present, and to comb your neighbor's hair and eat the 'bag' an honour and a luxury. They will also eat the grubs of wasps and bees, and in fact any larvae." [70] According to Cobo, one of our most reliable informants on Peru of the Conquest period, the Indians there ate lice "as if they were grains of sesame or candied anis." [71] Lice, incidentally, were collected as a form of tribute. The Incas "obligated Indians who could not work at ordinary tasks because of age, infirmity, etc., so that they should not be lazy, to collect such lice as they found on themselves or other persons and to pay them as tribute; also Indians who had no other goods to pay." [72] The present writer has observed the eating of lice among the Barama River Caribs of British Guiana. Says Castner of the Indians of Alaska, "I noticed one old medicine man without covering, catching mosquitoes and eating them. This they all do with the vermin they catch on each other's heads and bodies." [73] Among the Buganda of East Africa, "white ants are eaten alive or cooked. When eaten alive, the two wings are firmly grasped and the body is popped into the mouth. . . . When the ants are to be cooked, they are put into the pot alive, cooked, taken out, put into a leaf bundle, then cooked again with matoke. . . . Served either whole . . . or else dried in the sun and then pounded and mixed with salt or butter." [74]

The people of the Lepcha village of Pantoong are reported to have been serpent eaters; they would stone a snake, cut off the head, and eat the body raw. Most Lepchas habitually eat dead domestic animals and carrion found in the forest, when available.[75] "Frogs were much appreciated by the Incas, for their delicate flesh; and in the towns where there were no live ones, they ate them dried." [76] At the present time, small lizards are hunted on the coast of Peru and eaten fresh or dried, not only by Indians but also by the Creoles. They may usually be obtained in dried bundles in the public markets.[77] A paste made from the eggs laid by a certain kind of fly on the lakes is still extensively eaten in Mexico, and was a standard article of diet among the Aztecs.[78]

Cannibalism may be based on a variety of motivations, but among certain tribes in South America, Melanesia, and Africa, the custom of man-eating seems to be a method of satisfying a specific acquired appetite. Also, as Whiffen states for the Issa-Japura tribes, "it is possible that the salt in human blood may be one of the unrealized attractions that lead these people to anthropophagous habits." [79] That actual food cannibalism, regardless of religious or other types of cultural motivation, can become a cultural complex is supported by ample evidence, particularly from Melanesia and Africa.[80] For example, in New Britain human flesh was eaten and sold in butcher shops or markets.[81] Among the Ba-Huana of Africa cannibalism is said to be confined to men, but is general to the sex. It cannot be "ascribed to a craving for animal food, since game is plentiful in the Ba-Huana country. It is, in fact, due to a sincere liking for human flesh, of which the natives are in no way ashamed. . . . No special ceremonies are observed in connection with cannibalism, and the flesh is prepared and boiled in the same fashion as any other meat." [82] Cannibalism can also be motivated by other acquired cultural drives, such as the desire to gain prestige by eating an enemy, desire to honor a relative by eating a part of his body or bones, desire to gain supernatural power through magical ingestion of human flesh, and the like, but, as we have seen, it is possible for a society to inculcate in its members an appetite (acquired drive) for human flesh as such.

From the point of view of species survival, the ability of man to obtain nourishment from so wide a variety of items and "to learn to like almost anything" has been a great advantage, for these abilities have enabled man to live in environments where more specialized animals starve.

The discovery that healthy human beings can subsist entirely on a diet of animal products has been made by several societies (for instance, Eskimo: meat, fish; certain Mongol tribes of Central Asia: meat, products of horse milk). The arctic explorer Stefansson was perhaps the first to make this clear to our own society on the basis of his observations among the Eskimo and on an experimental basis. He and another man of white stock lived on an exclusive meat diet for a year. Beyond a diminished tolerance for carbohydrate, attributed to lack of the usual dextrose stimulus, these men showed no significant changes in blood, urine, or kidney functions, and no evidence of vitamin deficiency.[83] Nor are any of these difficulties reported for Eskimo living on an aboriginal meat diet. In fact, Price claims that the native dietary of the Eskimo is much more nutritional than the white dietary which displaces it, at least in Alaska. He says that the native Eskimo diet provides 5.4 times as much calcium as the white régime, 5 times the phosphorus, 1.5 times the iron. 7.9 times the magnesium, 1.8 times the copper, 49 times the iodine, and 10 times the soluble vitamins.[84]

Apparently foods from animal sources are more completely digested and utilized by the human organism than vegetable foods. According to McLester, the coefficients for digestibility are as follows: for protein from animals, 97 per cent, from plants 95 per cent; for fat from animals, 95 per cent, from plants, 90 per cent; for carbohydrate from animals, 98 per cent, from plants, 97 per cent.[85]

Price states that a certain amount of meat is required in all diets and explains this by the fact that the human body does not synthesize vitamin D, which must be obtained from animal tissues.[86] In general, he believes that modern "civilized" diet causes tooth decay, narrowing and con-triction of the jaws and dental arches, and physical, mental, and moral degeneration. His views need to be tested by further research along the lines on which he has made so excellent a beginning.

How far can hunger be resisted? Hunger, or appetite associated with it, seems to be a drive which rises periodically, in our society at least, and which seemingly must be satisfied to some extent three times a day. Is this characteristic of the species? It is obvious, even in ordinary experi-ence, that one can fast for various longer periods of time without per-manent damage. How long can a human being be trained to withstand hunger "as a regular thing" and still continue to function as a member of society? In many circumstances, such as traveling and nomadic life, it would obviously be an advantage if men could develop the custom of eating, say, only once in three days, for thereby they could feed at established settlements and save the energy and inconvenience of carrying supplies with them.

There is probably no absolute period of time at the end of which food deprivation becomes lethal. Survival depends to a large extent upon the amount of stored bodily energy the individual possesses at the start of the fast. One of the longest non-fatal fasts on record is that of Merlatte of Paris, who fasted for 50 days. Succi on the fortieth day of his fast had lost 25 per cent of his weight. Terence MacSwiney, Mayor of Cork, ended a hunger strike of 74 days in 1920 by death in a coma. Even in prolonged starvation, brain and heart lose only 3 to 4 per cent of their weight.[87]

Although no cultural system includes patterns for such extreme fasts, customary fasting of rather extended length is not unknown. For example, a warrior of the Papago Indians of the southwest United States returning from a raid in which he had killed a man customarily fasted for sixteen days after his return. Small quantities of corn meal and water were the only intake allowed. Really brave men would allow the corn meal to settle in the bowl of water and drink only the latter.[88] A Kazak (Central Asia) would customarily go without eating and drinking all day without any difficulty.[89] Musters reports of the Tehuelche of Patagonia that "their powers of abstaining from food are also very remarkable. When the disturbances and fighting were going on they rarely ate anything: also when traveling as 'chasquis,' or messengers, they will not infrequently go for two or even three days without tasting food." [90]

Drugs are used culturally in some societies to inhibit the rise of hunger drive and fatigue. Even at the present time Indian porters of the Andean region are accustomed to chew coca leaves instead of eating, when traveling over the mountains with burdens. The cocaine contained in the leaves inhibits hunger and fatigue and obviates the necessity of carrying food supplies in addition to the "pay load." [91] Fasts of two to three days, sustained by coca, are a regular part of a cargo carrier's routine.

Except for specialists such as cargo carriers or in unusual circumstances, all societies of which I know seem to have patterns for feeding at least once a day. Is this because of an absolute physiological necessity? Is it because the human hunger drive cannot normally be repressed without malaise for more than twenty-four hours? Again, further investigation is required.

Within the twenty-four-hour cycle, however, there is considerable cultural variability, even within the area of European civilization. Although each society prefers its own feeding schedule, it would be interesting to know what an optimum interval between feedings would be for the species. In North America the standard number of meals is three with an interval of from four to five hours between the first and second and from five to six hours between the second and third. Four meals per day was a standard in a number of peacetime European societies, for example, England, which inserted afternoon tea, and Germany, which inserted second breakfast into the three-meal schedule. In parts of Scandinavia five and six meals per day were *de rigueur*. In each society individuals were trained "to feel hungry" at the appropriate feeding times.

Turning to preliterate cultures, we find a similar variety, although usually in the direction of fewer meals per day. For example, the Nama Hottentots of South Africa have "no fixed time for eating. Only the morning meal, taken after the cows have been milked and driven out to pasture, has a special name, *sobas*. The time and place of other meals are regulated according to circumstance; in camp by the return of the herds from pasture; on the march by the progress; on the hunt by a successful shot, and so on." [92] The Tupinamba would work in their gardens in the morning without breakfast, eating only one meal per day after they returned to the house, either about noon or later in the day.[93] One meal per day is also customary for the Tanala of Madagascar, although a few cold scraps left over from the day before may be eaten upon rising.[94] Among the Bemba, whose food customs have been so well studied by Richards, a single daily meal is the rule, and it occurs at very irregular times during the day, depending upon the type of work in progress. "Men and women are accustomed to go to their gardens in the early morning to do the bulk of their work on what we habitually describe as an 'empty stomach.' They return to the village about noon, when the whole community awaits the evening meal." [95] The concentration on a single daily meal as in this pattern seems to require considerable training. Richards says that children are allowed to eat snacks all day long, and only as they approach adolescence do they succeed in emulating their elders. Among adults it is considered "undignified" to be eating at all hours of the day. Thus we seem to have the timing aspect of the eating customs operating on an acquired drive of prestige anxiety which overrides the hunger drive.

Other peoples eat two meals per day, for example the Tiv, who eat at dusk and at noon,[96] and the Quechua of the Inca Empire.[97] The Masai of East Africa take three meals per day: fresh milk in the early morning, a heavier meal about ten o'clock in the morning, and an evening meal.[98]

Perhaps these instances of varying meal schedules are sufficient to indicate something of the variety of the cultural control which is exerted over the hunger drive in the human species. We need more investigation on this subject if we are to be accurate in cultural planning in this field. What is the limit to which intervals between feedings could be stretched culturally? What is the optimum schedule for customary feeding? What auxiliary drives and what methods of training are most efficient in producing disciplined customary responses to hunger?

Limits of response to hunger. It would seem that the longer the interval between feedings, the larger the amount of food which would be consumed at a feeding. Therefore, the question of cultural training to resist or control hunger would seem to be correlated with the question of the amount of food which may be customarily ingested at one sitting without pathological aftermaths.

No absolute and conclusive figures can be given, and even accurate reports of prodigious eating on a customary basis are rare. An average Andaman Islander (and these people are Pigmy Negritoes) will eat from three to four pounds of food daily, and after a good hunt or at a dance may consume ten pounds of pork or turtle together with considerable portions of other food during the evening.[99] The old people among the

Lepcha complain that once they could eat fifteen pounds of meat per day, but can now eat only four pounds in comfort. Gorer gives a typical menu of food consumed per head at a feast lasting from 11:00 A.M. to 9:00 P.M.: three pounds of rice in two helpings; three bambu vessels of alcoholic "chi"; three cups of stronger drinks resembling spirits; two double fistfuls of popcorn; two pounds of meat; four helpings of tea; plus "as much curry, vegetables, and soup as are wanted." [100] Although a Kazak can refrain from eating all day long, when he has the opportunity he eats and drinks prodigiously. Levchine reports that "on one occasion a man ate a whole six-months-old lamb and said he was ready to eat another, which was supported by his companions' testimony." [101] It is said that the average daily consumption of steamed taro per head among the Hawaiians is about five pounds, in addition to various other foods.[102] Pigafetta was much impressed with the gustatory capacity of the Patagonian Indians. "They were very gluttonous," he says. "The two we caught would eat a basket of biscuits per day apiece and they would drink half a tub of water in a single swallow; they ate raw rats without killing them." [103]

In this section we have discussed briefly certain aspects of customs which seemingly are developed on the motivation of hunger, with a view to exploring the limits to which the development of such customs can be extended.

NOTES TO CHAPTER 12

1. Murdock, 1945, discusses this matter among others under the head of the Principle of Limited Possibilities; Gillin, 1944a, mentions species limitations as one of five corollaries of the Principle of Compatibility; see also Gillin, 1944b; Sorokin, 1941, Vol. 4, 709; Thurnwald, 1937. Part of the material in this chapter has been published in Gillin, 1944b. Thanks for present use are hereby expressed to Dr. Karl Zener, editor of *The Journal of Personality* (formerly, *Character and Personality*).
2. In the present chapter we shall devote most of our attention to overt actional customs. In theory, of course, the same type of analysis may be applied also to representational and mental customs.
3. Linton, 1936, pp. 272-274.
4. Damon and Randall, 1944.
5. The majority of these examples are taken from Behanan, 1937.
6. Behanan, 1937, pp. 193-194, 198.
7. *Ibid.*, p. 196.
8. Yeats-Brown, 1935, p. 262.
9. Behanan, 1937, p. 195.
10. Man, 1882-1883, p. 91.
11. Best, 1934, p. 364.
12. Métraux, Alfred. Unpublished notes on the Choroti, Chulupi, and Matako, on file in the Cross Cultural Survey, Institute of Human Relations, Yale University, New Haven, Conn.
13. Simpson, 1940, p. 424; photographic illustrations Nos. 31 and 42.
14. Covarrubias, 1937, p. 339.

15. Covarrubias, 1937, pp. 213-214.
16. Best, 1934, pp. 112, 436.
17. Gould and Pyle, 1897, pp. 473-474.
18. Benedict and Cathcart, 1913.
19. The periodical and book literature in this field is quite extensive. Among standard works are: Barnes, 1940; Gilbreth, 1911; Morgensen, 1938. Illustrations of work-simplification taken with a high-speed camera will be found in *Life*, October 13, 1941.
20. Barnes, 1940, pp. 145-173.
21. *Ibid.*, p. 145. Quotation by permission of John Wiley and Sons, publishers.
22. *Life*, October 13, 1941.
23. Hoke, 1922.
24. Young, 1941.
25. McLester, 1939, p. 253; Best and Taylor, 1937, pp. 959 *et seq.*
26. Cannon, 1939, Chapter 7.
27. McLester, 1939, p. 253.
28. *Ibid.*, pp. 243-256.
29. Cannon, 1939, pp. 138-139.
30. Marett, 1936.
31. McLester, 1939, pp. 80-87.
32. *Ibid.*, p. 256.
33. Best and Taylor, 1937, p. 959.
34. Cannon, 1939, pp. 70-86.
35. Tsang, 1938.
36. Bash, 1939a.
37. Bash, 1939b.
38. Young, 1941, p. 154. It seems to us more useful to reserve the term "appetite" to designate the "acquired hungers" (that is, secondary or acquired drives).
39. *Ibid.*, p. 154.
40. *Ibid.*, p. 130. In addition to Young, the other outstanding researcher on "free selection" is C. H. Richter.
41. Literature is plentiful. See, for example, National Research Council, 1943.
42. Osgood, 1937, p. 44.
43. Rochefort, 1665, p. 365.
44. Stefansson, 1935-36.
45. Hunter, 1940, pp. 23-36.
46. McLester, 1939, p. 145.
47. Richards, 1936, pp. 39, 52.
48. Warden, Jenkins, and Warner, 1940, Vol. 2, p. 734.
49. Sarasin, 1893, Vol. 1, pp. 401-409.
50. Schomburgk, R. H., 1837, p. 346; Dance, 1881, p. 177.
51. Gould and Pyle, 1897, p. 413, quoting Philos. Trans. Roy. Soc. London, 1700.
52. Gould and Pyle, 1897, p. 413.
53. Whiffen, 1915, pp. 124-125.
54. Westermarck, 1926, Vol. 2, p. 600.
55. Dickens and Ford, 1942.
56. Cobo, 1890-1895, Vol. 1, p. 243; Valdizán and Maldonado, 1922, Vol. 2, pp. 16-17.
57. Lawson and Moon, 1928.
58. Paz Soldán, J. L., in Raimondi, 1904, Vol. 4, p. 50.
59. Gumilla, 1791, p. 177; Crévaux, 1883, p. 287; de Goeje, 1910, p. 5; Koch-Grünberg, 1910, Vol. 2, p. 291. See Laufer, 1930, for a general résumé of earth-eating.
60. Bailey, 1863, p. 288.
61. Gorer, 1938, p. 56.
62. Osgood, 1937, p. 42.

63. Hodge, 1907, Vol. 1, pp. 467-468.
64. Conzemius, 1932, p. 88.
65. *Ibid.*, p. 91.
66. Murdock, 1934, p. 199.
67. Stefansson, 1935-1936.
68. Richards, 1936, p. 57.
69. Cf. Notes 27 and 28 above; also Linton, 1940.
70. Whiffen, 1915, p. 130.
71. Cobo, 1890-1895, Vol. 2, p. 278.
72. Herrera, 1728, Década V., Libro IV, p. 85.
73. Castner, 1900, p. 705.
74. Anna, 1940.
75. Gorer, 1938, p. 56.
76. Cobo, 1890-1895, Vol. 2, p. 140.
77. Gillin, 1947b.
78. Vaillant, 1941, p. 131.
79. Whiffen, 1915, p. 124.
80. See the numerous citations from the literature in Sumner, Keller, and Davie, 1928, Vol. 4, pp. 657-663.
81. Danks, 1892.
82. Torday and Joyce, 1906, p. 279.
83. Stefansson, 1935-1936; Lieb, 1926; Tolstoi, 1929; McClellan and Dubois, 1930.
84. Price, 1939, p. 275.
85. McLester, 1939, p. 151.
86. Price, 1939, p. 279.
87. Best and Taylor, 1937, p. 959.
88. Underhill, 1939.
89. Levchine, 1840, p. 318.
90. Musters, 1873, pp. 166-167.
91. Personal observations of the writer in Peru and Ecuador.
92. Schapera, 1930, p. 239.
93. Soares de Souza, 1851, p. 319.
94. Linton, 1933, p. 74; Kardiner, 1939, p. 254.
95. Richards, 1936, p. 72.
96. East, 1939, p. 147.
97. Rowe, 1946.
98. Merker, 1904, p. 32.
99. Man, 1882-1883, p. 7.
100. Gorer, 1938, p. 99.
101. Levchine, 1840, p. 318.
102. Miller, 1927.
103. Pigafetta, 1906, Book 1, "June and July."

CHAPTER 13

Human Resources as the Raw Material
of Culture (*Continued*)

CULTURAL REACTIONS TO TEMPERATURE

Man has established permanent residence in all parts of the globe except Antarctica, a range of adaptability which, so far as temperature conditions are concerned, is explained by two factors: the remarkably successful innate human apparatus for maintaining a more or less constant body temperature, and a wide variety of successful cultural response. Since man is a mammal and hence "warm-blooded" his internal economy demands the maintenance of a fairly steady temperature of the blood regardless of the temperature of the outside medium surrounding the body (air or water). A number of delicately balanced neuro-physiological mechanisms operate in maintaining body temperature, but there is a range of outside conditions beyond which their functions decay or break down completely. As the temperature outside the body approaches these extremes of high or low temperature which imply danger the individual becomes increasingly uncomfortable. We say, in psychological terms, that temperature drive begins to operate. Responses made under the influence of temperature drive may harden into habits and customs, thus becoming culture. It is our purpose here to approach some understanding, therefore, of the influence of temperature drive upon the development of culture.

Physiological psychology of temperature. Present evidence seems to indicate that there are two centers of temperature control, situated in a gland called the hypothalamus, which is located in the forebrain.[1] Although these two centers are probably coördinated to form a single functional mechanism of temperature control, heat is apparently controlled by a center in the anterior part of this organ (the hypothalamus), while cold control is centered in the posterior or caudal portion.

At birth the human infant's regulatory mechanism for temperature is not well developed and is inefficient. The result is that parents or nurses are required to respond culturally with some means of maintaining the child's proper temperature, and in climates where this is necessary, we invariably find some sort of cultural response to this need. In our own society, these measures in general are known as "coddling" and are associated with infancy. On the other hand, many cultures institute measures fairly early in accordance with the dictum of Aristotle:

> To accustom children to the cold from their earliest years is also an excellent practice, which greatly conduces to health, and hardens them for military service. Hence, many barbarians have a custom of plunging their children at birth into a cold stream; others, like the Celts, clothe them in a light wrapper only. For human nature should be early habituated to endure all which by habit it can be made to endure, but the process must be gradual.[2]

From the sixth month onward the daily temperature curves become more regular, until in adults a relatively stable blood temperature within one degree and a half, Fahrenheit, of 98.6 is normally maintained. In all races of men a maintained rise or fall outside this range is a harbinger of illness or death, unless promptly counteracted.

It is not necessary for our purposes to consider in detail the mechanisms whereby temperature control is maintained, but it is of some interest to review briefly the ways in which the "feelings" of cold and warmth are produced, because these feelings combine to raise the drives of cold and of heat. Only a relatively small range of temperatures arouse these drives—minus 10 degrees to plus 70 degrees Centigrade (minus 14 degrees to plus 158 degrees Fahrenheit). Above and below this range the organism usually feels only pain.[3] The sensation of cold or warmth is not entirely dependent upon the internal heat of the body, but rather upon the temperature of the skin. The sensations of cold and warmth are produced by stimulation of two types of specialized neuron endings in the skin, which are known as "warm spots" and "cold spots" respectively. Cold spots are not stimulated by warmth, nor are warm spots stimulated by cold. So long as a normal outward flow of heat is maintained by the blood, sensations of cold and warmth are not aroused. This point of indifference is known as physiological zero, and it is only when the skin temperature rises or falls from this point that drive is aroused and reactions are evoked. Among members of our own society in good health, resting in a room at 20 degrees to 22 degrees C. (68 degrees to 71.6 degrees F.), physiological zero is about 98.6 degrees F. under the tongue, 95 degrees on the normally clothed parts of the body, 91.4 degrees on hands and face, and 78.8 degrees on the earlobes.[4] It is true, however, that training and habituation can raise or lower these values somewhat.

Although cold spots are normally stimulated by temperatures below physiological zero, they also respond to temperatures considerably higher than physiological zero. This phenomenon, known as *paradoxical cold*, explains why, under certain conditions, one may have a sensation of cold upon grasping a hot object. This, of course, usually gives way to pain if the heat is sufficient to damage the tissues.

The chemical regulation of body heat is associated with the rate of heat production, a feature which is measured by the so-called basal metabolism rate. In average males heat loss equals heat production when the air temperature is between 84.2 degrees and 87.8 degrees F. Average female metabolism is, on the other hand, 14 to 20 per cent lower than that of males, which gives women an advantage over men with respect to heat loss, an advantage which is accentuated by the layer of subsurface fat characteristic of women. Thus women on the average withstand temperature of one degree less than men in the surrounding medium (air or water) without unbalanced loss of body heat. Furthermore, women sweat less than men, because of their lower metabolism at high temperatures. On the average, a woman does not begin to sweat until the air or water temperature is about two degrees higher than the point at which the average man begins to sweat.

It is obvious that many cultures, including our own, have "taken advantage" of these sex differences in heat regulation by developing differences in costume and associated culture patterns. The lighter clothing of women in our society thus has some basis in physiology, as well as in vanity.

Basal metabolism rates seem to be lower on the average in warm climates, and even persons born in the middle latitudes develop a lower rate after a few years in the tropics.[5] This may be regarded as a physiological adaptation to the situation. Although the human body is able to adapt physiologically to a limited extent, man lives in so wide a range of climates that culture must in many cases come to the aid of his physiological mechanism.

What alterations of internal body temperature are normally tolerated without fatal results? Within what limits may man get hot or cold, so to speak? Fevered patients seldom live with a blood temperature of more than 107 degrees F. for more than a few hours. Recovery from short periods of higher temperature than this have been reported, but usually associated with resulting destruction of brain and other nervous tissue. From the cultural point of view, then, if no cultural techniques or activity patterns exist which prevent or lower temperatures of 107 degrees F. or over, the society will suffer loss.

Abnormally low body temperatures, on the other hand, seem to be better tolerated. Patients have been reported living with rectal temperatures ranging from 75 degrees to 90 degrees F., although loss of memory for events is said to occur below 92 degrees F. and vocal responses fail below 80 degrees F.[6] Yet the normal internal body temperature of all races of man seems to range within a degree and one-half of 98.6 degrees F.

We have seen that the nude body at rest produces about the same amount of heat as it loses when the air temperature ranges between about 84 and 87 degrees F. It follows, then, that survival in climates and temperatures outside this range depends, in the long run, upon some sort of cultural protection for parts of the skin. Everywhere, of course, men have to sleep, so that they are at rest during at least part of every average day. Protection of some sort has to be provided, which maintains a layer of air of proper temperature next the major portion of skin surface. It may be an open fire below one's hammock, a furnace-heated room, or a sleeping bag, but the cultural pattern and equipment are necessary.

Cannon says that for a short time men may be exposed to dry heat at 239 degrees to 261 degrees F. without an abnormal rise in body temperature,[7] and Gould and Pyle,[8] quoting Gmelin, point out that men have lived where the air temperature falls as low as minus 157 degrees F. These extremes indicate on the one hand the remarkable natural stability of the internal body economy in extreme heat, and, on the other hand, the range of cultural adaptation and habituation which may be made to extreme cold.

Cultural reactions to the drives of temperature. Let us now turn to a few examples of temperature adaptation by cultural means gleaned from the literature of ethnography. The Ona of Tierra Del Fuego live in one of the rawest and chilliest, if not one of the coldest, climates of the earth. Temperatures ranging between plus 5 degrees F. and minus 12 degrees F. prevail for weeks at a time, and one series of observations showed a maximum mean daily temperature of plus 82 degrees F. and a minimum mean of plus 5 degrees F.[9] Here, warm days occur seldom, even in summer. To survive in such a climate would seem to be quite a feat, even with the best of cultural equipment. The Ona, however, were not well equipped culturally in the aboriginal state. The dwelling consisted of a conical arrangement of poles usually covered with skin on the windward side only, while the more southerly groups in the colder part of the island used very short poles and provided no roof for the shelter. Even so, these dwellings represented luxury, for when on the march or the hunt, the Ona relied upon a simple windbreak consisting merely of a sort of fence made of skins held up by a half-circle of widely spaced poles. Clothing was equally poorly adapted to the climate. It consisted, in addition to a loin apron of skins, of an untailored skin draped about the shoulders and body (usually leaving large surfaces of the skin exposed on the leeward side), a fur cap which covered only the forehead, and skin sandals. Truly, the human organism can "stand" a good deal.

The Eskimo of the American arctic, on the other hand, were well equipped culturally to withstand the low temperatures of their region. They provided themselves with carefully fitted and lined suits of skin and fur; their houses were weather tight (whether of snow, stone, wood, or skin), and provided with air traps and, in some areas, skin linings ingeniously contrived to prevent the escape of warm air. Nevertheless, the Eskimo illustrate also the adaptability of the human organism to temperature, the variations which it will tolerate if properly trained. As Birket-Smith remarks, "it is possible to experience all the climate belts of the world at once [in an Eskimo house]: at the feet the temperature is still arctic, waist-high the surrounding air is almost temperate, and the head sometimes projects a good way into the tropics." [10] On the other hand, a hunter must be trained to suffer extreme exposure to cold, despite ingeniously made clothing. In seal hunting, he must wait motionless for hours beside his quarry's air hole on the ice until the seal appears, then instantly harpoon the animal when it appears. "The hunter has to hold out, and this despite a temperature that not infrequently falls to minus 50 or minus 60 degrees Fahrenheit." [11] Knud Rasmussen describes Netsilik Eskimo of King William Island plunging into the icy river water—men, women, and children—to swim about and spear fish.

Exposure to cold was regarded as part of the training of every boy among many of the Plains Indian tribes. Among the Crow in all seasons most of the men were in the rivers before sunrise. Says the old warrior Plenty Coups in his autobiography as recorded by Linderman, "Boys had plenty of teachers here. . . . They would often send us into the water to swim among cakes of floating ice. . . . Cold toughens a man. The buffalo-runners in winter rubbed their hands with sand and snow to prevent their fingers from stiffening in using the bow and arrow." [12]

Among the northern Asiatic tribes similar accommodation to cold is part of the cultural training. Speaking of the arctic coast of Siberia, Nordenskiöld reports, "The men during their hunting excursions pass whole days in a cold of minus 30 to minus 40 degrees out upon the ice, without protection and without carrying with them food or fuel. . . . Women nearly naked often during severe cold leave for a while the inner tent, or tent-chamber. . . . A foreigner's visit induced the completely naked children to half creep out from under the curtain of reindeer . . . of the exterior tent which . . . is not heated. . . . Mothers do not hesitate to show their children one to two years of age in this temperature." [13] Among the Chukchi, "small children are left all day in the open air in winter. I have seen infants lying on the snow attempt to get out of their fur combination-units. The upper part of their bodies remained naked for a long time, but they did not show any signs of discomfort, though the cold was severe and the wind blew sharply. The women work with the needle in the open air even in March, at a temperature of 30 degrees blow zero, Centigrade. Their fingers remain unprotected for several hours at a stretch. The exertion even makes them feel warm and perspire so that they throw aside their ample fur bodices and remain half naked, or else even thrust large cakes of snow into their bosoms." [14] Bogoras says, "On the whole the Chukchi and the Asiatic Eskimo are more hardened to the cold than their neighbors on the southeast, because they live in far more exposed regions, with no fuel for fire. They do not even supply themselves with heavy overcoats, and while traveling sleep in the open without extra covering." [15]

Speaking of the Kazak of Central Asia, Levchine says, "Clothes are not made for it [the child] but it is simply wrapped in a cloth or in cold weather in a lamb-skin. Children wriggle out of these coverings and fall quite naked into the snow or hot ashes of the fire, thus being accustomed at a very early age to heat, cold, and changes of temperature." [16]

From these reports we see the influence of social training upon the patterns and types of response to temperature drives: we see, as it were, what culture can do with human beings whose innate physiological adaptations are relatively limited. Although a certain amount of natural selection doubtless accounts for the ability to withstand cold among at least some of these tribes, the evidence also suggests that early and continued habituation may modify the individual's reactions to low temperature and enable him to withstand certain degrees of cold in the absence of cultural equipment adequate to maintain the ideal air temperature at all times. On the other hand, we have numerous instances, including that of the majority of individuals in our own society, of high sensitivity to cold. The Mataco of the Gran Chaco of South America are said by Host to be very sensitive to cold and they shiver violently when the temperature goes no lower than 57 degrees F. above zero.[17] Numerous reports of Indians of the tropical forest regions of South America indicate their sensitivity to cold.[18] Fires are usually kept burning under hammocks at night even though the nocturnal temperature is usually only some 20 degrees F. below that of the day. In cases from tropical regions, of course, the possibility of malarial infection must always be reckoned with.

Let us now summarize some of the available evidence regarding the *influence of hot climates upon the human organism.*[19] The so-called direct "actinic" effects of tropical sunlight seem to be of little importance although they may add to the burden of overtaxed systems. What is important is the reduction in body-cooling power which occurs under conditions of high temperature. The greater the area of skin surface to body mass, the more efficient is the human cooling apparatus; and there is a possibility that the scrawniness of so many native peoples of the tropics is an adaptation to this principle, although nutrition deficiencies may be responsible as well. Whites going to the tropics usually show the following physiological effects: greater need of peripheral blood circulation robs the central organs of some of their needs with the resulting development of at least temporary organic complaints: in women there is a tendency to sterility, irregular menses, and post-puerperal hemorrhages; urinary secretion is reduced and the urine is more concentrated, with possible undesirable effects upon the kidneys; lower urea and chloride content is marked in the urine, due to excretion in sweat. Alkalosis tends to develop, but usually disappears under a régime of plentiful water drinking and exercise. Blood sugar may drop; phosphorus in the blood tends to be reduced and there is a decrease in suspension stability of the red cells. The number of red blood corpuscles does not decline in the tropics, but in hot desert climates they tend to increase. Hair and nail growth tends to be inhibited. There is also some evidence to indicate that the requirement per unit of food for B vitamins is higher than in cooler climates, while at the same time the supply of these vitamins in native meats is lower. In Panama shorter stature is characteristic of white children raised in the tropics as compared with their relatives raised in the United States. This is interpreted by Mills as due to excessive cellular combustion because of inefficient dissipation of heat and lack of vitamins. Women show late maturity and a lag in fertility after first menses.[20] Many of the physiological disabilities of tropical residence can be eliminated or compensated by regular and temperate habits of living and by scientifically planned diets, all of which are in themselves elements of culture. Nevertheless, no large permanent white communities or societies have succeeded to date in establishing and maintaining themselves from the resources of the country in the wet, lowland tropics.[21] Temperature alone is not the only factor in this failure, of course. In the light of present knowledge, however, it seems to be indicated that whites require special cultural adaptations, not required by other races, if they are to establish and maintain self-sustaining and self-reproducing societies in the lowland tropics.

Sweating is one of the most important human physical reactions to high temperature. The amount of salt in the perspiration is more concentrated in hard work than in easy work, and the salt content drops as one continues profuse sweating day after day. However, the heat regulatory apparatus can be improved with training. Adaptation of the individual to high temperature involves increased capacity to sweat, greater sensitivity of the temperature regulating mechanisms, and economy of salt.[22]

Cultural reactions to heat drive are many and varied. In high temperature the members of one society may go practically naked as a means of increasing heat loss, while in another society, such as that of the Arabs and among some tribes of the Sudan, loose-flowing garments are favored, which practically cover the entire body and exclude the intense external heat from contact with the skin. It is not necessary to catalogue the vast array of cultural patterns, techniques, and artifacts which represent cultural reactions to the drives of temperature. Housing, heating, clothing, systems of ventilation, use of certain foods and liquids as well as certain uses of narcotics may be better understood and functionally analyzed, however, if we know something of the limitations of the species with respect to heat and cold. Such cultural devices provide satisfaction of which the unaided organism is incapable.

As already mentioned, increase in either cold or heat above the optimum usually causes discomfort within a certain range of change, following which sensations of pain occur. We have very little information concerning the effect of training upon the increase of ability to withstand these painful sensations. One custom, found in a great variety of cultures, however, was thought for a long time to indicate trained ability to endure heat pain. This is fire-walking.[23] This spectacular feat has a wide distribution. It consists of walking barefoot through a trench of either red-hot embers or of red-hot rocks, and among native peoples the ability is usually formulated in terms of supernatural power or faith. The trenches vary from 11 to 25 feet in length and the hot coals or rocks are heated by burning large quantities of wood for several hours previous to the trials. Stone-walking on hot volcanic stones is found in Fiji, Cook Islands, Society Islands, and Hawaii, while ember walking on a red-hot bed of glowing wood coals is reported from East India and regions colonized by East Indians (Trinidad, Natal, Mauritius), the Navaho Indians, and Japan. In Bulgaria the peasants dance on the embers of an open wood fire which is not contained in a trench. Ember-walking seems to be the more difficult of the two general types. Elaborate investigations in England [24] produced the following conclusions. Fire-walking is not a trick; it is done in the normal manner of walking, with bare and chemically untreated feet. Moisture on the foot is a disadvantage because it causes hot particles to adhere and create blisters; nor is there any sudden formation of an insulating cushion of vapor between the feet and the embers, nor any abnormal callosity of the feet. Blisters usually result if more than two steps are taken with each foot; the only long training required is in self-confidence. An English university student performed the ordeal repeatedly without prior training as successfully as two East Indian magicians.

In summary the student of human life must consider the bearing of temperature change upon social life, custom, and cultural equipment. In planning cultural readjustments or in understanding past developments, one must direct attention to the following aspects of the problem: (1) the innate reactions to temperature and the mechanisms innately established for adaptation; (2) the degree to which these adaptations may be changed by training; (3) the effectiveness with which custom and cultural equipment provide adaptation under conditions to which the organism is innately incapable of adapting.

Theories of optimum temperature zones. Human geographers have accumulated considerable data which would indicate that health and work output are best all over the world in places where the temperature for day and night together averages somewhere between 63 degrees and 73 degrees F. Ellsworth Huntington, who has been perhaps the leading exponent of this point of view, has repeatedly argued that the normal cultural reaction of human beings to temperatures below this optimum range is more energetic than that above the range.[25] The "normal" response to high temperatures is to wear as little clothing as possible, stay in the shade and do nothing, whereas cool temperatures stimulate people to fashion clothing, build shelter, and engage in vigorous activity, if for no other reason than the fact that "doing nothing" is uncomfortable in a cool temperature. From this it then follows, according to the argument, that coolish climates are more stimulating to the development of culture and civilization than warm, tropical climates, and it is truthfully pointed out that few of the more complex civilizations have developed in moist, tropical environments. As cultural equipment and techniques increase the mastery of mankind over the environment, the optimum climate becomes one "in which the warmest instead of the coolest season has noonday temperatures of 74 degrees or so."[26] Gilfillan[27] seems to have been the first to develop the idea that the optimum climate changes in harmony with technological advance, although Stefansson[28] and Markham[29] seem to have arrived at it independently. The theory in general is known as the "coldward march of civilization," and is supported by the fact that many of the modern centers of complex civilization are located farther toward the earth's poles than were the predecessor cultures from which they were derived. For example, in Europe the centers of cultural development have since classical times moved from the Mediterranean basin to the more northern countries. The modern period has also seen the development of civilization in such relatively cold regions as Canada, Southern Australia, New Zealand, and South

Africa. To the temperature factor, as a stimulant of culture, Huntington has added the "storm" factor. He endeavors to point out that most of the modern centers of culture are located, not only in regions of cooler optimum temperature, but also in areas which are subject to fairly regular periodic storms of the cyclonic type (not to be confused with tornadoes or hurricanes). His point is that variation in the climate over short periods is stimulating to cultural activity and, combined with coolish optimum temperature, provides the setting to which the most energetic cultural responses are made.

The climatic theory of culture as usually stated represents an over-simplification of the processes of cultural origin and growth, since numerous other factors, such as diffusion, contact between societies, interests and orientations of culture, and the like, are not given their due weight by the average climatologist. Nevertheless, in the light of our present knowledge, the factor of climatic temperatures and their variations seems to be an important one which the student of culture must take into account. The climatologists have made an important contribution in bringing this aspect of the environmental component into clearer focus and in providing data of very great value to cultural anthropology.

THE DRIVE FOR AIR

Although there are few things as "free as the air," there are not a few situations in which men are driven by want for air to make special reactions of a cultural type. For example, any human activity under water or in the rarefied atmosphere of high altitudes requires cultural adjustment of some sort.

Physiologically, breathing serves the function of supplying oxygen to and eliminating carbon dioxide and other products of combustion (particularly lactic acid) from the system. Although the human organism is capable of storing nutrient substances which will preserve life for some time without eating, it does not store sufficient oxygen to care for its needs for more than a relatively short period. The "vital capacity" is the maximum amount of air which can be drawn into the lungs, and for the average white adult male it is about 4,000 c.c. Some 500 c.c. of this is "tidal air," that is, that which is drawn in and out of the lungs with each respiration when the individual is at rest.[30] The oxygen requirement (as distinguished from whole air) of a man of average size at rest is about 25 to 30 c.c. per minute and the maximal amount which can be taken into the body and used is said to be about 400 c.c. per minute.[31]

In conditions in which this even flow of oxygen into the system cannot be maintained, there are two general types of cultural reactions to which resort may be had. First, the individual may be trained within certain limits to make up or accommodate for the deficit. Second, he may use cultural equipment of one sort or another (oxygen masks, diving suits with hoses, pressure cabins in airplanes, and the like) to supply the requisite oxygen.

Some cultures apparently take advantage of the physiological mechanism of *apnea* to train individuals to "hold their breath." Apnea is largely due to excessive elimination of carbon dioxide from the blood and can be produced when an individual forces his respiration for a few minutes, following which he has no desire to breathe for a short time. It is said that the average person without training will lose desire to breathe for only about forty-five seconds after this exercise, but that voluntary apnea has been produced lasting as much as fourteen minutes.[32] This procedure apparently is used by certain Oceanic societies, for example, where men and boys engaged in pearl diving and underwater fishing are trained to stay under water for an average of about two to three minutes per dive.[33] The invention of the modern diving suit in our culture with air supplied from the surface through a hose has, of course, increased the length of time a diver may remain under water.

The Yoga cult has perfected exercises which, it is claimed, enable the practitioners to control their respiration, and to "hold the breath" for 100 seconds at a time, and even for as much as several minutes. These exercises are phrased in terms of promoting the spiritual welfare of the practitioners and are not, therefore, directly motivated by air hunger or oxygen need, but are of interest as indicating yet another cultural response which may be made on the basis of this basic primary drive, even though indirectly.[34]

Training is also beneficial in increasing the volume of air breathed and the amount of oxygen absorbed under conditions requiring vigorous exertion on land. That the sometimes onerous training techniques imposed upon athletes to improve their "wind" actually "pay off" in greater breathing efficiency has been proved, for instance, by studies of Schneider and Crampton.[35]

Before the invention of the airplane, cultural adjustment to the rarefied atmosphere of high altitudes was mainly a matter of slow adaptation or "acclimatization." The altitude at which mountain sickness and other anoxic symptoms first appear in persons habituated to low altitude varies with individuals, but usually is between 6,000 and 10,000 feet. However, white men have climbed on Mt. Everest higher than 27,600 feet without the use of oxygen masks, which gives some indication of the extent to which acclimatization can be attained through a régime of careful training.[36]

The development of high-altitude flying in Western culture of recent years has given rise to a whole complex of customs [37] and cultural equipment taught to aviators for the purpose of avoiding the untoward effects of air hunger. Unless oxygen is artificially (culturally) supplied, sleepiness, headache, feeling of fatigue, and "blacking out" may begin at about 12,000 feet, while the ability of the brain to coördinate muscular actions frequently becomes impaired at about 14,000 feet, and the reflexes deteriorate between 13,000 and 15,000 feet, until at 30,000 feet convulsions appear. Above 30,000 feet other problems show up which are not directly concerned with oxygen hunger; most important is aeroembolism, or liberation of gases from solution in the body fluids, due to decreased air pressure at these altitudes. At 33,000 feet the air pressure is only one-fourth that at sea level. For this reason, further cultural adaptations, in addition to those supplying oxygen, must be brought into play, such as pressurized suits and sealed cabins in which the pressure is artificially maintained.

Finally, in certain cultures the environmental component of given situations or the characteristics of certain artifacts in use may give rise to air drive and necessitate the development of appropriate customs and equipment to avoid asphyxiation, even at low altitudes. In our own society, the use of smoke eradicators on chimneys, blowers, and other ventilating systems in factories and kitchens, and air conditioning in all types of buildings are connected with this drive. (Air conditioning is also a cultural response to temperature drives.)

An example of the problem on a somewhat simpler level of culture is contained in the instructions furnished to castaways by the Navy:

> If a tent or other closed shelter is used, it must be carefully ventilated. A fire of any kind burning in a closed and poorly ventilated space may produce carbon monoxide, a deadly poisonous gas. . . . Make certain that the tent or hut has a hole at the apex and that some air can come in from below.[38]

THIRST

The need of human beings for water is more pressing than the need for food. As Cannon puts its, "The body can lose practically all stored animal starch or glycogen, all reserves of fat and about one-half of the protein which is either stored or built into body structure, and not be confronted by great danger. But the loss of 10 per cent of body water is serious and a loss of 20 to 22 per cent means certain death." [39] Thus it is that all societies are required to maintain a fairly regular supply of liquids available at fairly frequent intervals. The thirst drive itself is locally made manifest by an uncomfortable feeling of dryness in the throat and, progressively, by a parched feeling in the mouth, and swelling of the tongue and lips. The drive itself is probably more pervading,[40] but the average human being is driven to "do something about it" when these local symptoms appear. Consequently most cultural patterns are linked primarily to the alleviation of the local symptoms.

The mobile, protrudable lips which man shares with the higher Primates render containers with edges adaptable to human consumption of liquids, and, in some form, they occur in all cultures.

Since water is, in a sense, a "natural resource" the customs involved in obtaining it often lay a good deal of emphasis upon training in discrimination to stimuli indicating where it may be found, and so forth. Excellent examples of the way such customs may be built are contained in the instructions issued to personnel of the Navy which they may follow in case of shipwreck in areas where the usual civilized equipment and patterns for alleviating thirst are not available.

For men adrift at sea:

Drinkable water will be your most essential need. If your emergency craft is equipped with a still or chemical apparatus for removing salt from sea water, learn *in advance* how to assemble and operate it. [Necessity of adapting customs to artifactual component of a situation.] There will probably be some water in the craft, and you should rig gear to catch rain water. Use sea anchor, boat or sail cover, or any piece of canvas. Try to estimate how long you may be adrift and ration your water accordingly. A man needs about a pint a day to keep fit, but he can survive on two to eight ounces. Water will go farther if you hold it in your mouth a long time—rinse, gargle, and swallow. If you have no water, do not eat, since digestion uses up body moisture.

Preserving the water already in the body is almost as important as having water to drink. To avoid excessive perspiration, refrain from unnecessary exertion. If it is warm, remove (but do not discard) all clothing except headgear, shirt, trousers, and socks, which are necessary to prevent sunburn. Rig an awning which will protect you from the sun but which will not interrupt any breeze. Keep your clothing wet with sea water, so that the evaporation will cool the body, but discontinue this if you feel chilly....[41, 42, 43, 44]

It is not necessary for present purposes to recall to the reader the elaborate customs and artifacts which are involved in the satisfaction of thirst in our own society, ranging from the digging of wells to the "proper" type of glass tumbler on a dinner table.

FATIGUE

Physiological psychology of fatigue drive.[45] For present purposes we shall consider the "desire for rest" after activity and the "desire for sleep" as phases of a single drive, "the fatigue drive." Physiologists are not yet agreed about the details of the organic mechanisms underlying this drive, and further research may indicate that it is more proper to speak of two, or more, physiological drives rather than one. For purposes of cultural analysis, however, "fatigue drive" serves us well enough until more physiological material of cultural significance is made available.

In any case, muscular activity of any kind, if prolonged or intense, normally provokes a desire for rest, and prolonged wakefulness provokes a desire for sleep, which generally speaking has the effect of providing rest for the striped muscles of the entire body. It would seem that muscular activity is directly responsible for the rise of the fatigue drive, rather than mental or internal organic activity. In fact the internal organs of the body, such as heart, digestive organs, endocrine glands, and others, never "rest" completely, but continue their activities even when the individual is asleep, although often at a reduced rate. There is some doubt that the mental activities ("thinking" and the like) actually raise fatigue, although their continuance serves to maintain the tonus (tenseness) of the skeletal muscles, which in turn become tired, and, according to Kleitman's theory,[46] in such a case would send nervous discharges to the "wakefulness center" of the brain, eventually inducing the desire for sleep. It seems probable that a certain amount of "mental tiredness" which the ordinary person feels after prolonged mental activity is actually an expression of the drive for new experience, that is, the desire to escape boredom. However, at present this is merely a speculation. It is established, however, that, although consciousness is lost in sleep, a considerable level of mental activity is usually maintained in dreaming, and so forth. Prolonged wakefulness, nonetheless, eventuates in deterioration of the mental processes (hallucinations, reduction of memory, loss of attention, and the like), indicating fatigue of the cortical centers involved, or some type of disorganization of them.[47]

For reasons not entirely clear, the need for sleep seems to decline with age. In our society physicians generally hold that a new-born infant requires on the average from 18 to 20 hours per day, a growing child from 12 to 14 hours, a mature adult from 7 to 9 hours, and old persons 5 to 7 hours.[48] There are, of course, individual exceptions. It is not clearly established, however, as to whether the adult member of the species requires a certain amount of sleep *every* day for most efficient functioning, or whether the daily felt need or drive is a result of custom and training. In all societies the infant's sleep is of the "polyphasic" type, that is, it sleeps at all periods of the twenty-four-hour cycle, and its sleep is taken in periods broken by wakefulness of longer or shorter duration. As the child passes from infancy, it tends to form a "monophasic" pattern characterized by one long period of sleep during the twenty-four-hour period, although this may be supplemented by naps during other phases of the cycle.

No absolute period can be set at the end of which lack of sleep becomes fatal for human beings, although at least one case is on record of a young night-watchman twenty-four years old who kept awake for 231 hours during which he had only 5.25 hours of sleep, snatched in 10- to 30-minute periods.[49] In all scientific experiments with wakefulness, it has been found impossible to keep the subjects awake for more than about 50 hours without almost continuous muscular activity. As soon as they become quiet, they tend to go to sleep. This probably accounts for the reported ability of certain primitive people to stay awake for two or three days at a time during festivals, when they are kept continually exercising in dances, ceremonies, and the like.

In summary, we may say that the species is so constructed that the normal member requires rest from activity, and in the presence of such requirements the organism tends to make its needs felt by the rise of the fatigue drive. However, it is also apparent that the drive may be suppressed by training and may tend to rise at certain time intervals set by custom.

Some customary reactions to fatigue drive. As regards muscular fatigue, most societies endeavor to develop certain patterns of training intended to postpone the rise of the drive. The degree to which the organism can be trained to withstand fatigue of course enhances the efficiency of the society in those activities in which endurance is required. Any reader who has undergone the "toughening up" process demanded of recruits to the armed services is aware of how society may take a hand in this matter.

Among the Chukchi of Siberia, says Bogoras, "a fair amount of swiftness combined with endurance is peculiar to all tribes of the area described. Some of the Chukchi herdsmen are able to overtake a reindeer-buck running at full speed, while the ... hunters claim to be able to keep up with a wild reindeer fleeing for its life." [50] Among the Bena of East Africa the chief formerly trained special messengers for speed and endurance while they were boys. "It was apparently no uncommon thing for them to travel as many as forty miles in twelve hours over the most difficult country." [51] The Wapishana of British Guiana are good walkers and runners. "On the trail they walk very fast even with a heavy pack. In the savannah, where there is always a good trail, they will make 3½ miles an hour with a 60-pound pack; over the rough bush trails, 3 miles." [52] Among the Ovibundu of Southwest Africa a day's march is about twenty-five miles during which a man carries a 60-pound pack.[53] The Bemba men of Northern Rhodesia "will walk an average of 15 to

20 miles with 50-pound loads on their heads daily for a fortnight or so, and women commonly go two or three days journeys with a 50-pound load and a two-year-old baby in addition on their backs." [54]

At the start of the war in 1941 the *Infantry Journal* contained some authoritative remarks on the matter of walking endurance in the United States Army. "Sustained mobility on or near the battlefield requires that all troops be thoroughly conditioned to march exertions. Their endurance must be at the maximum." "A rifle regiment must be trained to the point where it can average 15 to 20 miles a day on foot without unusual fatigue. And, under reasonably good conditions of routes, weather and situation, it must be able to march 30 to 35 miles in 24 hours and be fit for battle at the end of the march." "Foot elements halt for 15 minutes after the first 45 minutes of marching and after that march 50 minutes and rest 10." [55] However, the Japanese army seems to have been able to stretch the endurance of its men farther than was customary in the American army before the start of the war. According to a report by a peacetime American military observer, Major Harold Doud, entitled "Six Months with the Jap Infantry," the Japanese training for infantry was rather rigorous. Major Doud accompanied infantry regiments on various occasions on field-training expeditions. He reports that "one day we marched 37 miles . . . Twice troops went three days and two nights without sleep except what could be snatched during 10-minute halts. Sometimes the men slept while walking [!]." "We started out at five in the morning and marched almost continuously until ten the next morning. In that time we covered 56 miles." In addition to these exertions the troops were kept on patrol duty at night. Remarks Major Doud laconically, "They know how to sleep. They used training [to establish customs] in how to stay awake." [56] It will be remembered that these cultural patterns of the Japanese army apparently caused considerable surprise to the British in the first flush of the Japanese conquest of Malaya, the defenders of which, according to contemporary press despatches, at first found it impossible to believe that any soldiers were capable of the forced marches which were required of the Japanese in that campaign. Although we cannot admire the secondary motivations of the Nipponese in their conquest of Malaya, this is a dramatic instance of the results obtainable when a society explores a certain aspect of its "human resources" and resolutely inculcates customs based on human abilities.

Customary responses to the desire for sleep are extremely varied and we can do no more than suggest their range here. In contrast with the "serene rest" mattresses and other paraphernalia which characterize at least the ideal patterns of our culture, we find that the Veddahs of

Ceylon always sleep on the side either on the bare ground or in the ashes of a fire.[57] And an early account of the Maori describes the method of composing oneself for sleep if a watchman: a closely woven mat is tied around the neck and forms a sort of thatch against the rain, after which the man squats on his heels and sleeps.[58]

Experimental evidence indicates that any outside stimuli tend to rouse the "wakefulness center" in the brain and to disturb sleep. A variety of customs and cultural equipment have been developed in certain societies to eliminate such stimuli: the quiet room, the soft bed and pillow, the drawn shades, and so forth, are familiar in our own culture. Nevertheless, it seems that in many a society the individual is able to satisfy his desire for sleep with equipment which sounds rather torturesome to an American. As a matter of fact it is only Western culture which has developed beds of great softness, and the steel-sprung bed is unknown outside the radius of this culture. Technical factors explain this to some extent, but steel springs are not required for making a "comfortable" mattress or pillow, which can be made by any one possessing something like a sack and some hay or feathers, for example. Yet, a large proportion of the earth's population regards a soft pillow as unnecessary for restful slumber. Perhaps the most uncomfortable type of "pillow" from an American's point of view is the wooden or bamboo headrest used in China, Japan, and among various tribes of Melanesia. This is a sort of bridge of wood which is placed under the neck, leaving the head "hanging over the end," as it were, but raised above the surface of the bed.[59] This gadget is usually used by people who wear elaborate coiffures and who wish to avoid mussing up the hair-do at night. It illustrates two points of interest to students of culture: (1) an acquired drive (prestige, perhaps) may override a primary drive (fatigue), and; (2) fatigue can customarily be lowered even in spite of such a sleeping arrangement, if the individuals involved have received sufficient training or habituation.

The ability to withstand the desire for sleep is systematically encouraged in some cultures. Among the Aztecs, during the five "useless" days of the final year of a fifty-two-year calendrical cycle, "children were marched up and down and kept awake, for fear that sleep on that fatal evening would result in their turning into rats." [60] Of the Copper Eskimo, Jenness reports that "for a few hours, or for two or three days, they could display phenomenal energy. . . . Even the children were inured to sleepless hunting trips of thirty-six hours; but they could not plod along day after day and week after week at an even rate of progress. . . ." [61] Among the Lepcha of Sikkim, according to Gorer, "a really good feast . . . lasts for three days and three nights. People doze intermittently . . . but on the whole little sleep is had; under such conditions the Lepchas seem to manage with very little rest and I have seen people after forty-eight hours of almost continuous eating and drinking go off, apparently quite fresh to work in the fields." [62] The reindeer herdsmen of the Chukchi, according to Bogoras, often go without sleep for two or three days. "A young girl will work for a whole day on skins, then watch the herd all night long, and in the morning return home and busy herself till evening, without any visible drain on her strength." [63] "When the herdsmen are too few for regular watches, they may not get time to sleep for two to three days in succession, and often are so tired that they drop to the ground and fall asleep against their will." [64]

Steady undisturbed slumber throughout the night does not seem to be an absolutely necessary feature of sleeping customs. A Barama River Carib (in British Guiana) usually is up two or three times during the night to stir up the fire under his hammock, have a smoke and perhaps a talk.[65] Likewise the Lengua of the Gran Chaco region in South America are intermittent sleepers. "They do not . . . slumber steadily the whole night through, as we do, but rise at intervals, sit up at the fire, light a pipe, and have a chat, and then retire to sleep again." [66] Irregular sleep probably has some effect on the structure of the basic personality, as Du Bois [67] points out for the people of Alor (Indonesia). "The lack of regular habits of sleep should be stressed. . . . At night a household is roused at least once and frequently oftener by some one who has dreamed and gets up to replenish the fire and tell his dream to the household. Often a pot is placed on the fire for a midnight snack at this time." A good deal of disturbance during the night is common in an Alorese village because of men returning from discussing finance, boys coming back from courting, and so forth. "There are also the night dances, which average one every eight days throughout the year, and during the dry season . . . may average as many as one every five or six nights," and no one pays much attention to the needs of small children for sleep. In Buka (in Melanesia) "it is considered silly to go to bed while the moon shines." [68]

In summary, we see the drive of fatigue motivating the establishment of numerous customs in every culture, whereas the outside limits which this drive lays upon human custom are not precisely known.

SUMMARY OF THE RÔLE OF BASIC HUMAN RESOURCES IN CULTURE

In the preceding two chapters we have dealt with muscular responses and with a number of innate physiological drives (hunger, temperature drives, air hunger, thirst, fatigue) in order to indicate the importance of considering these fundamental "wants" in the analysis of culture. When considering the customs of mankind, or of a particular society, we are often wont to take our point of departure at a considerable distance from the actual roots of custom, and to indulge in impressive statements regarding culture in its higher aspects, without being at all clear as to how culture is rooted in human wants, and without recognizing explicitly that some of these wants are inborn in the species, regardless of how they may be modified by training or overlaid by subsequently developed secondary drives.

Actually, we have been trying to emphasize that the raw material of culture must come from the "human resources" present in the species and from the manifested abilities to make response and to be motivated by wants. In the last analysis there is no other source of culture available for examination by science, and the culture of no society may transcend the resources of the species.

The reader may trace for himself the influence of the various other innate or universal drives mentioned in Chapter 11. In dealing with innate and universal drives of the species as the motivating springs of human custom, we must be careful not to oversimplify the situation. We have already seen that few of these wants appear in their pristine unmodified form. As soon as the new baby appears in a society, the other members of the group get to work on him, so to speak, with a view to modifying his innate drives and wants in conformity with the patterns prevalent in the culture. Then, as time goes on, there gradually develop secondary drives laid over, built around and on top of the innate drives, but still having their roots in the original human resources. In the next chapter we shall look into this matter a little more fully.

NOTES TO CHAPTER 13

1. Scott and Bazett, 1941.
2. Aristotle, 1336a, Book VII, Line 13 *et seq.*
3. Boring, Langfeld, and Weld, 1939, p. 615.
4. *Ibid.,* p. 616.
5. Scott and Bazett, 1941.
6. *Amer. Jour. Physiol.,* 129:434, 1940; Fay and Smith, 1941; *Amer. Jour. Clin. Pathol.,* 10:1, 1940.
7. Cannon, 1939, p. 22.
8. Gould and Pyle, 1897, p. 430.
9. Popper, 1891; Gusinde, 1931, pp. 194-199.
10. Birket-Smith, 1935, pp. 126-127. Quotation by permission of E. P. Dutton, publishers.
11. *Ibid.,* pp. 81-83.
12. Linderman, 1930, p. 12. Quotation by permission of John Day Co., publishers.
13. Nordenskiöld, A. E., 1882, p. 461.

14. Borgoras, 1904-1909, p. 37.
15. *Ibid.*, p. 243.
16. Levchine, 1840, p. 357.
17. Host, 1874.
18. For example, Gillin, 1936a, p. 42.
19. Sundstrom, 1927.
20. Mills, 1942.
21. For example, see Price, A. G., 1939, for a review of this subject.
22. Dill, 1938.
23. A few among the numerous references: Burke, 1903; Langley, 1902; Ingalls, 1939; Price, H., 1937; Roque, 1939; Girard, 1939; Morris, 1922.
24. Brown, B. G., 1938.
25. Huntington, 1924; 1945, Chapter 14.
26. Huntington, 1945, p. 401.
27. Gilfillan, 1920.
28. Stefansson, 1922.
29. Markham, 1944.
30. Best and Taylor, 1937, p. 546.
31. Cannon, 1939.
32. Best and Taylor, 1937, pp. 546-547.
33. Man, 1882-83, p. 47.
34. Yeats-Brown, 1935, pp. 174-176, 263-266; Brunton, n.d., pp. 201-203.
35. Schneider and Crompton, 1940.
36. Schmidt and Comroe, 1941.
37. See Armstrong, 1940.
38. Ethnogeographic Board, 1944, pp. 139-140.
39. Cannon, 1939, pp. 78-79. Quotation by permission of Harper and Bro., publishers.
40. See, for example, Morgan, 1943, pp. 440-445.
41. Ethnogeographic Board, 1944, pp. 9-10.
42. *Ibid.*, pp. 59-61, for tropical forests.
43. *Ibid.*, p. 141, for the arctic.
44. *Ibid.*, pp. 170-171, for the desert.
45. Kleitman is the outstanding researcher on sleep. See Gilbert and Patrick, 1896; Kleitman, and others, 1933; Katz and Landis, 1935; Best and Taylor, 1937, p. 1465; Kleitman, 1939; Edward, 1941; Morgan, 1943, pp. 375-385.
46. Kleitman, 1939.
47. See references in Note 45.
48. Best and Taylor, 1937, p. 1464.
49. Katz and Landis, 1935.
50. Borgoras, 1904-1909, p. 265.
51. Culwick, 1936, pp. 165-166.
52. Farabee, 1918, p. 71.
53. Hambly, 1934, p. 157.
54. Richards, 1936, p. 43.
55. *Infantry Journal*, 1941, pp. 68-73.
56. Doud, 1942, p. 32.
57. Sarasin, 1893, Vol. 2, p. 377; Seligman, 1911, p. 87; "A Vedda will never sleep on the ground if there is any rock upon which he can lie," because dampness is avoided by sleeping on a rock.
58. Fitzroy, 1839, p. 610.
59. For illustrations, see Lewis, Albert B., *Ethnology of Melanesia*, Field Museum of Natural History, Guide, Part 5, Plates 10-12.
60. Vaillant, 1941, p. 200. Quotation by permission of Doubleday and Co., publishers.
61. Jenness, 1928, pp. 161-162. Quotation by permission of the author, Diamond Jenness.

62. Gorer, 1938, p. 259.
63. Bogoras, 1904-1909, p. 37.
64. *Ibid.*, p. 82.
65. Gillin, 1936a, pp. 39-40.
66. Grubb, 1911, p. 61.
67. Du Bois, 1944, pp. 45-46.
68. Blackwood, 1935, p. 27.

CHAPTER 14

The Cultural Rôle of Acquired Drives

Although all adaptive cultural behavior is ultimately based on innate or universal drives of one sort or another, the everyday business of living and carrying on customs in most societies is motivated by secondary or acquired drives. One does not usually go to a restaurant under a drive of stark starvation hunger, but out of a desire to satisfy one's appetite for specific articles of food prepared according to cultural patterns—steak smothered in onions, hashed brown potatoes with gravy, or whatever the case may be. Ordinarily men and women are not driven by raw sex drive, but are motivated to seek the company of members of the opposite sex who conform to culturally defined ideals of beauty; who behave according to certain patterns of decorum, refinement, and "manners"; who are attired according to patterns approved by the group; and so on. Although people become thirsty in all societies, they are accustomed to slake their thirst with certain culturally prepared liquids; a glass of milk is as distasteful a means of satisfying thirst for a Chinese as is a foaming stein of beer for a Middle Western member of the W.C.T.U.; although unflavored water is regarded as a suitable thirst-quencher in some societies, in others it is considered little short of poisonous and fit only for washing and bathing the outside of the body.[1] Thus it is that all the basic drives are "frosted over," we might say, with culturally conditioned appetites, anxieties, and other secondary drives.

General types of acquired drives. The acquired or culturally conditioned drives which motivate so much of the cultural behavior of persons in all societies may be classified in a number of ways. Since they are built up, artificially so to speak, from innate and universal drives, we may classify them usefully from the point of view of the effect which cultural situations have upon actions motivated by the underlying drives. In this sense, we may speak of (1) acquired drives derived from punishment, (2) acquired drives derived from reward, (3) acquired drives derived from frustration. It is, of course, clear that all three factors of punishment, reward, and frustration, may be, and usually are, involved

NOTE: References for this chapter will be found combined with those for Chapter 15.

in the formation of an acquired drive, but one or the other influence is usually dominant. Those in whose formation punishment has been most prominent, we call *fears or anxieties*, those in which reward is the dominant factor we call *appetites or positive cultural desires*, while those in which frustration has been the principal recurring factor may be described as *acquired angers or hostilities*.

It is to be understood that the cultural system of each society is presented to the individual as a configuration or "set" of recurring punishments, rewards, and frustrations. There is a *regularity* in which artifacts and customs impinge upon the individual. These aspects of the culture are conveyed by the actions that are patterned and practised with regularity by other members of the society. And the individual customs are fitted together into a system or configuration from which there are no escapes other than flight or death for the individual, or cultural change for the society. Thus the individual is caught in a *press*, to use Murray's term, which not only molds his actions, but also his very motivations. We shall analyze cultural systems at more length later, but we emphasize the regularity, the recurring quality, the super-individual aspects, and the power of patterning at this point so that the reader may obtain some grasp of the concept of cultural drives. The individual in any society, to be brief, must learn to adapt his motivations to the cultural environment as he finds it—he learns to fear those aspects of the situation which are regularly punishing to him; he learns to want what is available to reward him; he learns to hate that which frustrates his attempts to reach goals.

Thus, if we are to classify acquired drives in specific terms, we can only speak with respect to specific cultures. For example, the typical individual in our society is motivated by a strong desire for money, which we may call the money drive. In a society whose culture does not contain the artifacts and concepts we call money, there can, of course, be no such drive. Many persons in our society have a fear of "hell fire," but numerous societies have never heard of this particular post-mortem punishment and hence have had no opportunity to develop an acquired anxiety associated with it.

Acquired drives are always supported by innate or universal drives. This is to say that, in the course of the socialization of the individual, his basic drives have forced him to react in cultural situations, and these reactions in given cultural situations have proved punishing, rewarding, or frustrating often enough so that they have been laid over by acquired drives. We might, therefore, classify the acquired drives on the basis of the basic drives which underlie them, speaking of the acquired drive based on pain, that based on sex, those based on hunger, and so forth.

The difficulty here, however, is that there is no one-to-one correlation between the basic drives and the acquired drives. There is no guarantee that a fear, for example, is developed solely on physical pain or that an appetite is based solely on physical hunger or that an anger is based solely on primary frustration. A combination of basic drives or of these together with acquired drives may underlie an acquired drive. One may have learned fear of persons in authority on the basis of both unrelieved pain and unrelieved desire for response; one may have an appetite for artichokes not only because they relieve hunger but also because their consumption enhances one's chances of forming closer contact with a marriageable partner; one may be angry with, let us say, "the laboring classes," because they actually block one's purposes and also because actions based on such anger tend to enhance one's prestige with the "upper classes." Most acquired drives are probably built up through experience on the basis of a combination of underlying drives. In some cases this structure may be quite complicated, so that the acquired drive in question may be thought of as supported by a whole pyramid of underlying drives, arranged in strata, each group supporting those above it.

The question may be asked, Are not acquired drives, then, to be considered a part of culture? The answer is no, for the following reasons. Only learned and patterned human *activities* are properly to be considered the content of culture. Drives, whether basic or acquired, are not activities, but the motivators of activity. A drive may motivate unpatterned and unlearned activity as well as habits and customs. Random activity, for example, is undoubtedly motivated, but it is neither patterned nor learned, so long as it remains random. There is, in short, nothing in a desire or drive per se which specifies the precise type of activity (custom or habit) which may be learned in order to satisfy it. Once established, an acquired drive occupies the same functional status as a basic drive, and a variety of customs may be learned to satisfy it. One may have an appetite for tobacco, for example, but this desire may be satisfied by a number of different types of customs and equipment—machine-made cigarettes, hand-made cigarettes, straight pipes, elbow and bowl pipes, water pipes, cigars, or others.

However, we may point out that, although cultural systems do not contain patterns for acquired drives themselves, they may nevertheless, and usually do, contain patterns whose effect is (*a*) to create acquired drives, (*b*) to arouse them, and (*c*) to satisfy them.

Let us now survey the various types of acquired drives. We shall begin with those based on punishment, and in order to make the matter more vivid, shall lead off, first, with a consideration of the basic drive of physical pain, and then consider certain acquired drives in which physical pain seems to be the main factor.

PAIN

The searing, stabbing, throbbing, wrenching qualities of pain are doubtless more motivating to the organism than are the goadings of any other basic drive. This fact is, of course, recognized in all societies for purposes of social control, which everywhere is based on the use of force as a last resort.

Physiological psychology of pain. Pain is apparently mediated by special receptors, called free nerve endings, which are located in the skin and in almost all organs of the body. They are separate and distinct from the nerve endings which receive stimuli of pressure and temperature. When the pain receptors are stimulated or injured the individual experiences pain drive.[2] Itching seems to be mediated by the same fibers as pain and the sensation appears when these nerve endings are stimulated mildly in certain ways.[3] Generally speaking, pain is an indication of injury or threatened injury to the organism, and the behavior which takes place under high pain drive is adaptive if it results in putting an end to such injury or threat. On the principle of anticipation an individual can learn to recognize certain cues indicative of painful situations and, by appropriately reacting, can learn to avoid them.

The organism has the ability to *adapt* to pain, that is, the unrelieved drive declines in its punishing effects if the pain-arousing stimulus remains constant and steady,[4] and this ability enables individuals to "withstand" pain to some extent. For example, the steady grinding of the dentist's drill is more punishing when it first goes into the pulp of the tooth than after it has been steadily working in the nerve for thirty seconds or so. This is only relative, however, and even with adaptation, the drive remains. Nevertheless, painful stimuli of everyday life seldom remain steady and constant, and the change in intensity and locale of the stimulus constantly rearouses the drive. This is why repeated strokes from a whip are so much more painful than if each lash were tightly bound against the skin after its stroke had been delivered. Finally, pain is an unusually punishing drive, because it frequently does not subside immediately after the drive-arousing stimulus is removed, but tends to linger on.

All parts of the body are not equally sensitive to painful stimulation and some portions seem to be totally insensitive, for example, brain tissue and the inside of the cheek opposite the lower second molar. Although certain pathological conditions render an individual unusually sensitive to pain, the evidence to date indicates that normal healthy individuals of all races have about the same innate thresholds, and that differences in apparent ability to endure pain are, so far as exhibited by groups, due to differences in cultural training. Research workers of the Cornell Medical College conclude that "all people, of all ages and both sexes, no matter how they react, and no matter how sensitive or insensitive they think they are, have exactly the same sensitivity to pain." [5]

Cultural responses to pain. Every culture contains activity patterns related to physical pain. A brief consideration of these customs and their motivations affords us an opportunity to consider certain aspects of the dynamic interrelation of drives with customs.

Use of pain as a counter-irritant. Many societies, just as our own, have discovered that locally applied pain may serve as a counter-irritant and bring its reward in the eventual reduction of more intense pain, inflammation, and other punishments. In all cases, however, social training is required, because the naïve organism's dominant reaction is to withdraw from any type of pain. Thus the small child among us frequently has to be held down by force when the mustard plaster is applied to its chest or while the searing iodine is applied to its scratches. Most societies have discovered that some pain *now* may avoid more pain, or possibly death, *later*. Thus, in most societies persons are trained to endure a certain amount of immediate pain. These methods are not in all cases based on reality, that is, the connection between the counter-irritant and the anticipated punishment may be a projected (symbolic) connection, rather than an empirically verifiable connection. Nevertheless, such customs afford us an opportunity to see how persons can be trained to endure pain, even though the motivation for such endurance is actually an unreal anxiety.

Among the Pima Indians of Arizona in localized inflammations, several cuts were made in the skin with a piece of glass and a little blood was allowed to flow out. [6] The Fishskin Tartars of Central Asia use cupping as a treatment for headaches. A small cup is filled with distilled grain spirits and set afire. "When the flame is going well, the cup is clapped to the forehead of the patient. It burns for a moment before going out, and so forms a vacuum sucking powerfully against the skin." [7] These same people regard pinching of the skin as a useful dispeller of aches and illness, and pinching is employed "as casually as we employ aspirins, and is resorted to for roughly the same range of aches, pains, colds, and 'not feeling well.'" [8]

The often painful joint twisting and "bone cracking" dispensed by chiropractors and osteopaths among ourselves are submitted to voluntarily by many patients for the reward of "good feeling" which comes in their train. Other cultures have invented somewhat similar treatments. For example, in the modern town of Moche, and among most of the common people of Peru, *chucaque* is a feeling of malaise. As a part of the treatment the operator stands behind the patient, grasping the latter's two arms which are folded across his chest.

With a swift series of jerks the patient is lifted off his feet and bent backward sharply by the operator. Usually the operator places his knee in the small of the patient's back and continues jerking until there is a cracking sound in the patient's vertebral column. Next, standing behind the patient, he places his right palm open against the lower right jaw of the patient and his left hand is held in position to steady the patient's head while, in a series of quick jerks, the right hand rotates the patient's head sharply several times until a cracking noise comes from the neck.[9]

One is reminded of the old saw, "It's like hitting yourself on the head with a hammer—it feels so good when you stop."

Among the Pima a small cotton ball about the size of a pea is applied over a painful spot and set on fire. It burns to the skin and leaves a blister followed by a pigmented effect.[10] The same people treat the pain of a toothache by sharpening a young branch, heating the point red hot in the fire and inserting it in the cavity.[11] According to Dobrizhoffer, "if a thorn of any plant happens to stick in their foot [referring to the Abipones of Paraguay] and to break there so that it cannot be pulled out by the finger, they will coolly cut the little piece of flesh" out with a knife. The same people when overtired claim that their blood is "angry" and "they have a ready remedy: they plunge a knife deep into their leg." [12] A similar treatment for fatigue is reported for the Macusi and Wapisiana tribes of interior British Guiana. They cut each other's legs with a piece of rock crystal, "an instrument to which they ascribed particular virtue, refusing my offer of a lancet instead of it." [13]

A rather unusual use of pain in curing is that reported for the Inca of Peru by Father Cobo. A species of ant was used "to unite the skin of the two sides of a wound. . . . [They apply] these ants, which bite and seize the two sides of lips of the wound, then their [the ants'] heads are cut off so that they remain attached to the wound as when they were alive." [14]

It is not necessary to continue the recital of further customs of this sort to convince ourselves that the endurance of pain is something which can be learned and incorporated in customs.

ACQUIRED DRIVES DERIVED FROM PUNISHMENT

Anxieties. Pain is undoubtedly a very punishing drive, but it is probable that its influence in social life under most situations is indirect rather than direct. This is to say that drives *derived* from pain and from other potentially unrelieved basic drives are responsible for a great many custom-motivations. This is explained by a psychological faculty highly developed in human beings. The man in the street may call it "imagination." The psychologists call it "anticipation." Even rats have some ability to anticipate punishments when they are introduced into situations which have been heavily punishing in the past. Man simply has more of this ability. Men consider each other "stupid" if they cannot learn to anticipate. Acquired drives based upon anticipation of punishment are called anxieties.

Any aroused drive is punishing until it is relieved. Pain perhaps mounts higher than any other innate drive, and anxieties are frequently based on anticipation of painful punishment. But hunger, fatigue, suffocation, and so forth, are also punishing, and experience may erect drives of anxiety based upon them. Or, a number of innate drives rather than only one may be unrelieved in certain social situations, and the anxiety may be based upon the combination of them.

Multiple anxieties. The normal person's anxiety regarding stealing is perhaps a compound of fears of being painfully handled by the police and of being deprived of food and warmth in a jail cell. Although some customs probably do operate on the basis of simple motivations, most social situations have the effect of raising a number of drives simultaneously and most customs are oriented toward this multiple-drive aspect of situations. A custom, then, (*a*) may be a cultural response to a number of drives operating simultaneously, or (*b*) it may be a response to the dominating drive in a hierarchy of drives all of which are aroused by the situation.

With regard to the first of these functions, we are justified in regarding the safety rules and mechanical guards, placed around machinery in most modern factories, as cultural responses designed to avoid pain from industrial accidents. Undoubtedly, the anticipation of painful injury is one of the motivations inducing workers to follow these patterns of "safety." However, a number of other motivations, of an acquired cultural type, may also be identified. For example, an economic motivation such as fear of loss of pay resulting from an incapacitating injury may be equally important, or a prestige motivation which moves a worker to avoid the loss of esteem in the eyes of his fellows and bosses which falls upon a careless operator, and so on.

All of these drives are anticipatory and therefore are acquired motivations (fear of pain, fear of economic loss, fear of prestige loss), but our point is that a given safety custom may reduce all of these drives simultaneously; also, it is apparent that an anxiety based upon social and cultural punishments can be as motivating as an anxiety based upon fear of directly painful punishment.

Some persons, usually classified as neurotics, have come to the conclusion (unconsciously, perhaps) that practically all situations are punishing, in which case we say that they suffer from "general anxiety," which remains continually punishing for them because they have mastered no techniques for relieving it. Although the cultural press of a total society may be so arranged as to raise a high degree of anxiety in practically all average persons, the culture also usually provides certain techniques for lowering it. This matter has not, however, been thoroughly investigated, and it is quite probable that certain cultures create more anxiety in their practitioners than do others.

The point to bear in mind here is that anxieties or fears, once aroused, are for practical purposes just about as punishing as the basic drives from which they are derived. In fact, they are in some cases more so. We frequently say that we would rather face certain death than suspense, and we remember the relief which swept Britain when the "phony war" of 1940 was ended with the invasion of the Low Countries. Military defeat is extremely painful for a society, but not so painful as a "war of nerves" during which the society is able to take no action whatever.

Another matter of importance is that anxieties may be developed on the basis of other anxieties. This sounds like a vicious circle, but is simply based on the rules, (1) that any unrelieved drive, basic or derived, is punishing unless relieved, and (2) that anxiety develops on the basis of anticipation of punishment. Thus, unless a culture provides techniques for relieving the drive tensions which exist in the species and those created by the culture, we may expect to see the rise of various anxieties in the society. In short, it is possible to create an anxiety on any type of drive or on presumably any combination of drives. An anxiety may be aroused by any stimulations or conditions which the individual or the group has learned through training or experience to associate with punishment.

The economy of anxiety. Anxiety is generally uncomfortable, but it usually serves an adaptive function for the individual if it motivates him to avoid or eliminate situations in which he will be punished. Anxiety also is economical from the point of view of a society as a whole. On the basis of anxiety the members of a society learn many customs which they might otherwise be forced to learn through the application of pain. About 99 per cent of our own population is law-abiding. In part this is because of the rewards which they receive, in part it is because of fear of punishment which is well diffused throughout the population. The example of what happens to a few law breakers is sufficient to induce most of us to toe the line when seized by unlawful impulses—the so-called deterrent theory of punishment. In this way each person, in a sense, becomes "his own policeman," which from the social point of view is much more economical than having to assign a human guardian to each citizen, an arrangement which would be practically impossible as a permanent thing in any society.

HOW ACQUIRED DRIVES MAY OVERRIDE INNATE DRIVES

We have chosen to discuss this point in connection with pain, because it is generally agreed that the latter is, of all the innate drives, the most motivating. One would think that in any situation in which painful motivation is involved it would win out over any other type of drive, especially drives of the "artificial" type which are created by training and experience. An examination of cultural activities in many societies as well as our own, however, indicates that this superficial judgment is by no means invariably true to the facts. People will actually arouse physical pain purposely as a means of lowering the punishing effects of anxiety.

Prestige drive in general may be defined as the desire to maintain or improve one's social status. It is an acquired drive probably based upon the universal species desire for favorable response of one's fellows as well as upon certain innate drives, but it is always connected with status as defined in a given society, as well as with the means of attaining and validating status prescribed in that society. The definition of status and the customs connected with it obviously may vary from one society to another. It very frequently happens, however, that, when prestige and pain are both involved in the same situation, prestige will override pain. People will actually forego responses which might reduce pain and in many cases they will actually invite pain, if by so doing the prestige drive is rewarded. Let us consider a few examples.

Among the Samoans *childbirth* takes place in the presence of twenty or thirty interested spectators. . . . The mother makes it a point of honor not to cry out in pain.[15] Among the Chukchi, "women are delivered with little labor. Custom strictly forbids the woman to groan, or to give way to the pain by any audible sign. Nor may help be given by another woman." [16]

Puberty ceremonies are often a mechanism whereby the young person validates his status as an adult. In Lesu, for instance, boys endure a painful ceremony of circumcision. Sometimes a stick is placed in the boy's mouth to prevent him from crying out.[17] In Kenya "each boy is circumcised in his teen age. Each patient must remain perfectly silent during the operation, as any who cry out are branded for life as cowards. . . .

The girls are required to go through a similar [operation] before marriage. . . . Any girl who cries out with pain is beaten." [18] In New Guinea, the adolescent girls are scarified. "With sharp flakes of obsidian, incisions are made by old women in the region of the chest, shoulders, breasts, thighs, arms, sides, and abdomen. The cuts are very deep and every day the girl is required to bathe in salt water until the scars are healed." [19] Among the Subanee in the Philippine Islands, it is reported that "upon arriving at the age of puberty many of the men and women grind and blacken their teeth. Sometimes the teeth are ground to the gums and the stumps fall out and painful ulcers ensue." [20] Thus will man submit to pain if thereby he may establish his standing before his fellows. Among the Subanee, this point is stated explicitly, by the "belief that pearly-white teeth belonged to animals and dogs and cats . . . and that man . . . [must change] his teeth if he wished to maintain his supremacy over the lower animals." Another seemingly painful operation on the teeth may be cited from the so-called Cliff Dwellers of Kenya. "The two lower teeth of both youths and maidens are removed. . . . The gums of the victims are cut with a knife between two teeth and on either side of them until the teeth are loose. These are hooked out with a bent piece of wire." [21]

Mutilation and deformation. Most of the painful mutilations which are voluntarily practised in various societies would seem to indicate the overriding influence of prestige (or possibly some associate acquired drive) on pain. "The commonest sight in west African villages," says Gorer, "is women stripped to the waist, their breasts which they crush as early as possible to give the appearance of fertility, hanging forward." [22] A similar custom is reported from the Bavenda of Africa. "They carry out . . . the operation of kneading her [an adolescent girl's] breasts so that they may ripen, a very painful procedure. It is done at home to the accompaniment of a song. . . . They do this until she weeps and drops some tears onto her breasts. When they see that she does not weep they abuse her. . . . Weeping they consider a sign of modesty, and if she does not, it indicates obstinancy, impudence, and an unbending spirit." [23]

The validating of one's status by mutilations which enable one to approximate the tribal ideal of beauty may often be a painful process, as many a Victorian lady of our own society realized as she was being laced into her corset, and as the average young lady of the present day may reflect as she plucks her eyebrows. But not all mutilations of the body are painful. For example, the deformations of the skull, which are practised by binding the head during infancy to deforming cradle boards or in tight bandages provoke no discomfort in the subject. But many another "beautifying" practice is far from comfortable. Among the Masai of East Africa, "there is something called em-bwata, which means the extracting of the two middle incisors of the lower jaw. A knife is used with which to perform the operation." After the teeth have been extracted, "donkey's dung is put on the face in order to cool it." [24] Tatooing, an essential feature of local beauty in Borneo, is described as follows by Hose. "The operation is usually painful, and the subject can rarely restrain her cries of anguish; but the artist is quite unmoved and proceeds methodically with her task." [25] Among a number of western Eskimo groups, the tatoo lines are made by sewing the skin with a sooted thread, not exactly a comfortable procedure, which is apparently borrowed from the tribes of Siberia.[26]

Practically every member and part of the human body is subjected to permanent deformation or mutilation in some society or other somewhere in the world. Dembo and Imbelloni [27] have published a review of these customs. Many deformations may be performed relatively painlessly, as we have already mentioned in the case of infantile deformations of the skull. But not a few mutilations of the body which have fairly wide currency throughout the world are definitely painful, at least when first performed. Among these are the following.

Cicatrization or *scarification* is the creation of designs on the surface of the skin by cutting the epidermis and causing scar tissue to form. Certain Australian tribes, for example, enlarge the scars by rubbing the wounds with clay and the juice of fresh plants. There is some evidence (the statuette of the Venus of Brassempouy, for example) to indicate that this custom goes back into upper Paleolithic times, perhaps 25,000 years ago. As previously mentioned, scarification produces its most noticeable decorative effects on dark skins, which, contrariwise, do not serve as good background for tatooing.[28]

Tatooing is more familiar in our society, at least, in certain social categories. The word "tatoo" is apparently Tahitian and is said to appear first in European languages after the voyages of the famous Captain Cook in 1770. The natives of Polynesia have elaborated this custom to perhaps a higher degree than any other people. Persons of high rank in the Marquesas Islands were in some cases tatooed from head to foot; practically every square inch of skin was covered with designs, including in some cases the mucous membranes of the mouth and the genitalia. The procedure was said to have been highly painful.[29] The Maori of New Zealand combined tatooing with a sort of skin carving of the face which produced shallow grooves in the skin, into which pigment was rubbed.

In general, there are only three methods of tatooing, regardless of whether the instruments used are primitive or modern electrical contrivances: (1) incision, (2) puncture, and (3) the sewing method (subcutaneous tatooing) which seems to have been an exclusive Eskimo and Siberian trait. In any case the skin has to be broken, and since the integument is everywhere plentifully supplied with free nerve endings giving rise to pain drive, the process can never be comfortable unless anesthetics are employed.

Facial deformations. Mention has been made previously of various deformations of the teeth. Orthodontic surgery in our society manages to get most of the snag teeth of children straightened without much pain, and it is only in certain social categories that persons still undergo the torture of the dentist's chair for the "prestige" purpose of being able to display gold caps and fillings on their teeth. We all know, however, that the best that modern dentistry is able to do does not make work on our teeth a noticeably pleasant experience. Yet, there were many people in history and some still living in societies where the pain of mutilating the teeth without benefit of anesthetics was and is bravely endured for the sake of social rewards. The decorative dentistry of certain regions of the Western Hemisphere was fairly advanced before the coming of the Europeans. The ancient inhabitants of the Esmeraldas Coast of Ecuador had a trick of setting "fillings" of metal or gem stones into holes bored in the anterior surface of the incisors. As a matter of fact this custom occurred also in prehistoric Mexico and constitutes one, among other, evidences of a prehistoric connection between the Middle American region and the coast of Ecuador.[30] Considering the fact that these peoples apparently had nothing better for performing these operations than stone or bronze drills (the latter have not appeared in archaeological remains) twirled by hand or with a bow drill, we have a right to expect that a good deal of squirming, to say the least, must have been the price paid both during and following the beautification.

Practically every other feature of the face may also be mutilated under the influence of social drive of one sort or another. In addition to tatooing and scarification, these mutilations usually take the form of perforations. The *ear* is most often perforated in the lobe, but the shell or helix may also be perforated. Distention of the lobe can be produced by hanging weights in the perforation or by inserting rolls of leaves or fiber which tend to expand the member. Among the Koto Indians of the left bank of the Rio Napo in eastern Peru the author observed men with ear lobes so expanded that they were able to wear disks of wood six inches in diameter held in place by the distended skin of the lobe. Perforation of the septum and wings of the *nose* is fairly common among primitive peoples and even among civilized peoples. For example, high caste Hindu ladies often still wear jeweled buttons set in perforations of one wing of the nose. The ferocious-looking boars' teeth of the Melanesians and the feather-tufted bird bones of various Amazonian tribes worn through the perforated septum probably represent the most spectacular use of this organ. The lips may also be perforated and decorated by setting in buttons (labrets), as among the Eskimo and the Tupinamba of Brazil, or may be distended by the insertion of large platters of wood or calabash shell, as among the Sara-Yenye and other tribes of Africa. The Tupinamba of Brazil also perforated the cheeks for the purpose of wearing decorative studs and skewers of wood and bone.[31]

Although all of these perforations are painful when made, they usually do not continue to be painful, once healed. However, most of the mutilations of the lips and nose are definitely inconvenient for the performance of the natural functions of these organs.

Mutilation of the genitalia of both sexes has already been mentioned.

One of the best known and most painful mutilations of extremities, and one directly based upon status prestige, was the old Chinese custom of deforming the feet of upper-class girls. The feet were bound in such a way as to "break the arch" and to disarticulate the bones of the metatarsus from their normal configuration. The process continued over a period of years and is reported to have been extremely painful. It must be admitted, however, that Chinese footbinding was not submitted to voluntarily, but was imposed on girl children against their will, although apparently most women, once grown up, seemed to feel the prestige worth the pain and inconvenience which they suffered.[32]

When we review even briefly the pain which peoples in many societies will endure to conform with the local ideal of beauty or to obtain an ineradicable mark of status, one can only conclude that social drives may undoubtedly become more powerful than even the most punishing of the innate drives. The "mental pain" of being socially ignored or degraded, the mental anguish of unrelieved anxiety of a social nature, can obviously be more punishing to human beings than the physical pain of childbirth or the unrelieved boring into the raw nerve pulp of the teeth. We think of pain as punishing, but physical pain, as we have seen, often comes off second best as a motivator of customs.

CHAPTER 15

The Cultural Rôle of Acquired Drives (*Continued*)

MENTAL SYSTEMS AND "UNREALISTIC" PUNISHMENTS

A MATTER which has puzzled observers since attention was first directed to the ways of man, is the fact that entire societies frequently hold *beliefs* which have no basis in reality when subjected to empirical scrutiny. Despite the apparent unreality of such beliefs, members of the society holding them act *as if* they were true. Perhaps even though the sophisticated readers of this book are aware that there is no empirical evidence that ghosts inhabit cemeteries and forsaken dwellings, nevertheless they refrain from visiting graveyards after dark and will involuntarily attribute to ghosts unusual nighttime noises in empty houses. All religious systems and beliefs in the supernatural, superstitions, and the like, are of this non-empirical type. The question is, how do we acquire such beliefs so firmly that we act as if they referred to empirically verifiable phenomena?

It is to be understood that a scientific explanation of such projective systems on the cultural level does not necessarily imply the judgment that such systems are without validity or merit.

On the contrary, we shall see that such mental systems play an important rôle in promoting cultural integration in many societies. In our own society the orthodox reply to a request for an explanation of our beliefs is ordinarily the statement that they are to be taken on "faith." It is often forgotten that other peoples take their beliefs "on faith" as well. The Japanese belief in the divinity of the emperor was a matter of faith, but does knowing this assist us operationally in restoring the Japanese people after their defeat to the circle of modern civilization? Obviously not, for "faith" is a description, not an explanation. When we are told that a given belief is to be taken "on faith" we are in effect being told that no explanation is necessary—certainly none is to be offered. In essence, the appeal to faith is a begging of the question, which may have some practical validity in maintaining the stability of our own belief systems, but which effectively hamstrings any attempt to understand and to handle these matters either in our own society or in others. In so far as our own beliefs and traditions possess demonstrable value for our society and for ourselves as persons, we need have no fear of inquiring into the general principles underlying systems of belief.

Adaptive functions of mental activity. It has already been mentioned that one of the types of activity which may be learned and patterned as custom is so-called "mental" activity which may take the form of thinking, forming "mental pictures," dreaming, fantasying, and the like. The details of the brain mechanisms involved in this type of activity are at present unknown, but the fact that the activities take place cannot be ignored by students of culture. Although an individual may have strictly private thoughts and other mental activities, they can be made manifest to other persons only through the medium of representational activities. One has to *tell* one's fellows "what is on one's mind" if the others are to have any comprehension of it, and the telling may be done by means of spoken or written language, by means of facial gestures and "expressions" understood by others, or by any other methods of representation. Thus, on the level of custom, the representational customs always serve as links, one might say, between the minds of men, and it is through the practice of representational customs that individual members of a social group come to share common types of mental activity which thus become customary.

It should be noted that all inventions appear first as mental activity in the mind of the inventor. A new idea of this sort does not always appear consciously at first: it may come into the inventor's mind as a half-grasped notion which gradually "takes shape" in his consciousness. In other cases the complete picture of a new artifact or the complete set of words for a poem, for example, may suddenly appear crystal clear to the inventor. In any case, the invention must be "represented" or communicated to others if it is to become a part of culture. In the case of a new artifact, one must describe it, draw a picture of it, or actually make a model of it, if others are to comprehend it.

This ability to perform mental activity, and to express it, is apparently one of the advantages which human beings possess over other animals. Not only is mental activity the source of all culture (in the sense that all inventions are mental in the first instance), but also the ability to "internalize" actional customs serves an important function in the preservation and stabilizing of culture. The actional customs, the artifacts which are their products and adjuncts, and representational customs can be "stored away" in persons' minds. Thus a culture, or at least part of it, may be said to exist, even if there is only one surviving member of the society which formerly practised it, so long as that member retains the mental patterns. Also a society may retain parts of its culture in times of adversity, and when conditions are more propitious the mental patterns can once again be translated into action and artifact. An excellent case of this is the Babylonian Captivity of the Israelites as recounted in the Old Testament. For nearly fifty years (586-538 B.C.) the people lived under restraint, removed from their native land, and prohibited from overtly practising their own culture in full, but that culture they retained mentally, and when the time of the captivity was passed the Israelites were able to return to Palestine and once again take up the actional patterns they had been unable to practise for a generation or two. In the absence of the ability to retain and practise mental customs, a society in such a case would be obliged to start building its culture "from scratch" all over again; it would have to solve its problems without the help of the past cultural solutions.

Mental systems. Although all individuals may have "free floating ideas," the mental activity common to a group is usually systematized to some extent. The individual "runs over in his mind" his ideas or thoughts which he shares with the group in a more or less orderly fashion. The canons of logic are an explicit set of rules for systematizing thoughts, but we must bear in mind that any particular logical system (for example, the Aristotelian system) represents only one type of order. Any system of ordering thoughts, mental pictures, musical tones covertly practised, and so on, may become conventional, provided it does not prove to be punishing and does provide some type of reward. An example is the fact that the words of any language are conventionally ordered according to a tacitly agreed system. Yet, the basic principles of lexical order differ from one language to another. For English-speakers it seems "right" that adjectives should precede nouns and that verbs should follow subjects, but to a German speaker it seems "right" that verbs should stand at the end of the sentence, while to a Spanish speaker it appears inevitable that most adjectives should follow the nouns they modify. These grammatical "rules" are usually not conscious to the members of the group, but nevertheless are practised in common. Likewise in music, each culture exhibits a basic system of order in the arrangement of musical tones. We ourselves use a twelve-tone scale and feel that musical tones put together by any other system—the five-tone scale, for example—sound disagreeable.

When we say that mental activities are systematized, we merely mean that they follow a pattern, they are "practised" in a more or less regular order which is the common property of the group. All cultural activities are patterned, and mental activities, therefore, are no exceptions. Thus it is that we may say that mental customs, like other types of customs, have both *content* and *organization*.

Do mental customs conform to the rule which requires that a custom to be learned or maintained must be rewarding? From the individual point of view, society usually metes out rewards and punishments which bring about conformity. Thus the individual who cannot learn to "think clearly" according to the system of thinking approved in his society is punished by denial of privileges and statuses (jobs, honors), while one who does arrange his thoughts and express them according to the norm of his society is usually given rewards in the form of wealth, prestige, power over others, and so on. Also one may learn to practise certain mental activity that is rewarded internally. A certain train of fantasy often has the effect of lowering anxiety in the individual. Most of us have some such patterns of mental activity which are strictly idiosyncratic, and we practise them because they are anxiety-lowering and ego-inflating. If you cannot get the raise you were after at the office, you can at least take refuge in "imagining" what you would do if you were boss, and thus obtain some relief from your anxiety. Such mechanisms are also often practised on a cultural level. Dr. Coué's method which induced thousands of persons to repeat mentally that "every day in every way" they were "getting better and better" was apparently rewarding in this way. The mental customs of Christian Science serve much the same function of relieving anxieties associated with physical illness and pain. And the beliefs (mental customs) of all those religions which promise reward after death for the endurance of anxiety and pain in this life serve a similar purpose of relieving anxieties and other tensions.

An important mechanism of mental activity is that of *identification*. It is the process whereby one can "put himself in the place of another," as it were, by imagination. It is this process which accounts for our interest in stories and other works of fiction. Once we have identified with a fictional character we are able to share his adventures *vicariously*, with the result that the predicaments through which he passes symbolically nevertheless have the effect of raising drives in ourselves, and the actions which he takes to solve his problems have the effect of lowering these drives. Hence the satisfaction we receive from the "happy ending" and other fictional techniques. In the same way we are able to identify ourselves mentally with persons in real life and to attribute to them feelings which we ourselves may have, a process which is known as *projection*. It is this mechanism which accounts for much of the social "sympathy" of which earlier sociologists spoke so much, and it often serves the adaptive function of preserving the solidarity of the group, although it also enters into conflict in cases where aggressive drives are attributed to (projected upon) other persons.

Realistic and unrealistic mental systems. Covert or mental activity is said to be realistic in so far as it internalizes events, objects, and relations as they actually occur in the external world according to the evidence of our senses. The inmate of the psychopathic ward who believes he is Napoleon and who insists that the attendants are soldiers who must follow his orders for the Battle of Waterloo is operating an unrealistic mental system. We say that "what goes on in his head" does not correspond with what goes on outside. Nevertheless, such an individual's mental activity is frequently well systematized and the delusion "hangs together" in an orderly fashion, if one grants the basic premise.

The mental customs of many cultures are unrealistic because of faulty techniques of observation which prevent the members of the society from ascertaining completely the real relations of the empirical world. The old tale of the three blind men, each of whom formed a different idea of what an elephant was after feeling it, is an illustration of how unrealistic mental systems may arise from faulty observation. The "primitive" belief that sickness is caused by the entrance of an evil spirit into the body is an unrealistic belief, but we can hardly expect a society to hold the germ theory of disease if it lacks microscopes capable of bringing pathogenic microörganisms into its ken.

In the matter of cause-and-effect relationships many errors have been made during human history, errors which have been incorporated into the mental systems of cultures. These systems are frequently supported by what appears to be empirical evidence from the real world. For example, a society believes that a painful leg is caused by the presence of a magical spider which has entered the member. A medicine man, with ritual procedures, makes an incision and by prestidigitation sucks out a spider, which he exhibits to the patient and onlookers as empirical evidence of the belief. The spider is real enough and its observation is no illusion. What has not been proved is the alleged causal connection between spider and swollen leg. This connection has been assumed or imputed. Thus it is that, in the process of ordering or organizing mental customs, a culture may construct relationships of cause and effect between empirical stimuli, relationships which by scientific methods of investigation can be shown not to exist empirically. Such a mental system then serves in turn as the basis for certain actional customs. So long as the latter are not unduly punishing and so long as no more rewarding customs are presented for trial, neither the mental nor the actional customs will be extinguished.

One of the reasons for the advance and diffusion of science, of course, lies in the fact that it is a complex of techniques for bringing the mental systems of a culture either into conformity with the external world, or discarding them in favor of systems which do conform, and of bringing actional and representational customs into consistency with both. In so far as the scientific complex proves more rewarding to more drives than does an unrealistic system with which it is competing, it tends to displace the latter. In considering these matters, however, we must always consider carefully all of the drives involved. In some cases an unrealistic system is actually more rewarding and hence successfully resists the introduction of science. For example, among people in whom anxiety concerning the after-life can be aroused, science has, up to now, had little to offer in the way of consolation.

Projective systems. Kardiner, Linton, and associates,[33] have demonstrated (in terms other than those of the present analysis) how mental systems come to be generated in early childhood as the result of the pressures of the particular cultural institutions of child care and training, family organization, and social relationships to which the average child is subjected by his society. These conditions tend to be generally uniform within a given society or group because they are governed by common cultural patterns, but they may differ from one society or group to another. The configuration of rewards and punishments surrounding the small child tends to build up in him a view of the world, or system of looking at the social life in which he must live as an adult. For example, in one society (Tanala) the child's life is dominated by the father who dispenses rewards, punishments, and frustrations, in another the father's authority over the children is shared by many adults (Marquesas), in still another both parents may be more or less equally frustrating in the eyes of the child (Alor). Depending upon the type of family in which the child grows up, he tends to view the world as dominated by an all-powerful male who must be placated, by males and females, or by no such omnipotent beings.

Kardiner makes the point that these commonly held mental systems (our term) tend to be *projected* into the outer world. Thus, in the case of a society in which children are dominated by the male parent, if there is no one to fill the parent's place in the childhood *Weltanschauung* when the child eventually reaches adulthood, he and his fellows will invent one. The system is projected into the adult world of the society—a king or dictator may take the parent's place in worldly affairs, and an all-powerful god may reflect the all-powerful parent in the religious scheme of things. A just and terrible male god becomes the adult equivalent of the just and terrible male parent of the childhood scheme. As one learned to beg favors and forgiveness from one's father as a child, it is customary to follow the same techniques with respect to the father-god. These are examples of only one type of projective mental systems which may occur in culture.

It thus becomes clear that although the mental customs of a culture may be "unrealistic" in the empirical sense it is possible to understand scientifically how they arise. Furthermore, even unrealistic systems are "real" in the cultural sense that they form a façade of stimuli to which response must be made customarily, and they can be interpreted as providing reward to many types of drives. Up to the present time no society has constructed a culture which is 100 per cent "real" in the scientific, empirical sense. A certain sector of cultural life in all societies is carried on in an unreal world structured and interpreted in terms of mental systems which are commonly held and which have been projected onto the "real" world of nature and of society. And the evidence seems to indicate that such structures and the overt customs practised in connection with them often bring satisfactions which are just as "real" psychologically as other, more empirically stimulated customs. No one can doubt the pleasure which the little child receives from his belief in Santa Claus, nor the feeling of security which many religious people obtain from their faith and practices.

However, occasions do arise when the mental systems show themselves to be excessively inconsistent with reality. The child some day discovers that there is no Santa Claus; not a few primitive peoples have discovered after conquest by the whites that their tribal gods seem to have lost their power. It is because of contingencies of this sort that the student of culture must be able to understand the principles underlying mental systems and to assess their function in the life of culture.

DEVELOPMENT AND MAINTENANCE OF MENTAL SYSTEMS

To an unbeliever or a foreigner many a mental system appears to be a mere "figment of the imagination," "a body of benighted superstition." This view, to be sure, seldom applies to our own systems, but to those of others. We may well ask how such systematized views can be inculcated into the members of a society and how they can be maintained, when the premises themselves often seem to fly in the face of readily observable "facts." Dr. John Whiting has made a pioneer analysis of these matters, particularly with regard to supernatural beliefs, in a tribe of Oceanic Negroids, the Kwoma of the Sepik River drainage of New Guinea. We can only sketch a few of the points brought out in Whiting's study,[34] but they should provide us with some insight regarding analogous cultural forms in our own and other cultures.

When an older member of the society is teaching a child the customs which accord with natural laws he has the support of the environment, which affords both motivation and reward to validate his teachings, but when his task is to transmit customs which do not accord with these laws, one would think his task to be more difficult.

The Kwoma have four types of unrealistic supernatural beliefs, and to each of the objects concerned is attached anxiety. (1) Marsalai are supposed to be huge monsters in the form of snakes or crocodiles which produce storms, earthquakes, and other natural cataclysms, and which are also present at the yam ceremonies to insure a plentiful crop. These creatures are believed to be dangerous. (2) Ghosts are believed to be the spirits of dead persons who live on the edge of the tribal territory; they are believed to attack living persons abroad at night; whistling or music-making at night tends to attract them. (3) It is believed that certain persons have the power to inflict injury or death by sorcery; they do this either by inserting a magical "poison" into the victim's food, or by burning certain materials which have been bodily associated with the victim, such as food leavings, blood, and so on. Accepting food from any one but a close relative, spilling one's own blood or the blood of animals one kills, and eating away from home where a sorcerer may pick up one's leavings are, therefore, all considered dangerous practices. (4) The Kwoma believe that food turns into blood in one's system, where it stays and deteriorates unless drained off from time to time. Fresh blood is thus necessary for the health of adults and for the growth of children. A number of customs involving periodic bleeding are based upon this belief. If a boy does not periodically let blood from his sexual organ, he will not grow up; and if he is not properly bled at the age-grade initiation, he will not become a man.

Now the question is: How are such "fantastic" beliefs inculcated and maintained?

Warning. A common technique of inculcation among the Kwoma, as among ourselves, is the warning of youngsters by adults. In effect, a warning is a drive stimulus whose function is to raise anxiety; but how does the child learn to heed the warning, especially if it is unrealistic? Whiting points out that the Kwoma develop from the first a strong habit of heeding *all* warnings given by adults, and we may remark parenthetically that a similar technique is used in all human societies to a greater or less degree. Most warnings issued by adults, particularly parents, are reinforced by punishments meted out by the adults themselves or by the environment. Before the child develops the use of language, objective warnings of this type are the only kind which can can be issued. Thus, if the child does not heed the warning, it is very probable that it will suffer the pain or punishment specified therein. If the toddler is told not to go near the fire or it will be burned, it usually finds out that the prediction turns out to be true. If he is told not to play with his father's weapons or he will be beaten, father usually makes good on the threat if the warning is unheeded. Thus, the child learns by hundreds of more or less bitter experiences that the warnings of parents and adults are "real"—there is nothing imaginary about the punishments which are connected with them. On the other hand, adults reward children who are obedient with food, caresses, words of praise, and so on. Thus by the time the child is large enough to understand more abstract language it has firmly established the habit of heeding warnings and believing the punishments which are specified in them. Hence, when it is told not to accept food from strangers because it might be magically poisoned, or not to go near swamps if it does not want to be attacked by the supernatural monsters living therein, the child is not in a questioning frame of mind. The warning tends to raise anxiety which is lowered by heeding the admonition.

Generalization. A second factor in making the supernatural beliefs "stick" in Kwoma is that many of the alleged dangers are described as similar to real dangers. For example, the fact that the marsalai are said to be like crocodiles and snakes raises anxiety based upon past experience with real animals of this description. By the principle of secondary generalization or transfer, when two objects are described by the same term, the individual tends to respond to them in a similar manner, because the term itself serves as a similar stimulus. Likewise ghosts are said to look and act somewhat like living men, although they can also assume the form of birds and animals. When animals or birds are heard at night, children are told that they are ghosts walking about. Thus behavior learned for men and animals and birds of the real world generalizes to ghosts. We have something similar in our "bogey-men" who are said to be like men, with the unpleasant and punishing attributes of men somewhat magnified. Fear of poisoned food is realistically reinforced by experience with putrefied victuals, which are fairly common in this society. Also the same root word is used to describe "poisoned" and merely spoiled food. It is probable that the beliefs regarding "bad blood" and the necessity for letting it are realistically enforced by experience with the sickness and even death which frequently follows puss discharges from wounds and sores.

Imitation.[35] In Kwoma, as in most other societies, children are rewarded for copying the behavior of certain other persons, especially those of the same social category, same family, and so forth, and they are punished when deviating from such models. Thus there is ingrained in most children the tendency to "imitate" older children and adult relatives, especially when the latter give evidence of being in a situation of danger, whether the danger be objectively realistic or not.

Chance usually plays a part in the maintenance of supernatural beliefs, although in many anthropological reports it is given all the credit. In

Kwoma, it is alleged that if one even accidentally molests the dwelling place of one of the supernatural monsters in a swamp, the latter will cause a storm. As Whiting points out, however, rain and thunder storms are of almost daily occurrence in this region, so that one has not long to wait for "proof" of the belief, if he has unwittingly trespassed on the domain of the supernatural.

Experimental evidence has shown that one experience of heavy reinforcement will establish and maintain habit strength even in the face of several succeeding unrewarded trials, especially if no alternative or inconsistent habit is offered.[36] We are all familiar with this principle in everyday life: if you have eaten an unusually fine meal in a certain restaurant, the chances are that you will go back several times to the same eating house "in the hope" of duplicating the experience, even though on several subsequent visits the cooking is nothing to boast about. If an individual has been very friendly to you on one occasion, your tendency is to seek his company thereafter, even though on several later occasions he may not seem overly interested in you. In short, a single heavy reward will often establish a habit or a custom, whereas a considerable number of later trials without reward may be required to extinguish it, provided no punishment is involved in the subsequent trials.

With respect to supernatural beliefs, this principle operates in both a positive and a negative fashion. A single case of heavy punishment for failure to follow an injunction based on a supernatural belief is often sufficient to maintain the enjoined behavior pattern for a considerable time thereafter. If you have a heavy stroke of bad luck shortly after walking under a ladder, the chances are that you will avoid this practice for a period in the future. On the other hand, a single heavy reward for behaving in consonance with a mental system will often convince an individual for a considerable time, even though no obvious rewards are forthcoming for some time thereafter. In our own society we have many instances of sudden religious conversion which illustrate this point, some of which have been recounted from the war. A pilot, for instance, finds himself in apparently lethal difficulties in the air from which there seems to be no escape but death. He decides to pray, something he has not done for years. He is miraculously saved and returns to base. Thereafter, no one has to convince him of the efficacy of prayer.

The reader will understand that we are not arguing against the efficacy of prayer or other rituals. But we are endeavoring to explain scientifically how individuals and groups establish and maintain the customs which are associated with the mental systems current in their societies.

Social sanctions. The mental systems are usually intertwined with the basic institutions of the culture. Malinowski and a number of sociologists have pointed out that an institution always has a charter or a tradition, the effect of which is to explain and to justify the practices involved. Such a charter is, of course, a mental system. In Kwoma the supernatural beliefs we have cited are bound up in various ways with several basic institutions, including the family, the men's secret societies, the age-grading system for boys, and so on. If the beliefs were removed, the institutions would lose their reason for being. Among ourselves, in many communities, at least, the beliefs of Christianity serve to unite and strengthen the family, the political organization, even business. Thus it is that the social group as a whole unconsciously guards and protects the mental system, because an attack upon the beliefs is regarded as an attack upon the stability of the overt content of the institutions or of the society itself. Any one who aggresses against or professes agnosticism concerning the beliefs is heavily punished by society.

It should be noted that mental systems are not all necessarily religious in the strict sense of the word. Among ourselves the institutions of capitalism are interwoven with a mental system, and any heretic, such as a communist or even a socialist, is vigorously attacked by the adherents of the capitalistic system.

Also we should note that mental systems do not *have* to be unrealistic. Modern technology, for example, is supported by a mental system of scientific theory, which is as realistic as constant investigation can make it, but which functions in the same way as an unrealistic system—that is, it provides the rationale for the techniques employed in applied science. Even among the scientists, however, who are supposed to be especially open-minded, there is the general tendency to protect the mental system against changes and innovations. Witness the furor created in the last century by Darwin's announcement of a new theory of the origin of species. Einstein's theory of relativity is still the subject of considerable debate. With respect to scientific systems, however, the way is open for testing them by all who have command of the procedures involved, so that critics can satisfy themselves as to the pragmatic "truth" of the systems. This is the main difference between realistic and unrealistic mental systems. The latter provide no practical possibilities for thorough test or the elimination of error.

Unrealistic drives. If one has followed the foregoing explanation of unrealistic mental systems which occur in culture, he is able to follow to the conclusion that such systems are capable of creating unrealistic drives which may be common to a social group or society. Thus, although there is no scientific proof of "hell" after death, some persons fear it sufficiently to follow certain religious customs designed to deliver their souls from its torments. In the more mundane realm most Americans have recently been sufficiently convinced of the likelihood of sundry punishments from vitamin deficiency so that they have incorporated a new complex of customs into their culture which have to do with gulping various fish oils in gelatine capsules, and so on. Scientific experts on nutrition tell us that the fear of vitamin deficiency is greatly exaggerated if not entirely unrealistic for the average North American citizen, but the motivation persists.

Unrealistic drives connected with the supernatural are very frequently sufficiently strong to become more motivating than realistic drives, such as pain, the desire for economic security, the desire for response from others, and the like. They may be either negative drives (fears or anxiety) or positive drives (yearning for beatitude, for the good-will of the deity, and so forth). As far back as upper Paleolithic times we have evidence that the hunters of Europe were in the custom of cutting off finger joints, presumably as offerings to the supernatural, and the bloody and painful sacrifices which are offered up to the divinities in so many cultures testify to the power of unrealistic fear and yearning to override the motive of pain. The Aztecs of Mexico, for example, systematically offered their own blood by drawing a cord through a perforation in the tongue.[37] The Macusi hunter of Guiana who wishes to secure supernatural aid in the chase follows a widespread pattern of this region and uses a string of fibers woven together in a sort of tassel.

He now takes one of these strings and, passing the thin end up his nostril, manages to bring it out through his mouth, and thus pulls the whole length of the string in at the nostril and out at the mouth. . . . Or he takes a small mat, about six or eight inches square, made of narrow parallel strips of the skin of a reed-like plant (Ischnosiphon), tied together somewhat as are the lathes of a venetian blind. . . . Between each two of these strips he inserts a row of living ants, their heads all one way. The strips are exactly at such a distance apart that the ants, which are of a large and venomous kind, bite most painfully. Or, in other cases, the huntsman looks for certain large and very hairy caterpillars, the hairs of which break off very readily and have a great power of irritating the flesh. These caterpillars he rubs on his chest or thighs, and thus produces a considerable and very painful-looking rash.[38]

The Sun Dance of the Plains tribes was a ceremonial search for power (phrased with some variation among different tribes). One of the widespread features of the ritual was that certain male participants "had skewers run through the fleshy parts of their backs to which thongs were attached, fastened at the other end to the dance pole." The men tossed themselves about on the end of the thongs, often tearing the skewers from their skins. Or the thong might be attached to a skull which had to be dragged about over the ground regardless of the obstructions.[39]

Many other such *masochistic customs* illustrate the power of unrealistic motivations.

We have only to remind ourselves of the ascetic cults which have flourished in all periods in Christianity, as in most of the other world religions, to understand that groups of men and women may be motivated to override their desire for earthly companionship and response in their yearning for divine approval through hermitage, to scorn their desires for food and other "cravings of the flesh" in their desire to identify with the deity, to cast aside their desire for economic security and wealth to satisfy an all-powerful desire for holiness. It is no denial of the nobility of such persons and their motives to conclude that, in the sense used here, they were unrealistic.

ACQUIRED DRIVES DERIVED FROM REWARD

The culturally conditioned motivations which we call fears or anxieties are based principally upon social experience with certain types of punishments and upon anticipation of their repetition in the future. Another type of acquired drive which we find in operation in almost all societies is based upon specific types of reward which have been experienced with respect to certain features offered by the cultural environment. We may call such acquired drives *appetites* or *positive desires of a cultural nature*. As is the case with all acquired drives the appetites or positive desires may, and in fact must, be associated with certain aspects of cultural situations; that is, people have acquired desires only for specific features which are present within a specific culture. Although not a few individuals in our society are motivated by desire for chocolate malted milk with ice cream, we do not expect to find this motivation among the natives of Tierra del Fuego, where aboriginally there was neither cow's milk, malt, ice cream, nor chocolate. In the realm of food not a few of the substances which are craved in our society are distasteful, even to out own infants when first presented to them. We say, with respect to green olives, for example, that "you have to learn to like them." Thus it is possible to learn to like almost anything in a culture sufficiently to have a craving or a desire for it, provided one's training and experience have been such as to make the cultural feature in question highly rewarding. The strength of such drives may vary from that of a mere "liking" to that of an imperious "craving."

Numerous examples of acquired appetites for food have been discussed in Chapter 12 and need not be repeated here. It must be understood, however, that appetites or acquired cultural desires may be oriented toward anything which gives satisfaction. The appetite for drugs, including tobacco and alcohol, for example, seems to be based less on food hunger than upon anxiety—most drugs have the faculty of relieving the feeling of mental stress temporarily and of creating in its stead a feeling of satisfaction and well-being which is highly rewarding. In this connection we should note a distinction between the customary *use* of drugs and the *desire* for them. Smoking and drinking, for example, may be practised as customs in the absence of a specific smoking or drinking drive. Thus we have persons in our society who smoke only when in groups where others smoke, and the custom for them may be presumed to be based on desires for prestige and response from others. Likewise one may gain a certain prestige in some circles by drinking his fellows "under the table," a motivation which is directly opposed to the soporific, anxiety-relieving effects which many a true addict desires from alcohol. This indicates that customs which satisfy one type of drive may be used to satisfy other types of drive as well.

Instrumental drives. Most cultures inculcate certain desires the satisfaction of which is instrumental to the satisfaction of still other drives. We shall postpone a full discussion of the instrumental aspects of culture until a later section, but the drive aspect should be mentioned here. For example, the *desire for money* may be regarded as an instrumental drive. In our cultural setting the satisfaction of this drive (that is, the acquisition of money) is not ordinarily an end in itself—it merely places one in a position whereby he is enabled to practise other customs designed to satisfy other drives. Money is an instrument for the satisfaction of other wants. Thus members of our society are trained to want money so that they can get something else. We are told that we "have no business to want fur coats, fine houses, or what-not, unless we have the gumption (that is, the drive) to earn the money to pay for them." It is obvious that in our culture the capitalistic system is well coördinated with this particular drive. We shall see that other types of cultural systems in other societies may also be coördinated with money drive.

Another instrumental drive of this sort which is generated in not a few societies is the *desire for prestige*. Although some cultures may make this an end in itself, it not uncommonly is actually an instrumental drive. In our own cultural setup a man who has achieved generally recognized prestige may use it to obtain "power" over other men, to obtain the type of mate he most desires, to escape punishment for his misdemeanors, to acquire money with which to satisfy still other desires, and so forth.

Thus, without going into more details, it is obvious that the members of a social group may be motivated by positive wants generated by the culture, (*a*) wants that may be directly satisfied, and (*b*) wants that stand in an instrumental position to the satisfaction of other wants. And, once these desires are established in the members of the society or group, the culture provides patterned customs which may be learned for their satisfaction.

ACQUIRED DRIVES BASED ON FRUSTRATIONS

Frustration drive. When a response leading to a goal of satisfaction is blocked, an innate drive, which we call frustration or anger, arises. In the naïve organism this drive motivates random activity, usually of an aggressive nature, against the blockage, until a rewarding response is found. The adaptive function of such a motivation is to goad the organism on to remove, by-pass, or avoid obstacles which stand in the way of the satisfaction of other drives, and thus to preserve the life of the individual and the species. If an otherwise successful response based on either food or sex, for example, could be stopped by a fortuitous blockage of some sort, many an animal (including man) would starve or would die without issue. Nature, therefore, seems to have equipped most animals with a frustration drive which motivates them to eliminate impediments which stand between them and goals.[40]

Now frustration, just as punishment, can be anticipated. Once an individual has had experience with a frustrating situation, the presentation of any significant element of the stimulus configuration of that situation may serve as a drive-stimulus to arouse anger. Likewise, on the principle of generalization, situations and elements which have some resemblance to those which have been associated in experience with frustration may also serve to arouse the drive. To take an example of anticipation, let us say that a fellow has tripped you at a party as you were about to ask a girl to dance with you. This has made you "angry with him." Next week when you see him coming down the street your anger arises upon first recognizing him. You don't have to wait for a repetition of the situation in which it was first aroused. This is anticipation of frustration and the part-stimulus gives rise to the drive. Let us say that, instead of the original culprit himself, you see his brother coming down the street. It would not be unusual if this sight also were sufficient to arouse anger. In other words, you generalize from the original stimulus to one you identify as similar to it. It is through this mechanism that feuds between entire social groups often develop.

General reactions to frustration. In general the organism can react to frustration by (*a*) aggression or attack against the frustrating object or objects, (*b*) by avoidance or circumvention of the frustrating object (withdrawal, by-passing, and the like), or (*c*) by suppressing the frustration drive and not reacting at all in the presence of the stimulus. The latter two alternatives definitely must be learned; that is, they must be based on past experience with the frustrating stimulus. They are usually learned on the basis of punishment or anxiety drives, which override the frustration drive. That is to say, one learns that aggression is punishing and painful. Hence, in the future, the stimulus situation may arouse frustration drive, but it also arouses an anxiety drive which is more powerful and motivating. Thus one makes the response which relieves the anxiety rather than that which relieves frustration. Psychoanalysis has shown that as a general rule, however, a suppressed frustration drive will often motivate delayed and disguised responses: aggression "seeks an outlet" in other ways than direct attack upon the frustrator. There is a fourth type of general reaction to frustration, namely, (d) displacement of aggression upon some other stimulus than the actual frustrator or block. This is also usually conditioned by fear of punishment from the actual source of the frustration. For example, a man frustrated by his boss during the day may abuse his wife when he comes home in the evening.

Cultural responses to aggression. Any of these types of reaction, not to mention some complications of them, can be learned and are therefore capable of being translated into customs.

In our own society patterns of direct aggression to frustration are enjoined upon small boys by their mothers from an early age. But the stimuli to which direct aggression is permissible are strictly defined by the culture. Boys should only attack other boys of their own size when attacked by them or when they obviously and intentionally stand in the way of practising socially approved customs. Margaret Mead has defined this as the "chip on the shoulder" attitude and in our society it is customary to think that this type of training promotes self-reliance and independence. The customary forms whereby boys respond to these instigations (fisticuffs) are entirely different in content from those taught to girls (snide remarks, and the like). Ours seems to be a culture in which the average individual is expected to practise a good many customs of aggression, either direct or indirect, and in general one cannot be a "success" unless he has mastered some of these techniques. On the other hand, the culture prohibits unprovoked aggression and attacks upon individuals who because of age, sex, size, or other disabilities are unable to defend themselves against the aggression. This is known as the "sporting attitude" (a mental pattern), which is supposed to be universally practised in our society.[41]

Directly aggressive customs are always patterned and may be *actional* as in the case of "scientific boxing," the techniques of jiu-jitsu, "shooting a pistol from the hip," and the like. They may be *representational*, as in the patterned verbal insult whose aggressive intent is understood by all.[42] And they may be purely *mental*, as when one performs a standardized fantasy to the effect that "the next time I see that blankety-blank I'll tell him to go straight to ——," or when one forms a mental picture of knocking the frustrating individual "cold" with a neat blow to the chin.

Indirect aggressive customs are usually learned and performed on the basis of a mixed motivation of fear and frustration. For example, practically all personal aggression in Carib society is carried on *sub rosa* by the indirect techniques of sorcery and magic. Practically the only exceptions occur when the individuals are drunk, a condition which seems to inhibit the rise of anxiety drive.[43] The practice of such indirect customs, of course, requires the existence of a mental system, as previously discussed; that is, both aggressor and victim must believe the efficacy of the magical techniques. Even when magical aggression is completely secret, it is rewarding to the individual who practises it, because it lowers his frustration drive. When the magical aggression is made known to the victim, it often has practical punishing effects upon him—any sickness he may have is psychosomatically complicated with anxiety, self-confidence is lost, and so on. In case the perpetrator of the magic is known to the victim, magic is merely a technique of direct aggression, but if the perpetrator remains unknown, we may regard it as a method of indirect aggression. It may be surprising to North Americans that magical methods of indirect aggression are still used by literate modern peoples in Latin America.[44]

Anonymous rumors and "whispering campaigns" are other types of indirect aggression, as well as all other round-about methods of putting the other fellow "in a corner." Indirect aggression, by maintaining the anonymity of the instigator, protects him from retaliation by the victim.

Group aggression. The foregoing has referred for the most part to customs usually available within a culture for individual aggressions within a society. When an entire society or group undertakes to aggress against another, the individual customs of aggression are usually organized and integrated together for group-coördinated action, often with certain patterns added which can only be practised by groups. Thus in modern warfare individual soldiers are taught the individualistic customs of fighting, but are trained to integrate the use of the knife, the gun, the fist blow, and the wrestling throw with a *plan* of attack. This is as far as customs of warfare go in some of the simpler societies.[45] However, most "civilized" societies have employed patterns and artifacts of warfare which are operational only by a trained group of individuals. For example, no individual alone can operate a battleship or a Superfortress. Even in Roman times, single individuals were incapable of operating the siege machines, such as catapults, which were available at the time, crude as they were.

Although warfare between nation-societies in modern times represents the peak of aggressive culture, we must bear in mind that aggressive patterns may also be adapted to the purposes of smaller groups both within and without the larger societies. Whites may aggress upon Negroes, "capitalists" upon "workers," the "upper classes" upon the "lower classes" within a nation-society. Likewise American corporations may aggress in foreign trade upon corporations affiliated with other nations, and so on. Before World War II, Nazi intellectual circles were aggressing on the United States, Latin American, and whatever other intellectual circles with which they could make contact. Organized proponents of Nazi "race" theories (mental systems), for example, were attempting to discredit and undermine the scientific anthropologists and their theories.

Aggression as an outgrowth of frustration was well illustrated in the civilian agencies of government in Washington during the war. The present writer was connected with a number of these agencies during the "emergency period" before division of labor and lines of authority had been worked out. The fact that these matters had not been settled satisfactorily before the emergency arose is an excellent illustration in itself of the practical need of cultural planning. But the writer, like many another new recruit to Washington who had joined the government service with the idea of "helping to win the war," was amazed to find that, although "fight" was one of the commonest words in the vocabulary of the bureaucrats, it was in that period applied to rival agencies much more often than to our national enemies. Thus one made the discovery that we had to "fight it out" with such-and-such a department, because it was trying to usurp the functions of our department; we had to "go to the mat" innumerable times with other groups of compatriots who were trying to block our own (that is, our department's) path to victory. In many cases animosities toward rival heads of bureaus were more intense than toward Hitler, Hirohito, or other enemies of our nation as a whole. It is and was entirely possible to *plan* the functions and activities of the various agencies of government, since they were cultural organizations after all, so that internal aggression need never arise. That is one of the themes of this book: we must learn the ways of culture so that we may plan customs and institutions to suit our own convenience and best desires as members of society, rather than becoming the servants, dupes, and victims of self-created cultural situations, whose effect is to lead us into mutual aggression.

In group conflict it is well known that the frustrating blocks which arouse anger among the members of the group in many cases must be presented to them mentally and representationally. Thus in time of war individual citizens who have had no personal experience with the frustrations imposed upon them either actually or potentially by the enemy must be convinced by argument, news stories, photographs, and other devices that the enemy actually does stand in the way of their personal goals as well as those of the nation. These techniques are sometimes described as "propaganda," a word which has rather an unsavory flavor among ourselves. The process of "arousing" the frustration drive by means of representations may be, of course, based on objective fact or the representations may be at least partly based on fantasy. Thus the aftermath of the war with Germany seems to have produced ample evidence that few, if any, representations made to our own people concerning German acts during the conflict were exaggerated. On the other hand untruthful "propaganda" is not uncommon, for which reason many of our people have become somewhat skeptical of all such representations. One example is the type of propaganda technique sometimes used in industrial relations. During the war the papers repeatedly printed "scare stories" regarding strikes which were said to be so serious as practically to cripple our war effort. This was true of a few strikes, but the object of this campaign, of course, was to identify the entire organized laboring movement in the minds of the "public" as a block to the common goal and to arouse frustration drive against organized labor. Actually, this was an exaggeration. Up to the end of June 1945, according to an official announcement by the Secretary of Labor, less than 1 per cent of possible total man hours available since the beginning of the war had been lost by strikes, and by renouncing the single holiday of July 4 of that year the workers made up all time which had been lost by strikes throughout the war period.

These techniques for arousing anger or frustration drive directed against groups within our own society must be carefully watched by intelligent citizens and responsible public officials. All of us have been trained in the practice of certain customs of aggression and when we practise them against groups within our own society on illusory grounds the stability of the social structure is threatened and the satisfaction of other drives often stands in jeopardy.

Competition. A good deal has been made by sociologists of competition as a substitute for conflict and aggression.[46] It is pointed out that when rules of competition are agreed upon and followed, as for example in organized sports, individuals and groups may carry on certain aggressive customs toward each other without the dire social consequences which often form the *sequelae* of true aggression. How is this? Remember that stress is always laid upon the *rules*. Why? Rules of competition imply also the cultural definition and the arrangement of the situations in which competition takes place. Thus a pair of football teams compete with each other before a crowd of spectators, on a field of agreed dimensions, with referees and umpires present to remind them of approved and disapproved behavior. What is the motivation of the players, coaches, and others involved under these artificial, culturally arranged conditions? In most cases of amateur competition the principal drive seems to be prestige, which we have already seen is an instrumental drive. Team A receives prestige if it gets to the goal of Team B, regardless of the blockages which the latter may place in its path. The rules, in other words, define the situation in such a way that a blocking tackle, for example, does not arouse frustration drive in well-trained men; he arouses even higher the prestige drive of the ball-carrier, who practises every customary technique he has learned from his coach to reach the goal despite the opposing techniques of the competing team. It is only when the rules are "broken," that is, when the cultural definition of the situation disintegrates, that true frustration drive is aroused.

Avoiding and circumventing customs. One cultural means of handling frustration is to pattern customs designed to avoid frustrating situations. Although other motivations are also involved, the widespread custom of the "mother-in-law tabu," which prohibits speech and other social contact between son-in-law and mother-in-law in many a primitive society, is a set of customs which has the effect of avoiding mutual frustration on the part of the occupants of the statuses involved. Many an American husband may wish that such a custom were incorporated in our own culture. Patterns which require the segregation of the races and minimization of the contacts between them have the same effect.

Many frustrations, however, cannot be avoided in the course of normal cultural life. Hence not a few cultural patterns are usually provided in every society for the circumvention of frustrations in case they are presented. In our own society a type of frustration very often encountered is mechanical failure. Obviously, this does not occur in societies whose cultures lack machines. Techniques of circumventing mechanical failure among ourselves range all the way from learning how to use fence-wire for tying together a drooping fender to the specialties of garage mechanics who are trained in detecting and repairing faulty distributors, clogged needle valves, and the like. In a hunting or fishing society frustrations are frequently encountered in what often appear to be the perverse habits of the wild denizens of the earth and the water. Some societies learned to circumvent these frustrations to a certain extent perhaps 10,000 years ago by techniques of *domestication* of animals. Where wild animals are still hunted customary techniques for avoiding the frustrations imposed upon men by their wild quarry range all the way from weird horns for producing "moose calls" to magical practices supposed to ensure "good luck" and other forms of supernatural aid.[47]

Conventional suppression of frustration drive. The socialization of the child in all societies and cultures involves unavoidable frustrations to its "natural" impulses. In fact, a person is not entirely "human" until he has undergone this process of "domestication," which involves establishing control over the reactions to certain drives and the channelization of such reactions in socially approved lines. The precise channelization of customs may differ from one society to another, as we have pointed out repeatedly, but, whatever the culture pattern may be, no normal child will be accepted into adult society unless and until he has submitted to a certain degree of frustration. If nothing else, the individual must learn to satisfy his innate drives at certain times and places and according to specific, conventionally approved patterns of custom. He must learn to eat, to eliminate, to express or react to pain and sorrow, to engage in sex activity, and so forth, according to the "rules" laid down in the culture of his society. He cannot do "just as he pleases," which means that he cannot habitually practise any one of the group of random responses which might be evoked by certain situations, but, on the contrary, he must learn to practise only that one or group of responses which is approved by his social group.

In this process of teaching the approved behavior, frustrations are inevitably placed in the way of children by the social group and its agents. This may be done in an organized fashion which tends to build up an integrated personality in the individual, or it may be done in a haphazard fashion which arouses frustrations without completely satisfying many other basic drives. Du Bois has described and Kardiner has analyzed very clearly the frustrations imposed in disorganized and haphazard manner upon children of the Alor tribe in Indonesia.[48] Children, for example, are constantly frustrated, even during the weaning period, in their attempts to satisfy hunger and the desire for favorable response. Mothers do not nurse their children at regular intervals or constantly and they usually leave them without nursing during the day while the mothers are at work in the fields. They fondle and support the child only intermittently and capriciously, and make no systematic attempt to satisfy the child's wants.

Not only in Alor, but everywhere, the small child's untrained response to frustration seems to be crying and random attack upon the frustrator, and when this proves inadequate, it resorts to temper tantrums. The latter is likewise an unrewarding response to frustration drive if parents or other persons continue their frustrating activity toward the child. If other persons pay no attention, the temper tantrums eventually extinguish through lack of reinforcement. If older persons are annoyed by such "unruly" behavior the childish displays may be eliminated by physical punishment. In either case the child eventually learns to "suppress" its direct reactions to certain types of frustration. This does not mean that the drive is eliminated or satisfied, but rather that the direct response to it is delayed or directed into some other channel. In Alor, for example, boys when they grow large enough, "take it out" on their elders by systematic robbing of fields and gardens.

Many a cultural system contains patterns which involve the suppression of direct aggression as a response to frustration. In our own society, for example, males are trained not to attack females physically no matter what the provocation. (This training is, to be sure, occasionally honored in the breach.) And the so-called "Battle of the Sexes" which James Thurber has so amusingly portrayed resolves itself into the use of customs of indirect attack, in which, according to Thurber, the women usually seem to get the best of it. One learns not to respond to frustrating and arbitrary actions of superiors with direct attack, although a conventional method of obtaining some relief is to engage in verbal aggression in the presence of one's fellows and out of hearing of the frustrating superior. Trade unionism is, of course, an institutionalized response to the frustrations imposed upon workers by "bosses" and other conditions of modern industry.

We say that every society frustrates its members in one way or another, but each society sets up its own kind of blocks to uninhibited activities. Thus it is that we may speak of *acquired aggressions,* which are connected to or aroused by certain objects or conditions set up by the culture. Thus "class anger," for example, which is common enough in Western society, is unknown in classless primitive tribes. On the other hand, local angers which are expressed in feuds between local groups in many primitive tribes seem to have largely disappeared in Western societies.

Customs of displacement. Under certain cultural conditions aggression of any kind, even indirect, against the true source of frustration is hedged about with so many punishments that such customs are eliminated. In this case we often find the development of customary aggression directed against some other object. The aggression, we say, is *displaced* from its true goal to a substitute goal. Thus the frustrations of the German masses were partially resolved by the Nazi institution of attack upon the Jews, a minority group from which retaliation could not be expected. Likewise, in the United States, the frustrations of the "poor whites" of the South are by custom directed toward the Negroes, rather than toward the superordinate and powerful white masters of their destinies.

A very widespread custom of magic among primitive and folk peoples involves the use of a doll or image which represents the object of one's aggression. The ritual involves the mutilation of this substitute in various ways, such as sticking pins into it, burning it, dismembering it, and so on. This practice is supported by a mental system which includes the belief that the indignities and physical injuries wreaked upon the effigy will magically appear in the actual human object. It is easy to see that such a custom is reinforced by the release of frustration tension experienced by the practitioner.

In our society, certain material equipment is customarily used for the release of aggression. Many a man, for example, after a frustrating day at the office has learned to repair to the gymnasium and to vent his spleen on a punching bag or an exercise machine.

Whenever we find established customs involving cruelty to animals and wanton destruction of property, for which no other motivation can be found, it behooves us to inquire how the cultural system has managed the problem of frustration. In some cultural systems, the only available customary responses to frustration involve displacement to animals or material objects.

Customary suppression and displacement of frustration responses has a certain functional value in preserving the solidarity of the society, and and it is doubtless for this reason that such customs survive in a given society. It is no accident that the customs of magical aggression seem to extinguish in societies which have developed institutions of secular justice which are available to all and through which members of the society can obtain satisfaction under rules which have social approval, for legal institutions and customs are also conventional patterns of handling aggressive reactions without producing permanent and disrupting antagonisms in the social group or society.

Generally speaking cultures with a high development of malevolent magic are characterized by suppression of freely used overt violence. The two types of customary response on frustration drive are not necessarily inconsistent (except in local cultural definitions), but a society which has developed patterns for the one mode finds it uneconomical to use both.

NOTES TO CHAPTERS 14 AND 15

1. For example, Gillin, 1947b, pp. 46-49.
2. Boring, Langfeld, and Weld, 1939, pp. 613-615; Morgan, 1943, pp. 258-268.
3. Rothman, 1941.

4. See references in Note 2.
5. Anonymous, 1939.
6. Hrdlicka, 1908, p. 246.
7. Lattimore, 1932, pp. 66-67.
8. *Ibid.*, pp. 66-67.
9. Gillin, 1947b.
10. Hrdlicka, 1908, p. 246.
11. *Ibid.*, p. 247.
12. Dobrizhoffer, 1822, pp. 34-35.
13. Roth, 1924, p. 332, quoting Schomburgk.
14. Cobo, 1890-1895, Vol. 2, p. 261; quoted by Valdizan and Maldonado, 1922, Vol. 2, p. 433.
15. Murdock, 1934, p. 67.
16. Bogoras, 1904-1909, p. 36.
17. Powdermaker, 1932.
18. Massam, 1927, pp. 68-70.
19. Pearson, W. W., p. 152.
20. Finley, 1913, p. 28.
21. Massam, pp. 145-146.
22. Gorer, 1934.
23. Warmelo, 1932, pp. 43-44.
24. Hollis, 1905, pp. 313-314.
25. Hose, p. 188.
26. Birket-Smith, 1935, p. 125.
27. Dembo and Imbelloni, 1938.
28. *Ibid.*, pp. 110-114.
29. Handy, 1922; Clavel, 1885.
30. Dembo and Imbelloni, 1938, pp. 158-187; Saville, 1913; Van Rippen, 1917.
31. Dembo and Imbelloni, 1938, pp. 36-158.
32. Virchow, 1903, 1905.
33. Kardiner, 1939, 1945; Linton has frequently referred to the "covert" culture, e.g., 1945, pp. 38-41; see also Kluckhohn, 1941, 1944. The term "symbolic activity" is generally used by behavior psychologists to refer to "mental" or "covert" reactions of the organism.
34. Whiting, 1941, especially Chapter 8.
35. For a general analysis of imitation, see Miller and Dollard, 1941.
36. Hull, 1943, chapter 9, and references cited there.
37. Vaillant, 1941.
38. Im Thurn, 1883.
39. Hodge, 1907, Vol. 2, p. 146.
40. For other views of aggression, see Young, 1940, pp. 378-380; Dollard, and others, 1939; Murphy, Murphy, and Newcomb, 1937, pp. 376-508.
41. Cf. Mead, 1942, pp. 138-157.
42. Roback, 1944.
43. Gillin, 1936b, pp. 140-154.
44. Gillin, 1947b; Valdizan and Madonado, 1922, Vol. 2.
45. Turney-High, 1942.
46. See Gillin and Gillin, 1942, pp. 604-655.
47. For example, Gillin, 1936a, p. 8 (hunting calls); pp. 180-185 (hunting charms and binas).
48. Du Bois, 1944; Kardiner, 1945, pp. 146-171.

PART III

Some Structures of Human Relationships

CHAPTER 16

The Organization of Human Relationships

IF HUMAN BEINGS must "come to terms" with nature, they must also be able to get along satisfactorily with each other. This statement is a truism, but, judging by the conflicts of the modern world, it is one which is little appreciated. Adjustment to the natural environment is provided for each group by customs and artifacts involved in its technologies. Adjustment between individuals and groups is furnished by the patterns of social organization. A faulty technique applied to a problem posed by nature (for example, inadequate housing in a cold climate) produces maladjustment for the members of the society. Conflicting patterns in technics (such as unrestricted profit-seeking or other types of unbounded exploitation combined with patterns of conservation of natural resources) also often result in lost energy, unnecessary conflict, and other forms of maladjustment. Likewise, inadequate or poorly coördinated patterns of social life tend to produce disturbances which exact their price from the members of a society.

A society, by failure to develop adequate patterns of social organization, may breed within itself the disease of decay and destruction. An illustration of this is to be found in an Indian tribe, the Kaingang or Botocudo of the Brazilian highlands, as reported by Henry.[1] Organized, if that is the word, into a number of extended families or bands, the tribe as a whole lacked cultural means whereby these component units could live at peace with each other. The extended families decimated one another in perpetual feuds and devoted the energies which might have gone into constructive activities to the refinement and intensification of murder. As Henry reports it, Kaingang self-destruction proceeded inexorably from the nature of their lack of social organization. "The very lack of fixity of relationships and the multitude of ways of forming them left the Kaingang with no device for controlling a conflict. Once a feud arose there was nothing, neither dominating ties of blood nor the voice of chieftainship or government, to stop or limit it."[2] In such a situation, there develops a personality type with very limited resources for security. The individual seeks the comfort of human contact within the restricted limits of his extended family. The embraces of sexual partners, the caresses

339

of members of his own sex, a suppression of overt aggression against members of the family group possess values bred of desperation. Yet the aggression seeks outlets, and the stay-at-home Kaingang between feuds vented his spleen in spiteful slashes at the trees and surrounding shrubbery, or savored a compulsive retelling of the blood-thirsty folk-tales which deal exhaustively with feud and homicide and which seem to be the only native art worthy of the name. The Kaingang merely document the proposition that a society whose culture lacks patterns of internal social adjustment cannot stand.

SOCIAL GROUPS, CATEGORIES, AND STATUSES

In a previous chapter it was mentioned that every cultural situation contains certain social potentialities in the distribution and characteristics of the population. We have also pointed out that a prerequisite of social life is social contact between individuals and groups, that is, possibilities of interstimulation and response. Given these conditions, an aggregation of human beings will tend, even before it has developed a common culture, to sort itself into groups, categories, and statuses, all of them focused around certain interests. A dramatic presentation of this principle is the theme of James M. Barrie's *The Admirable Crichton.*

Social scientists have never agreed on a thoroughly satisfactory definition of *society*. Perhaps the most useful is something like the following: *A society* is the largest relatively permanent group of people who share common interests, common territory, a common mode of life, and a common recognition of *esprit de corps* or "belongingness" whereby they distinguish between themselves and outsiders. Thus the members of a society all tend to have something in common. However, no human society is completely homogeneous. For, in addition to the interests common to all the members, which provide the basis for such unity as the society as a whole enjoys, subsidiary interests tend to develop, which in turn account for the development of subsidiary groups, social categories, and statuses within the larger society.

Subsidiary interests found in all societies. An interest is a focusing of attention or effort on certain objects or situations in anticipation of receiving satisfaction therefrom. Obviously the development of an interest is related to the *abilities* of individuals, for the anticipation of a certain type of satisfaction is based to some extent upon the abilities the individual may possess to achieve it. The basic conditions for certain types of interests are found in all societies and, consequently, a tendency for individuals sharing such interests to draw together into groupings of some sort. These universal group-forming factors are: (1) locality, (2) kinship, and (3) constitutional characteristics, particularly age and sex.

Individuals who share a common locality or territory within the society tend to have "something in common" with each other and on the basis of this common interest they tend to form a group. The same is true of those who belong to the same family or share a common set of kinsmen. Also, individuals of the same sex and of roughly the same age possess certain abilities which tend to draw them together and to exclude others.

Groups based on these factors are not necessarily mutually exclusive. A single individual may, and usually does, belong to at one and the same time a locality group, a kinship group, and an age-sex category. These universal factors of interest tend to cut across each other.

The differentiation and sorting of a social population on the basis of these universally present factors may be spoken of in terms of *basic social tendencies* leading to social organization. Such basic social tendencies toward differentiation and grouping, however, should not be confused with social organization itself, which is a matter of cultural patterning and custom. Thus, all societies tend to subdivide into subsidiary groups on the basis of locality, but this factor is in itself no basis for prediction of the details of organization and custom which will characterize the local groups so formed. In one society the typical local group may be a nomadic band, in another a peasant village, in another an "open-country" neighborhood. Even towns, for example, do not conform to identical patterns throughout the world. The dwellings and other buildings may be laid out around a central plaza or square, as in many parts of Latin America, or they may be strung out along a main thoroughfare, as in the "Main Street" pattern of Western towns in the United States. Patterns of behavior also differ in accordance with the cultural system. Within the town, persons proceeding in opposite directions along a thoroughfare may customarily pass each other on the right side or on the left side, according to the local rules. The factor of locality determines that certain people live together and form a group. But the culture determines how the group is organized and the patterns of interaction. The same is true with respect to groups formed on the basis of kinship and constitutional factors.

Although these basic social tendencies occur in all societies, the culture of each society tends to mould and to define the interests so generated. The average society which we are called upon to study is a going concern with cultural definitions, organization, and interaction customs already in operation, so that the question of whether or not kinship, for instance, is basically a non-cultural factor in grouping is mainly an academic matter. However, the universality of the factors mentioned account for certain underlying similarities found in all social organizations, just as the universal types of "components" occurring in cultural situations generally provide an underlying framework and set certain basic limits to the adaptive features of cultural organization, regardless of the detailed variations.

Cultural interests. The culture itself of a functioning society tends to create opportunities and to generate interests in certain individuals possessed of the abilities to take advantage of them. In many cases such "abilities" are the result of training, experience, and social position. One has no choice with respect to his sex, but he or his elders or friends may provide training or experience which will fit him to find a certain occupation, for example, particularly satisfactory and interesting. Persons with similar "acquired" interests tend to be grouped together within the society, and such groups become units involved in social organization.

Since such social units are formed on the basis of culturally generated interests, their general types are not as universal as those mentioned in the previous section. Perhaps the most commonly found general types are those based on *technological specialization, congeniality, political interests, economic interests, intellectual interests, and recreational interests.*

Again the investigator must be warned against assuming that the cultural details of organization and activity are necessarily the same in all groups of the same general type in various societies. Technological groups, for example, are found in almost all societies, but it is difficult to say that a given general type of technological speciality will form a group at all, or that, if it does, the details will be similar everywhere. Canoe-building, for instance, is carried on in Polynesia and in the jungle portions of Guiana. In Marquesas, however, this craft was carried on by organized groups or guilds of workmen, whereas among the Barama River Caribs, each man usually builds his canoe by himself. Hand cultivation or horticulture is a technique practised in many different societies. We may mention only two instances from similar tropical forest environments, West Africa and the Amazon Valley. In the former area organized work parties (groups) customarily do the hoeing and digging, whereas in the Amazon Valley horticulture is usually carried on by individual farmers working alone, or only casually together. Thus it is impossible to state categorically that a given technique, such as canoe-making or horticulture, universally serves as a basis for social grouping. And the same is true with respect to any other of the acquired or cultural interests.

It is therefore to be understood that not only the interests themselves, but also the patterns of cultural activity developed in groups based on such interests must always be considered in terms of the total culture of the society under study. The Holiness Church group of Plainville, U. S. A., and the murderous secret societies of various Western African tribes may both be classed as "religious" groups, although the details of the definition of interest and the actually practised customs differ radically in the two cases.[3]

Social units. The social organization of any society consists of an underlying scheme of relationships (a system of mental cultural patterns) connecting social units, plus the representational and actional patterns more or less appropriate to such a scheme. Although individuals are of course the carriers of culture in the last analysis, a social organization usually is set up and operates with respect to social units. These are social entities whose position and function in the system are defined by the culture and whose existence is not necessarily dependent upon the life span of specific individuals. It is only by thus divorcing the units of the system from the biological existence of human individuals that a certain stability in a social organization is possible. Thus, although many individual soldiers of a given military regiment may be killed in battle, the regiment as a unit in the army organization carries on: the individual casualties are replaced by other individuals trained to perform the activities expected of members of the regimental group. The social unit, as such, carries on independently of any specific individual, so far as its function in the social organization is concerned. A social system tends to develop around social units rather than specific persons with their individual peculiarities. And individuals are trained or otherwise prepared to play the parts expected of them in the social units in which they are involved. The general types of social units may be described, respectively, as groups, social categories, and statuses.

Social groups. A social group is a collection of memberships which is internally unified to some degree by means of internal patterns of interaction oriented toward some predominant interest or objective. The group usually functions as a unit and is characterized by cultural patterns which govern the internal interactions of the members. In other words, the internal interactions are, at least to some extent, patterned and organized.

Differing degrees and types of internal organization may be involved. If the interactions of the membership are predominantly of a primary type (see pp. 186-187) the group is called a *primary group;* if secondary or intermediate, and instrumental contact is predominant, we speak of the group as a *secondary group.* Groups may also be differentiated on the basis of permanency: we may thus speak of *temporary, intermittent,* and (relatively) *permanent groups.* Groups of the temporary type, such as street-corner crowds and mobs in our own society, however, seldom figure in social organization because of their transitory nature: no patterns of interaction are provided either for the membership within the group or for the group in its relations with others. An intermittent group is one which comes together and/or functions as a unit only at certain times or under specified circumstances. In Central Australia, for example, the tribal and local groups were mainly intermittent, for the constituent families roamed about the territory independently during most of the year, gathering food, only to come together in a larger group, in some cases, once a year for the annual corroboree. Likewise in many states in North America, the legislative assembly meets and functions as a group only once every two years. Relatively permanent groups, on the other hand, typically involve continuous interaction between the members and continuous function as a unit of the overall social organization. The typical family in most societies is a relatively permanent group, especially if it is organized on the "consanguine" principle and consists of a collection of blood relatives or other "permanent" kinsmen.

In any case, groups of the intermittent and permanent varieties usually possess special customs of their own—a sort of subculture, as it were—which are practised by the membership. Also they are related, by patterns of interaction, with the other constituent units of their society.

Social categories. Another type of social unit occurring in most social systems of the world is the social category. This is a socially recognized subdivision of the membership of a society, but it lacks the patterns of internal organization and unity, as well as the clear-cut functional attributes which are characteristic of a social group, properly speaking. Among the Barama River Caribs of British Guiana, for example, there is a category of medicine men, who are the repositories and practitioners of special techniques for contacting the supernatural beings and for the cure of illness. These techniques and the manner of their practice are unknown in detail to laymen. Yet the practising medicine men of the various communities of the tribe do not coöperate with each other, do not recognize a common bond of unity, nor do they function as a unit in the social system. Each man receives his training from a single established operator in a temporary group of neophytes, but when he goes out to "practise," he works on his own. Somewhat similarly, the smaller communities of the western United States have traditionally considered themselves incomplete without a "town radical." Such an individual practised culture of the mental and representational varieties, at least, which were distinctive from those of their fellow community members, but at the same time similar to those of other "radicals" in other communities. They were in a category by themselves, but, until recently, no attempt was made to organize them into functioning groups.

Social classes and social castes often partake of the characteristics of social categories rather than groups, in our sense. It may be recognized that the members of a given social class practise certain patterns of culture which are peculiar to themselves, but in many societies social classes or castes lack internal organization as well as explicit unified function in society. In our own society, intense competition, even conflict, may develop between members of a class category without in any way obliterating the recognition which society as a whole gives to the cultural distinctiveness of the category itself. The Joneses and the Browns may refuse even to speak to each other, but will still remain members of the middle class, both in their own eyes and in the judgment of others.

In our own society many "lone-wolf" criminals, hobos, and homosexuals are thought of as belonging to appropriate social categories. Groups may be formed within these categories, but the categories themselves are not internally organized units, although they each practise recognized (if not approved) special customs and enjoy special relations with respect to the other constituent elements of the overall social organization. That proper groups may develop from such categories is demonstrated both in our own and in other societies. In India, a good share of the law-breakers are organized into the so-called "Criminal Tribes" which operate as units with internal organization and leadership. Some of our own tramps and hobos are organized into a National Association. Among various non-Pueblo tribes of the American Southwest, homosexuals enjoyed a recognized and approved status called *berdache*, but they were not organized among themselves into a group. In Germany of the 1920's and 1930's, on the other hand, male homosexuals were organized into definite groups, such as the Schmeterling Club, which were tolerated within the social organization, if not wholly approved.

Status. Another type of unit in social organization is *status*. This term is commonly used to refer to the "position" occupied by an individual in the social system. Although a status is occupied by an individual, it is not, of course, the same as the personality manifestation of a particular individual—it is an entity of social organization which may be occupied by successive individuals provided they possess the training, experience, and other attributes required by the system. The status of President of the United States has remained constitutionally very little changed through about 160 years of history, but thirty-three different men have occupied the status. The status of husband, so far as cultural definition is concerned, is relatively stable in California, even though an occasional Hollywood lady may have induced five or six different men in succession to occupy that position in relation to herself.

A status in a social system is defined in terms of rights and duties which are expected of the occupant. In other words, each status has assigned to it certain cultural patterns which the occupant is supposed to perform and which relate his status to others in the system.

From the point of view of social organization, two types of status may be recognized: (1) those *derived* from social groups or categories, and (2) those which stand *independent* of other social units.

The *derived statuses* are of two subtypes: (*a*) ordinary derived status, and (*b*) distinctive derived status. Every group or category to which an individual belongs confers certain social position upon him simply by reason of his membership. His status in society in general is derived from the cultural patterns of privilege, obligation, skill, and so forth, which are the common property of the group or category, and society confers upon him its recognition of his ability and right to perform those patterns; it assumes that he has certain social and cultural characteristics because he is identified with a group or category whose cultural position is generally recognized. In our society one has a certain social position if he belongs to the Vanderbilt family, and among the Iroquois one had a certain place in society if he belonged to the Bear clan. It is to be noted, however, that status is of significance only in terms of the common recognitions (meanings) involved in a given social system. One has no place in modern American society by virtue of membership in the Bear clan, and one could claim no status in aboriginal Iroquois society simply on the basis of the name of Vanderbilt.

Distinctive membership status in a general social system grows out of the fact that groups are usually internally organized on the basis of leadership and followership, and other divisions of labor or function. This merely means that in a group itself (as distinct from a category) there is differentiation of status and function. Mere membership status carries with it a certain recognition in society. But distinctive status in a given group usually involves an enlargement of rights and duties in the social arena outside the group as well. Thus the general social position of the matriarch of the Bear clan is different (more important) than that of a mere member without distinction. The headman of a local group receives more attention in the tribal council than a mere resident of the locality. An American ambassador abroad receives more attention and has more leeway of action ("diplomatic privileges") than a simple American citizen. The definition of a distinctive membership status usually involves at least implicit recognition of the fact that such a status represents or symbolizes the place of the group in the total social system. A modest general of our army will usually make this explicit when receiving a medal, by indicating that he accepts the decoration not in his own person but as a representative of "the boys" who belonged to his command (social group) and fought under him. Although the occupants of distinctive membership statuses are often individuals of unusual personal ability, the fundamental factor in their general social position is their identification with the group. For this reason, it is not difficult to find mediocre or even degenerate individuals occupying statuses of this sort. For example, under the British colonial system in India, rulers of "native states" were accorded honors, annuities, formal respect, and other privileges, regardless of their personal characters, and despite the fact that it is well known that some of the men were profligates and incompetents. Likewise, as many a private in our army has complained, an occasional incompetent officer appears, let us say, as a company commander; but, so long as he occupies this position, the system demands that he be paid the respect which is attached to his status.

The type of status which stands independent of group or category affiliation is less common in most social systems than those previously discussed. Let us bear in mind that we are speaking of social systems, that is, going concerns, and the positions therein culturally defined. This is a different matter from the sort of thing permitted in many societies wherein an outstandingly gifted individual is able to make a unique place for himself through an unusual combination of abilities. So long as the "place" remains *unique* it is not a part of a cultural system of social organization.

However, not a few social systems do provide statuses which stand relatively independent of group or category. Among ourselves, for example, the status of "hero" is not dependent upon group or category affiliation. Recognition is given to certain "heroes" of the life-saving variety by the annual awards of gold medals by the Carnegie Institution. In wartime, heroes are recognized by standardized decorations provided by the armed services. In frontier society of the West, there was a status of "good fighter"—occupied by one who was ready with his fists and gun in the interests of socially approved moral principles.

Among most of the Plains Indian tribes of prereservation days, the status of warrior was well recognized in terms of "counting coup." This had nothing to do with membership in a recognized group or category. A man was able to occupy this well-recognized status if he had counted coup in one or more of the following approved ways: taking a scalp of an enemy, stealing a horse from an enemy, touching an enemy in battle, and (in some tribes) killing an enemy. Although warriors were wont to boast of their exploits to each other, they were not, in most tribes where this system pertained, organized into functional groups. In fact they were so distinguished in their special statuses that it was inappropriate to speak of them even as a category. In modern Western cultures stabilized statuses of this sort—independent of groups or categories, yet recognized in the system—are even rarer. In England the status of public hangman is officially recognized and is paid by the government (a political group-institution). Of late, it has tended to pass from one generation to the other in the same family, but in spite of this, as a status, it remains independent of groups or categories. Likewise, in the United States, such statuses as "heavyweight champion of the world" are not derived from groups or categories in the system (unless the crucial contests are "fixed").

Participation in statuses. It should not be supposed that statuses are necessarily mutually exclusive. On the contrary, a given individual may occupy several statuses at one and the same time. Thus a President of the United States may also be a Thirty-Second Degree Mason, father, husband, and head of his party, to mention only a few of his statuses. And each of them has certain cultural patterns attached to it. When on a campaign tour as leader of his party, the President may not hesitate to pass out cigars, kiss babies, and don the feathered headdress of an Indian tribe into which he has been "adopted"—patterns of activity not considered appropriate to his rôle as Chief Executive in Washington.

The combination of specific statuses occupied by an individual at a given time is often spoken of as his "general status" in society. However, this is an attribute of the individual, rather than of the social system as such. If a man is able to play the rôles pertaining to a dozen statuses, he may be regarded as prominent in his society, that is, receive a "rating" in the eyes of his fellows different from that of an individual who handles only three or four statuses. So far as the system of cultural patterns are concerned, however, the individual is still expected to perform the rôles of the specific statuses involved. The rôles are provided by the system; the fact that a single individual performs several rôles is unimportant to the system itself.

Furthermore, the average individual in any society not only changes status as he moves from one situation to another, but he inevitably assumes a series of statuses as he grows older and moves through his life cycle from infant to old person. Age-status is universally recognized, although more formally in some societies than in others, but nowhere does an infant or child occupy the same place in the social system as an adult or an old person.

Status and rôle. We have pointed out that a status is defined in terms of the formal (recognized) rights and duties pertaining to a position in a social system and that such a position is independent of the personalities of the successive or various occupants. Status is thus, in one sense, a static concept—it is a point or place in a social system. It is "placed" in the social system by means of cultural relations—that is, patterns related to other statuses which can and which cannot be performed by the occupants.

What about the activity aspect of status? What about the cultural expectations which are laid upon the occupant of a status? So far as these are defined culturally, we speak of them as the *rôle* which, in a given system, is assigned to the status. This is the dynamic, or active, aspect of status, and consists of the patterns of behavior which are considered appropriate to the occupant of the status. The rôles of many statuses are implicit rather than explicit. For example, the President of the United States cannot get drunk in public, although such a prohibition is not anywhere written down or proclaimed. Likewise, he can and must appear smiling in photographs under most conditions. Mr. Hoover ignored this aspect of his rôle—one of the factors which has been assigned to his failure of reëlection. In the case of the President, of course, many "do's" and "don't's" are explicitly set forth in the Constitution and laws of the land. The same type of analysis, nonetheless, is applicable to any status. What can the occupant do and what can't he do in terms of the cultural system?

It is obvious that *individual personality* enters the picture at this point. This is to say that one individual will play his rôle "well," in terms of the cultural definition of it, and another will play it "badly." Another way of putting this is to say that one individual will live up to the expectations set forth in his cultural system, another individual will fall somewhat short of them. A third type of individual may institute innovations in this system, thus setting the pattern for a redefinition of the patterns themselves.

In summary, a system of social organization is to be thought of as a collection of social entities connected with one another in a more or less integrated scheme by appropriate relationships expressed as patterns of custom. From the point of view of the individual such a system or scheme provides pathways through the system and ready-made patterns of stimulus and response whereby the individual is able to adjust without necessarily having to undergo the rigors of independent thought. From the point of view of the groups and categories involved, they likewise are provided with means of "getting along" with each other and also with means and methods for coöperating toward the common goals of the society and/or for mutual opposition according to the "rules" of the culture. In the latter case such competition or opposition as occurs within the pattern of the social organization is kept within preconceived bounds, patterns of expectation are provided, and the disorganization which signifies crisis in social affairs is avoided so far as cultural patterning can do so.

The patterning and rates of interaction. Not only do the patterns of social organization involve the timing, placing, direction, and content of the interactive customs linking the various elements of the system, but also, as Chapple [4] has pointed out, the rates of interaction themselves. The "specifications," we might say, of any system of social organization take account of all these aspects.

As with any other type of customary activity, those involved in social organization are specified with respect to time and place of their appropriate performance. This merely means that the patterned customs which relate one social entity to another are properly performed only in appropriate situations which are designated and defined as such by the culture. Such situations always involve at least an implicit specification of proper time and place for the performance of interactive customs. For example, soldiers are not required to salute officers in the midst of battle, but on a garrison post, yes. Direction refers to the unit in the system toward which the activity is directed. Aggressive military activity is supposed to be directed toward the enemy, whereas competitive activity in business is directed toward rival business groups. The members of a class direct "courteous" activity toward superiors, and "condescending" activities toward their inferiors on the local social scale.

Another aspect of such social patterning is the rate or frequency of interaction. On the football field the interaction between two teams is very rapid, whereas in the case of an obscure rural district petitioning a king or dictator, the pattern may be practised only once in a quarter century. In our urban family system the mother interacts (usually in patterned ways, of course) with the children much more frequently than does the father, who is away from home during a good part of the day. The question of who "originates" an interactive pattern and who "terminates" it is also of importance to an understanding of the system and of the statuses within it. In the army, officers customarily originate orders to enlisted men, who "terminate" the interaction. Leaders in all groups usually originate to their followers. It is to be understood that a rate of interaction and its direction may well be part of the pattern. However, the pattern can usually be modified by unusual individuals, who upset the pattern in favor of one of their own. In our society, one finds an occasional father who never gives orders or directions to his children, does not originate action to them. Again, in such an interactive pattern as debate or conversation, certain individuals talk rapidly, others slowly, some are "quick on the uptake," others "take their time." Such modifications of rate are often quite possible within the range permitted by the pattern. But the limits of the range are always important. In the classroom situation, for example, some students may recite frequently, whereas others only occasionally. The student who never recites, however, is not performing within the range permitted by the pattern, and he is usually eliminated from the group—"flunked out."

Criteria of membership in social units. How do persons become identified with groups, categories, and statuses? It is clear that units differ among themselves with respect to qualifications for membership or occupancy. An individual involuntarily finds himself in a given age or sex category, for example, but he must qualify himself by voluntarily acquiring the appropriate patterns, if he is to be taken into a professional group. Thus we may speak of two types of social units: *closed* and *open*. Individuals are *assigned* to the closed type of unit by the social system; such assignment may be on the basis of age, sex, birth, or rearing in a certain locality, birth into a certain family, or other criteria. Among the Caribs the accident of being born with six toes is almost a sure sign that the individual will be a medicine man. In Tibet, second sons were customarily assigned to the status of monks. Such assigned individuals are trained in the customs appropriate to the system, but they have no personal choice as to whether they shall be so trained or not.

Open social entities, on the other hand, admit and retain individuals mainly on the basis of voluntary qualification by the aspirant. To use Linton's terms, membership or recognition is achieved rather than ascribed.[5] One moves into a higher social class (in systems where this is possible) by acquiring the manners, wealth, and friends which such membership requires. In China one became a government official by passing written examinations. There are entities of the open type into which individuals are occasionally admitted "in spite of themselves," but they do not have to maintain their identification against their will. Sinclair Lewis was elected a Nobel Prize winner, but declined the honor (status); a man may be made a member of a Rotary Club by his friends (on account of his qualifications), but decide that he cannot spare the time to come to meetings and allow his membership to lapse.

Social organization as culture. A social organization is, of course, a cultural system. Like other aspects of culture, it consists of patterns for mental, representational, and actional customs. Typically a social organization also involves artifacts employed either in their utilitarian aspect or as symbols. The social organization is manifested objectively by patterns of activity which relate the various social entities to one another in patterned ways. The system as a whole may be thought of as a vast network of such patterns woven together, criss-crossing each other, but more or less adjusted together to permit and to promote at least a minimum level of function for the society as a whole. The customs thus patterned are of course acquired during life by the individuals who practise them.

A social system as a whole, however, is usually an abstraction of the scientific investigator. This is to say that members of a society seldom carry about with them a clear "mental picture" of the total system in all its details. An average individual tends to think in customary terms (to practise mental customs) only about certain bits and parts with which he is concerned, and he overtly practises behavioral customs pertaining only to the memberships and statuses which he possesses. He may share the mental customs regarding what is appropriate action in certain other entities, as when a man will know (mentally) the pattern of "lady-like" behavior even though he would be horrified to be caught practising it overtly. But this knowledge of the patterns of other entities in the system is usually confined to those entities which have some relation to his own activities in the system. The average man, for example, has a patterned idea as to how a physician should act toward him as a patient, even if he has no comprehension of the content of the medical speciality. But the average citizen usually has no idea of the patterned customs which physicians are supposed to practise with other physicians or with druggists, for example. Those relationships of physicians do not touch the sphere of the ordinary layman; nor is it necessary for the functioning of the system that he have even a mental pattern concerning them, so long as they work satisfactorily and do not interfere with his own patterns. The medical man, on the other hand, must be well aware of and well practised in all such patterned relationships if he is to function effectively in his area of the system.

Thus there is no absolute imperative that members of a society, in order to make it function, even be able to practise mentally all the patterns of their social system, to say nothing of being able to understand the underlying principles of organization which have been developed over generations. A social system will "work" within its capacities so long as the members of the society have been properly trained in their rôles and so long as they properly perform them. The members do not need to know the overall system or its principles in order to make it function, any more than they need to know the morphological principles and grammatical structure of their language in order to be able to speak it.

This fact is one of the principal reasons why we need a science capable of analyzing social systems as wholes. For a social system may continue to operate after a fashion, even though it is poorly organized, even though its patterns are poorly adjusted to each other, and even though their performance creates constant frustrations, annoyances, and conflicts in the society. So long as the internal inconsistencies do not cause a complete breakdown, the members of the society will continue operating the system, perhaps complaining and suffering, but without knowing what is wrong or what to do about it. Only expert scientific analysis can in many cases tell them what is wrong and recommend the necessary readjustments in the patterns. The present writer and a companion were once stuck in an automobile with transmission trouble in the midst of the desert country of Southeastern Utah. Three days of arduous amateur mechanical work on a sand dune enabled us to take the transmission apart and to put it together again so that the car would once more move. We were quite proud of our accomplishment. However, on the four hundred mile drive back to Salt Lake City, the car could not be induced to go more than 30 miles per hour, and it made a noise like a cement mixer filled with scrap iron. We could not understand what was wrong, for we drove with the greatest care. However, an expert in such matters (a garage mechanic) in Salt Lake City needed only about five minutes to discover that we had inserted one of the gears into the transmission backwards. The mechanical system would work after a fashion—sufficient to move the car—but not well enough to provide the satisfaction which we expected. Something similar is the case in many systems of social organization.

The analyst of social systems may require more than five minutes to put his finger on the trouble, but his services are nonetheless required in many cases. Furthermore, it is possible to diffuse the principles of social analysis throughout a society—to make them part of the culture, so that the average man or woman will be able to recognize difficulties himself, or at least be able to understand them when discovered by specialists. So far, however, no society has done this. Hence the need for more rather than less cultural science.

PRIVILEGE AND PREJUDICE

Systems of rank. The entities which constitute the points and places in a social system (groups, categories, and statuses) may be either ranked or unranked. An organization of ranked statuses always involves at least three cultural features: (1) a system of mental patterns whereby the respective entities are viewed on a scale of "goodness" and "badness," "higher" and "lower" or some other basis of invidious comparisons which involves a cultural system of values; (2) a set of customary behavior patterns differing with respect to the rights and duties projected in the customary relations between the ranked entities to the advantage of those higher on the scale; and (3) a system of customary symbolic expressions of the foregoing social relations.

We have seen that individuals and groups composing a society are never completely homogeneous. The differences between them are reflected in specialized cultural patterns practised by the various groups, categories, and statuses. However, it is not inevitable or universal that such social and cultural differences be ranked or rated in terms of a value system. Among ourselves, for instance, Republicans and Democrats compose distinctive groups, but there is no general agreement in our society that one is "better" than the other, nor over the span of history do members of one group rate special privileges not available to those of the other group. The same, except in special local conditions, is true of the Lions Club vis-à-vis the Kiwanis, physicists over against the chemists, and so on. Such groups are clearly distinguishable in the society, but their social positions one to another may be described as *horizontal*. Such non-invidious mutual relationships are also discernible with respect to social categories and individual statuses. The society has no general system of rating wheat farmers above or below hog farmers or dairymen, for example, and hardware merchants are not either higher or lower on the scale than grocerymen, so far as our culture as a whole is concerned. Likewise the status of amateur golf champion, for instance, is neither better nor worse, in the eyes of the general public, than the position of amateur tennis champion.

In social systems in which some or all of the social entities have, by common agreement, a more or less relative position on a scale of conventionally agreed values, the foregoing conditions do not pertain. The three most commonly encountered principles of ranking are rating, class, and caste. All three involve cultural patterns of the type mentioned at the beginning of this section. Rating complexes often tend to be relatively temporary or ephemeral, as in the faddish criteria upon which college men "rate" various girls as possible "dates." More permanent ratings are those comparisons made between such entities as "artist" and "businessman," "professional wrestler" and "golf professional," and the like. A rating, in short, usually involves a rather vague and informal consensus of opinion regarding the differential worth of various social entities, a consensus which is reflected in speech and other symbolizations and in a restriction of customary activity regarded as privileged on the part of those entities rated "low."

Ranking on the basis of *class* and *caste*, on the other hand, usually exhibits more rigidity and formality from a cultural point of view. A society organized on a class or caste basis shows a series of social groups or categories ranked on a "vertical" scale. Such ranked classes or castes are differentiated on the basis of certain cultural patterns which are assigned to each respectively. For example, in the town of San Luis Jilotepeque in Eastern Guatemala there are two castes, Ladinos and Indians. A Ladino is permitted to enter an Indian house at will and to eat a meal without formal invitation: an Indian is not permitted to enter a Ladino house without permission and is never invited to eat with Ladinos in the latters' houses. A great many other differentiated cultural patterns are assigned to the respective groups. In such a situation we may speak of an *unequal distribution of privileges,* because the patterns and goals which are considered most desirable by the society as a whole are usually reserved for members of the upper group. We may also speak of an *organization of prejudices,* which really amounts to a system of mental patterns and representations thereof which serve to rationalize and reinforce the ranked social positions. Thus the Ladinos in Eastern Guatemala, just as the whites in the Deep South, tend to assign "animal-like" qualities to members of the lower group, whereas the latter have developed a series of prejudices reflecting upon the morals and honesty of the members of the superordinate group.

An unequal distribution of privileges and a differentiated organization of prejudices are characteristics of both classes and castes. The principal cultural features which distinguish a caste system from a class organization are the following: (1) intermarriage and the whole complex of mutual kin recognition and relationships are prohibited or very restricted between caste groups; (2) membership in a caste group is usually determined solely by birth, and there are no techniques generally available whereby a member of one caste may "work his way out" of his caste either "up" or "down." There are occasional exceptions and some intermediate types, but these characteristics are generally found. Vertical mobility in a class organization, on the other hand, may be difficult, but it is usually possible, in the sense that cultural techniques are available and their practise is permitted.

These two principles of vertical ranking are by no means mutually exclusive, even in our own society, as various recent studies by Warner, Dollard, Davis, and the Gardners have shown. For example, Negroes and whites constitute two castes in the South, but within these groups class groups are also recognized. Except for the rules of hereditary position in the caste and the prohibition of marriage out of the caste, the upper-class Negroes practise cultural patterns considerably "above" those of lower-class whites.

Although most North American Indian tribes, for instance, were democratically unranked (an exception were the Natchez of the lower Mississippi), equality is by no means universal in the social organizations of all the so-called simpler peoples. Among non-literate societies, vertical ranking was characteristic of the social systems of the Incas of Peru, many regions of Polynesia, and the various native kingdoms of Negro Africa, to mention no other areas. The caste system of modern India is sufficiently familiar to require no extended discussion.

Although modern North American culture contains a set of mental patterns which are represented as opposed to class and caste types of distinction, there seems to be a tendency toward social stratification, especially in the older settled parts of the country and in urban communities. Even in pure white communities the class structure tends to harden with the passing of the years, as shown by studies on "Yankee City" on the part of Warner and associates. Nevertheless, color castes excepted, American ranked groups are organized into a system which provides techniques for passage from one group to another, with the result that most "upward mobile" persons in the society are constantly preoccupied with acquiring the patterns and the artifacts which will enable them to claim recognized status in a class higher than the one they at present occupy. Such a system generates a strong acquired drive of prestige, and many persons, because of the frustrations to this drive imposed by the cultural system, develop prestige anxiety. Thus the mental patterns of "equality" are inconsistent with certain actional patterns which have the effect of providing unequal distribution of privilege and opportunity among the ranked social classes. A culture such as that of Hindu India is more consistent in this respect. While Indian society is rigidly ranked by caste, the culture contains no universal mental patterns which pretend that equality is right or expectable in this life with the result that relatively few persons develop prestige anxiety or prestige drive with respect to the caste system itself.

In the following pages we cannot describe and analyze all the extant systems of social organization in detail. Our aim is to illustrate some variations in *form* with respect to certain phases of social organization in order to make clear the underlying *principles* of social organization and in order to provide a working notion of the *functions* which are served by diverse forms. We shall confine the discussion mainly to the fields of technics, local organization and kinship organization.

NOTES TO CHAPTER 16

1. Henry, 1941.
2. *Ibid.*, pp. 49-50.
3. Butt-Thompson, 1929; West, 1945.
4. Chapple, 1939; Chapple and Arensberg, 1940; Chapple and Coon, 1942, p. 51.
5. Linton, 1936, p. 115.

CHAPTER 17

Technics and the Cultural Adaptation to Things

MAN IS A tool-using animal in a sense more comprehensive than that which can be applied to any other of the animal species. Although apes, particularly chimpanzees, are not incapable of inventing and using crude tools under experimental conditions, the exercise of this ability is very restricted in nature. More important is the fact that the technical inventions of the apes do not seem to be passed on from generation to generation as a social heritage as is the tendency in man. We may only presume that their limitations with respect to representational and mental processes are at fault.

In the following discussion *technics* refers to the total complex of customs and artifacts concerned with a culture's adaptation to material things, including both raw materials and artifacts, the organization of the human element, economic organization, procedures for "getting a living," and so on. *Technology* is used to describe the organization of custom and artifact within the field of technics which is concerned with the application of human energy more or less directly to the conversion and use of material substances, but excluding derived economic organizations, declared values, and the like. *Technique* refers to those customs or skills directly involved in actual manipulation of materials or artifacts. Thus the technology of a given culture would include analysis of the fact, for instance, that groups of kinsmen are organized for the purpose of cultivating yams, but would not involve an elucidation of the arrangements for exchange or sale to other groups; techniques would involve the procedures of planting, harvesting, and cultivating together with an analysis of the customs involved in handling the tools. Technics would involve all aspects.

ELEMENTS OF TECHNOLOGY

Tools. Among the various material products of man's manual dexterity we may regard tools as those artifacts which are used to enhance the natural features of the human body for the achievement of human purposes. They are both logically and (apparently) chronologically the primary artifacts, for without tools many other material products of industry and social activity cannot be produced. In the archaeological record, long before there is evidence of permanent dwellings or household utensils, we find the remains of stone tools presumably used for killing game, dismembering it, removing the skins for clothing, and so on. And among historical peoples of very limited material equipment, such as the Tasmanians, the major part of the armory of artifacts at their disposal usually consists of a few simple and basic tools (including weapons). So also, in the industrial organization of modern Western culture, the tool, particularly the machine tool, is basic to other processes. Every one remembers that the power of United States' industrial organization could not be brought to bear in the 1939-1945 war until industry had had the time to "retool," and after hostilities had ceased the processes of "reconversion" were inevitably slowed by the necessity of once more providing the tools for the manufacture of other articles.

The earliest tools were of the *cutting and piercing variety* and this type is still basic to modern industrial processes. The reason that cutting and piercing are so basic a function of human tools seems to lie in the fact that without the performance of such functions few of the material objects or resources of the planet can be shaped for purposeful use by man. The species is poorly provided by nature with hereditary structures capable of cutting and piercing the materials available: unless these functions can be performed through the instrumentality of tools, man must take nature as he finds it, without attempts to modify it. Our finger-nails and teeth are paltry equipment with which to shape rocks, dig into the earth, kill animals, whittle wood, and so forth.

A second type of almost universal artifact may be called the *manipulative tool*, a gadget of one sort or another which is used to hold or manipulate either raw materials or other artifacts. Even in Old Stone Age times spear-wrenches had been invented for the purpose of straightening the shafts of spears and darts. In modern culture the wrench is still a basic item in the tool box, while the mechanical elaborations of the manipulative tool run from holding jigs to automatic machines capable of juggling slabs of armor-plate about like sheets of paper.

A third type of basic artifact is the *container*, which is not usually thought of as a "tool," but which, nevertheless, is designed to supplement the capacities of human hands and arms for holding materials. We have no direct evidence of containers in early Old Stone Age times, and it is not until the upper (Aurignacian) part of the period that crude, pecked containers of stone appear in the archaeological material. Judging from the cultures of the most primitive historical peoples, however, it is to be supposed that thongs, basketry, skins, and other materials were used very early in human culture for holding raw materials and enabling men to carry them about more efficiently. Aside from variations in size and shape, the principal improvements made in containers during the course of technological development have been three. (1) Inventions of various types were made to fit the container to hold liquids. (2) Improvements were made which enabled the container to withstand fire and other types of physical and chemical action. Although peoples who invented or adopted pottery solved both of these problems, many peoples, even up to modern times, had not developed containers which were both water-tight and fire-resistant. For example, the Apache Indians of Mescalero still use water bottles made of basketry, covered with pitch, which are water-tight, but not resistant to fire. (3) A third desideratum in the container is durability—resistance to shock and breakage. Although pottery may be both liquid-tight and fire-resistant, it has not been adopted by many peoples, even when they had the materials at hand, because of its fragility. It was not until men had learned to work metal that truly durable containers, satisfying the other requirements as well, were developed, and we find the first metal buckets, pots, and pans in use on a considerable scale in the so-called Bronze Age. In some tropical areas a temporary durability has been attained by the use of containers made of sections of green bambu of large diameter. The node or septum of the bambu joint provides the water-tight bottom, and the greenness of the wood enables the container to be used over a fire—although usually not more than once, for the green wood soon burns out. Another method of handling the problem was the so-called stone boiling process of certain Plains Indian tribes. A hole was dug in the ground which was then lined with a skin which in turn was filled with water. Then hot stones were dropped into the water as well as food products which it was desired to boil. The hot stones boiled the water and cooked the food products. Both of these methods were, of course, comparatively inefficient. No major improvements were made in containers for liquids following the development of metal containers until the adaptation of glass for the purpose, and it was only within the last few decades that heat-resistant and shock-resistant glass was efficiently developed. This major advance, of course, was one of the prerequisites for modern chemical and biological research.

Power. Any technological process necessitates the application of power from some source for the modification of natural materials to human purposes and designs. According to the archaeological record, the technological power available to man was exclusively provided (a) by *man*-power for a period of perhaps nearly a million years—until the full Neolithic period beginning eight to ten thousand years ago in the then most advanced parts of the world. As we have seen in comparing man with other animals, he is a relatively puny organism, considered as a power-producing machine. Consequently his technological results were strictly limited so long as they were dependent upon man-power alone.

Beyond question the most significant revoluntionary changes in technology to date have been directly dependent upon the discovery of new sources of power amenable to man's control. For nearly a million years the entire species was entirely dependent upon its own power output. Then, in the so-called Neolithic period of culture, a series of extremely significant inventions were made. We are not accustomed to think of the domestication of draft animals as inventions, because no such innovations of this class have been introduced in modern times, nor, in fact, for thousands of years. But five to ten thousand years ago (depending upon the part of the world involved) means were found to make available (*b*) *non-human animal power*. As has been the case in all revolutionary inventions which have improved the power potential available to man, this one was eventually followed by far-reaching changes in other aspects of technology—larger scale agriculture with the plough, wider ranging interchange of goods and migrations made possible by transport animals, development of machines driven by animal-power (wheeled vehicles, grinding mills, and so forth).

It is a curious and, as yet, not clearly explained fact, that the domestication of power animals was confined to a relatively few species, in restricted areas of the earth, and to periods relatively remote. No recent new domestications of animals have occurred. In fact, there have been no new animals domesticated during the period of recorded history in any part of the earth. Although the dog was possibly domesticated in late Paleolithic times and diffused to practically all parts of the earth, including the New World (it was only incompletely domesticated by some Australian tribes), the domestication of power-giving animals was not achieved until Neolithic times, and, even then, was relatively restricted. The ass was domesticated in the Near East; likewise, probably the ox, as a draft animal. And the latter, at least, appeared in Europe, in an elementary way, during the New Stone Age. The dog, which had been domesticated much earlier, was perhaps not converted to power production until relatively recently, for example, among the Eskimo and in the Netherlands. However, there is some evidence of the dog sledge in the circumpolar Neolithic of Russia. The horse as a riding animal was probably first domesticated in Central Asia. The camel seems to have been domesticated first in the southern Asiatic steppe or desert country whence it was later diffused to North Africa. The domesticated horse spread rapidly among the nomadic peoples of Central Asia, and from this center, it seems that the idea of domesticating the reindeer passed over to the tundra- and arctic-dwelling peoples of Northern Asia within relatively recent times. The reindeer as a transport and draft animal has definite limitations, mainly referable to its weak back and narrow shoulders. In southeastern Asia and the adjacent islands, the carabao, or water buffalo, was domesticated at roughly the same time, as an animal of major power production.

In the New World, the dog seems to have been imported as a domestic animal by the earliest settlers from the Old World, but it was not used as a power animal until the advent of modern Eskimo culture, a development of the last one thousand years, at the most. The dog was also used in Pre-Columbian times by some Plains tribes to pull a travois. However, independent domestication of one power animal was accomplished in the Andean area of South America. The animal in question was the *llama*. This beast, which belongs to the camel family, was domesticated sufficiently for the transportation of loads as a pack animal, but was never converted to draft purposes of any sort, for instance, it never pulled a plow or wheeled vehicle. None of the European domestic animals, except the dog, was introduced to the New World until after the European discovery.

Of minor importance is the fact that various other animals have been trained to carry loads on their backs as pack animals at one time or another and also to furnish subsidiary power. For example, even at present sheep are used as pack carriers in Tibet, likewise the yak. Dogs also have not been neglected as pack animals, as for example, among the natives of Tibet, and even in parts of modern Europe. The cormorant bird has been used for fishing in the islands off southeast Asia and also in the Caribbean. The method employed was to place a constricting ring about the elongated neck of the bird, and a restraining leash on its leg. It was then allowed to swim about and gulp up fish with its long beak. Because of the restraining ring about the neck, it was unable to swallow its prey, which thus became the booty of the fisherman. Likewise in the islands of the southwest Pacific and also in the Caribbean (possibly a borrowing) the ramora fish was used. This creature in nature is a parasite which attaches itself by means of a sucker cup to the under surface of larger denizens of the briny deep. Men, by attaching a line to the body of the remora, have found it possible to drag in the large game to which the parasite attached itself. Such examples of human ingenuity, however, can only be considered examples of domestication of power-producing animals in the widest sense. Likewise, the use of wild spiders to spin nets over branches or hoops (in Melanesia), and even the cultivation of the silkworm for the production of textile material, are of course, further examples of human capitalization upon non-human animal-power, of one sort or another. But in these minor cases the power involved is restricted to narrow fields and is not amenable to general technological application. Only the draft and transport animals are of major significance as sources of power in technology, and the importance of these, throughout human history, has largely been confined to agriculture (plough cultivation) and transport, especially efficient when the wheeled vehicle is available. Treadmills and similar crude mechanical contrivances for the use of animal-power are relatively late and comparatively unimportant in the history of technology.

It was a long time until man began to achieve practical control of (*c*) *artificially generated power*. The use of animal-power, whether provided by man himself or by his domesticated animals, definitely limited the advance of technology. But once a non-animate source of energy and power was discovered and under control, the basis was laid for a rapid proliferation of technological processes. The first source of artificially generated power tapped by man seems to have been *water-power*, although in the first century B.C. this was utilized in a comparatively inefficient manner, mainly for turning millstones for the grinding of grain. In what Geddes and Mumford have called the "Eotechnic Period," beginning about the tenth century A.D. in Western Europe, *wind-power* was used, in somewhat naïve machines, for grinding grains, draining inundated areas (particularly in the Low Countries), and even for powering relatively crude weaving machines, and so forth. Both water-power and wind-power, under Eotechnic conditions of technological advancement, suffered from one major disadvantage, namely, inconstancy: one could not depend upon a steady flow of energy from these sources hour in and hour out, day in and day out, whenever it was needed. Not until it was discovered how to generate electric power by these means, could the resulting energy be transmitted any great distance from the source.

As it is well known, a truly revolutionary "advance" in power development occurred in the latter part of the eighteenth century, with the practical development of the *steam* engine, which became a practical instrument of power production about the beginning of the nineteenth century. During this century *coal* became the principal source of energy for generating steam power, but toward the end of the nineteenth century the use of *petroleum* and its products as a fuel began to come into increasing prominence. This was the result of a series of technological inventions having to do with the development of *internal combustion engines* of various types—gasoline and Diesel. At about the same time great technical improvements were made in the *generation of electricity*, and the use of steam, internal combustion, and water sources of power for the generation of electricity, rather than for the production of direct power, developed.

In 1945 a method for the production of power by *fission of the atom* was announced. This has been hailed as the most revolutionary technological development of all time; an assessment and prediction of changes which may be expected to be associated with this invention depend upon a more complete knowledge of the technical processes involved, which are at present secret.

Thus we see that the discovery of energy sources and their harnessing and application in the form of power is basic to the technological development of any culture.

Materials. The type of cultural products of a material nature which may be involved in a society's technology depends also upon the raw materials which are available for use. For example, the great architectural achievements of ancient Mesopotamia were constructed of mud and brick because the region is devoid of suitable building stone or wood, and the form and permanency of the buildings, therefore, compares in some respects unfavorably with those of Egypt and Greece. Although physical lack of certain materials may dictate choices in technology, it not infrequently happens that the customary traditions of a society will likewise force a selection from among the resources actually available. For example, the Indians of the Northwest Coast of North America (Kwakiutl, Tlingit, Haida, and others) have a certain amount of clay physically available with which they could have made pottery. However, the tradition of these cultures led the emphasis on the manufacture of containers into other channels most containers for liquids were made from wood, which was in some cases first cut into thin boards, then bent into shape and sewn together with thongs. It is obvious that the techniques involved in the working of wood are considerably different from those successful in molding clay, which are in turn different from those successful in stone, and so on. The making of clothing from animal skins dictates techniques different from those required for weaving from yarn, which are in turn different if the available material is bark cloth.

As a general rule the technology of a society is of course limited by the effective natural resources presented by the environment. Such environmental limitation may, however, be overcome by cultural means. In the first place, materials which are not physically present may be imported, which of course requires the development of patterns of transportation, and, usually, patterns of trade or interchange with foreign groups controlling the supply of imported materials. On the other hand, discoveries and improvements in processes may increase the effectiveness of the natural materials available. Thus the iron ore of the Mesabi range was physically available to the pre-Columbian hunting Indians who occupied that territory, but for lack of appropriate processes, they were unable to make use of it effectively as a natural resource.

Methods, principles, motivations, and techniques. Any type of technology is a part of culture and is controlled and integrated by cultural patterns. Tools, power, and materials do not combine of their "own volition" to produce artifacts of human design and for human purposes. There must be some plans back of the whole business—plans of thinking and plans of action. In the terminology used in this book, we say that every technological complex includes mental patterns and actional patterns. The mental patterns constitute the overall scheme of what has to be done in order to achieve certain results, and the actional patterns constitute the "tricks of the trade" which must be practised if the overall plan is to be carried out successfully. In ordinary language, we may speak of these two aspects as *method* and *technique*.

When a technological complex is developed, which appears first, the method or the technique? There seems to be no basis to believe that either is necessarily prior to the other, although evidence seems to indicate that perhaps the majority of the earliest advances in technology grew out of "play with technique." Despite the fact that complete new processes are now worked out on the drawing boards of industrial laboratories before the techniques of operation are actually devised, it is fair to say that, even today, "play with technique" is an important, probably the most important, breeding ground for new methods. In short, most methods of technology probably have been—at least until recently—pragmatically derived through trial and error. That method is adopted which, after numerous trials with other methods, seems to work best.

In modern industrial technology another type of mental pattern is involved which stands back of the methods, as it were. This is the set of scientific principles upon which the methods are based. The principles provide the explanation as to why the methods and techniques should be expected to produce the desired results. They are of value, when scientifically based, because they eliminate in advance the necessity of a considerable amount of trial and error.

The presence of principles does not seem to characterize all technological complexes without exception, although there is always a tendency toward their development. Principles, of course, do not have to be based upon scientific procedures, and, in fact, scientifically organized and derived technological principles seem to be a feature almost exclusively confined to Western civilization. Other peoples, however, frequently have explanations of one sort or another for their technological methods and techniques. For example, the Pokomám of Eastern Guatemala hold fast to a principle that the dark of the moon exercises a baleful influence on newly planted maize. The Maya of Chan Kom base their agricultural activities on a system of weather prognostication called *xoc-kin*, which assumes that the weather of the first twelve days of January respectively corresponds to that of each of the succeeding twelve months, while the weather of the succeeding twelve half-days respectively likewise predicts the weather of the succeeding twelve months; that is, the weather on the morning of January 13 corresponds to the weather of January; in the afternoon it corresponds to that which will prevail during February, and so on.[1] Appropriate methods and techniques based upon these "principles," have been developed in both of these cultures. Analogous complexes may be found in many of the cultures of the world.

Also included among the cultural patterns of a technological complex is some idea or *statement of the purposes* of the complex. In other words, the individuals practising the complex have some agreed notion of "what they are trying to do." This agreement on purposes constitutes part of the culture, of course, but it does not necessarily have to agree with the "facts" which may be brought out by objective analysis of the cultural function of the technology. Thus, in certain cases, the purpose of one of our own industries may be stated and believed to be "raising the general standard of living by the provision of low-cost household conveniences to the general public," or something similar, whereas an analysis will reveal that in effect this and all other objectives are actually subordinated to the purpose of making profits for the owners or managers of the business. Nevertheless some idea of the purpose of activity is usually required, whether "true" or not, from the lower to the highest levels of technology. When a savage starts chipping a piece of flint, he usually has in mind the objective of making a definite artifact, an arrowhead perhaps, and his methods and techniques are different from those he would employ were he starting out to making a scraper or a flint dagger.

To be considered in connection with the stated purposes, of course, are the *drives or motivations* which psychologically underlie the activities involved in a technological complex. The motivations involved may be either primary drives, such as hunger, or secondary drives, such as "the profit motive." In most complexes a combination of motivations is involved. As we have just mentioned, there is no guarantee that the representational patterns of the complex will necessarily state the actual motivations clearly, and it often happens that the members of the group who perform the patterns of the complex are unconscious of their true motivations. The matter must always be considered, however, when studying the technological complexes of a people, for if the technology fails beyond a certain point to satisfy the drives of the performers, serious maladjustment is almost bound to occur. Thus if a technology does not satisfy the basic needs of workers for food, clothing, and shelter, one may prate at length about the "dignity of labor" without getting the workers to perform their functions at all, or to perform them as efficiently as they otherwise might. On the other hand, it should not be inferred that primary physiological drives play a part in the motivation of all technological processes and economic activities. Somewhere in the technology of a society these needs must be satisfied to a minimum degree, but a specific technological complex may have little or nothing to do with them. The elaborate techniques of the Hopi pottery-maker seem to be motivated entirely by desire for prestige mingled with some religious motivation. And the infinite care which was expended upon the carving of the Marquesan ceremonial clubs, which as tools were too unwieldy for hunting or war, offered no direct satisfaction to physiological needs.

Methods and techniques may, of course, vary in efficiency and consistency. Such matters may be studied and corrected scientifically, and the profession of industrial engineering is concerned with them in our own society.

In this connection we should mention one principle which has had a far-reaching effect upon technology where it has been adopted. This is the principle of rotary motion and its basic artifact is the *wheel*. Rotary motion and the wheel are fundamental to practically all mechanical processes, and only slight reflection will convince the reader of the pervading influence of the principle and artifact in our own culture. The application of the wheel to technological purposes of significance seems to have been an invention which occurred only once. It first appears during New Stone Age times in Egypt and Mesopotamia, and its technological application in other parts of the world seems to be explained by diffusion from the ancient center. However, the wheel as a toy was probably independently invented in aboriginal Mexico where it was used on toy animals of clay, which were provided with clay disk wheels.[2] However, there is as yet no evidence of the use of wheels on vehicles or machinery in the aboriginal cultures of the Western Hemisphere. Although all the centers of civilization in Eurasia had adopted the wheel by the beginning of the Christian era, it is noteworthy that as a technological artifact it had never reached the New World previous to the discovery by Europeans in the fifteenth century. Thus the high developments of civilization in the Western Hemisphere in Mexico, Yucatan, and the Andean region were completely unmechanized and devoid even of wheeled vehicles. Even after four hundred years of European civilization, the natives of these regions today perform most of their work and transportation without the use of machines or wheeled vehicles. Even in modern times the wheel had failed to reach or to be adopted by many other functioning cultures of so-called primitive peoples.

Any culture devoid of the wheel is at a technological disadvantage for the basic reason that this simple artifact reduces friction and thus permits an infinitely more efficient application of power to almost any technological process.

Another very basic principle of importance to technological culture is the principle of combustion, in other words, the fact that the splitting of certain types of molecules gives off energy in the form of heat. The *control and use of fire* seems to have developed early in human cultural development, for even in the earliest stages of the Old Stone Age we find evidence of hearths and fireplaces. When human beings first learned to make fire as well as to use it, we do not know with certainty, but the discovery was apparently made independently in various parts of the world. However, some primitive peoples, for example the Andaman Islanders, according to Brown had not learned to make fire, even in modern times.[3]

The energy produced by fire was early used for such homely purposes as cooking raw foods and for providing heat when the temperature was low. For this reason, it has often been alleged that the hearth and its fire was an early and basic material component in the family complex. From the point of view of technology, fire has been fundamental to many advances. Its energy is necessary for hardening water-tight pottery, for smelting metal ores, for producing steam, and even (apparently) in the preliminary stages of preparing the uranium from which atomic energy is derived.

Social and economic organization. A final component of any technological system is the organization of the individuals who engage in the activities involved. Technology may be performed by individuals working separately or they may be organized into groups for given jobs. The average man may be a jack of all trades or there may be varying degrees of specialization of function. Every man may be his own boss, or there may be various ranks of command and direction of the work. These matters are usually patterned by the culture and the individuals involved are taught their respective rôles in the system and trained, not only in the technical details of their functions, but also in their relations with other participants in the system. In the highly complex organization of modern technology the relationships between such groups as workmen, technical designers and engineers, and managers, have become crucial, not only to the well-being of the society as a whole, but also to the successful accomplishment of the technological objectives involved.

Summary. The technics of any culture are to be considered as a complex or institution involving, at the least, the elements of tools, power, materials, methods, principles, motivations, techniques, and organization of the human element. The success of a technical system depends not only upon the efficiency with which tools, power, and technical patterns are applied to materials, but also upon the organization of the working elements, the satisfactions provided, and the general consistency of all these factors one to the other and with a system of values.

SKETCH OF THE DEVELOPMENT OF TECHNICS

THE OLD STONE AGE

Prehistoric Archaeology is the science which attempts to reconstruct the life and culture of extinct societies which have left us no written record. It is of necessity largely concerned with the technical developments of early times for the reason that the cultural materials available for study consist almost exclusively of material objects made and left behind them by the peoples concerned. Obviously only the more durable materials and artifacts withstand the ravages of the ages and, therefore, the archaeologist is never able to reconstruct *in toto* the culture of very ancient peoples, except by inference from the remains which he is able to recover. Inferences must in all cases be made on the basis of actual observation of living "primitive" peoples having similar artifacts, or from a knowledge of certain general principles of technics and of culture. Here again we see the essential unity of anthropology, the science of man, for archaeology is closely dependent upon ethnology, or the study of living peoples, for its interpretations.[4]

We recall that the first truly manlike creatures appeared during the early Pleistocene, perhaps a million years ago. Although these creatures may have made and used wooden tools, most of the earliest clearly human artifacts that we have were made of flint, chert, or similar stones.

Systematic investigation of prehistoric archaeology has been most thoroughly carried forward in Europe, the Near East, and the United States. Since the story in Europe extends backward to far greater antiquity than that in the New World, it has been customary to use the terminology developed there to describe the series of industrial periods or stages through which mankind developed in Europe for comparison with other parts of the world. Speaking in general, the feature of this development which strikes us perhaps most forcibly is the fact that technology developed extremely slowly at first. Significant innovations, or "new models," of stone tools appeared at intervals of tens and hundreds of thousands of years. The coup de poign, or fist axe, the scraper, and a crude borer were *the* three outstanding types of tools in the human kit-bag for perhaps over half a million years (of the total of a million or so years since the first appearance of evidences of early man), and, although certain refinements appeared, no basically new model or new process of manufacture was developed during all that time at least (the Lower Paleolithic or Old Stone Age). In other words, it seems that mankind put in a technical apprenticeship which lasted perhaps a half-million years. The Upper Old Stone Age, involving a number of new techniques and significantly new types of tools and materials began about 12,000 to 25,000 years ago in Europe and the Near East, more or less coincidentally with the appearance of sapiens type of man in the area. Each succeeding technological period following was of shorter duration. Inventions and innovations of a technical nature appeared with increasing frequency, until at the present time in modern civilization they pour by the thousands each year from the patent offices.

In the following pages we shall briefly sketch the more important advances in technics, so far as they are known, from the beginning of human culture. Obviously in the space at our disposal the discussion of many details and implications must be omitted, but we hope to make clear certain principles involved in technics and their relationship to other aspects of culture.

The Lower Old Stone Age. Mankind apparently started out "to make a living" in the world as a simple hunter and gatherer during early Pleistocene times. The earliest artifacts which have been recovered are the much discussed *eoliths*, crude flakes which are alleged to show human workmanship and fashioning. Although it is not improbable that our earliest ancestors may have fashioned and used something similar, it is difficult to accept all so-called eoliths as human artifacts for two reasons. (1) Many are so crude in technique that it is difficult to rule out the possibility that they are merely flint flakes chipped by natural causes. (2) Many of the best examples come from geological levels identified as Pliocene, a period previous to the time when we have any definite evidence that manlike creatures (as distinct from apes) had evolved; and some alleged "eoliths" have appeared as early as the Miocene, a geological period which we know almost definitely saw the development of no human-like forms, for even the great apes had not fully evolved at that time. Also, although the most convincing eoliths—those from the sub-Red Crag deposits in Southern England—are in some cases associated with what appear to be the remains of hearths, no eoliths of late Pliocene or early Pleistocene date have yet come to light directly associated with the remains of clearly manlike creatures.

Somewhat more convincing are the so-called *Pre-Chellean* implements found in Western Europe in geological formations of early Pleistocene date (Gunz glaciation). These implements are crudely made from both cores and flakes of flint. The age is roughly the same as that of the Java Ape Man.

From this time forward for several hundred thousand years one of the principal industries of early men was the making of tools and implements from flint. This substance, usually found in the form of metamorphosed nodules in beds of sedimentary limestone, is particularly adaptable to the earliest and crudest techniques of stone working. Flint is somewhat like glass in that it is usually rather homogeneous in texture; this quality enables it to be chipped in all directions, instead of shattering along planes of cleavage as is the case with sedimentary, laminated rocks, such as limestone and shale. Also flint is brittle, like glass, so that it can be chipped into the desired shape (provided the chipping technique is adequate), a feature not shared with some of the tougher types of stone. Finally, the edges of flakes chipped off of flint are sharp like the edges of broken glass and thus provide the operator with a keen (although brittle) cutting tool.

The working of flint can be quite an art, but the earliest flint-workers apparently knew only one simple technique, which consisted in knocking off chips from a core by means of *percussion* with a hammer stone held in the hand. Direct percussion of this type produces a relatively ungainly result because of the difficulty of controlling the force of the blow and consequently the direction and extent of the chipping. The early flint-workers, of the *Chellean* type of industry (so named from the type site, Chelles, France), were primarily interested in implements fashioned from *cores* of flint, rather than in what they could do with the chips taken off the cores. Although scrapers and rough knives were made of flakes, the major effort was expended on a type of implement called by the French a *coup de poign* or *fist axe*. These implements were large, heavy, somewhat triangular implements of flint, shaped by the removal of large and irregular flakes. The fist axe was probably a general utility weapon and tool, perhaps used for killing animals in hand combat, for cutting wood and carcasses, and for hacking notches in tree trunks for climbing. The only surviving people in modern times having such an implement were the now extinct Tasmanians, who used small fist axes for climbing trees, cutting branches, and for general utility purposes. Chellean industries appear in Egypt during the First Interglacial period, perhaps 600,000 years ago, while full-blown Chellean forms in England and France date from the Second Interglacial period, possibly 450,000 years ago. Piltdown and Peking men were living in the Second Interglacial period, but, although both of these forms were found with some cultural material, it is not clear that they were either the originators or the users of Chellean tools.

The succeeding period of flint technology is known as the *Acheulean* and still shows primary interest in the fist axe, which, however, was now made with greater skill and fineness, still with the percussion technique. The fist axes are smaller, more regular in outline, straighter (less wavy) along the edge, and thinner in cross-section—all of which effects depended upon the development of better control of the percussion technique. Rough scrapers continued to be made from flints, with some of them now achieving discoidal form. Apparently the early technicians struggled along with the Chellean techniques for about 150,000 years, for the Acheulean continues in the Near East and in Western Europe about that length of time after the first appearance of the Chellean. Acheulean implements are characteristic of the Second Interglacial period in Egypt (say, 450,000 years ago) and of the Third Interglacial period, with perhaps some slightly earlier development, in West and Central Europe.

As we have said, the main emphasis of the Chellean and Acheulean technics was upon the making and use of core implements. Contemporary with these two developments, however, a number of early industries grew up in other regions of Western Europe which concentrated on the making of implements from flakes. These styles are variously known as Levalloisian, Clactonian, and Micoquean, depending upon their location. In one of the Clactonian sites a portion of a wooden spear has been recovered. All of these industries together are usually grouped into what is known as the Lower Paleolithic or Lower Old Stone Age.

The Middle Old Stone Age, *or Paleolithic,* was ushered in perhaps 125,000 years ago (latter part of the Third Interglacial period) in the form of the *Mousterian culture.* The cultural remains known by this name (from Le Moustier, a cave site in France) are definitely associated with the Neanderthal type of human remains, and thus represent the earliest horizon at which we have extensive data both as respects artifacts and the type of creatures who used them. Since the Neanderthals and their Mousterian culture continued in Europe through the Fourth Glacial period, during which time they inhabited caves for protection, their mode of life may properly be described as that of the Cave Men. Some rather important innovations both in workmanship and in variety of tools appear for the first time. In the first place, the two trends in workmanship which had been developing during the Lower Paleolithic—emphasis on cores and on flakes, respectively—seem to converge in the flint work of the Mousterian. Small, well-made, pointed fist axes were made and (presumably) used with skill by the Mousterians, thus carrying on the core tradition. But increasing ingenuity was shown in the handling of flakes. From the latter were made points, side-scrapers with crescentic edges, knotched "spoke shaves" (probably for smoothing spear or dart shafts), and even tanged spear or dart points. All of these flake implements were comparatively finely made by reason of the use of a new technique in addition to that of percussion. This new technique, which seems to have been invented in its earliest forms in the Mousterian culture, is known as the *pressure technique*. Instead of knocking off chips with blows of a hammer, an operator using the pressure technique employs an implement of bone or wood with a blunt point, and with this he presses off chips of flint in the places desired. Any reader of this book may experiment with the technique by using the end of an old toothbrush on pieces of glass and will find that it is not too difficult to make a passable arrow-head by this procedure. It is particularly useful when shaping or "retouching" the edge of a flake. Many of the finer Mousterian implements show evidence of this type of retouching, which seems to have been a major invention of this phase of culture. However, the flakes themselves were still removed from the cores by percussion, and the pressure technique was applied only to flakes so removed.

In the Mousterian deposits not only dart or spear points with re-touched stems are found, but also an increasing variety of scraper tools, probably used for cleaning the inner side of fresh skins. Likewise bone tools appear in this horizon for the first time as a regular part of the tool chest; colors made of mineral substances are also fairly common, indicating a more developed aesthetic interest. The use of fire was an unquestioned and regular feature of Mousterian culture, and several cases of ceremonial burial during Mousterian times are on record, showing an awakened interest in the fate of the soul and the after-life.

We recall that the Neanderthals eventually disappeared and were replaced (either by extinction, amalgamation, or both) by a sapiens population. So likewise their Mousterian culture faded out. The process of change-over began perhaps as early as 25,000 years ago in some areas, but Neanderthal men and Mousterian culture had finally disappeared everywhere by about 15,500 years ago. The sapiens men introduced a number of new ideas in technology, and from the time of their advent in Europe each technological advance appeared at a progressively shorter interval than the previous one.

Upper Old Stone Age. The Upper Paleolithic phase, known also as the Gravettian series of culture, began with the so-called *Aurignacian culture* (known also as Capsian in North Africa and Sebilian in Egypt). From the technological point of view a number of definitely revolutionary changes were introduced with the beginning of the Upper Paleolithic.

1. Making of implements from cores of flint was practically abandoned, and flint-working technique was concentrated on fine and delicately retouched implements from flakes.

2. Greatly improved proficiency in the pressure technique was achieved. In Aurignacian culture the flake instruments were not only retouched, but the workmen apparently invented a process of removing the flakes themselves from the cores by pressure or *indirect percussion*. In the latter process the bone instrument of the type used for retouching is held in position against the "striking platform" (a relatively flat surface) of the flint nodule, and the butt of the instrument is struck with a hammer. At all events, the Aurignacian people were adept at producing long, thin, razor-like blades which were skilfully removed from cores of flint. This technique requires a thorough practical knowledge of the characteristics of the material as well as a working knowledge of the principles of force carefully controlled. It is a procedure definitely difficult to duplicate even with modern tools.

3. The *variety* of flint tools thus made greatly increased: fine knife blades, chisels, engraving instruments, shaft shavers, end-scrapers, and so forth, appear in profusion.

4. *Bone artifacts* for the first time come into prominence. It would appear that their manufacture was dependent upon the previous development of the fine cutting and engraving tools of flint previously mentioned. For bone, as a material, differs radically from flint—it cannot be usefully chipped either by percussion or pressure, but on the contrary must be carved or abraded into shape. This is technically impossible without appropriate tools. We see here one of the earliest illustrations of the general principle that one technological development often lays the foundation for succeeding developments, and that the history of technologies is a story of inventions and discoveries being built one upon the other in an irreversible sequence. Bone artifacts of the Aurignacians included bone awls presumably used for punching holes in skins; dart points, some with split bases for attachment to the shaft; spatulas; a few needles with eyes, apparently indicating the use of sewn clothing; dart shaft wrenches; and various pendants and other ornaments of bone and ivory, including toggles (crude buttons), bracelets, and rings. Some of these bone objects were decorated with incised designs of carved lines, but the Aurignacians did not develop the decoration of bone to the degree which was achieved in later cultures.

5. Actual objects of *art* occur for the first time in this phase of culture, and these likewise seem to have been dependent upon the prior invention of delicate and manipulatable stone tools. Sculptured heads and full figures in the round—always female—are fairly frequent and in some

cases show surprisingly "modernistic" treatment in economy of effort, simplicity of design, and forcefulness of effect. Most of the full figure female sculptures exaggerate the reproductive features of the female body, from which it has been inferred that they represented idols of a fertility cult. Otherwise the representational art work of the Aurignacians was mainly concerned with the depiction of animals of the chase, most frequently bison, deer, and mammouth. Figures of these animals were engraved on cave walls, and also painted in single colors, usually in black or red lines. Animals were usually depicted in profile, but in some cases foreshortening and shadowing were used in an elementary way. On the whole the Aurignacian cave art is pleasing to the "modern eye," for it combines realism with a sophisticated economy of line and suggestion. It has been highly praised by modern critics.

6. Perhaps associated with the interest in art in general was an interest in *personal ornament*. Perforated beads and pendants of bone and shell and fish vertebrae are common, all of which, together with the increased attention to clothing as evidenced by needles and toggles, would seem to indicate an increasing appreciation of the individual personality.

7. The first steps in a new technique of stone-working appear among the Aurignacians. This is the *pecking or abrading technique* whereby granular and sedimentary stones are shaped into vessels. At least one such vessel, probably used as a lamp, has been recovered from an Aurignacian deposit in France.

Taking everything into account we get an impression of a more "human" type of life from the material products of Aurignacian culture. Nevertheless, these people were hunters, who, at least in cold seasons, still lived in caves, probably following a nomadic type of life in relatively small groups.

The Aurignacian culture was succeeded in a rather restricted area of Europe by the *Solutrean phase*. Most of the tools of the preceding phase survived, but the outstanding feature of the Solutrean was a great efflorescence of the pressure-flaking technique in flint. Not only were elaborate spear points, dart points, and knives made, with and without stems of various types, but also large daggers and spear points. The outstanding feature of the technique was the accuracy of control in the flaking and the remarkable aspects of the results were regularity and symmetry of form and the effect called "ripple flaking" covering the entire surfaces of thin, delicately made blades. Some of these implements were used to hunt wild horses, for the skeletons of over 100,000 of these animals were found at the type site, Le Solutre.

The Magdalenian culture followed the Solutrean and during this phase the various techniques of bone and antler working came into their own. Flint instruments were still made, but apparently for strictly utilitarian purposes, that is, for use as bone-carvers primarily. The Magdalenians' most spectacular bone product was the harpoon head, which developed through several "models," the better examples of which were provided with double rows of recurved barbs and incised designs. Small points, very much like arrow points, were made from bone, as were also spear throwers for casting darts or spears, daggers, shaft wrenches, spatulas, buttons, and so on. Some of these objects were decorated with realistic incised depictions of animals, such as wild horses, while others carried apparently ritualistic, stylized designs possibly of ceremonial significance. A few of the designs ("tectiform") look like the frameworks of tents or houses with pitched roofs, the first hints we have thus far of definite structures. The Magdalenians also made mortars of pecked-out granular stone for grinding wild seeds as well as "lamps" and other containers of the same material. And they carried the cave-painting art of the Aurignacians forward with such technical improvements as polychrome painting.

The Magdalenian period lasted perhaps 6,000 years in Western and Central Europe and came to an end in those regions perhaps 7500 B.C. It was the last outstanding cultural development of the Old Stone Age and in Europe faded out through a series of transitional cultures (Azilian, Tardenoisian, and others). The Old Stone Age had lasted for almost a million years, during the whole of the Glacial epoch. Although technological progress and improvement were achieved as we have seen, they came slowly, almost unbelievably slowly from the point of view of the present day. And after all, man was still a nomadic hunter, living in small groups, gathering a large part of his sustenance, but without permanent settlements or many of the finer arts of life.

During its first million years mankind did not achieve any of the technological procedures which are basic to modern civilization. In many respects the conditions of human life at the end of the Paleolithic were farther removed from our own mode of life than from that of mankind's apish ancestors. The real foundations of civilization were laid during the past 15,000 years or so.

THE NEOLITHIC REVOLUTION

While the inhabitants of Central and Western Europe were still chasing the deer and elk across the bogs of Europe from which the glaciers were reluctantly retreating, a revolution in the pattern of human life was getting under way in Egypt and the Near East. This is traditionally called the Neolithic or New Stone Age, but the changes in technics which were developed were far more important and pervasive than any mere innovations in methods of working stone, for they laid the foundations of civilized and settled life upon which all the more developed cultures have been built to this day. Many societies exist in the Neolithic phase of culture even at the present time. We can do no more than to sketch here some of the salient features of this new technological complex.

1. *Stone-working* continued to be a major industry in Neolithic cultures. In fact, the name New Stone Age was first given to the culture because of the greater emphasis upon grinding, pecking, and polishing techniques in the making of artifacts. Although these procedures are highly developed in full Neolithic cultures, the chipping of flint was continued, often with great skill, in the Neolithic of the Near East and of Europe. In fact, the ripple-flaked daggers, sickles, knives, and points of flint coming from Egypt during this period outclass even the best Solutrean work. Polished stone products were also well made as the tricks of the trade were better learned. Among the products appeared a significant new tool, namely the axe, which represents an important advance in control of the environment. With the axe, albeit of stone, house materials could be cut from forests with greater ease and in greater quantities than previously, while the forests themselves could be cleared for the cultivation of crops.

2. Hunting was raised to a new level of efficiency by the introduction of a novel weapon, the *bow and arrow*. It is possible, but unlikely, that this contrivance was used in the Upper Old Stone Age, but it certainly was not well developed until the Neolithic. By applying the force of elasticity in the wood of the bow, the weapon not only increases the range of the marksman's effectiveness, but also his accuracy and the economy of materials, for an arrow is less expensive, and therefore more expendable, than a spear.

3. At the same time that hunting became more efficient, it became less necessary. For by far the most important of the Neolithic innovations were the *domestications of animals and plants*. At the present point we shall not review the various speculations as to how these discoveries may have been made. It is known that the so-called Badarian Neolithics of Egypt were cultivating emmer wheat at least by about 5000 B.C., and it is probable that some domestications had occurred earlier. Although, so far as definite archaeological evidence goes, the earliest Neolithic domestications seem to have occurred around the eastern end of the Mediterranean, it is quite apparent that certain other species were independently domesticated in other parts of the world as a part of the general Neolithic phase of culture. We have previously mentioned the fact that the llama was independently domesticated in the Andean area,

and a long list of domesticated plants were first cultivated in the New World, independently of Old World suggestion: for example, potatoes, tomatoes, cacao, coca, maize, olluco, quinoa, and others. Most poultry birds were probably first domesticated in Southeastern Asia, although the turkey seems to have been independently domesticated in Mexico. The horse was probably domesticated in south central Asia. Cattle, sheep, and asses seem to have first come under the sway of man in the eastern Mediterranean area and reached Europe from there. The cat may have been domesticated in Egypt. Dogs were probably first domesticated at the very close of the Paleolithic. There is some evidence that the wolf-hound type of dog was first developed in Abyssinia or thereabouts. Barley and wheat seem to have been first domesticated in the Near East (an area which includes Egypt), whereas rye and oats may be products of more northern centers of cultivation. The banana, on the other hand, was probably first grown in Southeastern Asia or the nearby islands, also probably the home of the yam; manioc, another tropical root crop, is a product of tropical South American culture.

Without attempting to trace out the origins of other common crops and animals we may content ourselves here with the observation that domestication is basic to most of the other developments of civilization. Why should this be so? The domestication of plants and animals on any substantial scale has a most important effect of (*a*) providing a more steady food supply than is usually possible when reliance must be placed entirely on hunting, gathering, or fishing. (*b*) The cultivation of plants practically demands a settled mode of life, at least during the planting, growing, and harvesting seasons. Even in those regions, such as the wet tropics where the leaching of the soil exhausts its fertility after a few seasons and requires periodic movement to new fields, the cultivators are settled near their fields and gardens while the latter are in production. Once cultivated plants become a principal source of food supply, the establishment of permanent buildings, villages, and towns becomes imperative, together with the development of the techniques of architecture and public works, as well as systems of social organization and control of a more stable and complex nature than are required, as a rule, among nomadic hunters living in small bands. (*c*) Domestication, as the techniques improve in efficiency, not only provides a steadier supply but also a larger supply of food. This has several important effects upon the development of society and culture. First, it permits an increase in population. And we have seen in examining the general principles of culture that the patterns of a culture inevitably become greater in number and more complex in organization as the population of a society increases. The larger food supply also permits specialization of certain members of the society, who have the leisure for the development of arts, intellectual pursuits, technical invention, and the like. Domestication, in short, is a method of providing sustenance which is more highly efficient than any of the earler methods. The output of food per producer is greatly increased. If cultivation involves the raising of storable foods, such as small grains, the efficiency is raised even higher, for food can be laid by for long periods during which a considerable part of the population may not (because of weather) or does not (because of other occupations) devote itself intensively to food production. All the so-called higher civilizations have been raised on a cereal foundation. Wheat, barley, oats, and rye were the basis of the Mediterranean and European developments. The civilizations of the Far East were in large part based on rice. And those of the Mayas, Aztecs, and Incas of the New World were reared on maize. Thus it is that, even today, a steady supply of cereals is the prerequisite for the development and existence of civilization. Although there is no society which lives on cereals alone, there is no complex "higher" culture which exists without them, for cereals are economical in the sense that they provide high nutritive value per unit of productive effort, and they are stabilizing in that they can be stored comparatively easily during the "off season" and even for years, when crops are poor or disasters threaten the immediate food supply. It should also be noted that the so-called "coldward march of civilization" of which certain geographers speak is connected with improved cultural ability to produce storable foods in the shorter growing season of the higher latitudes.

It is for these reasons that we say that the Neolithic cultural developments laid the basis for modern civilization.

It should be noted that there are in general two types of plant cultivation: (a) hand tillage or horticulture, and (b) agriculture, properly speaking. The latter involves the use of the plough and other implements usually too heavy to be operated by human power alone, while the techniques of hand tillage employ digging sticks, hoes, and other implements that can be operated by human power alone. There are some plants which, even today, apparently are not amenable to cultivation solely by plough (for example, grape vines), but in general the introduction of the plough is an advance in efficiency, because it represents an increased application of power for each unit of man's time and effort. It should be noted, however, that until modern times and the invention of power-producing engines, the plough could nowhere be developed by a culture which did not previously possess domesticated animals suitable for providing the necessary traction power. In other words, the domestication of large draft animals—oxen, horses or mules, camels, or water buffalo—was a necessary prerequisite for agriculture.

This relatively simple case illustrates a type of linkage between elements, complexes, and other parts of a culture which it is important to grasp, not only for the purpose of understanding "progress" and development of cultural life, but also the functioning of cultural systems as going concerns. Invention A must be made in the culture, or introduced from outside, before B can be developed at all. Likewise, once the system is in operation, anything which interferes with the functioning of A will usually paralyze or seriously cripple the functioning of B. This interdependency of various parts of a culture is apparent, not only in technics, but also in social organization and other phases of cultural activity as well, and it will be mentioned from time to time in subsequent chapters.

Associated with the stabilization and proliferation of society afforded by the domestication of plants and animals were several concomitant inventions and innovations also first introduced during Neolithic times.

4. *Construction of permanent buildings and settlements* became an important part of Neolithic technology. Although the Paleolithic people may have had tents, pit houses, and shelters of brush, it is not until Neolithic times that structures were made sufficiently durable to leave many archaeological remains. Various techniques were evolved by the Neolithic builders, using materials provided by the different environments: adobe, wattle-and-daub, sun-baked brick, stone, and wood. In Europe the two most spectacular types of Neolithic structures were the Swiss Lake Dwellings and the stone dolmens, menhirs, and alignments. The Lake Dwellings were built of wood on piles out over the lakes, as a means of protection from landward attack, and several Melanesian peoples, for example, still dwell in somewhat similar villages.[5] The dolmens were chambers made from huge slabs of stone, one set on edge for each of the four walls and one laid on top as a roof, with the whole structure later covered with earth. The dolmens were apparently religious structures and were often associated with huge stones set upright in the ground singly (menhirs) or in lines and geometric patterns (alignments and circles, for example, Stonehenge in England). These constructions not only indicate interest in religion and organization of effort which the Neolithic form of life permitted and stimulated, but also the development of *engineering techniques*, for the individual stones often weigh as much as twenty tons.

5. *Pottery-making* came into its own during Neolithic times. Despite substitute expedients, such as stone-boiling in rawhide containers and the use of green bambu containers for boiling, only a pottery-using people can enjoy boiled foods and such preparations as soups, broths, and gruels conveniently and on a large scale. Pottery is not necessarily confined to people of settled life, however, and there is a strong probability

that some pottery developed in late Paleolithic times in Eurasia and was transmitted to the New World, where it enjoys a wide distribution among nomadic and semi-nomadic hunting peoples of the Woodland area and northward. The linkage is not between pottery per se and settled life, but between the latter and the elaboration of pottery forms and uses.[6] It is this greater prominence of ceramics in art and as utensil that characterizes the Neolithic development.

6. *Weaving* was also a part of the new Neolithic complex. Although the domestication of plants and animals is not an absolutely necessary prerequisite for the development of this art, domestication does provide a more abundant supply of easily handled fibers. Cotton was domesticated early in India, and the Neolithic people of Europe raised considerable quantities of flax for its fiber, from which they wove the fabrics for clothing. The fibers of sheep and goats were early adapted to weaving in the Neolithic cultures of the Near East and Europe, while the domesticators of camels in south central Asia and the llama herdsmen of Peru likewise made early use of these animals for fibers. Clothing in a Neolithic culture is normally provided in greater and steadier quantity than in a hunting-gathering-fishing economy. Weaving also permits a wider variety of raiment, adapted to a larger range of seasons and temperatures than is usually possible when the supply is confined to animal skins or unwoven vegetable products.

7. The *wheel* was an important invention of the Neolithic in the Old World. The otherwise Neolithic cultures of the Western Hemisphere lacked this very important mechanical device except in the form of toys. The same was true of certain cultures of the Old World to which, although they contained most elements of the Neolithic complex, the wheel either did not diffuse or in which its use was not adaptable because of environmental conditions or other factors. Thus the Polynesians lacked the wheel aboriginally, although they shared in certain other traits of Neolithic culture, likewise numerous agricultural societies of Negro Africa, some of which even developed metallurgy before adopting the wheel. In the strictly Neolithic (pre-metallurgical) phases of Old World cultures the wheel was used in crude, solid form on vehicles such as ox carts; it was also used in pottery-making in the form of the potter's wheel, and in a few other simple mechanical devices. But a pervasive application of the wheel and the principle of rotary motion was not characteristic of Neolithic culture which, we might say, was not basically mechanically minded.

8. Another group of Neolithic inventions centered about *transportation* and methods of increasing human mobility. Thus it is that, although cultivating communities in a Neolithic type of culture have more settled

places of residence than is the rule among more nomadic Paleolithic peoples, they are also often in a position to enjoy greater contacts with the world. The Swiss Lake Dwellers, for example, had dugout *boats* for lacustrine movement, and even earlier the Neolithic farmers of the Nile Valley had developed craft for movement on that river. Poles, paddles, and oars were the earliest devices for the application of *human energy* to the propulsion of water craft, but a few Neolithic cultures (for example, those of Egypt, the Northwest Coast tribes of North America, Polynesia) harnessed the *power of the wind* through the use of sails. The adaptation of *animal power* for the transportation of men and goods was likewise accomplished in the Old World Neolithic cultures. Although one would logically assume that the riding of animals would have preceded their use with vehicles, it is doubtful that this was the case. The riding of horses is first mentioned in Babylonian records of about 2300 B.C. (where the horses are described as the possessions of certain barbaric tribes to the north), but they do not appear in Egyptian history until about 1700 B.C. On the other hand the use of oxen with wheeled carts is clear as early as the sixth millennium B.C. in the Near East and in the full Neolithic cultures of Europe somewhat later. The employment of the ox as a draft animal, or possibly a beast of burden, may be presumed to have developed even earlier.

This Neolithic development of transportation undoubtedly had a favorable effect upon culture development in general. By the interchange of goods, artifacts, and ideas between communities a stimulus was given to the adoption and invention of new elements of culture and that process of cultural accumulation, which is another of the features of advanced civilizations, was set in motion.

The use of domestic draft animals in agriculture for the purpose of pulling plows and other implements likewise increased food output, with its attendant features of greater efficiency, division of labor, increased specialization, and advancement of both the technical and fine arts.

9. The technical innovations we have sketched undoubtedly produced reverberations in the *patterns of human relationships* characteristic of the Neolithic world. Such patterns do not leave complete material remains which may be reconstructed by archaeologists, and the Neolithic peoples did not develop the techniques involved in keeping written records which might have described their social life for us. Therefore, our remarks with respect to this aspect of Neolithic culture must be based on inference from archaeological material and from the practices of certain peoples who have preserved a phase of Neolithic culture in modern times. First, the culture must have developed a greater *specialization of function* than had previously existed. The freeing of certain portions of the populace

from the necessity of spending all their time trying to fill their bellies enabled them to devote their energies and talents to the development of specialities, such as pottery-making, building design and construction, clothing and ornament, political functions, art and aesthetic pursuits, and religion. Second, a necessity arose for the development of *more elaborate patterns of personal and group intercourse* than those presumably sufficient in Paleolithic times. Chiefs, councils, and other governmental mechanisms of a more stable and complicated type were required. Ideas of property must have developed, particularly as regards real estate, because the individual's and the group's stake in land and its improvements increased enormously once they had settled down to a cultivating mode of life.

THE MAKING OF METALS

The next great step forward in technology came with the discovery of the usefulness of metals and the technical procedures for their production. In Egypt the smelting of copper began about 5500 B.C. and the technique of alloying it with tin to produce the harder and tougher bronze was established by about 3000 B.C. This was succeeded by metallurgy in iron, which in the Near East seems to have been developed between 2000 and 1500 B.C. In Europe these phases all appear later, indicating the lag in diffusion from the Near Eastern center. In Western Europe, for example, copper did not come into general use until about 2500 B.C., bronze 500 years later in the most advanced centers, and the so-called Iron Age did not get under way until about 1100 B.C. The Iron Age did not reach Scandinavia until the beginning of the Christian era, or later.

Although the metal industries of early Europe seem all to have derived from the Near Eastern center, the smelting of ores was also independently developed in other parts of the world. For example, the people of ancient Peru were accomplished workers of copper, bronze, silver, and gold, although neither they nor any of the other New World peoples ever learned to smelt iron previous to the European conquest.

Many of the more familiar articles of modern times survive in much the same patterns as when first invented and made during the early metal ages in Europe. The curved barbed fish hook, the horse bit, safety pin, brooch, grain sickle with curved metal blade, the metal bucket and basin, the metal dagger and sword, and the flat axe all appeared in Bronze Age Europe. Scissors, pliers, horse-shoes, spades, trident spears, boat hooks, and perforated axe-heads were made and used during the European "Iron Age" in practically the same forms as they appear among us now.

The achievement of metallurgy, wherever it has occurred, has had important general reverberations in other departments of culture. Specialization of function is increased, for metallurgy, even in its simpler forms, is a complicated technique requiring considerable training and apparatus. In almost all metal-working societies the metal-workers are specialists. Agricultural implements increase in efficiency, for metal-bladed hoes and metal-tipped digging sticks, metal plows, and other such implements all do their work with a considerable saving of effort and material in contrast to stone and wooden implements. Warfare may become more lethal and better organized because of the greater "efficiency" of metal weapons, and a people possessing these instruments of aggression is enabled to enlarge its territory at the expense of its less well equipped neighbors. This is particularly true if the aggressive society possesses horses to increase the mobility and combat advantages of the warriors. The horse is most effectively managed with metal equipment in the form of bits, shoes, spurs, buckles, and so on.

In connection with the technology of the early metal ages several points of contrast with modern metallurgical economies should be noted. During none of the early phases of metallurgy—not even in Roman times—were the techniques adapted to large-scale output or to the production of heavy objects made of metal, such as production machinery, girders, ship plates and other bulky products which constitute so large a part of the output of modern metallurgy. The products of the smith were on the whole confined to tools, utensils, weapons (including defensive artifacts such as shields and armor), and articles of personal adornment and dress. It is also to be remarked that machinery was practically absent from the metallurgical complex. Although bellows are an essential part of the forge equipment, they were in early times always worked by man-power. Machinery was neither used to produce articles of metal nor did it figure to any extent among the products of metallurgy. Consequently there was no mass production, no factories in the modern sense of the word, and no "labor force" engaged simply in the routine motions of machine manufacturing. Metallurgy was hand work and was carried on by specialists on a more or less individualistic basis. The situation must have been somewhat like that in many rural towns in our own country until very recently, where a blacksmith, a tinsmith, and a general repair man supplied most of the needs for metal goods in response to individual orders of the customers.

In the Mediterranean region and in various of the cultures of Asia (particularly China) the achievement of early metallurgy was also accompanied by the invention of practicable *systems of writing*. There does not seem to be a necessary functional connection between writing and the other technical advances included in the Neolithic and metallurgical economies, other than the fact that the increased independence from nature which they permitted provided more leisure and opportunity for experimentation along these lines. Increased population, of course, renders a system of records especially desirable, for the purpose of controlling personal and group activities, for the preservation of traditions, general culture and history of past events, and for the standardization of communication as the relations between members of a society become necessarily less personal. In the New World, the Mayas and Aztecs did develop systems of writing, whereas the societies of the Andean area, although they were expert cultivators and metal-workers with a highly organized social system, depended upon a crude and somewhat clumsy system of keeping records by means of knotted cords, called *quipus*.

Notes to Chapter 17

1. Redfield and Villa, 1934, p. 133 for Chan Kom. For Pokomám, unpublished field work of author. .
2. Ekholm, 1946.
3. Brown, A. R., 1922, p. 472: "The Andamanese are perhaps the only people in the world who have no method of their own of making fire."
4. Supplemental reading on primitive technology and organization will be found in Boas, and others, 1938, Chapters 5-8 inclusive; Peake and Fleure, 1927-1936 is a useful summary of the archaeological aspects in Europe. Current materials and reviews of the archaeological discoveries in this field will be found in *American Antiquity*, Menasha, Wisconsin. Useful discussion and illustrations of primitive tools and other artifacts will be found in Sayce, 1933, and Mason, 1907. Economic aspects of life in non-literate societies are discussed in Thurnwald, 1932, and Herskovits, 1940.
5. See Mead, 1928.
6. Linton, 1944.

CHAPTER 18

Technics in Western Civilization

UPON THE technological bases already described the culture of the Roman world developed and prospered for several hundred years. But with the sack of Rome by the Barbarians and the collapse of the Empire, Western culture fell into a period of disorganization and desuetude which is usually known as the Dark Ages, and from which it did not begin to emerge until about the tenth century. During the past 1,000 years the technics of Western civilization as we know it have developed. Although the original equipment was the technological wreckage of the Roman Empire, which in turn was a relatively modest elaboration of the basic inventions and discoveries of the Neolithic and Early Metal ages, modern Western technics have developed a configuration and a content vastly different from those of Rome. We shall try to sketch in the broadest possible terms the basic steps in this growth, as a background for understanding something of the relationship of technologies to other aspects of culture, especially our own culture of the present day.

The machine. If we are asked to name one trait which by its prominence distinguishes the technology of Western culture from that of all others, we should have to mention the machine. It is not that machines of certain types were totally unknown in all other cultures, but that Western technology is the only one in which machines have had fundamental and pervasive importance. From the point of view of material equipment, the history of Western technological culture during the past 1,000 years has been a history of the increasing elaboration and proliferation of machines in all technological processes.

Whereas a tool supplements or enhances the natural features of the human body with respect to its ability to do a certain type of work, a machine substitutes for the human body's direct application to the job in question. A sickle in the hands of a man cuts grain more efficiently than the man can tear it down with his bare hands, but a mower or a reaper automatically cuts the grain without the man's having to apply his labor directly to grain-cutting at all. It is this feature of automatism which distinguishes machines from tools, and this feature itself also permits the application of non-human power to work and allows greater output of work per man involved in a given job. At the same time we must remember that machines, even the most advanced automatic models, have to be designed by human beings and they have to be tended and cared for by them. Likewise the machine is designed for only one job or one series of jobs, and, like all automatons, is quite inflexible and unadaptable in itself. Thus the machine can become the servant of mankind, releasing an increasing proportion of the energies of man from sheer back-breaking work for the cultivation of other values. Or, on the other hand, the machine by its very rigidity, repetitiveness, and impersonality is capable of converting human beings into slaves and automatons which are mere caricatures of its own likeness. This is one of the paradoxes of Western civilization and creates some of our major dilemmas.

Simple machines appear in almost all cultures, at least those of Neolithic status or better. The bow and arrow might be said to be a machine of the simplest type, certainly the crossbows and rock-throwing ballestas of Roman times were. The bow-drill, in which the shaft of the drill is spun by the string of a bow which the operator moves back and forth, is also a simple machine. The plow, so long as it is manipulated entirely by hand, however, should probably be considered merely an animal-powered tool, and, in fact, it seems to have evolved in Egypt from the hoe; in its earliest forms it is merely a hoe dragged through the ground by animal-power.

In Western culture the development of the machine as an automatic contrivance has been associated with the application of the principle of the wheel (rotary motion) and the increasing exploitation of non-human sources of power. One of the reasons that the native cultures of the New World were relatively innocent of machines is the fact that none of them had the wheel, which is so fundamental an element in machine design. In the Old World the water-wheel was one of the earliest fully automatic machines and is was developed by the Romans for the grinding of grain, but the invention of other machines for the use of water-power was relatively inhibited until the Middle Ages and later.

Grinding mills and water lifting in antiquity. The application of principles of rotary motion proceeded very slowly in the ancient cultures. The potter's wheel was invented during Neolithic times and a type of lathe during the Copper Age in the Near East. Following this the next invention employing this basic principle of mechanics was the rotary quern or grain-grinding mill operated by hand. The precise time of this invention is unknown, but we hear in Xenophon of rotary mills operated by donkeys about 400 B.C. in Greece, while the earliest actual examples of such machines which have survived archaeologically date from the first century Rome. Not only animal, but also human (slave), power was used to operate these rotary mills. In the same century two types of water-mill were invented in the Mediterranean world. First, and simplest, was the water-wheel with a vertical shaft, which requires a race or chute to direct the water against the sides of the paddle-wheel, but which requires no mill-pond or dam. It depends upon the natural force of the current and is usually found in hilly country where the streams are swift. Curwen regards this as a peasant improvement on the rotary quern, or hand mill. At any rate, it was the first employment of inanimate power since the invention of the sail. The second type of early water-wheel had a horizontal shaft and may have been invented by the Roman engineer Vitruvius (20-11 B.C.). This contrivance was more sophisticated for it requires the invention of wooden gears for the transmission of power from the horizontal axis of the water-wheel to the vertical axis of the milling stones; in its "overshot" form it requires a pond, dam, chute, and sluice, for the overshot wheel operates by the weight of the water which falls on it, rather than by the force of the current. Because of these requirements, it appears that the undershot wheel was the earliest: it operates on the force of the current, and requires no dam. It is interesting to note that the water-wheel of Vitruvius was apparently not brought into general use in Roman territory until the latter part of the fourth century A.D. because of the opposition of the Millers' Guilds which preferred to maintain their current installations operated by donkeys or slaves. When Rome adopted Christianity the use of slaves was discouraged, and the water-wheel was adopted as a "labor saving" device. This illustrates once again the intimate connection which exists between all components of a technological complex, especially the importance of the component involving social and economic organization of human beings.[1]

Another type of early application of rotary motion, although not always in the form of automatic machines, may be seen in connection with the water supplies of ancient cities and irrigation projects. The development of irrigation itself is, of course, associated with the domestication of plants, and previous to Neolithic developments we have no evidence of artificial water supplies whatever. Once wells were dug, however, or once it was desired to lift water from a stream into an aqueduct or irrigation ditch, an impetus was given to the invention of some mechanical aid to water lifting. The earliest such invention involved the use of the lever with a bucket on the end of it, which has survived until recent times even among ourselves and which was in use in the Old Kingdom of Egypt, in ancient Babylonia, and in China under the Han dynasty. A bucket or buckets on a rope or chain was another expedient, and the winch, using the rotary principle, but operated by human power, was applied for raising the containers quite early. Endless chains of buckets running over crude pulleys are mentioned for Babylonia in the Bible (Ecclesiastes, 12) and were used in Egypt by the end of the second century B.C. A more sophisticated and radical employment of the rotary principle was the water screw, invented by Archimedes (287-212 B.C.) and widely used in Roman mines in Spain and Southern France. It consisted of a wooden cylinder containing a helical copper vane or screw, and motive power was supplied by men working in treadmills.[2] Waterwheels on boats floating in the Tiber were used to lift water in Rome in the late sixth century.

Thus we see that the rotary principle was known to the ancient world of the Mediterranean and also of China, but the cultures of antiquity lacked the impulse and the technical orientation to carry them onward to the development of automatic machines on any but a relatively crude and elementary level. This was a feat reserved for Western European civilization of the second millenium of our era.

The clock. Mumford has pointed out correctly that the mechanical clock is the model of the automatic machine which is characteristic of Western culture. Its success depends upon a close measurement of energy and a fine analysis of the principles of motion and transmission of power through gears and cogwheels. It works automatically and it turns out a standardized, accurately measured "product"—seconds, minutes, and hours—a product which is the creature of the machine rather than of man directly. Although mechanical clocks appear to have been invented in the thirteenth century it was not until 1370 that von Wych produced a relatively perfected model. From this time on the clock became increasingly accurate and increasingly common. At present it is the most ubiquitous of all machines.

In 1345 the hours and minutes on the clock were respectively divided into sixties and the basic measurement of time which is still in use was established. The hour of constant length and the calculation of time on a sexagesimal system (using sixty as a basic unit) had been introduced in Babylon, but not generally adopted because of lack of mechanical means of measurement. This measuring of time mechanically should not be underestimated. Not only did the clock serve as model and prototype for many other types of machines, but it created a new framework for living—measured time, divided into seemingly discrete units which could be counted and predicted. Other cultures, to be sure, had invented methods of "keeping time"—sundials, water clocks, hour glasses, and others—but only after the appearance of the mechanical clock was the accurate measurement of all time—past, present, and future—possible. Time ticks away, inexorably into the infinite future, and each unit may be identified with human action either accomplished or omitted. Thus a technique is at hand for the ordering of human relationships with a precision never before attained, but the technique is based upon the product of a machine, entirely artificial and unrelated to the rhythms of growth, of the seasons, of night and day, of the other periodicities of nature. The fact that the day should be divided into two halves of twelve hours each by the face of the clock; the fact that each hour should have sixty minutes and each minute sixty seconds—all of these are purely cultural facts. As men are trained to order their actions and to plan their lives in terms of these markings on the clock's face, they in effect learn to adjust to a set of conditions which are totally artificial, totally cultural, totally uncorrelated with the phenomena of external nature or of human physiology.

It is important to understand the clock as a mechanism for creating a "world that nature never made," for it illustrates, not only some of the basic features of a machine-dominated culture, but also demonstrates the power of culture to structure situations in its own terms. Men must learn to adapt to cultural conditions as well as to "natural" conditions, and customs must be consistent with such "artificial worlds," if maladjustment is to be avoided. In Western culture punctuality came to have value, often measured in monetary terms, and the model was provided also for accuracy and measurement in all other aspects of culture.

Printing. The clock produces a product which, although very real and of tremendous importance, is nevertheless intangible. The printing press, on the other hand, was the first machine in Western culture to be perfected for the production of a completely standardized tangible product, and in this sense it serves as a prototype of many later machines of mass production. The printing press and movable type seem to have been invented in China from where the basic idea was diffused to Europe. We hear of movable type (of pottery) being invented by Pi Sheng between 1041 and 1049, but it was not until the twelfth century that printing from wooden blocks is reported from Europe. Wooden type was invented in Turkestan about 1300 and metal type in Korea in 1390. Not until the 1440's, however, did Gutenberg and Schoeffer perfect the printing press in Europe. Paper, another originally Chinese invention, was first made in Europe in 1144 in Spain, and by 1190 at Herault, France, with another paper mill at Ravensburg, Germany, a century later. By the end of the fourteenth century, paper was fairly common in Europe.

Once mechanical printing had been perfected in Europe, the process and its product spread throughout Western culture much faster than it had in Asia, although the basic inventions were made in the latter area. This is an interesting illustration of the principle of consistency in culture. By an historical accident, it happened that a relatively simple, phonetic alphabet employing only a couple of dozen characters (originally invented by the Phoenicians) was in use in Europe, whereas the Chinese were tied to an ideographic system of writing involving thousands of characters, each one of which represented a distinct word or idea. The use of movable type in printing employs a basic principle of mass production, namely, standardization and interchangeability of parts for specific functions. The phonetic alphabet is based on this principle also, in a manner of speaking. The standard letter "l," for example, may represent a given sound regardless of the length or meaning of the word in which it occurs. It is obvious that the mass production of reading matter by printing from movable type was much more consistent with European systems of writing than with the Chinese systems of writing, and hence more readily assimilated by European culture.

It is unnecessary for us to review the influence of the printed word upon our culture. A few outstanding functions only may be mentioned. (1) Knowledge and other cultural material can be both diffused and "stored" (accumulated) with an accuracy and in quantities never before possible. These features themselves are important prerequisites for a vastly increased and elaborated culture content. (2) Control and integration of social relationships and cultural activities may be greatly extended and standardized through the printed word. Laws and regulations may be disseminated accurately to a literate population; printed forms and blanks for the collection of data greatly decrease the labor of activities such as census taking, tax collecting, and voting, not to mention business operations and scientific investigations. (3) The printed word is also a mechanism for standardizing thought throughout wide sections of a population and over extensive areas. Although this is an advantage in many respects, it also carries with it a tendency to stifle individual and local initiative.

Glass. Glass beads and small bottles were known in Egypt as early as 1500 B.C., and cruder glass work occurs in Egyptian tombs of the fourth millennium B.C., but the technical perfection of glass-making is one of the basic technological achievements of Western culture. For through the use of glass not only was light shed in the literal sense on the everyday world of men, but enlightenment in the metaphorical sense was made possible on a vastly greater scale, while new worlds, both of microscopic life and of interstellar space, were brought within human ken. We may mention a few of the basic functions which glass plays in our technology. (1) The use of clear glass windows permits work to be carried on indoors in inclement weather, thus eliminating much of the "seasonal factor" so far as manufacturing conditions are concerned. It also permits clarity and accuracy in indoor work which is impossible in the obscure interiors of windowless buildings. (2) Seasonal factors in diet can also to some extent be reduced through the ability which glass hothouses confer on a society to grow summer or tropical products during the wintertime. Hothouses were in use in France as early as 1385. (3) Artificial lighting is considerably increased in efficiency, even when it is produced by combustion of oil or tallow, by the use of glass wind protectors on candles and lamps; even today, with the use of incandescent filaments and gases, glass is essential to efficient artificial lighting. Glass thus plays an important part in "extending the summer into the winter" and also in "turning night into day." (4) We have earlier mentioned the importance of glass as a material for containers. From a technological point of view this is especially significant in the development of chemistry, for not only is glass transparent, but it is resistant to most chemical mixtures and compounds. (5) Although the useful manufacture of lenses must be preceded by a suitable theory of the refraction of light, the actual creation of lenses is dependent upon clear glass. It has been suggested that the revival of learning in Europe was brought about in large measure by the invention and use of spectacles which were widely employed by the fifteenth century at about the same time that the development of printing created a need for them. By the end of that century the concave lens had been introduced for the correction of near-sightedness. In 1590 a Dutch optician, Zacharias Jansen, invented the compound microscope, and in the middle of the seventeenth century Leeuwenhoek founded the science of bacteriology when he discovered under the microscope strange "monsters" in the scrapings from his teeth. In 1605 another Hollander, Johann Lippersheim, invented the telescope with lenses and thus provided Galileo with the tool for making his astronomical observations. Thus, through the invention of glass lenses, the world was extended in space and Western man discovered a whole universe of new beings and entities.

(6) Although mirrors of obsidian, glass, copper, or other materials were invented in antiquity and even by certain "primitive" peoples, a clear and distinct reflection of one's own face and background awaited the perfection of the glass mirror. By the sixteenth century, the technique of making smooth mirrors backed with quicksilver had been perfected by the Venetian glass-makers, and the hand mirror had become a relatively common possession. Mumford has pointed out how this development made it possible, perhaps for the first time, for a person to see himself somewhat as others saw him. The "looking-glass self," which the sociologist Cooley described with such insight in our time, was purely metaphorical prior to the invention of the modern mirror. At all events, from this time onward Western culture displays greater interest in the individual, in introspection, in analysis of the ego.

Scientific method. Another cornerstone of Western technics is the scientific method. Although the basic method of science was invented in the sixteenth century, it did not come to play a crucial part in technological development until the later nineteenth and twentieth centuries. Nevertheless, the main lines of careful investigation and testing of hypotheses were laid down and gradually applied to technics, or at least to certain departments. Early Western scientists were mainly concerned with investigation of the laws of nature and of the universe, but on the basis of these fundamental discoveries and with the use of the procedures thus developed, "applied science" has developed until, at the present time, it plays a vital part in many of the basic technological processes, ranging from the synthetic creation of new materials (such as plastics and sources of power like gasoline and atomic energy) to the systematic invention and improvement of machines and work patterns. Up to the present, science has been applied in Western culture mainly to the first four components of technology, namely, tools, power, materials, and techniques of work, but has been little used to solve the problems of the fifth component—social and economic organization. Unless our technological progress is to be stultified it seems essential that the scientific solution of its human problems must be not only permitted but actively stimulated and encouraged.

PHASES OF WESTERN TECHNICS

During the past thousand years Western technics have passed through a series of phases, which we shall attempt to describe briefly. They have been designated as the Eotechnic, Paleotechnic, and Neotechnic phases, respectively.

The Eotechnic phase. Even if we did not have evidence from other sources, we would know from the history of Europe and its dependencies that a "phase" of culture is not uniformly distributed among the population of the society to which it pertains. When we speak of the Eotechnic phase, therefore, we are aware of the fact that outlying "marginal" groups may have lingered in a Neolithic economy entirely, some perhaps even in a fishing or hunting economy. We are interested in the most advanced technology of the several periods.

The Eotechnic economy was one which, so far as *materials* were concerned, depended primarily upon *wood*. *Power* was supplied principally (in addition to that of men) by *wind* and *water*. The water-wheel was used for grinding grain and pumping water, also for pulping rags for paper, for running hammering and cutting machines in iron works (Dobrilugk, Zausitz, 1320), sawing wood (Augsburg, 1322), beating hides in a tannery, spinning silk, beating felts, and turning grinding machines of armorers. Metals were mined and water-power was used for pumping purposes, but metal as a major material of technics had not yet come into its own. The power of the wind was used primarily for land reclamation, but also for other industrial operations. The wind turbine is mentioned as early as 1438.

Tools, however, and such machines as existed, were made mainly of wood. Carpenter's tools were of wood (except for cutting edges), also the rake, ox yoke, cart, wagon, washtub, bucket, and broom. The spinning-wheel and loom (machines) were of wood; also pump cylinders, water-pipes, cradles, beds, houses, ships. The lathe, the most important machine tool of the period, was also of wood except for the cutting edge. In fact, metal was used mainly for cutting instruments, coins, and weapons. Furthermore, the principal fuel was wood, so that such metal-working as took place was dependent upon forests.

In transportation, sails supplanted the use of oars, but it was not until the fifteenth century that the two-masted ship came into use and not until about 1500 that the three-masted ship and a technique for beating against the wind appeared, which made possible long ocean voyages. The Eotechnic period also saw the development of inland water transportation, for it was the epoch of canal-building. Under Eotechnic conditions, of course, the efficiency of a single man and horse, or of a man with a pole, is much greater on a canal than on a highway. Finally, the magnetic compass (invented in China) and the astrolabe permitted more or less accurate navigation out of sight of land.

It was during the Eotechnic phase also that the experimental method in science was developed, although it had little influence on the technology of the period. It did, however, have the effect of producing an orderly, rationalized world, at least for the intelligentsia, a world dominated by "natural law." Order was supported by method, and the social order was bolstered by rationalization having a "scientific" aura. During this period the scientific academy, the industrial exposition, and the university (although usually devoid of experimental laboratories) became parts of the culture, while the laboratory finally found a niche for itself outside academic purlieus.

In the social organization of the Eotechnic period, the university was, in some ways, the prototype of the factory. In both cases, the human element was regimented with respect to time of activity and with respect to function. There can be little doubt that such social inventions increased, through organization, the efficiency and energy-output of society.

Many another technological invention of the Eotechnic period, notably the blast furnace, came into its own only in later periods. Labor was still organized under the guild system, management and ownership of economic enterprises were usually united; only in mining did the beginnings of capitalistic enterprise, in the modern sense, begin to appear. Factories were still small-scale affairs, mainly concerned with the making of armor and woven fabrics. The pattern of the medieval town and its commercialism still dominated the Eotechnic phase. It is worthy of note, nonetheless, that the importance of metals steadily increased and the methods of their production foreshadowed many of the developments of later periods.

The Paleotechnic phase. With respect to materials and sources of power, the distinctive feature of the Paleotechnic phase of Western technics was the use of *mineral resources*. Iron was the great source of materials, coal the great source of power. But to characterize the Paleotechnic culture thus is vastly to oversimplify it, as well as to fly in the face of the general principles of culture. From the technological point of view, the Paleotechnic culture represents an, if not the, "industrial revolution," but the reverberations of this mode of life extended far beyond mere questions of materials and power.

It is probably not too much to say that peoples of a later period will look back upon the Paleotechnic age as one of the most barbarous negations of human values in the history of human culture. The fact that Paleotechnic culture still lingers with us to some extent, especially in our thinking, makes the discussion of this development all the more significant.

Dates are difficult to fix, but the Paleotechnic phase is usually reckoned as having become established about 1750. Whereas the Eotechnic economy was mainly dependent upon the currently available products of nature—forests, cultivated plants, domestic animals, wind, and water—the Paleotechnic development planted its foundations deeper in the earth, upon the stored products of nature—coal and iron. Mining technology was thus central to the complex and many of the characteristic technical developments of the age were children of mining necessity. Thus the steam-engine was first developed for pumping water out of mines, railways were first used for handling coal and ore underground, the elevator and the escalator were first adapted to transporting men and ores from the ground surface to the mineral veins and vice versa.

During the second half of the eighteenth century the steam-engine was perfected sufficiently to provide power for large-scale manufacturing operations by machine. By the second quarter of the nineteenth century the *factory system* had been established in certain European countries and the Paleotechnic civilization was on its way to full bloom and boom. So much has been written concerning the factory system that we need do no more than mention a few significant cultural changes which it brought about. First, the new technology of the factory was expensive, and required *capital* in comparatively heavy amounts. Although capital was of course in use previously, the development of factory techniques required larger amounts than most earlier types of operations, and consequently gave greater power to those able to control and dispose of such properties. Second, the factory technology required labor in large amounts as well; and it was the essence of machine production that the skill and creativeness required of the average individual worker was decreased. Standardization and interchangeability became the order of the day, and the worker tended to be reduced from the status of craftsman to that either of an automaton performing a mechanical function in operations not completely automatic, or, on the other hand, a sort of shepherd or attendant of automatic machines. In the third place, this new system of production enormously increased the production potential of the areas where it was used. For the first time in human history, it was technically possible to supply the basic necessities and even what had formerly been considered the luxuries of life to the entire population. Artificial power and machine production placed an army of mechanical "servants" at the disposal of human society which far outnumbered the slave workers of the greatest states of antiquity. Human beings could have been freed from practically all manual labor, the possibilities of raising the standard of living were technically almost unlimited, and opportunities for art, intellectual cultivation, and recreation could have been brought for the first time within reach of the bulk of the population almost everywhere it was applied. Increased proficiency in agriculture and transportation did, in fact, increase the means of bare subsistence. But many of the social and cultural advantages which the technology made possible were never realized in Paleotechnic culture.

There are several ways in which this system could have been organized, or—to use the terms set forth in Chapter 21—there are several possible orientations which could have been given to it. For example, the new technology could have been developed for the benefit of society as a whole, "for the greatest good of the greatest number," for the purpose of raising the living standards of all to the highest possible level, for freeing the bulk of mankind from animalistic drudgery, as a basis for the development of more truly human activities and potentialities.

However, as every one knows, the system was in fact developed around the concept of private property, control was vested in those comparatively few individuals who possessed or controlled the instruments of production or the financing of them, and the principal motivation of the property owners and managers was defined as the desire for profits.

It is a mistake to say that this was "planned out" in advance or even that the majority of businessmen were necessarily unscrupulous or heartless exploiters of their fellow human beings. As the situation was culturally defined, the average businessman had to operate according to the rules of the game—he had to make profits or suffer disgrace, loss of position, and other punishments. As a businessman he received no rewards for services to society; it was only after such a one had proved his success as a profit maker that he might voluntarily distribute some of his gains as a philanthropist and receive therefore the reward of prestige from a grateful society. Even philanthropy was not a part of the system, however, and many a tycoon could omit such generosity without suffering seriously in social position.

A mental system of rationalizations, called laissez-faire economics, soon appeared in order to justify the social usefulness of the capitalistic system based on Paleotechnic production. The world was assured that, if left alone in free competition and in a free market, the privately controlled units which made up the system would distribute the benefits derivable from the new technology to all mankind. Although the critics of this reasoning have termed it the "law of the jungle" it is still heard to this day and, despite numerous cultural changes which have rendered invalid most of the arguments which had any basis in reality when first enunciated, the laissez-faire mental system is still taught in many of our schools and colleges as a basic part of our culture. Laissez-faire was never realistically descriptive of conditions in a modern society, and during the past fifty years it has become increasingly fantastic.

One of the basic tenets of the scheme was that all units in the system were supposed to be in free competition with each other, and that such free competition would hold prices down, in a free market, for the benefit of the "public" (that is, consumers of the products). By a quaint bit of reasoning it was held that an individual laborer was a "unit" in the same sense as the owner or manager of a factory or other large production or distribution mechanism. It was assumed that a worker, who had nothing to offer but his energy and/or skill, was in the same bargaining position as a man who employed hundreds of thousands of workers and controlled millions of dollars worth of investments. Obviously, this was contrary to fact so long as labor was plentiful and unorganized and the worker was forced to accept the wage offered by the employer. Thus it was that, during the first phases of the so-called industrial revolution, large groups of workers—the "proletariat"—were drawn into the system under conditions which reduced their mode of life to a level scarcely, if ever, plumbed even by the slaves of so-called barbarous nations. Crowding, filth, labor of women and children, physical and mental stunting were the lot of the new machine tenders forced off the land into the murky industrial cities of the industrial revolution. Since entrepreneurs bought only the labor of the workers, not their lives or persons, the workers were often in worse straits than domestic animals or machines, whose general well-being had some economic value to their owners. A man, woman, or child would be worked sixteen hours per day without compunction if "competitive" conditions permitted, and dismissed when worn out, whereas a good dray horse would be put in the barn after ten hours for fear it might die before its time and have to be replaced as a capital investment. Machines were cleaned, oiled, and repaired with care lest their owner run the risk of having to buy new ones prematurely.

Thus the new technology brought with it certain changes in human relations, and as time went on new types of arrangements for the organization of the personnel involved emerged. First, the capitalists banded themselves into joint-stock companies and corporations, which were organized pools of investments. The increasing capital outlay required by the advances of machine technology gradually surpassed the resources of the average investor who, in the Eotechnic phase, could own and operate a small-scale manufacturing or mining business himself. Since such was no longer economical in Paleotechnic economy, the device of the stock company enabled investors to pool their interests and shares of ownership. However, a new class gradually arose from these arrangements, the managerial class, whose function was to manage the operations of stock companies, although they often did not own them or any part of them. The manager's function was defined in terms of obligations to his stockholders without regard to his duties toward his workers, or to the general social welfare. In the second place, workers, in order to improve their impossible bargaining position, endeavored to organize into unions for purposes of collective bargaining. The general effect of both of these social aspects of the technology was to increase the depersonalization of relations between owners and workers, and to establish a line of conflict of interests between workers on the one hand and managers and stockholders on the other hand.

Although it was not generally realized at the time, the system built around this technology was at many points at odds with the interests of society as a whole. Since the prevalent belief held that profits were the primary goal, little attention was paid to other types of values. Not only were health, nutrition, and recreation ignored or in some cases actually flouted, but the aesthetic aspects of the industrial cities were sacrificed to the convenience of industry. Smoke-laden air, poluted streams, dingy dwellings for the mass of the population, and narrow, crowded streets were characteristic of the industrial cities of the era. Furthermore, the technology was wasteful of natural resources as well as of human resources. Iron, the metal of the age, was used in prodigious quantities for everything from hitching posts and lawn statues of deer to the construction of ornamental (?) facades for factories and business buildings. Coal, the power source of the period, generated steam in prodigious and unnecessary quantities. Lumber, although no longer a prime material, was stripped from the forests in reckless quantities for building, mining, and packaging operations. Much of this waste was, of course, due to the comparative crudity of the technological processes of the period.

Curiously, the age was hailed as a period of "progress." Theoretical and apologetic systems wedded to the notion of ever-increasing size and activity of all things material flourished without stint. The announcement of the Darwinian theory of evolution was pounced upon by technological and economic apologists—survival of the fittest became the slogan of the nineteenth century. It was the "basic law of nature." The peoples of Western Europe and North America, by reason of the fact that the marvels of Victorian technology had developed in their midst, were obviously the superior race, the Chosen People, the acme of evolutionary trends. "Proofs" were not lacking that such paragons enjoyed a "natural right" to exploit foreigners, primitive peoples, and even the "lower class" members of their own society.

Without doubt the Paleotechnic culture was progressive, in the sense that technology and social forms continued to develop, even at a terrible cost in human values and natural resources. But the culture of the period contained basic inconsistencies, of which we in North America are only becoming aware in this day, and at a very high price. The troubles which have beset Western civilization during the twentieth century are without doubt chargeable in large degree to our unwillingness or inability to recognize these inconsistencies and to take effectual measures for their solution.

The machine and power technological system, motivated by the quest for profits, is, even in the words of its most enthusiastic apologists, an "expanding economy." In other words, the technology of the exploitation of natural resources and manufacture of finished goods during Paleotechnic times reached a stage where production was technically capable of almost limitless expansion. The question at issue, of course, is "production for what?" The answer, "production for the market at the maximum profit." So long as the purchasing power of the masses was rigidly restricted by low wages, the expansion of the market was confined to two possibilities, (a) a growing middle class (since the consuming power, as distinguished from purchasing power, of the wealthy group was insignificant), and (b) foreign markets. Both of these sources of consuming power, however, were definitely limited, so long as the goal was ever higher production at ever higher profits. The middle class, based on small property holdings and income from services, was definitely limited both in size and in purchasing power. The same was true of foreign markets, even as rival nations and outlying parts of the globe became settled and in turn industrialized.

The inconsistency of the system should have been obvious to any one. (1) Technically and physically, production can increase more or less indefinitely. (2) The product must be sold at a profit, that is, the highest possible price. (3) The income of workers, who form the basis of the "market"—the purchasers—must be kept to the lowest possible level. Quite apart from any social or ethical considerations these tenets of the system do not make sense. No amount of casuistry by learned economists can make such a system workable in the long run. If the profit motive is to remain, the only answer is that increased production must be accompanied by increased purchasing power. And as the great majority of potential purchasers become directly or indirectly dependent upon their earnings in industry, an increase in said earnings is inescapable—if production and profits are to continue to expand.

During the closing phases of the Paleotechnic culture—in which we unhappily still linger—various changes in pattern were attempted in the economic system. One method was war. Although economic causes are not alone at the root of the wars of the twentieth century, few authorities will deny that they did play important rôles. As the various expanding nationalistic Paleotechnic economies ran into difficulties due to rivalry and competition for foreign markets and sources of raw materials, one or the other would seek to redress matters to its own advantage by war. It is even arguable that war is an essential feature of such a culture. The first heavy industry of the modern era developed about the manufacture of armaments, while the most prodigious technological advances and activities of recent times have always occurred during war. The Paleotechnic economy is in some respects better adapted to the production of instruments of destruction than to the artifacts of peace and human progress. And the human element, under the system, despite the vast sufferings wrought, finds surcease and some sort of reward, at least at the start of each major war. Workers and many of the middle class envision in war an escape from the drabness of their peacetime lives under capitalist economy, despite the horrors and destruction which "total war" may bring to them. And few, if any, of the rich or the mighty suffer as a result of the orgy of destruction. On the contrary, industry finds in war a guaranteed and profitable market, and relief from the increasingly difficult task of seeking new markets. During the Second

World War, it is reported, corporations in the United States averaged three times the annual profits, *after taxes*, which they realized in the years preceding its outbreak. War is a natural and recurring feature of the system, and will probably continue to be so, unless or until technological advances destroy everything.

Another device for avoiding the inconsistencies of the system of Paleotechnic capitalism was to tinker with the system itself, still in the interests of profits. Essentially this means restriction of output, although various high-sounding names, little understood by the common people, were employed, such as rationalization of industry. As the technology of production continued to develop in the absence of any comparable development of distribution, markets, or purchasing power, it became increasingly obvious that something should be done about the "expansiveness" of the system. The answer, of course, was to control production so that a certain "optimum" quantity of goods was produced and sold, the optimum being the largest quantity which could be sold at the highest price. In other words, a balance between quantity and price must be found and production limited at that point. For example, it may be possible to sell 10,000,000 razors at fifty cents each and only 5,000,000 at a dollar each. If the profit at the dollar price is as good or better as at the fifty-cent price, why bother to produce and sell twice as many? Obviously this sort of scheme will not work under conditions of "free competition," so that an essential part of its success depends upon agreements between producers to divide up the available markets and natural resources, and to restrict production to the quantities of goods which can be absorbed at the prices agreed upon. It is a matter of public record that some of the largest American corporations had entered into such agreements with German producers before the war, and in certain cases could be dissuaded from continuing the arrangements, even after the country had gone to war, only by action of the federal government. Such "cartels" were supported by technological "progress." As technical efficiency increased, larger and larger manufacturing plants, laboratories, mines, transportation systems, and so on, were required. Such agglomerations of capital equipment required financing on a scale never before dreamed of, financing which was available only from government or from monster banks, insurance companies, and other financial institutions. In capitalistic cultures, governments did not dare to enter many such fields, so that financial institutions were able to weld technological facilities together into gargantuan units, each of which tended to dominate its own field of activities or a sizable portion of it. Thus we have the Aluminum Company of America controlling 90 per cent of aluminum production in the United States, and the General Motors Corporation

controlling somewhat more than 45 per cent of the automobile manufacturing. "Competition" in fields dominated by big business thus becomes
a figure of speech which, at best, has little relation to its meaning when
applied to earlier conditions of small rival units.

Thus, although the shibboleth of "free enterprise" is still shouted
from the housetops by defenders of the system, very little free enterprise in the sense of open competition is any longer possible, at least in
fields dominated by big business.

Our main point is to bring out the fact, once again, that a functional
relationship exists between technology and social organization. It is highly
probable that big business, with its tendency toward cartels, restriction
of output, and fixing of prices would never have arisen except for the
technological developments which rendered such organizations possible
if not inevitable in a culture dominated by a profit-seeking ideological
(or mental) system. Nevertheless, once the system was in fact altered by
big business—regardless of the fact that many a citizen remained unaware
of the changes—various sequelae of a social and cultural nature appeared.

Is a Neotechnic phase emerging? It is clear that, from a purely technological point of view, a new cultural phase is developing in Western
civilization. Whether changes will be made in the economic and social
organization consistent with the new materialistic inventions seems to be
one of the fundamental problems of our time, for we are still trying to
operate a New Age technic with an antiquated system of organization
and values.

On the technological side, the most spectacular neotechnic development is the conquest of a new source of power—atomic energy. It seems
likely that, if fully applied, this new power is capable of completely
revolutionizing most present-day production processes, not to mention
travel and communication. Other characteristic neotechnic developments
are applied electronics; the making and use of synthetic materials, including plastics and pressed wood; the development of the light metals
as materials replacing many of the former uses of iron; perfection of
the airplane as a vehicle for travel; and so on.

The solution to the human difficulties produced by the inconsistencies
of the Paleotechnic technological and economic system does not seem
to lie simply in the vociferous advocacy of some doctrinaire system of
reform. The problem in essence is this: our technological culture has now
developed to the point where practically every one in a modern society
could enjoy all the necessities and most of the comforts of life, provided
the products which the system is capable of producing were appropriately
distributed among the consumers. Furthermore the technology is capable
of providing a constantly rising standard of living for the whole popula-

tion at a decreasing cost in terms of human effort. Technologically the entire population of a modern industrial society could be well fed, well clothed, and well housed according to any standard, and still have ample time for recreation, advanced education, cultivation of the arts and religion, and so on. For the first time in human history the material basis for a full life and a good life is technically within the reach of every one, even in the mammoth populations of modern societies. The fact of the matter is that these potential benefits are not, however, being enjoyed in the degree to which they might be. Instead of our technology actually being the servant of the society, millions of society's members are slaves of the technology and its attendant economic organization.

There is no theoretical reason why the science of culture cannot be applied to the solution of these dilemmas, just as other sciences have solved the materialistic problems whose mastery was necessary for our present technological progress. Sciences of culture are at present sufficiently well developed to analyze the inconsistencies of patterns which account for much of the present blockage toward the true goal of a Neotechnic economy. These inconsistencies can be eliminated and new patterns can be planned, just as inefficient processes are replaced by better adjusted patterns in industry. Furthermore, there is no reason to believe that the "profit motive" and "private property," for example, have to be eliminated in the readjustment of our technology to the rest of our culture. It is customary to raise the cry of "Red" or "Communism" or "Socialism" when any suggestion of scientific or rational readjustment is brought forward. There is no reason to believe in advance, however, that the scientific solution of modern problems will conform to either Communism or Socialism as at present stated in dogmatic or doctrinaire form. The value of a culture rests in the satisfactions it provides for the needs and wants of the society that practises it, and when the bulk of the people come to realize that culture is their servant and that there are scientific means at hand to adjust it to their purposes, they will no longer be frightened by shibboleths and red herrings.

Notes to Chapter 18

1. Curwen, 1937, 1944.
2. Clark, 1944.
   The student interested in Western technics should read Mumford, 1934, *Technics and Civilization*.

CHAPTER 19

The Organization of Local and Territorial Relationships

ALTHOUGH THE FAMILY may be the most basic social unit in a philogenetic sense, we begin our survey of social organizations with those based on the principle of locality, because of the fact that the latter show, at least in their simpler forms, the most obvious correlations with the technologies of subsistence. In whatever society, people have to live *some*where. The question is: How do they live? In what kind of groups? It seems that at least the basic features of local grouping are controlled to a considerable extent by the system of food production and distribution developed in the technology.

PHYSICALLY UNSTABLE SETTLEMENTS

Bands. The most primitive type of local grouping is the band, which seems to be universal among the peoples who have carried technology no farther than the gathering, hunting, and/or fishing configuration of subsistence. The band is also found occasionally in other types of technologies, depending on circumstances. For example, it is adapted to the conditions of pastoral nomadism, and is not inconsistent with certain types of semi-nomadic (for example, slash-and-burn) hand tillage. From a sociological point of view the band is characterized generally by the following features.

1. Size is limited by the exploitative techniques available, which are never highly developed (so long as band organization persists). A hunting band, in most environments, is limited in size and stability by the availability of game and the conditions for hunting it successfully. Only under exceptional circumstances can a large group of human beings exploit the game of even a limited territory successfully without either destroying it or driving it away. Most hunting bands therefore range in size from 50 to 150 individuals.

A fairly typical idea of this sort of life may be obtained from Eyre's description of bands among the Central Australians.

The number traveling together depends, in a great measure, upon the period of the year and the description of food that may be in season. If there is any particular variety more abundant than another, or procurable only in certain localities, the whole tribe generally congregate to partake of it. Should this not be the case, then they are probably scattered over their district in detached groups, or separate families. At certain seasons of the year, usually in the spring or summer, when food is most abundant, several tribes [that is, local groups or bands] meet together . . . for the purpose of festivity or war, or to barter and exchange, or to assist in the initiatory ceremonies.[1]

Sharp[2] made a study in 1933-1935 of a native population of Northern Australia on the west coast of the Cape York peninsula which gives us a more precise notion in statistical terms of the nomadic band type of life. Although these people are at present somewhat acculturated by contact with a mission station, conditions and culture at the time of the study were on the whole aboriginal. Four so-called tribes here had a total population of 393 persons. Utilized land required a ratio of 2.4 square miles for the support of each person. The ratio of males to females under twenty-five years of age was 132, whereas above this age the ratio was only 84, probably reflecting the lethal effects of fighting and hunting on mature men. Of native marriages not made in missions, 20 per cent were polygamous (men had plural wives); on the other hand 20 per cent of the persons over twenty-five years of age had no mates. The ratio of fertile to non-fertile women was 4 to 1, and the fertile women averaged 2.3 children each. However, the population at the time of the study was declining, for the vital index stood at only 67 (100 is required for mere replacement).

On the Great Plains of North America, an exceptional circumstance was provided by the presence of buffalo (bison) herds. These animals could be successfully hunted in large coöperative drives or surrounds by hundreds of hunters. Together with subsidiary food-producing techniques (minor hunting, some gathering, a little tillage) sufficient subsistence could be regularly provided by such methods to support fairly large local groups ranging (rarely) up to a couple of thousand in population. Such hunting techniques were enhanced by the introduction of the horse, obtained by the Indians at first indirectly from Europeans. Apparently the average size of the Plains bands was therefore based on a combination of two rare conditions: the presence of large herd animals easily hunted coöperatively, and the high mobility provided by a domestic riding animal, the horse.

Peoples depending upon slash-and-burn hand tillage are also often confined to relatively small semi-nomadic bands. These techniques of cultivation limit the area which can be exploited from a single center, and they also produce rapid exhaustion of the soil, requiring periodic moves in search of new land. In our times such conditions pertain with respect to many indigenous peoples occupying non-volcanic soils in the deep wet tropics, where the rapid exhaustion of soil fertility is also hastened by the leaching action of heavy rains. Most local groups in the Amazon and Orinoco jungle regions, New Guinea, interior Borneo, and similar environments, are consequently of the semi-nomadic band type. Early neolithic tillage in middle latitude areas apparently required semi-nomadic life, also. For example, an early cultivating culture seems to have appeared north of the Huang Ho River in China about the beginning of the third millenium B.C. It depended upon hoe tillage of millet, sorghum, and a few root and leaf plants, and possessed the domesticated dog and pig. The people lived in small unfortified villages of pit dwellings, eight to ten feet in diameter, and entered through the roof. Such villages, however, seem to have been moved frequently, because of exhaustion of the soil under the current methods of cultivation.[3] Although neolithic culture lays the basis for settled life, the actual techniques are not in all cases adequate to provide for permanently stable settlements, particularly in the earlier stages of development.

2. The restricted population of the band makes for predominance of primary contacts between the members, and hence for intimacy in social relations. However, such relationships are apt to be somewhat unsteady and fluid and tend therefore toward informality. Conditions of band life are not generally favorable to differentiation of status between families and individuals; "vested interests" have little opportunity to become fixed.

The band type of local group has been called a "campsite community."

3. The band typically claims a certain territory through which it roams and from which members of other groups are excluded by force, if necessary.

4. Usually a series of campsites or temporary centers is laid out within the band territory, for such groups do not usually wander over the countryside aimlessly, but rather on a sort of circuit, which is regulated by the seasonal presence of game, fish, and gatherable natural products (or pasturage, in the case of pastoral nomads). The tendency to recur to formerly occupied sites is a response to a need for security: a recurrently occupied site requires less labor, return to the same areas enables reëmployment of knowledge and techniques previously found satisfactory in the area; familiar stimuli evoke familiar, patterned cultural responses. In some nomadic bands (for example, Plains tribes' such as the Dakota, Nama Hottentot of South Africa) the camp is always set up according to an established pattern in which each family unit has its

assigned place.[4] Pioneer wagon trains of the American Far West often adopted a similar scheme as a temporary expedient.

5. Private property is usually confined to movable goods (including domestic herd animals, among pastoral peoples), and the artifacts in general are adapted to frequent movement.

6. Membership within the group is relatively flexible, in cases where alternative bands are present. Although there are exceptions, the typical band member may change his allegiance, and outsiders may "join up," after a proper probationary period; even in unilateral kinship bands outsiders may be "adopted."

7. Internal organization of the band tends to be relatively simple. Probably the band tends to be the most democratic of all local groups, because the conditions of life which characterize the average members depend upon the development of a high degree of individual or family self-reliance. Division of labor and distinction in status are both sharply limited. Every man and woman, and every family, owes its position in largest measure to its mastery of the available techniques and to individual initiative. Hence, rigidly differentiated and mutually exclusive social entities based on birth or property or other assigned qualifications of distinction are typically rare in the band type of local organization. Control is usually in the hands of a council of men. Leadership is usually based upon personal qualities, such as strength, skill, and congeniality. Well defined social classes are rare. The apparent partial exceptions to the latter rule—which still holds in general—are to be found in nomadic band groups organized for raiding and pillage. Such bands are often fairly well organized internally, although, even among them internal differentiation based on birth or wealth is rare unless the band settles down as conquerors of a sedentary people. The Ruwala Bedouin of interior Arabia and the Tuareg of the Sahara live in bands whose principal livelihood, at least during recent periods of history, has been the raiding of settled peasant or town-dwelling people in the oases or on the margins of their areas. Among these peoples captured victims may be converted to the status of slaves, but typically such individuals are actually considered auxiliaries to the social group as long as they remain in that status—much the same as domestic animals. Typically the status of such "slaves" is not hereditary, and their offspring are free men. Furthermore, such raiding bands do not really live from their own productive techniques—they do not depend primarily upon hunting or gathering. Rather they live on the produce which they can steal from settled peasant-village peoples who employ techniques of cultivation, husbandry, and handicrafts.

Steward, who has made a special study of band-type units, points out that so far as marriage regulations and residence after marriage are concerned, we may distinguish two types: the composite band and the unilineal band. The composite type consists of unrelated families and there is no rule of exogamy requiring band members to marry outside. In surveying the cultures of the world, Steward finds that this type tends to occur where the size of the group exceeds 100 persons. Examples are to be found among the Southern Bushmen, Andamanese, certain Algonkians and Athabascans of Canada.[5]

The unilineal band incorporates in one social unit, not only the principle of locality or territory, but also that of kinship, so that all members of the local unit are also considered to be real or putative kinsmen through a single line. Although such groups could theoretically be either matrilineal or patrilineal, the former seem to be very rare and have been little studied. All patrilineal bands studied seem to be partilocal as well (that is, kinship is reckoned through the father's side and the married couple live with the husband's group after marriage). The type seems to occur where adjustment to the environment "prevented group size from exceeding 50 to 100 individuals and where emphasis upon hunting or other factors tending toward male dominance made it patrilocal."[6] Examples are to be found among the Northern Bushmen, African Negritos, Semang, Australians, Tasmanians, Fuegians, and in Southern California. If there are any matrilocal bands in which hunting is the basic subsistence technique, the present writer has not come across them. Male dominance would seem to be almost inevitable in this type of subsistence technology, for reasons discussed in Chapter 7.

Certain *socio-cultural results* of the band type of life and the technology with which it is generally associated should also be mentioned. Although in anthropological works it has been customary to regard "primitive" cultures as unusually stable and conservative, there is reason to believe that those which are practised by bands of nomadic or semi-nomadic type and of small population are particularly susceptible to change within themselves and to the budding off of new cultures at a comparatively rapid rate. (1) Practically all experience of contact between such cultures and European peoples, for example, has shown the small band cultures to be highly vulnerable to the impact of Western civilization. Among "primitive" societies it is the settled, village or town type of society, such as that of the Pueblo Indians of Arizona and New Mexico, which seems best able to survive contacts with modern civilization without disintegration.

Even in conditions which do not involve contact with more developed cultures, however, the band-borne type of culture probably tends to be relatively unstable and changeful. (2) Because of the small population of the group the sex and age ratios to which the culture is adjusted tend to be particularly unstable. For example, the loss of a dozen or so individuals through disaster of any sort in a band of fifty or so may make the patterns of organization and activity, simple as they are, unworkable or unrewarding for another generation. Under such conditions the patterns of custom will usually change if the group is to survive. For instance, if a dozen able-bodied men are unexpectedly killed off in a band whose total number is fifty persons, warlike patterns, most hunting activities, paternal dominance in the family, and many other patterns of custom may have to be abandoned and new ones developed to take their place.[7] Disease which sweeps away the old people may upset the pattern of political control by older men, whereas loss of small children or infertility of women over a period of even a few years may require the development of patterns of raiding and adoption of captives if the group is to maintain its integrity. (3) On the other side of the coin is the fact that growth of population in the band will tend to force budding off of new bands in order to take care of the surplus, due to the fact that the technology of band-type groups is usually able to provide for only a definitely limited population in the area to which the culture is adjusted. Due also to the fact that such technology usually requires a relatively wide area of exploitation, the new groups in many cases will tend to become isolated from the parent band, with a tendency to lose the old customs and gradually to develop new ones of their own. (4) Although the chances of men of genius appearing are statistically less in small groups than in large ones, the individual of strong personality, good intelligence, or more than average physical attributes has a greater opportunity for influencing the culture and changing the customs in a band-type society than in a larger group with more complicated culture. The man with ideas of his own would have a better chance of convincing a group of, say, 100 persons that a new pattern was better than he would have in a society of thousands or millions of fellow-members.

Certain restricted areas of the world are characterized by a wide variety of cultures existing in a small territory. In each such area, within a few hundred or a few thousand square miles, literally dozens of distinct cultures occurred aboriginally. It is worth noting that in three such areas—Eastern Bolivia, Central California, and New Guinea [8]—most of the peoples involved now live or were known to have recently lived in band-type groups supported by subsistence economics based primarily on hunting-gathering-fishing and/or tropical slash-and-burn hand tillage. Of course, it is not to be understood that band-type local organization is inevitably associated with high diversity of independent cultures. The Eskimo, for example, lived in local, often very mobile bands; yet, despite some local differences, Eskimo culture was remarkably uniform throughout the Eskimo area, which comprises some 3,000 linear miles of the litoral of North America and Greenland.[9] The explanation for this uniformity may lie in the fact that Eskimo technology was provided with excellent means of travel (dog sled, umyak open boat, kayak decked canoe) which the people of the various local groups used for maintaining effective contact with each other. Prodigious trips on foot and by dog sled were a regular part of life in most Eskimo groups.

In sum, the factors mentioned above seem to rise inevitably from the band type of local organization and they seem to have the effect of stimulating cultural change and the budding off of cultural types. Whether new cultural configurations actually result from the budding-off process would seem to depend upon whether or not effective isolation is maintained between the parental groups and the offshoot groups. Geographical barriers and lack of cultural techniques for travel and communication are perhaps the most important conditions for the maintenance of such isolation.

STABLE SETTLEMENTS

The fundamental prerequisite of a settled mode of life and local organization is a subsistence technology capable of supporting the population of the settlement without the necessity of seasonal or other periodic moves in search of food. We have seen that, as a general rule, most societies have been able to fulfil these conditions only on the basis of the cultivation of storable cereals, the surplus of which supports the population during the "off season" of growth. However, certain societies have been able to achieve stability of settlement, if not large local populations, under special conditions which do not involve cereal cultivation. Many areas in the tropics, such as the Amazon and Orinoco forest regions, interior Borneo, and the like, do not permit permanently stable settlements supported by hand tillage, because the relatively poor soil is rapidly leached by the tropical rains and the group is under the necessity of constantly preparing new fields or gardens. However, this is not generally true of thick volcanic soils. Permanent settlements, supported by hand tillage of root crops, were therefore possible in certain tropical areas—for example, many volcanic islands of Polynesia. Another relatively rare environmental condition sometimes supports stable settlements, even without cultivation of any kind. This is a constant and abundant supply of fish and sea food in nearby or surrounding waters. If the society living in such conditions has developed adequate techniques for exploiting the sea, the necessity for nomadic wandering is reduced or eliminated. Most of the Indian groups living on the islands and along the shore of the

Northwest Coast were settled local groups, supplying their needs entirely from the sea and from supplemental food gathered and hunted in the forests. The same was true of not a few Polynesians living on coral atolls.

The size of a settled local group depends primarily upon two types of cultural development in technology: capacity to produce food and other basic commodities in large quantities, and/or development of means of transportation to bring such commodities to the settlement from outlying areas. Large concentrations of population in towns and cities inevitably means either that the subsistence technology is capable of producing surpluses over and above the needs of the food-producers themselves, or that such surpluses are obtained from other societies by trade or conquest.

Peasant farming villages. The oldest type of settled local group seems to be the rural farming village, typically composed of families and individuals whose principal occupation is the cultivation of the surrounding lands and the care of domestic animals. The peasant farming village is still the most common of human settled local groups in many parts of the world. In the Old World it generally appeared with the establishment of well-developed Neolithic culture, and peasant villages may have been developed as early as 8000 B.C. in Egypt and Mesopotamia. By 5000 B.C., at least, the small farming village was the typical local unit of the Nile Valley and Mesopotamia. By the middle of the third millenium B.C. a settled village type of life had developed in China, in the upper Huang Ho Valley. The culture is known as the Yang Shao, and the people lived in villages of pit dwellings surrounded by mud walls. Within the following few hundred years it had spread down the Huang Ho Valley into the Wei and Feng drainages and to southern Manchuria, forming the rural base for the later urban cultures. Even today the country village is the basic unit of Chinese local life outside the great cities.[10] Millet and wheat, a relatively late introduction from the west, were the staple cereal products of early rural China; rice cultivation appeared later, and was confined for the most part to the south.

Settled farming villages probably grew up in the Indus valley of India in the second half of the fourth millenium B.C. Wheat, dates, melons, and cotton were cultivated with the help of domesticated cattle and buffaloes. Sheep, goats, pigs, and elephants were also domesticated. In the New World settled village life apparently developed somewhat later and, of course, independently of the early settlements of the Old World. The archaeological picture is not entirely clear for the older areas of the New World, and we know the details of the shift from band life to settled village and town life only in the region of the Southwest, where this change apparently took place about the tenth and eleventh centuries A.D. All the evidence, however, points to the conclusion that the earliest villages and towns probably developed in the highland regions of Middle America and the Andean area, perhaps during the last 500 years before the beginning of the Christian era. The basic foodstuffs were corn, beans, and squash, plants which must have first been domesticated in relatively dry regions, where heavy rains did not leach the soil and rotation of a legume plant (beans) maintained the nitrogen fertility. Settled life in the New World was not dependent on domesticated agricultural animals, for the Indians of this hemisphere never domesticated any animal suitable for drawing plows and other agricultural implements.[11]

In summary, then, settled village life is a relatively late development in human culture. It may be 10,000 years old in Egypt and Mesopotamia, and is certainly more recent in other areas where it developed. Nevertheless, it has proved so rewarding that the settled village life or urban elaborations upon it have been maintained by all cultures possessing the technical facilities to do so.

In general, village and small-town life provides cultural conditions of the following types. (1) Stability of residence permits greater stability in social organization. The statuses of individuals and families can be more firmly fixed in the social scheme; reckoning of social position becomes more accurate and, in the eyes of the group, more important than in band life. (2) Since the basis of social stability is in large measure brought about through attachment to soil and other immovable objects, concepts of property upon which the members agree tend to become clarified and organized. This does not necessarily produce patterns of private property in land or other real estate, but may do so. On the other hand, settled village life with communal ownership of land, as in the early ayllu of the Andean highlands, may be quite successful over long periods of time. Either private or communal ownership of land in a settled group, however, requires the development of rules for its management and agreed definitions of the rights and duties of individuals, families, and other social units, if conflict is to be avoided. The identification of social status with immovable property is now possible. (3) The settled village is usually limited in size by the distance which men can travel to their fields, work during most of the day, and return to the village at night. Such settlements are therefore usually limited to a few hundred or at most a couple of thousand individuals. Relatively small size permits the retention of primary contacts, considerable informality in social relationships, and consequently a good deal of democracy in political affairs. Social control usually requires no elaborate legal codes or police officials. However, such delegation of authority as occurs tends to be of a more permanent nature because settled life permits public servants to devote constant attention to their duties. (4) Settled life permits the development of arts and crafts. Domestic architecture and other construction receive more attention. During the off-season, when work in the fields is at a standstill, leisure is available for non-food-producing pursuits. Furthermore, sufficient food may often be produced to support a few specialists who devote all their time to the arts, crafts, religion, political affairs, learning, and so on. (5) The dependency of most agricultural villages on the weather and the seasons in the cultivation of crops tends to promote cultural anxieties about the supernatural and the development of customary (religious) patterns for the supposed control of natural phenomena or for the relief of anxieties. The stage is set for the appearance of religious specialists who frequently devote their entire time to the study of natural phenomena, the accurate reckoning of seasonal changes, and the relations between these and the traditional powers of the supernatural. Religion and the intellectual aspects of culture thus tend to be elaborated in settled village life. (6) The peasant village is typically self-sufficient in most respects, and therefore tends toward a certain social and cultural isolation or "ingrownness."

Urban communities. Towns and cities are larger concentrations of population than villages, but, in addition to increased numbers of people, they possess distinct problems of social organization as well. No lower limit of size in absolute numbers marks off towns or cities from villages. The principal difference between an urban community and a village is the fact that, whereas regular primary contacts are normally possible among all adult members of the village, the average individual living in an urban community is not in a position to enjoy such face-to-face relations with all the other members of the group on a frequent or regular basis. Furthermore, although a peasant village may supply its needs almost entirely from its own exploitation of its surrounding territory, the development and continued existence of an urban community implies, not only a scheme of grouping within the town or city itself, but also the organization of human relationships covering a considerable territory outside its boundaries. For no large community of this sort can subsist on the food-producing efforts of its inhabitants alone. The territory necessary to support an urban community is usually larger than can be worked during the day by men who return to their community at night. As a result the subsistence requirements of an urban population are usually supplied by a hinterland of farming villages or by transport from distant areas which supply foodstuff in trade for manufactured products made in the city or in *some* city. In short, the very existence of an urban community implies a form of cultural organization in which considerable numbers of town or city inhabitants are entirely relieved from the direct production of food. City life therefore universally implies the presence of cultural patterns concerned with a fairly high development of arts and crafts, manufacturing, and services. It implies specialization and a comparatively elaborate division of labor. It tends to produce groups centering about culturally generated interests. All this requires organization. And, since every man cannot be in intimate contact with every other, instruments of communication and coördination are required. By far the most ancient and still the most universal of such instruments are human beings—political administrators, group representatives, judges, policemen, councilmen—individuals who specialize in performing functions upon which depend that minimum of coördination and order which the numerous groups and diverse interests of urban life require. In brief, urban life requires *government* as an institution, with specialized statuses and consolidated complexes of behavior. The band and the village can both function (although it would be wrong to say that they always do so) with informal governmental or political arrangements operating with part-time or amateur "officials" who require little special training and who perform relatively unspecialized functions. Not so the town and the city.

Urban life is by no means a recent development confined to modern culture. In some areas it developed among peoples who actually had no means of writing. But nowhere has it developed without a surplus-producing subsistence economy, some form of control over considerable areas outside the boundary of the urban area itself, relatively stable political institutions, and some method of keeping records (even though this not be writing, properly speaking).

The earliest full-fledged urban community of the Old World seems to have been the Sumerian city of Uruk (the biblical Erech), founded about 3500 B.C., in lower Mesopotamia. In the period between 3500 and 3000 B.C. various cities grew up in Mesopotamia—Kish, Ur, Susa (in Western Iran)—while the ancient cities of Memphis, Heliopolis, Thebes, and Heranconopolis flourished in Egypt. About 3000 B.C. a number of real cities were founded in the Indus valley—Chandhu-Daro, Harappa, Mohenjo-Daro—apparently by people who had been in cultural, if not personal contact, with the earlier Sumerian developments. In China the earliest known city seems to have been founded by the so-called Shang dynasty in the sixteenth or fifteenth century B.C.; its ruins have been excavated at Anyang in the lower Huang Ho valley.

In the Western Hemisphere,[11] urban communities like all other cultural developments until modern times, appeared later than in the Old World. By the fourth century A.D., if not earlier, urban developments had appeared in Middle America, the Mexican area, and on the Peruvian coast. The early Maya cities seem to have been primarily ceremonial centers with elaborate stone temples and associated architecture, but not residential centers for a large population in the true urban sense. The Chimu cities of the Peruvian coast (for example, Chan Chan, founded *ca.* 1000 A.D.?) definitely contained large permanent populations. Tiahuanaco (*ca.* 600 A.D.) the great pre-Inca city on the shores of Lake Titicaca in the high plateau of Bolivia was apparently predominantly an urban community. In late pre-Columbian times, Cuzco (*ca.* 1200 A.D.), the capital of the Inca empire, flourished as a true city, and much of its street plan and portions of its architecture are still to be seen in the modern Peruvian city of Cuzco. Likewise, the Aztecs developed a true city in their capital, Teotihuacan (modern Mexico City). In the Southwest area of the present United States the so-called Pueblo Indians achieved community developments in their huge "pueblos" which, if not cities, were certainly large towns. The ruins of many of these communities—both on open sites and in huge shallow caves (the so-called Cliff Dwellings) are a source of tourist attraction at the present time. It is estimated that Pueblo Bonito, for example, accommodated a population of about 5,000 persons in its heyday. Outside the areas mentioned true urban communities failed to develop in the New World until the coming of Europeans. It is worth noting that, although the cultures of Middle America had developed non-alphabetic writing, the urban communities of Peru and the Southwest were illiterate.

It is important to understand that the development of the urban mode of life was and is something distinctive in the world. The town and *the city inevitably creates a special, man-made environment.* People who live in a band or village are "close to nature", but the fundamental exigencies of urban life tend to interpose a screen between the populace and the physical surroundings. The typical East Side child of New York who has never seen a cow is perhaps an exaggeration of the urban picture, confined to metropolitan areas, but something similar is true of all genuine urban dwellers.

The following physical aspects of urban existence deserve mention. Both dwellings and public buildings in a town or city have invariably shown a trend toward permanent construction. This matter involves not only the "artistic" aspects of architecture, but such practical matters as the floor plan of the average house, the disposition of dwellings along the streets, the disposal of edifices devoted to public services (such as markets, administrative buildings, and others) and structures intended for public relaxation and amusement.

Furthermore, "practical" arrangements are required of cities and towns, if large numbers of people are to live together in close juxtaposition. For example, how about the necessities of water and disposal of sewage and garbage? These are problems which still beset modern

American communities, but which received some kind of attention even in ancient times. The Indus valley cities, for instance, had both water and sewage systems.

In sum, the individual who is accustomed to a city environment frequently lacks the patterns and customs of the "country." The regularity of structures and streets, the patterned characteristics of houses and dwellings, the expected material manifestations of public-service features, sometimes the transportation facilities, are all a part of urban life. But we must recognize that urban life is culturally created, that the individual who learns customary responses to these constructions is not responding to "nature in the raw," but rather to something which his group has culturally constructed. It is said, for instance, that the streets of Boston were originally "cow paths." In any case, the winding streets of the Puritan City are a different configuration from those of the regular grid network which characterize the greater part of Manhattan New York or Salt Lake City, for example.

Urban life almost inevitably requires *social differentiation* not insisted upon in simpler types of local grouping. The early cities of the Old World, for example, were almost always characterized by distinction between peasant cultivators and urban artisans and administrators. Typically the population of an urban center is subdivided into wards, barrios, or neighborhoods. In these units the individual still has the opportunity to engage in primary contacts and social activities, but their presence requires some scheme of coördination, assignment of function, specialization of jobs, and overall management. Finally, the diversity of interests within an urban environment tends to create a great variety of interest groups within the town or city itself—artisans, merchants, transportation groups, religious organizations, landowners, art groups, recreational groups, and so on. The Pueblo towns seem to have been exceptional in that little or no ranking of groups or persons was practised. But elsewhere there has been a tendency from the earliest times to create social classes or other forms of ranking in cities. Differences in wealth, birth, and alleged prestige become more easily marked than in the simple band or country village.

Town and city life is thus a special culturally created world not only in the material sense, but also in its social aspects.

We have omitted description and analysis of the precise details of community and governmental organizations and institutions in this general consideration of the basic factors of locality and territory in social organization. Likewise we shall not enter into a discussion of the variety of political institutions whereby local organizations are extended over districts, regions, and nations.

NOTES TO CHAPTER 19

1. Eyre, 1845, Vol. 2, pp. 218-219; for pastoral nomadism, see Myres, 1941.
2. Sharp, 1940.
3. Turner, 1941, Vol. 1, p. 407; Bishop, 1942, p. 7.
4. Steward, 1936; 1938.
5. Southern Bushmen, Schultz, 1907. Andamanese: Radcliffe-Brown, 1933; Man, 1882-1883; Algonkians: Speck, 1915, 1918.
6. Steward, 1938, p. 259.
7. C. F. Krzywicki, 1934, pp. 285-290.
8. Métraux, 1942; Kroeber, 1925; Reed, 1943, pp. 15 ff.
9. Weyer, 1932.
10. For an excellent review of the rise of urban communities in the Old World, see Turner, 1941, Vol. 1.
11. For an overall view of the native Western Hemisphere urban cultures, see Vaillant, 1941, Chapter 1; Means, 1931, for the Andean area; Roberts, 1935, for the Southwest; Morley, 1946, for the Mayas.

CHAPTER 20

The Organization of Familial and Kinship
Relationships

Some basic factors leading to kinship organization. Man is not the only animal requiring some care from adults immediately after birth and for a period thereafter. But he seems to be the only one who "sorts out" and attempts to identify his relatives or kinsmen, and the only one who erects more or less elaborate structures of social organization on the basis of the recognition of kinship. Every human culture makes use of this tendency to recognize kinsmen in its system of organizing social relationships, although some cultures lay more emphasis upon this factor than do others. Indeed, when speaking of social relationships we have to recognize that the first social relationship experienced by the average human being anywhere in the world is that with his mother who is, of course, his kinswoman. The only exceptions to this rule are relatively rare cases in which the mother dies at or shortly after birth, or is physically or mentally incapacitated in such a way that she is unable to react with the new-born child. Survival of the child in such conditions requires social relations ("nursing care") offered by some other adult member of the society, at least during the period of infancy.

In an earlier chapter we examined some of the incapacities which child-bearing lays upon women. No culture has developed a set of patterns whereby the average woman can support herself entirely by her own efforts during the period she is bearing children. It is true that some societies have discovered ways whereby the mother can get along without her husband's presence and even his economic assistance during this period, but in such cases she is required to rely upon some one else for assistance. The point is that the new-born infant normally is immediately introduced upon his entry into the world, not only to social relationships with his mother, but also to relationships with other persons who are older than he. The most usual first group encountered by the child, and it is found in some form everywhere, is the immediate family, consisting of the mother, her husband, and previously born children. Although families in the immediate sense are universal,

417

the ways in which the relationships between members of an immediate family are organized are by no means the same throughout the species. Even this small intimate type of social group offers possibilities for a considerable variety of manipulations by culture. For example, a little reflection will show that there are eight familial statuses possible everywhere, namely, those of father, mother, son, daughter, husband, wife, brother, and sister. Likewise, it is apparent that a number of types of relationships may connect these positions within the nuclear family. These are, for instance, the relationships of father to mother, mother to father, father to son, mother to son, father to daughter, mother to daughter, husband to wife, wife to husband, brother to sister, brother to brother, sister to brother, sister to sister, son to father, son to mother, daughter to father, daughter to mother, and so forth. But we remember that a culture always tends to define the details of statuses and relationships, and that such details may differ decidely from one culture to another. In one culture, the father's position may be dominant, and in another the first-born child may actually dominate his parents; sisters may be subservient to brothers, or brothers and sisters may be allowed to approach each other only formally, and so on. If there are so many possibilities in the cultural organization of the immediate family, it is obvious that opportunities for cultural manipulation multiply rapidly as we pass to the various kinsmen who may be recognized outside the family.

There is no culture which ignores *all* kinsmen beyond the family, and the reasons for this universal tendency to extend kinship relations are fairly obvious. In the first place, the nuclear family is rarely ever socially isolated. The parents have had kinship relations with their parents and siblings before they formed a family of their own through marriage. It is natural that they should continue to practise, even in attenuated or modified form, the patterns which they had learned in their own respective families of orientation. Since they carry on social relationships with their immediate relatives, they must teach some pattern to their children who naturally become involved in such inter-family patterns. The husband must have some pattern for dealing with his wife's relatives, and vice versa, for even if the in-laws do not care much for their son- or daughter-in-law they become interested in the children. Thus the circle of kinsmen which begins for the individual with an introduction to his mother, tends to widen first to his immediate family, then to an expanding series of other families, and so to other groups of kinsmen.

Only man among the animals seems to have any flexibility in the use of symbols, and in sorting out and keeping track of one's kinsmen, symbols are almost essential if the number of such relatives is of any size. Thus it is that every society has developed a *kinship terminology* whereby "relations" may be recognized and, sometimes, classified into groups or categories.

The widespread tendency to extend the patterns of social interaction characteristic of the immediate family into a wider social sphere may be explained psychologically on the principle of generalization (p. 244). Although the family is an agent of discipline, it must be remembered that for the average individual the earliest and most fundamental satisfactions are also obtained in the family. The basic drives receive their first satisfaction in this type of relationship and many of the acquired drives are generated and nurtured within the circle of intimate kinsmen. It is therefore not surprising that many societies have developed cultural means for enlarging the basic family situation in one way or another and for carrying the satisfaction-giving patterns of family life into the larger area of adult social participation.

From the point of view of social organization, the kinship principle when applied to a whole society usually provides unusual stability of relationships and patterns of interaction. However, the organization of a total society on a kinship basis is not consistent with all types of culture. A culture which is adapted to a large population of millions, such as modern North America, seems to be unable to rely upon kinship as a principal mode of organizing social relations throughout the society, although kinship has not been entirely discarded. A culture in which there are a great many alternative and specialized patterns tends to lay emphasis upon other factors of organization, such as cultural interests. Likewise a culture which permits a high rate of either physical or social mobility is generally inconsistent with a pervading kinship structure. A thoroughgoing organization on the basis of kinship requires conditions under which kinsmen may maintain a certain degree of social interaction, also that they have a sufficient number of cultural patterns in common to be able to interact meaningfully. Large population, heterogeneity of culture, physical and social mobility seem to militate against such conditions.

FAMILY-TYPE ORGANIZATIONS

General features of family-type structures. Regardless of the details of pattern and organization of the family type of organization in any given culture, we everywhere find the following general characteristics. (1) A *marriage bond* between two or more members of the group is typical. In our own culture only two members of the group are so united, but in *polygynous families* one husband may have two or more wives; in *polyandrous* families, one wife may have plural husbands; in *extended* families the spouses of children may be included within the organization.

The marriage bond is dissolvable by death in some cultures, but in others (Hindu India, for example) a physically widowed spouse is not permitted to remarry or may actually be required to follow the deceased partner to the other world. The Mormon marriage "for time and eternity" is typical of a good many other systems which do not regard death as the end of the marriage relationship. Likewise, divorce may break the marriage bond in some societies, but in others it is strictly forbidden. In general the simpler pre-literate societies permit remarriage more readily, because in such cultures it is often impossible for a widowed individual to function adequately without the reciprocal services of a partner.

(2) A recognized actual or assumed *blood or biological relationship* bond between the children of the spouses and other members of the group is universal. This relationship is a real biological one in the normal state of affairs, but exceptions are usually permittted. The blood relationship bond may be of a potential nature only, as in the case of childless marriages in our own society; however, many "primitive" societies do not permit family organization to be set up or to continue if the wife shows herself to be infertile; in such a case the group is broken up and new partners must be sought. The blood bond within the family may be only putative in the case of adopted children and other adopted members of the group, stepfathers or stepmothers, affinal relatives of the blood members who are taken into the organization by marriage, and offspring resulting from secret adultery of the wife.

(3) Family organizations involve a *residence* or a series of residences which are jointly occupied at least from time to time by members of the group. Associated with the residence is a typical complex of cultural equipment for housekeeping. In polygamously extended families, each wife and her children sometimes occupy a separate house or apartment, as was characteristic in Mormon Utah previous to 1890 and among most South African Bantu tribes at the present time.

(4) The specific *functions* of the family type of organization differ from one culture to another, but practically universal are the following: (*a*) The patterns include some directed toward the *physical care* of the members. Such patterns commonly involve (1) *protection from bodily harm and illness*, and care of the victim or invalid if they occur, including care of mother and child at time of birth; (2) provision and distribution of *food* to the members; (3) provision and distribution of *shelter and clothing* to the members; (4) patterning of *sex activity* of the spouses and sometimes for other members. (*b*) Patterns for the *transmission of cultural patterns* to children are universal features of family complexes. The first training in eating, elimination, reaction to pain, in speech,

cleanliness, use of clothing and ornaments, and in social interaction is usually given in the family. In many cultures the training for adult occupations, which our culture has largely given over to specialized institutions, is included in the family complex. (*c*) Some *economic functions* are usually included in the family patterns. (1) Sexual and age *division of labor* within the family is universal, and (2) the group is usually invested with rights of ownership and/or control of specified types of *property*, either corporeal (a dwelling, farm, shop, for example) or incorporeal (a tradition, a motto, a magical formula, for example). (*d*) Finally, the family complex always includes some patterns for what we may call *social care* of the members. (1) *Status* is given to the members through the family almost everywhere. A family name is not universal, but where it occurs it serves to symbolize family status and to identify individuals in the total social organization. Most cultural systems have extra-familial statuses in addition, but the family unit serves this function almost everywhere during the first years of the individual's life, if not later. (2) *Social protection* is another aspect of social care, protection from insult and defamation, bankruptcy, and other forms of attack upon the individual member's social standing. (3) The patterns of the family complex also always involve some control of the *courting and marital activities* of the members. Marriage and sex activity is universally prohibited between any members of the family group other than the recognized spouses. In many cultures spouses are chosen for marriageable members by the family group or a designated agent, and supervision of courting and marriage itself may come within the complex. (4) In many cultures family interest also extends to *general social activities* of the members, choice of occupation, political, religious, and recreational patterns.

Basic possibilities of organization. Several possibilities of family organization are to be found universally, and it is necessary to mention them if we are to understand the ways in which a given culture may emphasize one or other of these possibilities in its patterns of organization.

(1) First is the fact that every individual in whatever society actually during his life may belong to *two types of immediate family*, viewed from the point of view of his status within the family unit. (*a*) An individual's *family of orientation* consists of his parents and siblings (brothers and sisters). (*b*) His *family of procreation* consists of his spouse and children. In his family of orientation the individual is usually subordinate to his parents or to one of them, whereas in his family of procreation he is usually superordinate at least to his children. Exceptions occur; for example, in Marquesan noble families, the first-born son was superior in status to everyone, including his parents, in his family of orientation.

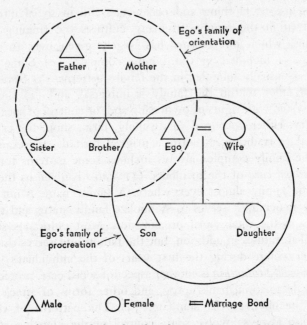

Schematic diagram of the family of orientation and the family of procreation.

(2) We have seen that there are a variety of possible social relationships within the family type of group. Emphasis may be given to one or other of these relationships with the result that the composition and the organization take on special features. We shall mention only the two possibilities one or the other of which is most commonly emphasized among the cultures of mankind. (*a*) If emphasis is laid primarily upon the relationship between the spouses, we may speak of the *conjugal family*. Conjugal families in some form exist everywhere, although in some cultures they are of little importance in the general scheme of social organization. (*b*) If emphasis is laid upon the blood bonds of the members of the unit, we may speak of the *consanguine family*.[1] In such cases the kinship bonds between the spouses and their respective blood kinsmen are considered more important than those between husband and wife. Linton has called such an arrangement a "nucleus of consanguine relatives surrounded by a fringe of spouses." The Hopi social organization, sketched on page 509 ff., makes such an arrangement one of the pillars of the entire social organization. Another example is that of the natives of the Trobriand Islands, northeast of New Guinea.[2] Here the functional family nucleus consists of a woman and her brother. Although the woman cohabits with a man who is recognized as her husband and the brother

also has his own wife, the organization is so patterned that the wife's brother is the functional head of her family with certain rights and responsibilities not given to the husband in his own household. The wife's brother is supposed to supervise the economic activities of his sister's household and to see that it does not suffer want. He disciplines the children, and his property and social position are inherited by his sister's children rather than by his own. The husband has similar status with respect to the household of his own sister. The husband is tolerated in his own household for his personal characteristics, but not because of his recognized social functions. The conjugal family exists, to be sure, in such a society, but it is greatly overshadowed by the consanguine organization imposed upon it.

Consanguine family organization has the advantage over the conjugal type in that it is generally more stable, since it is established by birth rather than by choice. Brother and sister or other consanguine relatives involved have usually been raised since childhood together in the same family or kinship group, so that problems of personal adjustment which frequently plague spouses have usually been settled or accommodated by the time they take on the responsibilities of the family themselves. Death, divorce, and maturation of the children may all destroy or alter the conjugal family group, with consequent need for reorganization of the surviving members, whereas such incidents do not necessarily disrupt the stability of the consanguine type of family. Except for sex activity, the general functions of family groups discussed above seem to be as well performed by the consanguine type as the conjugal type.

THE ORGANIZATION OF THE CONJUGAL RELATIONSHIP

The relationship of husband to wife and vice versa may be arranged in a variety of ways, either in prospect or in actuality. We have space to do no more than mention some of the problems and possibilities for their cultural solution.

Courting and mate selection is the first step toward establishing a marriage.[3] The problem here is how to bring the respective conjugal partners into social relations which may lead to marriage, and, as most readers who remember the "awkward" period of adolescence realize, the existence of established, socially approved patterns for meeting and courting are a great help in this matter. Although the mental patterns of our own culture lay great emphasis on the "independent" status of the pair involved, the fact of the matter is that in almost all societies a marriage and, consequently the approaches to it, are affairs which involve the establishment or intensification of some type of social relations between groups, usually the families or kin groups of the pair involved. This is so much stressed in some cultures that courtship, as we think of it, can hardly be said to exist. In the traditional culture of China, for example, all preliminary arrangements to marriage were made by the families of the bride and groom, or their go-betweens, so that the happy couple often met and saw each other for the first time at the wedding ceremony itself.

In the first place is always the question of *tabued and preferential mating*, for nowhere among mankind does a person marry "just any one." On the tabued side the most common barriers are those of *incest* (marriage or sex activity between kinsmen of a certain specified degree), place, and status. Incest rules have had a fascination for many students, because it seems difficult to explain upon what they are based. No society permits marriage between mother and son, although a few societies have permitted marriage between full brothers and sisters of certain categories. For example, the later Inca emperors married their full sisters, and Cleopatra, the Egyptian queen, is said to have been the product of fourteen generations of marriages between close blood relatives.[4] Although various theories in explanation of the universality of an incest tabu of some sort have been advanced, including the idea that "familiarity breeds contempt" and lessens sexual attractiveness, the most plausible seems to be the following. Marriage as a recognized union of members of the opposite sex always has the effect of increasing the "social resources" of the parties involved. Thus a man by getting married usually adds his wife's family to the number of persons with whom he may deal intimately and upon whom he can rely for aid. Obviously incestuous marriages taking place within the same family do not confer this advantage, with the result that such marriages would suffer in competition with the non-incestuous type, except under unusual circumstances, such as a desire to preserve the "purity" of a royal line, as in Peru and Egypt. By trial and error the successful exogamous (out-marrying) families would become convinced of the rightness of their mode of mate selection and tend to institutionalize it. Since these conditions are almost universal throughout human societies, it is not unnatural, therefore, that incest tabus of some sort should be found everywhere.[5]

Tabus upon marrying outside the community or territory of which one is a member lead to rules of *local endogamy*. Endogamic rules, requiring one to marry within the group, may be applied to almost any sort of social group, except the immediate family. In our own society, marriage outside one's own race is illegal in many states. Likewise, the culture may require one to marry within the social category or general status in which he finds himself. This is usually true in social systems which contain ranked units, such as classes and castes. *Exogamy*, on the other hand, is the rule that one must choose his mate from outside the group or category to which he belongs.

Preferential mating may often be merely the obverse of the tabu rules. Among types of preferential mating not found as general patterns in our system are *cross-cousin marriage*, which requires that one should always seek the offspring of his father's sister or mother's brother or their kinship equivalents; the *levirate*, which requires a woman to take succeeding husbands from among her first spouse's brothers; and the *sororate*, requiring that a man choose succeeding wives from among his first wife's sisters. The levirate and sororate may be practised either with monogamy or with polygamy.[6]

In so far as individual choice enters into the selection of a mate, it is usually strongly influenced by culturally conditioned mental patterns of what is to be considered desirable in a spouse. The typical individual in any society is trained from his early years to seek certain qualities in a partner, even though his choice may not be dictated by such formal patterns and sanctions as those involved in kinship, status, and locality rules. Just as in the case of personal beauty, there is no universal cultural criterion of the qualities considered desirable in a mate. Even sexual attractiveness is not a universal desiratum, as we know in certain circles of our own society and in Europe. Among one of the castes of the Nayars of the Malabar Coast of India, a man was married to a girl in a simple ceremony and thereafter never saw her again.[7] Chastity is considered of great value in a bride in some cultures, whereas fertility is the *sine qua non* in others. For example, among a number of Mohammedan cultures of North Africa (confined mainly to the Sudan, parts of Abyssinia, the Niger Delta, and the region south of the Nile Cataract), physical chastity is of so high a value that young girls between the ages of five and nine are subjected to the operations of clitoridectomy and infibulation: the latter renders them physically incapable of sexual intercourse until the performance of a second operation which takes place at or after marriage.[8] Elaborate patterns of chaperonage and of seclusion of unmarried women in other cultures are also oriented toward the highly prized value of chastity. On the other hand, other peoples consider a girl useless as a prospective wife unless she has proved her ability to bear children. For example, the Bushongo girl of Africa is betrothed in childhood, but does not go to her husband until she has had a child (usually by another man), which is left, after her marriage, with her parents as theirs.[9]

Economic productivity or worth and ability to keep up his or her end of the domestic division of labor is perhaps the most universally sought trait in a spouse, and the courtship patterns are often arranged to prove that these qualities are present. Tests of strength, hunting, and agricultural skill may be required of the groom. Demonstrations of ability to keep house, make textiles and pottery, and cook may be required of the bride, depending upon the culture. Love is not, of course, exclusive to our society, but there are few cultures which institutionalize the tender emotion to the extent that ours does.

In summary, the patterns of mate selection and courtship are a means of bringing two persons and, frequently, two groups of persons into a new set of social relationships which are supposed to be solidified by marriage.

Marriage. If we consider the number of persons directly involved there are, of course, only four "forms" of marriage: (1) monogamy, involving one man and one woman; (2) polygyny, one man and two or more wives; (3) polyandry, one woman and two or more husbands; and (4) group marriage, involving a group of husbands and a group of wives. The term *polygamy* is used to refer to plural-type marriages in general, that is, to both polygyny and polyandry. By far the most common arrangement, even in societies which permit others, is monogamy, and patterns for the monogamic relationship are found in every culture. Polygyny is especially congenial to cultural configurations in which each woman is considered an asset on account of her economic worth or productiveness or her ability to bear and raise children. Polyandry is much rarer and found in socially recognized form in only a few cultures: formerly among certain families of the Todas in Southern India, the northern Tibetans, the Marquesans of Polynesia, certain East African tribes such as the Bahima, occasionally among the Eskimo, the Shoshonean Indians of Nevada, and a few others. Where the natural resources are definitely limited and property is inherited through the male line, polyandry is sometimes consistent with the total culture, for it eliminates many conflicts over inheritance, especially of land. Among the Eskimo it was occasionally practised in conditions under which it was impossible for one man to support a family by his unaided hunting efforts. Group marriage is not universal in any culture, and occurs in a few rare cases such as the Chukchi where "second or third cousins, or even unrelated men desirous of cementing a firm bond of friendship, will form a group exercising marital rights over all the wives of the men concerned." [10]

Marriage rites,[11] like all other rituals, serve to symbolize the mental patterns involved in the new social relationships set up. In practically all cultures they involve (1) publicity, whereby the new relationship is made manifest to the society in general, and (2) festivity, whereby the interaction patterns and rates of the spouses and their kinsmen and friends are "given a good start." The symbols of the bond of matrimony take various forms, such as an exchange of rings, tying clothing together, drinking from the same cup, mingling of blood, and the like. The symbols of status of the partners after the rite may be symbolized by the woman kneeling before her husband, his carrying her in his arms, and so on.

Essentially a marriage differs from a casual liaison in the publicity and social sanction which is accorded to it. In effect, the ceremony is a public advertisement of the fact that the parties involved expect to carry out the established cultural patterns of persons and groups in this relationship and that other members of the society may henceforward act in accordance.

The established patterns for behavior between the spouses after the marriage rites are finished and they are "settled down," vary widely from culture to culture. Most universal is a cultural definition and assignment of rôles, so arranged as to provide a division of labor in the household and outside it. It is impossible to say that such division of duties always is equitable, from any point of view. Among the families of higher status in Marquesas, for example, the wife of the polyandrous household was not even expected to care for the children, except for an indifferent and artificially shortened period of giving the breast, and these tasks devolved upon her secondary husbands.[12] Weaving textiles and making cloth is considered men's work among the Hopi Indians, for example, whereas heavy field labor is expected of most wives in West and Central Africa.

Among ourselves, sexual fidelity is a firmly established feature of the marriage institution, at least in theory, but this again is by no means universal in all cultural systems. Among the Mongwandi of Africa a curious definition of marital fidelity occurs. After a man has three or four children he may "lease" his wife to another man for a period of ten to twelve months. Any child born to the woman during this interval is the property of the "tenant," but it is required that the wife be faithful to the lessee during the period of the lease.[13] Among the Ila, another African society, extramarital liaisons are raised to the status of an elaborate institution. One type of such arrangement is called *lukambo*. This is an arrangement made between a husband and another man, whereby the latter pays the husband a number of cattle and in return receives the favors of the wife for a specified period of time during which she lives in her lover's hut. The arrangement is quite public, and occasionally serious litigation arises between the husband and lover, not because of sexual jealousy, but over the economic aspects of the contract. If the lover does not pay according to agreement, he is subject to penalty, and if the wife is unfaithful to the lover during the period of contract, her husband is required to make compensation to the lover.[14]

Such customs emphasize for us the distinction between the concepts of biological and social status, and help us to gain some insight into the fact that kinship is actually a social rather than a biological relationship. We have mentioned previously that the family universally confers status upon the children born or brought into it. However, in most cultures little attention is given to the question of physiological paternity. Of course, there are some peoples who do not understand the male rôle in reproduction, but even among those who do, the important matter from the point of view of the society as a whole is not, "Is A actually the biological father of child X?" but rather, "Is the family in which A plays the rôle of father and husband willing to acknowledge child X as one of its members?" If the latter is the case, A and X may proceed to play the rôles (follow the patterns) prescribed for fathers and children in their culture, regardless of the actual genetic relationship between them, if any.

Rules of residence. Where the happy couple sets up housekeeping after their marriage has been solemnized frequently has a good deal to do with the organization of their relations with each other and with the rest of society. In general, there are three patterns possible: (1) matrilocal residence, that is, in or near the family of orientation of the wife; (2) patrilocal residence, with or near the groom's people; and (3) independent residence. It is obvious that any one of these schemes in the interests of consistency calls for certain peculiar patterns of custom governing the respective partners to the marriage and other persons.[15] Thus it is not unusual to find that in matrilocal systems the ownership or control of property is vested in the hands of the wife or of her kinsmen, that the husband at least during the early years of marriage plays a somewhat subordinate rôle, and that children are much more under the influence of their maternal relatives.

GENERAL TYPES OF KINSHIP RELATIONSHIPS

Before proceeding further with a consideration of the various methods of organizing social relationships on a kinship basis it is well to mention briefly the types of kinship relation which may be recognized in terminology, behavior, and cultural patterning. Two general types of kinship may be mentioned: "blood" relatives, or consanguine relatives, and *affinal* relatives, or kinsmen by marriage.

1. *Consanguine relatives* always have one or more ancestors in common or are assumed to have them. The common ancestor of two consanguine relatives may be their mother, or it may be a grandmother several generations removed. It is obvious that there are two types of "blood" relatives which one may have: lineal and collateral. (*a*) *Lineal* relatives are always connected by a line of descent; of two persons in

such a relationship, the first is always the ancestor of the second, who, of course, is the descendant of the first. Parents and children are lineal relatives, as are grandparents and grandchildren. Consequently two persons who stand in a consanguine lineal relationship to each other are never of the same generation. For a given individual, we say that his parents are in the first ascending generation, his grandparents in the second generation; on the other hand his children are in the first descending generation and his grandchildren in the second descending generation; and so on. (*b*) *Collateral* consanguine kinsmen, on the other hand, are not connected by direct lines of descent. One is neither a descendant nor an ancestor of his collateral relatives—for example, brothers and sisters, cousins, uncles, aunts, nephews, nieces. Nonetheless, the lines of descent of collateral relatives may always be traced back to an ultimate common ancestor or ancestors. Thus, though my maternal first cousin and I are not directly connected by descent, we are both descended from my mother's father and mother. My nephews and I share my own grandparents as common ancestors, and so on. Collateral relatives may be either of the same generation as oneself or of any other generation.

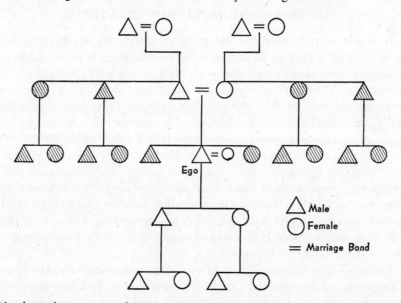

This chart shows some of Ego's collateral kinsmen. Lineal kinsmen are shown in white symbols; collateral kinsmen are shown in shaded symbols. Ego's wife, although shown as a white symbol, is not normally a lineal kinswoman.

2. *Affinal relatives* are those with whom relationship is established by marriage, either your own marriage or that of some other kinsman of

yours. At the time of your marriage you may enter into a new series of patterns with a whole group of your wife's consanguine kinsmen. Most systems of social organization recognize affinal kinsmen to some degree and lay down patterns of interaction between them, although the size of the affinal group for which customary interaction is patterned varies with the system in question. Our own organization, for example, provides definite patterns of interaction usually with only the immediate family of orientation of one's spouse, with rather vague, unpredictable behavior resulting when one meets more distant affinal relatives. In some societies marriage between certain consanguine kinsmen of the collateral type is permitted or even required, so that one's affinal and one's consanguine relatives tend to become merged to a certain degree. Marriage with a first cousin is required in many so-called primitive societies, and is not uncommon in modern Europe. In many Carib tribes of South America marriage between a man and his sister's daughter was customary, if not universal. No systems, with the exceptions previously noted, permit regular marriage between brothers and sisters.

THE RECKONING OF KINSHIP RELATIONS

It should be plain that the biological or genetic factors in themselves ordinarily play a very small part in social organization. It is not the genes which one may have in common with his kinsmen which enable him to enter into a framework of customary interaction involving coöperation, avoidance, or conflict. It is the accident of being born into a particular family and thereby being introduced to a number of relatives *socially* which gives him a chance to participate in a kinship organization. It is notorious that among human beings it is relatively difficult to detect blood relationship by gross physical inspection alone. The individuals of a kinship organization need some way of identifying their relatives and some way of handily labeling the respective relationships if they are to know whom to interact with and how, according to the design of their system of organization. It is for this reason that we find some type of *kinship terminology* in every culture.

Essentially the terminology must symbolize two things: (1) the extent of the system of kinship, and (2) the different statuses and their respective interaction patterns within the system. No kinship system recognizes all of one's relatives, living and dead. For example, in the question of lineal relatives, provided no consanguine marriages had taken place, any one would be able to count up, in the twentieth generation ascending from his own, no less than 1,048,576 lineal ancestors, not counting those in the intervening generations. Likewise, with respect to collateral relatives it is possible to continue counting them "on either side" of one indefinitely. The reckoning of kinship is socially useful only for determining categories, groups, and statuses of social participation and must therefore be related to practical realities. Thus it is common that a terminology contains terms only for relatives of a certain degree of distance from Ego, beyond which vagueness or void intervenes.

Within the system itself there are three general methods employed for identifying kinsmen. (1) A *particularizing terminology* in pure form would have a separate term for each kinship status within the system. In effect, each individual kinsman would be identified by a separate term. In our own system only the terms *mother* and *father* are of this type: only one person can occupy the status of *mother*, only one person can be properly designated as *father*. (2) A second method is to lump several relatives into a single category under one term. This type of terminology has been called *classificatory*. In our own system *aunt*, *uncle*, and *cousin* are classificatory terms. Many cultures use terminologies all terms of which, unlike our own, are classificatory. (3) The *mixed type* of system combines both particularizing and classificatory terms. Our own system is of this type. Actually there are no systems which use only particularizing terms, so that for practical purposes we have to deal only with the classificatory type and the mixed type.

It is hardly necessary to go into the technical details of the variations [16] which may be found in classificatory systems so long as we understand clearly that such a system is a symbolic means of sorting relatives into categories and groups with whom the individual in question carries on expected interaction according to the pattern in force. One reason, perhaps, that members of our own society have some difficulty in grasping the significance of classificatory terminologies is that we are accustomed to think of certain kinsmen in terms of their biological relationship to us. For example, many a classificatory terminology makes no distinction between father and father's brother; both relatives are called by a single term. If the father's brother is called "father" (we would call him paternal uncle), it is consistent that his son should be called "brother," which is what one calls all male offspring of "fathers." Thus a certain type of cousin (in our terminology) is equated with "brother." Now, if I call certain cousins in my own generation brothers, it is consistent that "father" in his generation likewise equates *his* paternal cousins with "brother" when he is speaking of or to them. It then follows that I call not only my biological father "father," but also apply this term to his biological brothers, and also to his parallel cousins. Thus the term "father" is applied to the biological father and also to a whole group of "classificatory fathers" as well. If one bears in mind that the same extension may apply to other terms such as those we would think of as "mother," "sister," "nephew," "niece," and so forth, it will be easier to grasp many behavior rules which, in terms of our system, seem impossible to carry out. For instance, one reads that a man's funeral should always be conducted by his sister's son. The student asks, Supposing he does not have a sister or that she does not have a son? If one understands the classificatory principle he will realize that usually there will be some classificatory sisters and classificatory sisters' sons.

It should not be inferred that those people who operate according to a classificatory terminology lose sight of their immediate families. Everywhere one's real father and mother, brother and sister, are known and identified as a general rule. Everywhere it is clear that the classification of kinsmen is an extension, an attenuation, perhaps a specialization, of relationships first experienced in the immediate family, but it is also realized that these extended relationships are not identical with those of the household. Just as a soldier is able to distinguish between the sergeant of his own outfit and sergeants in general, so the ordinary man has no difficulty in distinguishing between his father and his classificatory fathers. At the same time, by being able to identify a man as a classificatory father, he is at once able to start the practice of a pattern of behavior generally appropriate for interaction with that status, just as the private soldier shifts into the pattern of behavior expected toward sergeants, once he has made the identification.

Reckoning of descent. Any sort of kinship system is necessarily based upon some agreed rules of reckoning descent. It is by virtue of one's descent from a certain ancestor or ancestors that one establishes his membership in a kinship group or is able to prove his relationship with

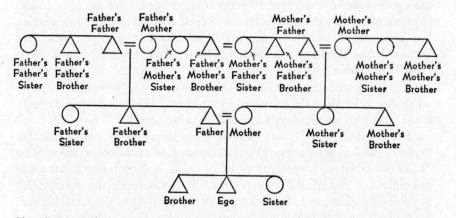

This diagram shows some of Ego's kinsmen as reckoned by rule of bilateral descent. Note that the kinsmen of both father and mother are recognized.

other persons. There are four general principles of descent reckoning, which may be summarized as follows. (1) *Bilateral descent* is the type familiar to us. Kinship and affiliation is reckoned through *both* the mother's and the father's lines. One is equally related with all four grandparents, and all possible lines are given equal prominence. In our own system the only lack of equality in this respect is the fact that the surname descends in the paternal line, so that with respect to surname one is affiliated with the male and unmarried female members of the father's line of descent and other relatives are excluded from the use of this name. This is about as close as we get to one-sided, or unilateral, kinship reckoning in our culture. (2) *Unilateral descent* reckons only through the mother's *or* the father's line (not through both). Ego is affiliated with only one grandparent. (*a*) *Matrilinear descent* [17] is reckoned only through the mother's female line. One reckons as kinsmen only those related through his mother and her female ancestors. Among his four actual grandparents, Ego is affiliated only with his mother's mother. (*b*) *Patrilinear descent* is reckoned only through the father's male line. Among his four actual grandparents Ego is affiliated only with his father's father.[18]

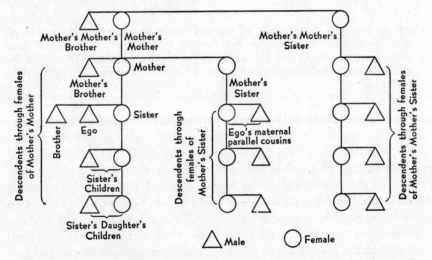

Here are shown five generations of kinsmen as reckoned by matrilinear descent by a male Ego. Note that, although male offspring of the maternal lines are reckoned among the kin, none of the children of these males belongs to the matrilinear kin. Ego's father's "relatives" are excluded altogether.

(3) *Mixed descent* is relatively rare, but occurs in some systems. There are two varieties. (*a*) In *sex-linked descent*, males are affiliated with

the father's male line, and females are affiliated with the mother's female line. This setup is found in the Sula system of Indonesia, for example.[19] (*b*) In *cross-sex descent*, males are affiliated with the mother's father, whereas females are reckoned with the father's mother.[20]

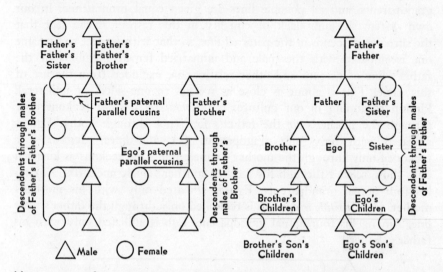

Here we see five generations of Ego's kinsmen as reckoned by a rule of patrilinear descent. Although the female offspring of the paternal lines are reckoned among the kin, none of the children of these females is included among Ego's patrilinear kinsmen. Mother's "relatives" are completely excluded.

(4) *Double descent* is even rarer than the types of reckoning previously mentioned. It is a combination of matrilinear and patrilinear descent, with the two modes followed concurrently. It differs from bilateral descent in that all possible lines are not given equal emphasis, but only two lines are emphasized. Thus Ego is affiliated with both his maternal grandmother and his paternal grandfather, but not with his other two grandparents. Double descent is almost always found in social systems containing a complex set of kin groups, wherein the normal individual belongs at the same time to both a matrilinear and patrilinear group.[21]

ORGANIZATION OF THE CONSANGUINE RELATIONSHIP

An agreed system of reckoning descent and a properly developed system of terms for symbolizing kinship relations provide the tools or instruments, as it were, for the organization of groups, categories, and statuses of kinship united by a web of customary behavior patterns. It is most convenient to begin a survey of such organizations with a discussion of "larger kinship groups." The one general feature of groupings of this type is that members of a given kin group consider themselves to be related to each other symbolically, at least, by "blood." The actual genealogical relationship is sometimes difficult or impossible to trace, while adoption or formal initiation may replace, sociologically, the lack of it. In some cases the common ancestor from which the members of the group are supposed to be descended is frankly a mythological figure, as is the case with the Ganda gentes, the Venda, the Orokaiva.[22]

1. **Informal or vaguely recognized groupings.** These groups are usually not discrete units within the general social organization, and they are usually relative to a particular individual. Therefore they tend to overlap each other. For example, in our society the group I call "my relatives"

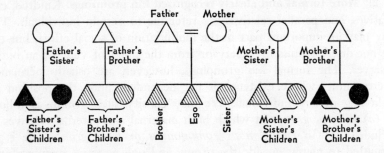

This diagram shows first cousins of Ego. Ego, his brother and sister, and their parallel cousins are shown by hatched symbols, cross cousins are shown in black.

is rather vaguely delimited; it contains some individuals included in the group which my cousin calls his "relatives"; but the two groups do not coincide. We may mention two types. (*a*) *Kindreds* are "groups of relatives" as found for example in our own society. The reckoning is bilateral, but there is no distinct line of limitation for the group which, for practical purposes, owes its real existence to the intimacy and intensity of unformalized interaction which takes place between the members. In stable rural communities of our society such groups usually tend to be larger and better defined than among urbanized mobile sections of the population. (*b*) *Parallel and cross relatives*. The recognition of these two groups among one's kinsmen always involves a unilateral system of reckoning. To enable the reader to understand the meaning of these terms, let us give the following examples. *Parallel cousins* are offspring of brothers or of sisters, in other words, they are offspring of siblings of the same sex. Thus my father's brother's child and my mother's sister's child are both my parallel cousins. This relationship of "parallelism" may be extended into any generation "up" or "down" from Ego and the whole group thus reckoned becomes Ego's "parallel relatives." Conversely, *cross cousins* are offspring of siblings of opposite sex; thus my cross cousins in the first degree are the children of my father's sister and mother's brother. This type of relationship can likewise be extended up and down in the generation lines, and it is possible for me to sort out a group of "cross" relatives, referring not to their dispositions but to their position in the kinship system. Among the Caribs of British Guiana, for instance, parallel and cross relatives are distinguished bilaterally (both through the mother and through the father), although the two groups are not formally organized. The incest tabu usually generalizes to parallel relatives, and the members of the "parallel group" are designated by incest terms generalized from the immediate family.[23]

2. **More formal and clearly recognized kin groupings.** Kindred, cross relatives, and parallel relatives are referable to certain individuals. They may play an important part in the mobilization of social effort, but they are not discrete units in society or from the point of view of an outside observer. The formal kin groupings, however, are usually permanent, discrete units whose existence is not dependent upon the position and reckoning of any individual. We may classify such groups as follows.

(*a*) *Bilinear groups* in which both maternal and paternal relatives are included. (i) In *endogamous communities or local groups* one is not permitted to marry outside the group, and one possesses membership in the group by virtue of one's father's and mother's membership. The Ainu of northern Japan,[24] for example, usually marry within their own village which thus becomes a bilateral kinship group. In the later Inca Empire of Peru, a man was constrained to choose his wife from his own community, although not from near relatives.[25] (ii) *Endogamous status groups,* such as castes, are also bilateral kinship groups. The classic example of caste organization is India.

As it exists in India, a caste (of which there are thousands) is a group of families bearing a common name which is associated with or denotes a special occupation. They claim descent from a common mythical ancestor, human or divine, profess to follow the same calling, and are regarded by outsiders as forming a homogeneous unit. A caste is typically endogamous, requiring marriages to take place within the caste itself. It is "a closed corporation, in theory at any rate rigorously hereditary; equipped with a certain traditional and independent organization, including a chief and a council; meeting on occasion in assemblies of more or less plenary authority, and joining in the celebration of certain festivals; bound together by a common occupation, observing certain common usages which relate more particularly to marriage, to food, and to questions of ceremonial pollution; and ruling its members by the exercise of a jurisdiction the extent of which varies, but which succeeds, by the sanction of certain penalties and above all by the power of final or revocable exclusion from the group, in making the authority of the community effectively felt." [26] There are thousands of castes in India at the present time, all traditionally growing out of the four original castes which arose after the Aryan invasion of India in the second millennium B.C. These four original castes are ranked in the following order: Brahmans (priestly caste), Kshatriyas (soldier caste), Vaishyas (merchant caste), and Sudras (workers caste). The numerous secondary castes which have grown around occupational, religious, racial, local, and other differences, real or imaginary, are all rigidly ranked within the social system, and elaborate patterns of avoidance have been evolved to prevent pollution of a high-caste member by a person of lower caste. Every one within the caste system is pollutable by some other group, for outside the system of caste is a group called the Pariahs or outcasts who pollute all caste members, but are polluted by none. "When a Brahman received a gift from another Brahman, he had to acknowledge it in a loud voice; from a Rajanya or Kshatriya, in a gentle voice; from a Vaishya, in a whisper; and from a Sudra, in his own mind." [27] In Madras a Pariah is said to pollute a high-caste Hindu by approaching within a distance of sixty-four feet. A whole scale of uncleanness is in operation: a Nayar may pollute a man of higher-caste by touching him; members of the Kammalan group, including masons, blacksmiths, carpenters, and leather workers, pollute at a distance of twenty-four feet, toddy drawers at thirty-six feet, cultivators at forty-eight feet, and so on. [28]

Several features of the caste type of groups should be noted. Membership is determined by blood and inheritance as in the case of other blood groups we have discussed. [a] However, ranked status is emphasized. It is probable that caste in India originated in the racial differentiations between various populations, the lighter colored, dominant invading group (Aryans from the northwest) assuming an aloof and superior position to their subjects. Since the Aryan invasion, differences of economic function, religion, and of many other kinds have given rise to caste groups. The rudiments, at least, of caste organization are not unknown in modern American society. Witness, the relations between the white and the colored racial groups. [29] [b] The caste is endogamous. The only exception in India is the rule of hypergamy which obtains in some castes, whereby men are allowed to marry only women of their own or higher castes. Caste groups and tendencies may grow up in any society when a social group for any reason seeks to preserve its distinctiveness and privileges by heredity and consequent refusal to intermarry with other people. All stratified hereditary social groups may be grouped under the general head of caste-type groups; slaves, freemen, nobles, and royal families are familiar in the history of our civilization. In present-day America there is a tendency toward an endogamy of wealth and of social position, that is, wealthy and "good" families taken together form a group which is in fact, though not formally, endogamous and which passes on membership and privilege by birth. The door is still open, in America, however, for "climbers." Until it is finally shut and barred, and individuals are no longer able to move from lower to higher groups at all, as is actually the case now with Negroes vis-à-vis whites, the wealthy classes will remain classes with a caste tinge. The caste system has not yet become solidified in this country.

(iii) *Endogamous sibs*, *phratries*, *moieties*, and the like must also be included under the heading of bilateral groups of a more or less formal type. They are discrete, easily recognizable units of a society which, however, as a rule prohibit their members from marrying outside the group. The Todas, that interesting tribe of India, are divided into two endogamous halves (moieties), called Tarthar and Teivali. A Tartharol may marry only in the Tarthar division; a Teivaliol only in the Teivali group (with a few exceptions). The Tarthar moiety owns all of the higher sacred herds and dairies which are so important in Toda religion, while the Teivali moiety furnishes the sacred dairymen, who are in fact the priests of this society. Thus the two endogamous moieties share in division of labor.

(b) *Unilinear groups.* One of the most widespread types of social unit in primitive societies is the unilinear kinship group. These units are permanent, in the sense that their existence is not dependent upon any specific constellation of particular persons. Membership in such a group is reckoned through one line of descent only, either the maternal or the paternal line, and one remains a member of his group for life. The incest tabu and the rule of exogamy usually apply to all members, and they regard themselves as being related to each other by blood. Often this relationship is kept in mind by the custom of members calling each other by relationship terms also applied to the immediate family, for example, *brother*, *sister*, *father*, *mother*, and so forth. Technically several varieties of such unilateral groups may be distinguished.

(i) *Lineages* are unilinear groups the members of which trace actual genealogical relationship to each other. They are small and often compact groups. Both matrilinear and patrilinear lineages may occur, depending upon the rule of descent current in a given society.

(ii) *Sibs* are usually larger social units which are distinguished from lineages by the fact that the unilinear relationship which unites the members is often only assumed rather than being genealogically demonstrable. Among many of the Bantu tribes of South and East Africa sibs with tens of thousands of members are not unusual, and there is evidence to show that some of these units have been formed through absorption of other groups. Nevertheless the members hold to the belief that they are all descended from a common ancestor in one line. There are two types of sibs: *clans*, which are matrilinear sibs, and *gentes* (singular: *gens*), which are patrilinear.

Sibs may be localized or unlocalized. In the latter case members of a given sib may be found in many or all local communities of a society. Among the Iroquois the various clans were not only composed of many different households in various communities, but sib membership even crossed tribal lines, so that the Bear clan for example was represented in five Iroquois tribes.

A sib always has a name and usually possesses a certain array of ritual and ceremonial equipment and usages for the exclusive use of the sib members and for their benefit.

In our own society we have nothing resembling the sib, and therefore we often find it difficult to understand the part which the idea of unilateral descent plays in the thinking and behavior of individuals who live in such a system. The nearest we come to this idea is the unilateral descent of our family names in the male line. When the male members of the Gunderson kindred, for example, get together, we have a unilateral group slightly resembling a sib. The members of such a group, however, do not ignore their mothers' relatives, nor as a general rule do they attach any more importance to their Gunderson relatives than to others. Sib members, however, carry the idea of unilateral descent much farther. Thus, if you are a member of a society organized into gentes (patrilineal sib groups), you do not consider your mother's relatives in connection with your gens life at all. They are ignored and are excluded from your gens. The mother of a gens member is not a member of the gens. This is a type of social organization which has played a very important part in many societies, even in certain civilized societies of antiquity, such as early Greece and Rome. Unilateral social grouping, however, tends to disappear in societies having large populations and extensive internal migration and mobility. When the members of a population are moving about from place to place and are changing their occupations and social positions, it seems to be difficult for them to maintain the ties based upon unilateral blood relationship.

The functions of the sib, where it is found, are so numerous that we have space to do little more here than mention them.

[a] Religious functions are frequently associated with the sib, and one aspect of sib religion, namely *totemism*, has attracted much attention. Totemism consists of patterns of behavior based upon the idea that a group of people is associated in some mystical manner with a species of plants, animals, or a class of other objects of nature. Such beliefs and practices are not confined to sibs. They may be associated with any social group, even the members of an army unit in modern times.[30] Nor are sibs

invariably totemic. However, the sib does form a group to which totemism is particularly adapted. Frequently the idea is current that the common ancestor of the sib members is an animal or plant; the Bear clan feels, for example, that a special connection exists between the members of the clan and bears; it may be forbidden for members to kill or to eat bears; special ceremonial behavior may be enjoined to increase the number of bears; patterns of reverence may be demanded when a clan member meets a bear in the forest, and so forth. This totemistic behavior tends to unify the members of the group and to heighten the idea of the group's exclusiveness. Members of other sibs do not enjoy this particular relationship with bears which is the privilege of the Bear clan membership.

[b] Group responsibility in economic, legal, political, and other matters is usually exhibited by the sib. In these respects the sib acts somewhat as an enlarged family. When an individual gets into trouble his sib members help him. If the member of one sib has committed a wrong against a member of another, it must be adjusted between the groups as units, rather than between the individuals or their immediate families. Among the Iroquois the political officers of the tribe and confederation were chosen from and by certain clans. Among the Ganda certain officials of the royal court are chosen only from certain gentes. Political function is usually conferred upon sibs in societies thus organized. Property is often held by the sib and passed down in sib lines, as a sort of group form of ownership. In some societies division of labor is based upon sib lines, each sib specializing upon a hereditary or permanent type of work.

[c] Marriage relations and social position are usually bound up with sib membership. Owing to the fact that all members of the sib consider themselves to be relatives (siblings) and usually call each other by terms which are merely extensions of those used in the immediate family (*brother, sister, father, mother*, and so on), it is considered incestuous to marry within the sib. Consequently, the rule of *exogamy* prevails. In many cases, however, the sib group as a whole takes a certain responsibility in arranging the marriage, in assisting at the ceremonies, and providing the economic exchanges which accompany marriage. Children born into a sib naturally assume the social position common to the members of the group, and since it is impossible to "resign" from a sib, they are destined to share the social fate of the sib for life.

Without going into more details, we may say that the sib patterns are in major part extensions of family patterns. Excluding reproduction, practically all of the functions fulfilled by the family are attempted by the sib. The fact that the sib may not be a primary group, however, while the family always is, results in a certain loss of intimacy and an attenuation of functions. Thus an individual usually responds more completely to a family brother than to a clan brother, and he distinguishes in his behavior between his actual father and the older members of the sib whom he may call father, and so on.

(iii) *Phratries*. Sibs may exist side by side in a society more or less independently of other sibs, just as families do. However, in some societies certain sibs are grouped together into larger units which are termed *phratries* (brotherhoods), because the component sibs are thought of as "brother-sibs." Thus the Crow Indians, for example, were divided into thirteen clans, which in turn were grouped into six phratries, five of which consisted of a pair of clans each, while the sixth included three clans. The usual attitude is that the members of the several sibs included in a phratry are related to each other. Exogamy prevails in marriage, and special patterns of reciprocity and coöperation exist between the members. The unilateral principle obtains. Phratries may be either patrilinear or matrilinear.

(iv) *Moieties*. Many societies on the so-called lower levels of culture are divided into exogamous halves, called *moieties*, or dual divisions. In cases such as the Dieri of Australia, in which the tribe is composed of two moieties, which do not contain component sibs, the moiety is simply a large sib. These are called *simple moieties*, in contrast to *compound moieties* which contain sibs and/or phratries. In any case membership follows unilateral principles. There is usually a pattern of reciprocity between the two moieties. For example, one moiety will perform the funeral rites for the other; athletic contests are arranged between the two halves; mutual exchange of presents may be customary. The moiety organization serves as a means for releasing feelings of opposition toward an "out-group" while, through the reciprocal activities, maintaining a fundamental unity within the society.

Sibs, phratries, and moieties are all somewhat similar in being unilateral, hereditary groups of real or assumed relatives who regard each other as brothers and sisters, parents and children, and so on. The functions which they fulfil vary from society to society and are dependent upon the cultural configuration. As a general rule these unilateral kinship groups are of the unstratified type, that is, they are not usually ranked from the point of view of the society as a whole.

(c) *Groups with Mixed Descent*. These groups are relatively rare and are so foreign to our own type of organization that we need only mention them. They are groups based on sex-linked descent, or upon cross-sex descent (see section on rules of descent above).

(d) *Groups with Double Descent*. Throughout a large area in Australia, tribal societies group their members into exogamous moieties. These moieties are in turn divided into marriage "classes" or "sections," which may be illustrated simply as follows, for a "four-section system with indirect patrilinear descent" :

Moiety I	Moiety II
Section A	Section C
Section B	Section D

A man of Section A must marry a woman of Section C, their children then becoming Section B. A man of Section C must marry a woman of Section A; children are Section D. A man of Section B must marry a woman of Section D; children are Section A. A man of Section D must marry a woman of Section B; children are Section C.[31]

This setup is peculiar in that children do not belong to the section of either parent. (In groups of the sib type the child always belongs to the group of either its father or its mother, depending upon whether descent is patrilinear or matrilinear.) Lawrence has shown that these groups are based on double descent. The affiliation is determined by tracing descent through both the maternal and paternal lines through alternating generations. In the above four-section system a man's paternal grandfather and his maternal grandmother both belong to his section. From North Ambrym in the New Hebrides a similar type of grouping has been noted.[32]

Double descent is also found occasionally in connection with groups which are, as groups, organized on unilateral principles. An individual may belong to a patrilinear sib and to a matrilinear sib at the same time. The Herero tribe of Africa,[33] for example, has non-localized clans and localized gentes. Both are exogamous and totemic, but the clans are primarily social in function whereas the gentes are religious. Ordinary property is transmitted within the clan to a man's brother or to his sister's son, whereas sacred property descends in the gens from father to son.

NOTES TO CHAPTER 20

1. Linton, 1936, pp. 159 ff.; Goldenweiser, 1937, pp. 361-374, discusses some examples of conjugal families under the heading of "unilateral families."
2. Malinowski, 1929.
3. A survey of courtship practices, somewhat biased toward a "survivalistic" interpretation, will be found in Westermarck, 1922, Chapters 13 and 21.
4. Thomas, 1937, p. 195.
5. This theory was advanced in Gillin, 1936b, p. 93.
6. Lowie, 1920, pp. 26-38.
7. Panikkar, 1918.
8. Dembo and Imbelloni, 1938, pp. 222-223, and references cited there.
9. Thomas, 1937, p. 245.
10. Lowie, 1920, p. 51.
11. For survey of the variations in marriage rites, see Westermarck, 1922, Chapters 24-26.

12. Kardiner, 1939, p. 154. (Sketch of Marquesan culture by Ralph Linton.)
13. Johnston, 1908, 2: 677.
14. Brelsford, 1933.
15. Titiev, 1943.
16. On kinship terminologies, see Spier, 1925; White, 1939; Lowie, 1929; Kroeber, 1909.
17. For example, Crow Indians: Lowie, 1935.
18. For example, the Ganda of East Africa: Roscoe, 1911.
19. Kennedy, 1937.
20. For example, the Mundugamor "rope": Mead, 1935, pp. 176-180.
21. Murdock, 1940.
22. Roscoe, 1911; Stayt, 1931, p. 190: one sib, for example, regards a baboon as ancestor; Williams, 113-115: in Orokaiva each sib has a plant emblem referring to a semi-mythical ancestor who had a plant name.
23. Gillin, 1936a; this system seems to be typical of Carib tribes: see Kirchoff, 1932.
24. Batchelor, 1927; Murdock, 1934, pp. 175, 180.
25. Rowe, 1946.
26. Risley, 1901, pp. 517-519.
27. Russell, 1916, 1: 20.
28. *Ibid.*, pp. 72-73. For a discussion of how classes and castes may originate, see Weber, 1922, pp. 631-640.
29. Davis, Gardner, and Gardner, 1941; Dollard, 1937.
30. Linton, 1924.
31. Radcliffe-Brown, 1930-1931; Lawrence, 1937.
32. Deacon, 1927.
33. Murdock, 1940, p. 558.

Thanks are hereby expressed to the Macmillan Co., publishers, for permission to use certain material, including kinship diagrams, published in Gillin and Gillin, 1942, chapter 9.

CHAPTER 21

Representations and Symbols

PERHAPS THE MOST distinctive feature of human social behavior is the symbolic quality which pervades a large share of it. Not only is a considerable part of every culture passed on from one generation to the other by means of symbols, but also the everyday operation of a culture would be impossible without this means of creating and maintaining common understanding in the minds of the practitioners of the culture.

The need for symbols. We have previously pointed out that the internalized, mental patterns held in common by the members of a social group constitute an important aspect of their culture. A certain agreement among the mental patterns held by constituent members of the group or society forms a basis for the body of common or conventional understandings whose existence and functioning is an absolute prerequisite for social unity of the culture. Cultures differ in respect to the area of common experience covered by the system of mental patterns of conventional understandings; likewise they differ in the degree of integration or organization characteristic of the system. Furthermore, societies may differ among themselves with respect to the extent to which the common mental attitudes and other patterns are diffused among the members. But a certain minimum of mutual understanding and common attitudes is absolutely essential to the existence of the society and to the operation of other aspects of the cultural system.

As a general rule, rents in the web of common understandings, so to speak, are made manifest by social phenomena usually considered undesirable. Two of the most common results of the failure of the mental system are (1) conflict, either between groups or between individuals, and (2) lack of social coördination, with resulting "loss of morale," apathy, and degeneration on the part of individuals.

If the successful functioning of any culture and the society which it serves depends upon the dissemination of a body of common understandings or mental patterns, the question is, By what means is this accomplished? In view of the fact that a good many cultures have been and at this moment are functioning, at least with a minimum of efficiency, it is obvious that some general principle of culture must have been developed

444

which serves this function in all such cases. Common understandings and similar mental patterns are not, so far as we can determine, created in the minds of the members of a group or a society spontaneously. Nor does it seem likely that "mental telepathy" and other means of "extra-sensory" communication,[1] even if such processes can be proved to operate, offer a valid explanation for the development of common understandings in a social group.

The answer seems to lie in the general processes of symbolization which are everywhere employed in human social situations. No human social group is known to have existed longer than momentarily without the use of symbols, and no culture has been discovered which lacks patterns for the production and manipulation of symbols. In fact, these patterns taken together constitute that important part of the total configuration which we have called the representational culture.

Signs and symbols. Both signs and symbols have the function of "standing for" something other than themselves, something which is not presented directly to the organism as a stimulus. This is to say that they both have "meaning." They also share the fact that the meanings associated with them have to be learned in one way or another by the organism. However, signs differ from symbols in certain ways which are worth mentioning briefly in the interests of clear understanding of their functions.[2]

Perhaps the outstanding feature of a sign is that it always forms an actual part of a total situation or configuration of conditions, past, present, or future. When the total situation is not presented the organism which has learned the meaning of such a sign reacts in the presence of the sign alone as if the total situation were present. The type of learning process which is most prominent in the establishment of such meanings is called *conditioning*.

It is obvious that in general there are two types of signs: natural signs, and arbitrary or artificial signs. The existential association between a natural sign and the situation to which it refers is not dependent upon culture, although a given culture may contain patterns for teaching members of the society to notice and to interpret such relationships. Thus, smoke is almost everywhere a sign of fire, and the association between these two phenomena does not depend upon conventionalized, artificial, cultural understanding between men. Likewise, moving tree-tops are almost always a sign that the wind is blowing. Heavy ridges on the bones of a skeleton signify that the owner in life was a male. A bulbous swollen head in a baby indicates that the infant will develop into a hydrocephalic idiot. Much of human adjustment, of course, depends upon our ability to learn to read such signs of nature, but the process itself is one which we share with other animals. Likewise, other animals often show a considerable ability to learn to read artificial signs and to react properly to them in absence of the complete presentation of the situations to which they refer. Thus Pavlov showed in his experiments demonstrating conditioned learning, that the sound of a bell, for example, may be arbitrarily associated with food, and that dogs, after the requisite training, will learn to react to the bell alone almost as they do to the total situation of food-and-bell. The sound of the bell is not a configuration given by nature, but an artificial sign. Human beings also learn to associate artificial signs to referents, and one hardly needs to expatiate upon the use of bells for such functions in modern culture. Every normal human being is called upon to interpret hundreds of such signs or clues every day. The successful practice of many professions and trades rests primarily upon ability and training in reading signs. A large block of stocks appears on the market indicating to the experienced operator that a changed, although not yet completely visible, situation has arisen in financial circles. A sudden weakness on the battle front signifies to an experienced general a different situation behind the enemy lines. The presence of arrow-heads of a certain size in an archaeological deposit gives the clue to an archaeologist for a picture of a long-dead hunting culture. The appearance of a marked bill in a store is a sign to the detective that the criminal he is tracking is probably in the vicinity. And so on.

A sign, then, refers to a situation, and for those who understand it, the item has been at some time during their experience a part of the situation with which they associate it. In the case of artificial signs this association may be quite arbitrary and may depend entirely upon customary manipulation of situations by human beings.

A symbol, on the other hand, refers not to empirical situations, but to ideas or other mental products in the minds of men. Infra-human animals, especially dogs and apes, have shown themselves relatively adept at learning signs. But on the evidence at hand it seems that they are very poor in the production of ideas, fantasies, mental pictures and other internalized "brain work." It is for this reason, as we have seen in our earlier review of the behavior of the non-human Primates, that they are apparently unable to use true symbols to any significant degree. A symbol serves as a stimulus for action, but there is no requirement that a symbol be learned as part of an existential (as distinguished from a mental) situation; it refers to a concept or set of concepts which presumably are in the first instance products of the cortex of the brain rather than of external nature or actional manipulation. Thus, you may react in a patterned manner when some one uses the vocal symbols "murder" or "rape." The fact that you react in a predictable manner to these symbols, however, does not require that you should at one time have been involved in an actual murder or an actual rape.

To conceive a thing or situation is not the same thing as to "react toward it" overtly, or to be aware of its presence. In talking *about* things we have conceptions of them, not the things themselves; and *it is the conceptions, not the things, that symbols directly "mean."* Behavior toward conceptions is what words normally evoke; this is the typical process of thinking. . . . Signs *announce* their objects . . . whereas symbols lead [one] to conceive their objects. The fact that the same item . . . may serve in either capacity, does not obliterate the cardinal distinction between the two functions it may assume.[3]

Some writers, for example Langer, have pointed out that symbolization involves two principal functions: *denotation* and *connotation.* Denotation is the association which the individual makes between the symbol and some object in the external world; connotation is the relationship developed by the user between the symbol and his conception (idea, mental picture, and so forth) of the object. Thus, if some one uses the verbal symbol "Jim Smith" in your hearing, the words denote a certain individual and also connote the idea which you have of him or the idea which is associated with the sounds "Jim Smith." Therefore, symbols may be said to have a two-way reference, one to the outer world of action or objects, the other to the inner world of mental activity. It is for this reason that in an earlier section we spoke of representational activity as serving as a link between action and artifacts, on the one hand, and mental activity on the other hand.

Cultural signs and symbols. Strictly private or idiosyncratic signs and symbols may, of course, be developed by individuals. In our own society certain persons possess sets of signs and symbols peculiar to themselves which they use for recalling names of new acquaintances or for remembering errands to be done during the day, for example. A cultural symbol, on the other hand, must, like any other cultural element or artifact, be shared and understood by at least two or more members of a social group. Observation, of course, shows us that all societies have developed social symbols, patterned them, and made them part of their culture. These are the parts of culture which we have called the Representational Patterns. Indeed, a culture without such patterns is a contradiction in terms.

Although natural signs do not owe their meanings to culturally arranged conditions, all artificial signs and symbols derive their functional importance from man-made conditions and from conventional social agreement among their users. All cultural signs and symbols are, like all other cultural items, in the broadest sense inventions rather than discoveries. One may say that the association between smoke and fire is something which men have discovered in nature. But there is nothing in nature untouched by culture which demands that existential fire be denoted by a vocalism which we pronounce as "fire." The association which English-speaking people have between a certain class of combustion and this particular sound is purely arbitrary and the meaning attached, as we say, to the sound is entirely conventional. An examination of the vocabularies of other languages will show that a very wide variety of other vocalisms are used in various parts of the world to refer to actual fire. We can trace historically the process whereby this and certain other words came into our vocabulary and how they came to assume certain symbolic functions, but we are forced to admit that the symbolic function itself depends upon the conventional agreement and similar training among the members of our society. The meaning of all types of signs and symbols must be learned by human beings, but in the case of cultural signs and symbols, it is impossible to learn the conventional associations except in social situations.

Although the sounds of speech are the most widely used of all human cultural symbols, it is obvious that other types of human behavior and their products may likewise serve symbolic functions. The expression of the face, the tone of voice, the posture of the body, or the performance of a customary pattern may all indicate, to the initiated, the state of mind, attitude, intentions, or thoughts of the performers. Many a custom, which serves a utilitarian or objective goal, may also serve a representational or symbolic purpose, either by its very performance, by its omission, or by the "manner" of its performance. Suppose you are arriving at an airport some distance outside of the town you are visiting. Some kind of a custom has to be performed which has the utilitarian function of transporting you into town where you can make contact with your host. Although physically you will be about equally well off in any case, it "makes a difference" as to how this matter is handled. Does your host meet you personally? Does he send a servant? Does he leave you to fend for yourself in a taxi? And so on. The particular choice of pattern has a symbolic significance, likewise the manner of its performance. International diplomacy often seems to rely primarily upon non-verbal symbols of this sort. The United States sends the body of the Turkish ambassador back home on its largest battleship, which seems to be a way of symbolizing that we are interested in maintaining the status quo of the Dardanelles. A diplomat fails to attend a tea party given by the Secretary of State, thereby indicating his government's displeasure over recent negotiations.

Finally, many symbolic patterns can be reduced to material form through the employment of artifacts. A system of artifacts (and the customs for producing them) which reduce verbal behavior to material form we call *writing*, and, as we have seen, there still exist not a few societies which have not achieved this level of symbolism. Nevertheless, there are certainly no current human societies which do not use some type of material objects in a symbolic way. It must be plainly understood that the physical form of the symbolic object or artifact in itself is of no great importance. It is the system of mental patterns associated with it that is of moment to our understanding of its cultural function. The author, for example, has seen painted images of the Holy Virgin in rural Latin American churches which would not be out of place, from the point of view of their physical appearance alone, in the Chamber of Horrors of a side-show wax museum. Yet these crude and ugly sculptures serve as the focus of attention for the performance of truly lofty and unselfish thought patterns and overt religious rites. Literally any type of physical object can be made to serve a symbolic function. Its cultural significance depends solely upon the training or social experience which the practitioners of the culture have had with respect to the object. Although the solemn symbols employed in foreign cultures frequently appear ridiculous to us, we must remember that one's sense of humor in such matters depends upon one's point of view, and one's point of view is mainly a product of one's own cultural background. Who is to say which is the funnier as a symbol of social status: the distended lips of the Ubangi women, or the millinery confections of our own ladies?

The economy of symbols. All the evidence indicates that man is the only animal which has developed the use of symbols to any significant degree, and the conclusion seems to be inescapable that this ability, together with the abilities to perform "mental" activity and to learn, accounts for the present world dominance of the human species. Certainly the development and mastery of symbols (always combined with the requisite training) results in an enormous saving of energy and effort for human beings. We may mention only two aspects. (1) Through the use of symbols a human individual may absorb a vast amount of experience during a relatively short period. In fact, if the average individual had to absorb the lessons learned by his culture, even in the most "primitive" tribes, by personal exposure to all the types of situations anticipated by the "lore" of his society, he would require several lifetimes. Lacking instincts for the solution of his problems of adjustment, the average human would probably not survive, could he not learn symbolically. By means of words, verbal descriptions, for example, of problems and situations he is likely to confront, the average individual is able to develop and to practise mentally problems of adjustment which will serve him successfully when such situations actually arise. (2) The use of material symbols is a form of "storing patterns," as it were. This is particularly obvious in those cultures that have systems of writing, but the same function is served by all types of material symbols—images, status marks in clothing and ornament, direction markers, and so on and so forth. Symbolic material artifacts save man-power and thus increase the efficiency of human living. The Barama River Caribs, to mention a very elementary example, indicate the trail to be taken at a forking by setting up a split sapling with a pointer fixed in it. This relieves an advance party of the necessity of leaving a man behind to direct the following group. The present writer, on the other hand, by living in the jungle with the Caribs for several months, was able to turn out a book which, he thinks, covers most Carib cultural patterns. A student may study this report in a few hours or days, and thus form an acquaintance with this culture which required the better part of a year and a certain amount of mild hardship on the part of the author. Thus the reader is saved the necessity of expending the time and effort required to obtain the material for the original report. But the latter would have been impossible had not our culture contained complexes involving the material artifacts of symbolism which we know as paper, typewriter, linotype machine, book-bindery, printed book, and so forth.

The neutrality of symbols. Because of the meaning they convey for us, there is always a tendency to regard the meaning of symbols as something inherent in them, as a part or quality of them. Even certain schools of philosophy were unable for centuries to rid themselves of this attitude, and it is not strange that many persons still maintain it in all societies. In fact, this tendency to see or feel power or personality or some other quality inherent in a symbol itself helps us to understand certain features of culture which will be discussed below. The image which symbolizes the saint comes to be regarded as a person in its own right. The phrase which represents a series of concepts in a ceremony is looked upon as having a magical power of its own. A social organization, such as a caste system, may be regarded as sacred in its very form, and meddling with it is discouraged even more than tampering with the concepts which it represents.

A calm study and comparison of symbols, however, will convince us that such inherent qualities as symbols possess in and of themselves have only an accidental connection, if any, with their function of conveying meanings. As Judas demonstrated, a kiss may symbolize assassination as well as brotherly love. The Holy Spirit may be symbolized as well by a makeshift altar on the field of battle as by an elaborate structure covered with gold and silver in an expensive cathedral. Any concept can be symbolized by practically any sound (word), as an examination of a series of foreign vocabularies will show.

It is not the form or content of the symbol, as a pattern of action, a material object, or a series of sound waves which holds the meaning. Anything which can be perceived and discriminated as a stimulus will serve as a symbol for any concept, provided the association has been established and mutually understood by a social group. Symbols are thus neutral conveyers of meanings.

LANGUAGE

How do we acquire language? By far the most ubiquitous type of symbol system used by human beings is spoken language. Because most normal persons beyond the age of infancy speak their "native" language rather automatically, they are often inclined to think that it is a gift of their biological inheritance, somewhat like walking or breathing. When we point out that there are thousands of languages in use throughout the world, differing among themselves in numerous details and in no way correlated with racial or other heritable features of their speakers, the average man will usually still ask if speech is not an "instinctive" human attribute.[4]

The ability to speak articulate language is, apparently, a feature in which the human species is unique. However, there are no specialized physiological organs of speech, properly so-called. The sounds of language are produced by the throat, nose, mouth, tongue, teeth, and lips and are received as air vibrations through the ear. In reviewing the Primates, we have seen that the great apes, at least, are provided with oral structures which would be quite capable of enunciation of words and that they have auditory acuity comparable to our own. Successful speech is not a matter of a specific specialized organ alone, but of a whole complex of structures the most important of which seem to be the association areas in the cortex of the brain. In short, an animal unable to use concepts is unable to speak in the human sense, because words are symbols and a language is merely a conventional method of handling verbal symbols meaningfully. Thus we come to the conclusion that language is learned by the individual, that it is socially shared by the group of speakers and is, therefore, cultural, and that it is a symbolic system.

In spite of the fact that language as such is not "instinctive" there seems to be a natural urge to vocalize in children. The almost constant babbling of the small child from babyhood onward is familiar to every one. We may regard this as trial-and-error vocal behavior, whereby the child experiments, one might say, with its vocal apparatus and puts the results to the test of experience. This random behavior, like the random trial-and-error activity exhibited by so many other parts of the child's body seems to be motivated by what we have called the "activity drive." The drive for response from others is probably also involved in certain situations, as well as other motivations, although it has been often observed that children characteristically vocalize even when alone and free from any other wants than the mere urge for activity. At all events, we know that these random vocalizations apparently do not become fixed into a symbolic system (language) except as a result of social experience. The few authentic cases on record of children who have survived the period of infancy and childhood in the company of animals, or otherwise devoid of human society, show that such children were normally able to vocalize, but had never developed articulate speech. Thus we must postulate that the members of the social group or society who normally surround a child during its period of random vocalization are a necessary factor in the development of speech in the individual. They help to select meaningful sounds from the great variety of babblings produced by the infant. Older members of the society gradually reinforce certain sounds, not only as to pronunciation, but also as to the objects and concepts which are considered their proper referents by the society in question. And by a constant application of small punishments and rewards the child's older companions establish the proper patterns of syntax and grammar, so that the words are connected together according to a scheme which makes sense to other members of the group. Therefore, a language, like any other complex of cultural patterns, must be passed on from one generation to the next through the agency of human beings.

The variety of human speech. Despite the fact that all normal human beings speak, one of the features of anthropology which has attracted interest from the earliest times is the great variety of tongues used among the various societies of mankind. Not only do vocabularies differ from language to language, but the very principles whereby the words are organized together into meaningful expressions show profound divergences in some cases. These features demonstrate the wide versatility of the human vocal potentialities and also show that no language makes complete use of the entire range of possible vocal products. Rather, a language in fact consists of a narrow selection of sounds organized into a limited number of basic patterns whereby the sounds are grouped into meaningful combinations.

Aspects of linguistic organization. Although the methods of verbal representation are enormously varied, if one makes a comparison of the world's languages, there seems to be no worth-while way of rating languages on the basis of "highness" or "lowness" or usefulness. Earlier allegations that certain primitive tribes had vocabularies of only a few dozen words and forms of expression "scarcely above those of the animals" have been shown to have been derived from inadequate and hasty observations by travelers and explorers who did not have or did not take the opportunity to study the languages in question. On the basis of modern studies we know that there is no society which lacks the linguistic facilities to express adequately all the concepts which come within the ken of its culture. When we say, "express adequately," we mean to add "for social purposes," since there is always some question as to whether or not any type of symbolization represents completely certain types of mental activity. But every people is able to talk intelligently about its own culture. Seeming deficiencies in another language, from our point of view, are often reflections of the fact that that culture lacks traits with which we are familiar. For example, inland Arabic is said to possess no words for the various parts and attributes of an automobile, of which there are several thousand in use in English. But Arabic has about 6,000 names for "camel" and its peculiar characteristics.[5] The study of a vocabulary of a language therefore provides a fair clue to the content of the culture, and also certain hints as to its past relationships with other cultures and other regions, provided one takes into account loan words and borrowed expressions. So far as we know, however, every language is able either by borrowing or by circumlocutions and other devices to accommodate itself to new elements of culture and new communal experiences and thus to serve as a vehicle for expression among the members of its society. The fact that languages die out and are superseded by other languages must be attributed to other factors than symbolic insufficiency: a language may disappear as a result of conquerors' prohibiting its propagation, as a result of loss of prestige, or because of the disappearance or absorption of its former speakers into some other population.

Underlying vocabulary are the morphology and syntax of a language. These, as Sapir has pointed out, represent an unconscious patterning of verbal behavior. Thus, few except special students are aware of the rules that govern the "grammar" of their native language, but study demonstrates that every language follows some such "rules." A language is truly a system for symbolizing concepts, for concepts are usually in some sense generalizations or abstractions of hundreds of individual experiences. Thus the word *boy* by itself refers not to one unique experience which the speaker has had, but to a general idea based upon a series of experiences. If the word referred to a unique personal experience, it could not serve as a symbol in social intercourse, because it is certain that the listener has never had just that particular experience or one exactly like it. What the listener has had is a series of experiences from which he has formed a concept generally similar to that of the speaker and which is associated with the vocalization, *boy*. Thus language would be impossible without this human ability to form concepts. Furthermore, in the interests of convenience, each group must agree, over the course of time and usually unconsciously, on certain other limitations whereby the symbols for concepts are classified into categories and linked together in certain limited and conventionally understood ways.

To quote Sapir, "It would be impossible for any language to express every concrete idea by an independent word or radical element. The concreteness of experience is infinite; the resources of the richest language are strictly limited. It must perforce throw countless concepts under the rubric of certain basic ones, using other concrete or semi-concrete ideas as functional mediators." [6]

Simply as elementary illustrations of the general problem of linguistic pattern we may mention a few instances that contrast strongly with the patterns familiar to us in English. *Word order* in the sentence itself is, of course, one evidence of conventional patterning, and English speakers feel a certain incongruity in the German pattern of placing most verbs at the end of the sentence, for example, or in the tendency of the Romance languages to place adjectives after the nouns they modify.

Languages involve *patterns of classifying words and the concepts to which they refer*. The use of three sex genders for classifying nouns is familiar to those who have studied Latin or German. The Bantu languages of Africa, on the other hand, have seventeen to nineteen "genders", that is, categories of nouns, but no sex gender.[7] "Animate" and "inanimate" is another type of classification, used by many American Indian languages. In Haida nouns [8] are classified according to shape: "long," "round," "angular," and so on. Likewise verbs may be classified in ways which are strange to us. In Haida (spoken by certain Indians of the Northwest Coast of North America) prefixes are used to indicate whether the action denoted by the verb is accomplished by carrying, by shooting, hammering, pushing with the hands, pulling, floating, stamping or treading upon, kicking, chopping or clubbing, by means of the shoulder, with the fingers, by means of a stick, by the voice, by a stream of water pouring out, with the lips, and so forth. In Hupa [9] (an Athabascan language of California) the evidence for a statement is indicated in the form of the verb, as well as the character of the action (hypothetical, contingent, qualified and others).

The form of sentence structure and syntax also varies widely among the languages of mankind. English has lost many of the elaborate inflections found in Latin and certain other Indo-European languages, although still retaining some, as in he *does*, we *do*. Chinese, on the other hand, has no inflections whatever, and the sense of a statement depends almost entirely upon the order of the words. At the other extreme, we find languages in which a whole statement consists of one word, or more accurately, a series of vocal elements so closely linked together that no one of them can stand alone. For example, in Chinook (of the Northwest Coast), Boas gives the example of *anialot*, which may be translated as "I give him to her." This may be analysed into *a* (tense); *n*, I; *i*, him; *a*, her; *l*, to; *o* (direction away); *t*, to give. "The weakness of the component elements and their close phonetic association forbid us to consider them as independent words." [10]

Influence of linguistic forms upon thought and action. Although the matter has not been exhaustively studied, there seems to be no doubt that the categories and forms of a language influence the form of thought and world view of the people using them, once they are established. The language of the Hopi Indians of the Southwest is a case in point. Hopi verbs have three tenses, but they are not past, present, and future, as in our linguistic system; the Hopi tenses have the function of distinguishing between the *factual* (which may be either present or past), the *future*, and the *generalized;* in short, the form of the verb tells at once whether one is dealing with the report of an event, an expectation, or a generalization or law about the event. A second feature of the language which conditions thinking is that the verb forms often distinguish between a *static* and a *vibrating* action. For example, wuku'ku, "he takes a step without moving from his place," becomes wuku'kuta, "he is dancing in one place"; ho'chi, "it forms a sharp acute angle," becomes hochichita, "it is zigzag." This is consistent with the general Hopi world view that human beings and other entities have place in a vibrating or oscillating universe with definite limits. [11] As Whorf remarks, "According to the concepts of modern physics, the contrast of particle and the field of vibrations is more fundamental in the world of nature than such contrasts as space and time, or past, present, and future, which are the sort of contrasts our language imposes upon us." [12] Time, in Hopi language, is not expressed as length, but as duration, "a becoming later and later." "Summer," for instance, is not objectified as a noun, but is expressed by a sort of adverb meaning "while the summer phase is occurring." Likewise, numbers are not used as abstractions or applied to them, but only to entities which actually form an objective group and can be counted. Thus the forms of the language itself seem well fitted to express certain fundamental ideas of the Hopi view of the universe: vibration and oscillation of beings within a limited sphere; becoming and fulfilment of all things; emphasis upon groups and categories, not only of human beings, but of other things in the universe which have "real" existence. We have no way of knowing whether the forms of the language originally developed in response to these ideas or vice versa, but the fact remains that the characteristics of the language as it exists at present set characteristic patterns and limits for thinking among the Hopi.

The analysis of languages. Although many of the remoter languages of mankind have been barely studied or recorded, the linguists, who form a highly specialized brotherhood, have been able to classify and to indicate the probable relationship of the languages of the major portion of mankind at present. These studies are, of course, of value not only for the elucidation of symbolic processes and their relations to other aspects of culture; they often, also, shed much light on the historic or prehistoric relations of societies and groups of people. Thus, the fact that all the European languages (except Basque, Hungarian, Turkish, and Finnish) belong to the same family of languages as Persian and the Indic tongues is evidence for an early dispersal of the speakers of such Indo-European languages from a common center. Such a common origin would scarcely be deduced merely from a superficial analysis of the present-day cultures, which in some cases are widely divergent.

In analyzing a language we are first interested in its *phonetics*, that is, the collection of sounds used. As previously mentioned, each language fixes upon a rigidly restricted series of sounds selected from the almost infinite variety in the innate human repertory. This infinite possible variety, however, may be classified according to the organs primarily concerned in their production and the parts of the throat, mouth, and nose in which they are made. In general all human vocalizations are made either by vibrating a current of air or by stopping it temporarily in various parts of the vocal apparatus. All of these manipulations of the vocal apparatus are muscular habits which, for any given language, are learned by the speaker. In the case of one's native language the habits are learned early in life and it is often difficult for one to learn the habits required of another language, particularly if its phonetic system is considerably different: hence the "accent" of one who has not completely mastered the muscular habits of a new language.

Once one has a fair idea of the phonetics of a language, the next subject of importance is the *phonemic system*. A phoneme is an elementary sound pattern, the smallest element of a language, which cannot be further broken down without destroying its function in the system. The two *i* sounds in *lip* and *leap*, for example are two separate phonemes of English. The *l* sound in both words is the same phoneme, and the *p* sound in both cases is the same. In the actual pronunciation of a language by its native speakers, one frequently hears variations of different types in the pronunciation given by different speakers. This is often the same sort of performance variation which we find around the pattern of any other custom, and such variation is tolerated so long as it does not transgress the conventionally recognized limits. Once the variation in performance passes out of recognized range, the symbolic quality of the phoneme is lost, that is, it either turns into some other phoneme or becomes meaningless. The phonemic system, in a word, consists of the socially recognized meaningful sound patterns of the language. And the discovery of the phonemic principle has led linguists to devote the major part of their attention to the study of these patterns rather than to a minute acoustical recording of numerous individual phonetic variations around the norm.

In comparing the vocabularies of two languages with a view to determining their possible relationship, attention must always be given to both the *sound* and the *meaning* of the words. Unless a larger than chance proportion of words agree in both phonetic structure and meaning, the chances that the two languages share a common origin or source are slight. For example, French *lame* (blade) and English *lamb* (young sheep) sound much alike, but do not agree in meaning. In comparing phonemes it is always necessary also to consider the possibility of "phonetic shifts" which often are found as we pass from one language to another of the same family or stock. A well-worn illustration is the shift from *pes, pedis* (gen., Latin), to *fuss* (modern German), to *foot* in modern English. If it is observed that a similar series of shifts occurs with fair regularity in a whole series of cognate words, one is able to work out a "phonetic law," such as the famous Grimm's law for the Indo-Germanic languages, which enables one to identify cognate words in their respective vocabularies, despite the seeming lack of resemblance in sound.

Finally, to mention one other aspect, the linguist studies the *morphology* or *structure* of the languages of the world. Various classifications of language on this basis have been made, none completely comprehensive, because many languages show features of two or more classes. For example, one scheme differentiates analytic languages, such as Chinese, from synthetic languages, such as Eskimo which unites long strings of forms into single words. Another classification divides languages into four types: *isolating*, which use no compound forms (for example Chinese); *agglutinative*, in which the various forms are "stuck on" to each other in sequence (for example, Turkish); polysynthetic (for example, Eskimo); and inflecting (for example, Latin), which indicates various aspects of meaning by changing the form of the root or basic concept word (as in "declining" nouns, for example).

Some major language families. By these studies experts have been able to identify the relationships, or lack of them, as between the major languages at present spoken in the world and to group them into large stocks or families. As work on these matters progresses, similarities appear between these stocks in some instances, so that the number of large families recognized as independent is becoming smaller.

The most widespread family of languages is Indo-European which is represented by native speakers in most of Europe, parts of the Near East, India, and areas colonized by Europeans in other continents. The Western Hemisphere is, of course, predominantly Indo-European at present, although considerable numbers of people still speak native Indian languages, especially south of the United States border. Of the Indo-European languages, the most widely diffused is of course English, probably followed by Spanish. The Indo-European family includes several subfamilies: Indic, Germanic (in which subfamily English is classified), Slavic, Romance, Persian or Iranian, Armenian, Albanian, Greek, Baltic or Lithuanian, and Keltic (including, Scots, Cornish, Irish, and Breton). The second largest language family of the world is *Sinitic*, which includes the subfamilies of Chinese, Tibeto-Burman, Thai or Shan-Siamese, and Lolo. The *Ural-Altaic* stock covers a good share of Northern and Central Asia, including such branches as Mongolian, Tungus-Manchu, Turkish, Finnish, and Magyar. The latter three languages represent the only penetration of representatives of this stock into continental Europe. *Samoyed* is confined for the most part to tribal peoples of North Central Asia. Another great stock is *Semitic-Hamitic* with four branches: Semitic, Egyptian, Berber, and Cushite. The present-day Semitic languages include Hebrew, Aramaic (isolated groups in the Near East), Arabic and Ethiopian (including Tigre, Tigriña, and Amharic). In antiquity the Semitic branch included Babylonian-Assyrian, Canaanite, Moabite, and Phoenician. Egyptian died out, to be replaced by Arabic in the seventeenth century, although one language of the Egyptian branch—Coptic—survives in the liturgy of certain Ethiopian Christians. Berber is spoken at present by descendants of the native inhabitants of North Africa and the Sahara, although it has been supplanted in parts of these regions by the Arabic of later invaders. The Cushite branch is found to the south of Egypt, and includes a number of languages, such as Somali and Galla.

South of the Sahara a broad belt of grassland extends across most of Africa, inhabited by speakers of a number of languages not yet fully known. These are sometimes grouped together as the *Sudanese* stock, including Wolof and Ful in Senegal, Yoruba and Ewe on the Guinea coast, Haussa in the central Sudan, Nuba, Dinka, and Masai in the Anglo-Egyptian Sudan and southward into Kenya. South of this group the rest of Africa is occupied by speakers of the *Bantu* family, with the exception of a relatively small southwestern section occupied by speakers of two independent stocks: *Hottentot* and *Bushman*. The former enjoys a certain fame because among its regular phonemes are a series of clicks, somewhat like we use for "clucking" to horses.

As previously mentioned, *Basque* remains an isolated language now spoken in the Pyrenees mountain region on both sides of the Franco-Spanish frontier facing the Bay of Biscay. It is thought to represent a remnant of the languages spoken in Europe before the spread of Indo-European over that continent.

Turning to Asia we find the following families among a number of other languages not yet definitely classified: *Hyperborean* or *Palae-Asiatic* (including Chukchi, Koryak, and Kamchadal) of Northeast Asia; *Ainu*, belonging to the aborigines of Japan, now living mostly in the northern islands; *Japanese;* and *Korean*. In the Caucasus region, two families are usually recognized, *North Caucasian* and *South Caucasian*. Among the languages of the latter family is Georgian, said to have been the native tongue of Premier Stalin of Russia.

In the south of India, as distinct from large regions of the north which are Indo-European, we find the *Dravidian* family with at least sixty million speakers at present. This was probably the dominant language group of all India previous to the invasions by Indo-European and Iranian speakers. *Munda* languages are spoken by three or four million people, mainly forest-dwelling primitive tribes of the hills around Chota Nagpur in Central India and on the southern slope of the Himalayas. Another important linguistic stock of Southern Asia is *Mon-Khmer;* the most important of its languages is Annamite. Some experts see similarities between Munda, Mon-Khmer, and the Malayo-Polynesian family and have united all three into the so-called *Austric family*. More study will be required to "prove" this relationship.

Malayo-Polynesian speakers cover the islands of the Pacific, important regions of Malaya and Indonesia, and Madagascar. This family consists of four branches: Malayan or Indonesian, spoken in Formosa, the Philippines, Java, Bali, and Madagascar; Melanesian; Micronesian; and Polynesian. Other families of the Pacific are not definitely studied: usually designated as families are *Papuan*, spoken in New Guinea and adjacent islands, and *Australian*.

Among the native languages of the Western Hemisphere we find more stocks or families than in the rest of the world together. Some conservative scholars see as many as 150 stocks, with several thousand dialects and languages, among the Indians of the Western world. This high number may be in part due to the fact that many of the languages, particularly in South America, have not been thoroughly studied, but it is certain that our part of the world saw a great proliferation of native languages in pre-European days. In North America the most important aboriginal language families are: *Eskimoan, Athabascan, Algonkian, Iroquoian, Muskogean, Siouan, Mayan,* and *Uto-Aztecan.* In South America the best known stocks are: *Chibchan, Quechua, Aymara, Araucanian, Arawak, Carib, Tupi.* In North America the aboriginal languages having the largest numbers of current native speakers are Eskimo and Navaho (belonging to the Athabascan family). In South America some six million persons speak Quechua as a native language, and in Latin America as a whole it is estimated that twelve to thirteen million persons still use one or other of the native tongues as their primary language.

WRITING

Although all cultures contain elaborate complexes of symbolic patterns which we call language, relatively few have developed patterns for reducing language to material form, that is, to writing. Writing of any kind developed relatively late and only in certain cultures: all originally invented systems more complex than picture writing seem to have developed in cultures of post-Neolithic status. Also, it is only in a few of the most modern societies that the patterns can be said to be universal to the culture, that is, practised by anything approaching 100 per cent of the population. This is in part because of the fact that writing consists of a whole set of patterns and equipment which, from the point of view of behavioristic response, has nothing to do with language itself. Thus, while the performance of oral language patterns requires the learning of a series of responses involving muscles of the throat and mouth, the learning of writing patterns involves the mastering of a series of coördinated habits involving the hands and arms. Likewise the ear is involved in the reception of language stimuli, whereas the eye is the organ of reception for writing. Consequently the patterns of literacy require special training and equipment as well as considerable time for their mastery, with the result that in societies lacking universally available institutions of education specialized for such teaching, the customs of literacy have remained a speciality of a small class rather than being diffused throughout the population.

Writing of whatever kind is, of course, merely a conventionalized and socially understood system of reducing speech, and consequently the referents which it represents, to material form which can be interpreted through the eye. The "material form" consists of a set of symbols. The advantages which this technique confers are obvious; it provides relative permanency as well as transportability for the mental patterns expressed through speech.

All systems of writing seem to have derived ultimately from drawing. So-called *picture-writing* has developed in a number of cultures, some relatively simple when viewed as a whole. The "winter counts" of certain Plains Indians, for example, were painted on buffalo skins and consisted of a series of pictures arranged in a series portraying the outstanding event of each year, and thus constituting a sort of history. Such methods of representation, of course, do not attempt a fixed relation between the forms of speech and the material symbols used. And they suffer from the further disadvantage that many words and ideas are not amenable to pictorial representation.

The actual symbolization of language itself seems to have begun with the writing of whole words, rather than syllables or phonemes, and several important writing systems still use this method. It is called *word-writing* or *logographic* writing (sometimes mistakenly termed "ideographic"). The Chinese system is the best-known example of this type in modern times. Basically, such a system consists of a series of characters, each one of which represents a word. In any case, it is relatively uneconomical, since it requires the memorization of a large number of symbols or signs. In case these are realistic drawings, a word-writing system is frequently unable to represent words referring to abstract ideas, relationships, attitudes, and so forth, but such words can be represented by means of purely conventional characters, of course. A certain economy may be obtained by the development of *rebus-writing* which was achieved, for example, by the Aztecs of Mexico. This is based on the principle of the school-boy game in which a word like Milwaukee, for instance, is represented by pictures of a mill, a sidewalk, and a door key placed in line. In a sense this is a step toward phonetic rendering; it enables one to get along with a reduced number of characters, and affords the possibility of being able to represent abstract words, provided the latter can be analyzed into syllables or other elements which are picturable. Also certain relations and qualities may be indicated by using diacritical marks or "classifiers" in connection with the word symbols. Although very clumsy and difficult to learn, a word-writing system has the advantage of not being tied to the phonetics of any particular language. Thus, although the Chinese speak a variety of mutually unintelligible languages and dialects, the same system of writing serves for all, and it has in part even been taken over to represent Japanese, a language of an entirely different family.

From the rebus type of writing some systems developed *syllabic writing* in which each character represents a syllable instead of a whole word. Ancient Babylonian cuneiform writing, for example, had reached this stage, although it continued to use logographs as well. In modern Japan two sets of syllabic characters are used to supplement the logographic characters derived from China.

True *phonetic writing* involves the development of symbols which represent, not whole words or syllables, but phonemes, even though crudely and imperfectly. Such a set of symbols is called an alphabet (from the first two letters of the Greek system, *alpha*, *beta*). All systems of alphabetic writing now in use seem to have derived ultimately from Semitic alphabets invented during the latter years of the second millennium B.C., apparently in or around the Sinai peninsula and North Arabian desert region. The earliest Semitic alphabets had signs only for consonant sounds, the vowels being inferred from the context or conformation of the word. The Egyptians had made some steps in this direction in later times, and the Asiatic Semites were undoubtedly influenced by Egyptian and Mesopotamian systems. The Phoenicians took over and modified the early Semitic system and carried it to various parts of the Mediterranean, notably to Greece. The Greeks modified some of the Semitic consonantal symbols and made them serve the purpose of representing vowel sounds. The Roman alphabet was borrowed from that of the Greeks, with some modifications, and from Rome the system was taken into Central and Western Europe with still further changes, including the development of capital letters and decorative forms, such as Gothic. The Slavs, on the other hand, borrowed their alphabets directly from the Greeks, adding some new symbols with which the better to represent their phonemes. It is not germane to our present purpose to trace the various other diffusions of the alphabet. But we may point out in passing, that, from the original Semitic center in the Eastern Mediterranean were derived such systems of alphabetic writing as the Aramaic, quadratic Hebrew, Arabic, the Indian alphabets, Tibetan, Pali of Ceylon, Burmese, Cambodian, Siamese, Javanese, Sumatran, the Philippine types, and Korean. Nestorian Christianity served as a medium for the diffusion of other forms of the original alphabet to Persia, Turkestan, the Turks, the Mongols, and the Manchu of Northern China. Thus two great arms of alphabetic writing spread around Asia from the west, almost encircling China which, even to the present, has maintained its logographic system.

Native America never developed alphabetic writing within any of its own cultures. The writing system of the Maya civilization of Yucatan and Central America, only a relatively small part of which has been deciphered to date, seems to have been primarily logographic.

The application of an alphabetic system from a single source to many different languages of diverse phonetic structure has, of course, resulted in numerous modifications of the original forms. The tendency to take over alphabetic systems which are not completely representative of the receiving culture's sound system has also resulted in some loss of accurate phonetic representation. Every one is aware of the lack of consistency in English spelling of the sounds of the present language. In a word like *chthonic* ("earthy"), for example, the *ch* symbolizes no sound, but serves merely as a sign of borrowing from the Greek prototype.

Even though many of the alphabetic systems at present in use suffer from lack of consistency and bear the scars of historical accidents, the advantages of even a clumsy form of phonetic transcription are so great that this system of keeping records has superseded all others almost everywhere except in China and Japan.

It should be noted, by the way, that even our system retains a number of word-symbols which are not at all phonetic. The "Arabic" numerals, 1, 2, 3, and so forth, are pronounced in a variety of different ways among the various peoples who use them, but, as written symbols, are well understood across language barriers.

Other materializations of speech. We have already commented (pp. 389-390) upon the significance of printing and allied processes whereby writing may be mass-produced. The recent development in our culture of phonographic recording of various types is another approach to the problem of preserving in relatively permanent form the symbols of speech and the ideas and notions to which they refer. Recently inventors have devoted themselves to the task of perfecting devices which will transform spoken language directly into written language, without the necessary intervention of the human hand or arm—for example, a typewriter that will type out words as they are spoken into a microphone. If such a device should become widely used, it is conceivable that the custom-complexes involved in handwriting would decline even further in our culture than they have in this day of the typewriter, when educated persons are seldom able to produce an easily readable script with the pen or pencil.

OTHER CULTURAL SYMBOLS

We have seen that practically anything—either action or artifact—may do service as a cultural symbol, provided it is associated socially with a mental pattern. These mental patterns may be logically arranged ideas, fantasies, emotional attitudes, projective or imaginary mental systems, and so on. Mental experiences must be communicated by means of symbols if they are to be shared socially and thus become cultural.

Verbal language and its extensions through writing, printing, and other mechanical techniques and artifacts, is the most flexible and comprehensive type of symbolic system developed by human beings, but there is no culture which depends exclusively upon spoken language or its substitutes for symbolic communication. Despite the great range of language, there are always some aspects of mental activity which seemingly cannot be completely or adequately represented by words. Facial and bodily gestures are customary accompaniments of spoken language in many cultures for indicating emotional tone and emphasis accompanying the words, although it is true that in some cultures such gestural accompaniments are more developed than in others. Likewise, when words cannot be used at all, as among deaf-mutes or between peoples of mutually unintelligible speech, a certain range of ideas and attitudes may still be symbolized by gestures. A highly conventional system of finger and hand gestures, or "sign language," was developed by the Indians of the Western United States, whereby communication was effected between tribes from Texas to Canada and from the Missouri River to the Rocky Mountains.[13]

ART AS SYMBOLISM

In addition to such cultural complexes whose function is primarily communication in the form of words or substitutes for them, we must recognize another type of representative pattern, that embraced by *the arts*. Except in the case of literature, the arts do not use words as symbols. But they are always devoted at least in part to the representation of emotions, emotional attitudes, or feelings. In some cases, particularly in its so-called "realistic" forms, art may serve as vehicle for the representation of concrete objects, actions, and ideas concerning the world of affairs, but always with a certain emotional tinge. In the less realistic forms of art, for example, symphony music, the emotions and attitudes tend to be *suggested* rather than precisely *represented*. Yet, even a slight acquaintance with the art conventions of various cultures will convince one that the success, that is the social understanding, of an art style depends upon conventional agreement among the members of society regarding the meaning of the symbols involved. There are few persons trained in our own tradition who "feel a message" or "see beauty" in the grotesque, agorophobic bas-reliefs which characterize the major part of Mayan stone carving, or in the contortionistic depictions of eight-armed goddesses and bull-headed gods often seen in Hindu sculpture. Yet we know that these, to us strange, forms carried their symbolic loads to the people of their culture as well as, if not perhaps better, than our art does to us.

It is even doubtful that "beauty" itself can be given an absolute, culture-free definition. Beauty· is so many things in so many different cultures. However, there are certain technical devices which seem to have fundamental power in arousing the feelings which are an essential part of all art appreciation. These "tricks of the trade" are used in hundreds of different ways, depending upon the medium and upon the cultural tradition or style, but they appear universally in art complexes. We refer to the use of *rhythm, symmetry, balance*, and *delimitation* or *artistic unity*. These are often called the general formal principles or the canons of form, and we may see their applications in even the most "primitive" art forms. The techniques of application and the elaborations thereon in any given culture determine the *style* or styles current in that particular culture.

Without continuing a further discussion of art as a symbolic system at this point, we should add that the ideas, emotions, and attitudes represented in a culture's arts always are, at least in part, closely associated with the *values* of the society, which are also to be regarded as deep-lying aspects of the culture in question.

THE GENERAL SYMBOLIC FUNCTIONS OF OVERT CUSTOMS AND OF ARTIFACTS

All overt or behavioral customs and the artifacts associated with them may be viewed in a double aspect: (1) from the point of view of their utilitarian functions in the actual cultural or social situation, and (2) from the point of view of their symbolic functions. In the representational type of customs and associated artifacts, which we have just been discussing, the symbolic function is the more prominent and in some cases the utilitarian function is almost indiscernible. Speech and music for example are almost incapable of directly modifying a situation except through their symbolic effects; although a shout or a blast from a trumpet may rattle the windows by its very physical force, this in itself seldom has any significant effect upon the situation. In so-called decorative art, on the other hand, the utilitarian function is fairly well balanced with the symbolic: an artistically moulded water jar, for example, not only conveys a more pleasing emotion, but is also easier to carry water in, because of its fine balance, a fact which is appreciated on both counts in many simpler cultures. Modern "functional" architecture and industrial design are explicit attempts to unite the two functions of artistic communication and utilitarian efficiency in action and product.

If we turn to other customs and artifacts that are usually not thought of as representational in any sense, we usually discover after intimate acquaintance with the culture that they, too, carry a symbolic load and "mean something" to the members of the society who practise them or are familiar with them. When a surgeon starts getting out a certain set of instruments, a good nurse does not need to be told in so many words to prepare for an abdominal operation. The college freshman who grabs his fork in a certain way and talks with his mouth full is immediately identified by his dining-hall mates as from the lower classes. Among the Caribs of British Guiana, if you see a man building a little conical house of palm leaves, you surmise at once that some member of his family is ill and will receive a curing session in the structure from a medicine man. The experienced observer can often tell from the way a man walks down the street whether he is a cowboy or a sailor. Tools of the trade, costume, and customary actions enable us to "place" individuals constantly, even when special symbolic forms are not present, such as badges or other status marks, spoken words, signs, and so on. And the "placing" or identification of an individual or even of a custom or artifact means something to us, if we are familiar with the culture. One may see a yoke of oxen pulling a plow, and say to himself, "The farmers in this region must be backward." One sees people on the street of a town he is passing through attired in clothing of a certain style and quality and concludes, "This town must be fairly well-to-do and prosperous." One may drink a cup of tea and call to mind the coolies who work on the plantations of Ceylon and all the middlemen between there and here; the quality of the steak in the restaurant is a symbol of the current operations of the livestock market; the way the brick-layers work down the street may reflect the current condition of the labor market and its organization.

After an outsider has learned the interrelations of the various elements of a culture and their implications, he may "read" the culture and appreciate the significance of actions and artifacts which previously made no sense to him. Many of the meanings which are thus interwoven with the utilitarian aspect of the culture are not customarily put into words by the practitioners themselves, or it often happens that verbal representations are inaccurate if taken at face value. It is for this reason that a scientific understanding of a cultural system cannot usually be obtained by the interview method alone, but must be supplemented by direct observation, and a certain amount of participation on the part of the investigator in order to get a feeling for the implications which the participants themselves perceive. To take an example from among cultures foreign to our own, Margaret Mead is able to state in her report on the Arapesh (of Northern New Guinea) that "the fundamental premises of Arapesh culture are organized on an affective [emotional] rather than upon a cognitive [intellectual] basis. Two things are associated, or stand together ... not because of some logical connection, but because both are symbols of the same emotional attitude." [14] It is quite clear that this symbolic theme which runs through the culture of the Arapesh was not stated explicitly to Dr. Mead by the natives, because the statement is preceded by some fourteen pages explaining the variety of techniques she used for coming to an understanding of the culture, and the bulk of the monograph (of which the work under reference is only the second of five parts) is devoted to a demonstration of this conclusion through an analysis of traditional activity, myth, ritual, and artifact.

Ritualization. As the symbolic function of an overt custom increases in importance, there is a tendency for a process of formalization to set in, which we may call ritualization. Such a process may have been personally experienced by some readers in connection with customs current in their family or group having to do with "table manners" and other matters of etiquette. The conveying of food to the mouth and associated activities at table may be predominately utilitarian in function and, in fact, is just that in many lower-class groups. But as one aspires to rise in the social scale it is made plain that such seemingly mundane acts may have symbolic significance, so that increasing attention is given to the *form* in which the practical object of feeding oneself is accomplished. "Good table manners" thus become a symbol of social status, of "breeding," and of "refinement." In certain situations the customs of ingesting food and drink may become almost entirely symbolic, as in the forms of taking communion in certain Christian congregations.

Ritual as symbol always implies, of course, a system of mental patterns which are symbolized by the formalized customary actions and which lend "importance" and "meaning" to actions that might otherwise be of merely utilitarian significance.

The same passage from a primarily utilitarian function to a primarily symbolic function may be observed in connection with some artifacts and other *materialistic symbols*. In our tradition one needs sometimes to be reminded that the Cross was once a utilitarian artifact used for punishing criminals and that the shield was once a piece of defensive armor. Furthermore, artifacts may retain their utilitarian functions and take on a symbolic function at the same time, so that the hammer and sickle, which are still commonly used utilitarian artifacts, become the symbols of communism, or a hammer held in a muscular forearm becomes the trademark (symbol) of a company manufacturing baking soda.

Finally, we shall do no more than mention a somewhat analogous change which may affect the use of words. Vocal expressions and words, of course, never have a direct utilitarian function, but they may undergo changes in meaning (that is, their referents may change) and a certain overemphasis may be placed upon the form of the word or vocal expression so that the linguistic behavior itself becomes formalized and ritualized. In all languages there seems to be a tendency toward *metaphor*, although some languages are "richer" than others in this respect. The process consists essentially in attaching a new referent to a word or expression; it seems to satisfy the drive for new (mental) experience and also often represents an economical use of the resources of a language. Thus most persons will understand from the context the "primary" meaning of "donkey" referring to a domestic animal and the "secondary" meaning when used to refer to a human individual of certain characteristics. Both may be used informally and in ordinary conversation. In the case of some words and verbal expressions, however, the secondary meaning may come to be associated with certain fundamental values of the culture, in which case they tend to become ritualized, and care must be taken with their pronunciation and with the circumstances under which they are used. Such an expression as "The Blood of the Lamb" is now almost always used in its metaphorical sense and in ritual contexts.

Another aspect of the ritualization of language is seen in the tendency to attach special (often "sacred") meanings to archaisms or to vocalisms that are frankly unintelligible as language to the society in general. Thus the Eskimo medicine man (angakok) in his seances uses a special "language" which turns out to be a mixture of obsolete words, especially pronounced current words, and nonsense syllables. The Northern Algonkian shamans, studied by Hallowell, always use, when inside the sacred "shaking tent," not only a special variety of vocalisms, but a special, ritual tone of voice. The priest's use of Latin, which can be understood as language by few if any communicants, in the Roman Catholic mass is another instance of the ritualization of archaic language. Likewise in those Christian communions which read the Scriptures in English, the archaic verbal forms of the King James version are preferred, and the reading of the Bible in modern language, especially in church or other ritual situations, appears to the communicants as somehow disrespectful and sacrilegious.

The formalization of language is common as a means of symbolizing secular as well as religious concepts. Thus the formal greeting, "How do you do?" does not imply an inquiry into the other person's health; if the latter is the real object of inquiry another form is used. Spanish is well provided with ritual words and phrases which, when used in ceremonial context, have practically no connection with their "literal" meaning. "Distinguido" (literally, distinguished) is applied to almost any one with whom one entertains or may entertain cordial social relations, regardless of whether he has made his mark in life or not. Analogously we apply the term "Honorable" to office holders ranging from august Supreme Court justices to minor office holders of doubtful honesty.

Prayer is usually ritualized language which may be formalized either with respect to the words used or the form of the prayer as a whole, or in both respects. A good example of the emphasis on total form is found in the ceremonial invocations of the Navaho Indians of the Southwest. Gladys Reichard,[16] who has studied these rituals most intensively, tells us that, although the language used in the Navaho prayers is often richly metaphorical, little attention is paid to special vocabulary or to exotic words. In fact, the language used is much like that of everyday life, and was easily understood by Dr. Reichard at a time when she had acquired no more than a conversational mastery of the tongue. The ritual emphasis is placed upon repeating the prayer in its exact approved form without any error whatever. The people believe that an error made in repetition of a prayer is dangerous to the performer and, in some cases, to the whole community. The idea back of this demand for precision is the belief that each word exerts a compulsive effect upon the supernatural powers and that a wrong word, omission, or other deviation from the established pattern may have the effect of bringing down undesired supernatural power on the performer or his clients. We might liken it to the requirement of absolute precision in handling the switches of a high-tension electrical transmission station. The mastery of a Navaho prayer is a truly remarkable performance considering the length and the manner in which it must be learned. One of rather ordinary length analyzed by Dr. Reichard, for example, runs to 399 lines.

The Navaho must learn a prayer, not by frequent repetition of it line by line, but by hearing the whole thing, then, if there is repetition it is of the whole. Ideally not one word should be repeated out of its setting, hence correcting in the ordinary sense of the word is impossible. . . . A single mistake not only renders the prayer void, but may bring upon the one praying the wrath, instead of the blessing, of the beings implored. There is, of course, a prayer to correct such error, but if one makes a mistake in one prayer he may do so in the prayer to correct his mistake. This may involve him hopelessly in the circle of bafflement which is his symbol for combined fears or confusion of ills.[17]

Thus in ritualization, whether it be of actional customs or verbal customs, the form comes to have first importance, because the primary purpose served by the performance of the custom is the symbolization of mental patterns or states, rather than the direct or immediate effect it may have on the situation.

Semantics.[18] Perhaps even so brief a mention of various symbolic aspects of human culture as the foregoing is sufficient to indicate that men in society do not live by overt actions alone, but also by means of a more or less intricate fabric of meanings intimately interwoven throughout the whole framework of their customary lives, meanings which are symbolized in a great variety of ways.

Because of the very intricacy and, in some cases, subtlety of the symbolic function of culture, mistakes are not uncommon. This is particularly true of language, partly because it is always a relatively flexible symbolic system and partly because it is manipulated (as a set of symbols) without conscious thought by its native speakers. Thus a variety of meanings may come to be attached to a single word without the members of society coming to complete agreement regarding the referents. Let the reader attempt to determine with a group of people either the objective, ideological, or emotional referents of such words as *democracy* or *success*. He will probably find that these symbols "mean different things to different persons."

The study of meanings is called semantics. It is obvious that maladjustment of both a personal and social nature may arise from semantic difficulties. For example, neurosis and other types of mental derangement may arise when individuals associate words with mental patterns which either have no referents in the outer world or are associated with referents other than those commonly understood by society. Likewise social maladjustment may arise when certain words or linguistic expressions in common use become detached from a body of clear, commonly understood meanings. If words like *honesty* and *patriotism*, for instance, become symbols to which the major part of a society no longer responds in a predictable manner, there is danger of cultural disorganization and social confusion. Thus semantic confusion on the social level is one aspect of the larger problem of cultural inconsistency—the linguistic patterns of representation become inconsistent with mental and/or actional patterns.

Another source of semantic difficulty lies in the tendency to look upon words as "things" in themselves, containing power, personality, potentiality for action, or whatnot, rather than regarding words simply as symbols for ideas and mental states, which latter may be our concepts of the concrete or objective external world. People may thus come into conflict over what they believe to be the "inherent quality" of words and find themselves unable to solve the real problems to which the words refer. Much of the current discussion of "communism" and "fascism" seems to suffer from this type of difficulty with the result that energy is lost and misdirected which might more usefully be directed to the study and possible resolution of differences in actional custom and mental pattern which these two words originally implied.

We have no space to attempt to expound the details of semantic science in an introductory treatise of this sort, but the reader who would understand human life in culture more profoundly is advised to continue his study of meanings in human life with the aid of some of the references given in this chapter.

NOTES TO CHAPTER 21

1. Rhine, and others, 1940.
2. For orientation in the science of symbols, see Langer, 1942; Dewey, 1938.
3. Langer, 1942, p. 61. Quotation by permission of the publisher, the Harvard University Press.
4. For readable general introductions to linguistics, see Sapir, 1921; Bloomfield, 1933.
5. Thomas, 1937, pp. 68-69.
6. Sapir, 1921, p. 88. Quotation by permission of the publisher, Harcourt, Brace and Co.
7. Johnston, H. H., 1919-1922, pp. 19-20.
8. Swanton, J. R., in Boas, 1911, Vol. I.
9. Goddard, P. E., in Boas, 1911, Vol. I.
10. Boas, 1911, Vol. I, p. 29.
11. Thompson and Joseph, 1944, p. 39.
12. Whorf, 1936, p. 131.
13. Clark, 1885; Mallery, 1881.
14. Mead, 1940, p. 339.
15. Weyer, 1932; Hallowell, 1942.
16. Reichard, 1944.
17. Ibid., p. 12, quotation by permission of the author, Gladys A. Reichard.
18. Korzybski, 1933; Chase, 1938; Johnson, Wendell, 1946.

PART IV

Patterning and Coördination
of Culture

CHAPTER 22

Analysis of Cultural Patterns

IN OUR FIRST discussion of culture we pointed out that this feature of human life and adaptation may be studied on three levels, those of cultural activities, patterns, and artifacts respectively. And in subsequent discussions we have repeatedly alluded to the fact that culture is patterned. Up to this point we have been exploring the problems of culture content, that is, we have been dealing with culture primarily on the activity level, acquainting ourselves with the principles and processes whereby customs are learned and maintained by the members of a social group. It is now time to consider the principles of patterning in more detail. These principles have to do essentially with the organization of the culture content.

It is therefore necessary to have clearly in mind the distinction between two aspects of culture: the activity aspect (or level) and the patterning aspect (or level). The activity aspect involves the principles of learning and performance of customs, regardless of the abstract structure of the customs themselves. The patterning aspect, on the other hand, takes for granted that customs can be learned and performed. It has to do with the way in which customs and groups of customs are constructed and connected together. In the real world the two aspects are mutually interdependent. But it is useful to distinguish them for purposes of analysis. It is obvious that maladjustment may occur in either of the two aspects. A custom may be perfectly patterned, but never properly learned or performed. On the other hand, an inefficiently patterned custom may be perfectly learned and performed. If corrections are to be made, we must be prepared to analyze both the activity and the patterning aspects. Many well-meant schemes for improving social life fail because they are not based on fundamental principles of cultural dynamics.

In a broad general way we may distinguish two types of patterning: (1) the internal patterning of customs, and (2) the patterning of co-ordination of cultural systems. The first applies to the organization of activity within unit-customs, the second to the organization of customs one to another within the total culture.

475

THE INTERNAL PATTERNING OF CUSTOMS

Unit-customs. The basic units of any culture are the unit-custom and the goal. The unit-custom is the smallest socially shared unit of learned behavior that has function within a cultural system. By "having function" we mean that the activity involved in the unit-custom is so organized that the proper performance of the custom will achieve a goal, as defined in the culture, and that the custom in question when properly and fully performed is capable of operating in conjunction with other customs of the cultural system. It is "geared into" the cultural system, fitted to play a more or less coördinated rôle with the other customs involved. If the unit-custom is broken up it loses cultural function or significance.

Unit-customs are thus not to be confused with simple learned responses of a neuropsychological type. It is possible to distinguish minutely the reactions of various parts of the body and to describe them in terms of stimulus and drive as response units. All of us are aware that each single muscle or muscle fiber in a group of muscles is often capable of responding independently to certain types of stimuli, a fact which most of us have appreciated occasionally when one or other such muscle begins to "twitch." Glands may also react more or less independently, as we understand when one of the small glands in the lid of the eye begins to "water" excessively so that it is brought to our attention. Each one of these simple neuropsychological response units may usually be learned if it is properly reinforced.

However, the mere fact that a response is learned does not necessarily signify that it is a custom, unless it is also patterned. In general, it is one of the distinctive characteristics of culture that it possesses the tendency to connect together into adaptive, functional performance on the social level various unit responses of which the species is neuropsychologically capable. In a relatively simple custom such as brushing the teeth, for instance, a neuropsychologist could identify perhaps fifty simple response units, each of which could be isolated and described independently. At least that many individual muscles are involved in the simple act of scraping a brush back and forth across the incisor teeth, not to mention the learned (or conditioned) reactions of the salivary glands, taste buds of the tongue, and so forth, involved in the performance of the custom. Yet, without a knowledge of the pattern as a whole and its relation to other custom-patterns, our neuropsychologist's careful investigations would have little significance in terms of individual or group life in its social aspects.

Thus the unit-response is the basic unit from the neuropsychological point of view, whereas the unit-custom is the smallest unit from the point of view of cultural anthropology. This unit is frequently called a "culture trait" or "culture element" and in this chapter we must analyze its general characteristics in more detail. From what has just been said, however, it is obvious that cultural anthropology is not mere "behaviorism" or a mere translation of psychology from the individual to the social level.

Patterns. We must readily admit that a pattern, in the sense we use it here, is often an abstraction. It must be deduced from the manifest content, that is, the performance of the custom we are studying. Such a process of abstraction is common in all scientific work, and in fact is that aspect of scientific activity which renders direct empirical observations meaningful. Thus physicists are unable to observe directly the pattern of relationships between the electronic particles which compose an atom, for the lines of attraction and repulsion that make up the pattern would not be directly visible even if the atom were large enough to be examined with the naked eye. The physicists *deduce* the pattern of the atoms.

It has been previously mentioned, on the basis of the work of the Gestalt psychologists, that visual stimulus configurations, at least, may be comprehended as patterns, but it is doubtful that the pattern of a custom, as such, is always learned automatically at the same time as the content. Especially does this seem to be doubtful if the learning situation involves no clear-cut model of performance or of representation. Although there is evidence to show that a comprehension of the pattern seems to hasten learning, it appears that many customs are learned through the process of "nudging" the individual by repeated rewards and punishments toward the underlying pattern which may not be consciously comprehended as a complete organization. Thus, all language is patterned and organized behavior. Most persons, however, learn to speak their "native" language without abstracting the pattern, that is, the "grammar." It is to be presumed that the unit-customs of the language are learned bit by bit through a constant press of reward and reinforcement.

It seems to be practically certain that the practise of coördinating customs one with another can be learned—and usually is so learned—by the members of a society without learning the pattern which underlies the integration. If the patterns of integration were known to all there would presumably be no difficulties arising from cultural maladjustment, and there would be no need to study the principles of cultural anthropology, for we would know it all to start with. It is largely because of the fact that the learning of customs does not necessarily involve the learning of patterns of content and integration that we must develop internalized systems of concepts to aid us in analysis.

In summary, it appears to be true that individuals who practise culture are not necessarily aware either of the unit-responses from which their unit-customs are constructed, nor are they necessarily aware of how the customs are organized, either internally or with respect to each other.

In spite of this, patterning always seems to be everywhere present in cultural phenomena, even though unconscious or unclear to the practitioners. This is the "strain toward consistency" of which the sociologist Sumner was wont to speak. Members of a group always recognize a "right" way and a "wrong" way to perform a given custom, even though they are unable to describe it or even to demonstrate it perfectly. But the custom is usually thought of as an activity or series of activities rather than as an abstract pattern. We remember that customs are solutions to problems which the individual and the group have to face. The strain toward consistency, therefore, seems to be explained on the basis of results achieved. The well-executed custom is more rewarding than the capricious variation, so that the individual is constantly pushed toward conformity with the seemingly most successful or most approved type of performance.

For our purposes we may think of the underlying patterns as the blue-prints, plans, or specifications for the customary activities of a group. As we have said, they may be discovered in all cultures, although only in certain cultures have they been made explicit and accurate by representational techniques. In our own culture, the patterns of various actional as well as mental customs are made explicit by the development of the very representational artifacts and associated customs which we have just mentioned—namely blue-prints, plans, and written specifications. Thus in our culture the means are at hand for "planning" any type of custom scientifically, rather than relying upon trial-and-error procedures which have been followed in most societies and in many departments even of our own culture. The advantage of advance planning lies in the fact that it is capable of eliminating the punishment which is likely to be attached to some of the errors of the trial-and-error process.

General structural aspects of customs. Although one custom may differ from another in terms of content, it appears that all customs are organized according to a basic scheme. In simple terms, we may say that every custom has a *starting point*, *a course*, and an *end point*. In so far as the observer-analyst specifies these features, he is able to distinguish one custom from another on this basis as well as from the point of view of content.

These concepts are general scientific tools to aid us in analyzing customs, and to be meaningful in any particular case they must be specified. There are usually no obvious signs hung on customs saying "this is the starting point"; no bells ordinarily ring when the custom has reached its end point; there is no whirring noise to signify the course. But the anthropologist who has the concepts in mind and knows what to look for

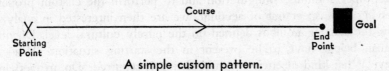

A simple custom pattern.

(the criteria) may identify the actual parts of a culture-pattern in terms of manifest signs even though they may not be so explicit to the naïve observer as those just mentioned.

The starting point of a custom is always identified and described in terms of a *starting situation*. Such a situation is characterized by all the types of components which compose the situation of the total culture and which have been mentioned in chapter 12. Also presence or absence of artifacts must be considered. But, since it occurs within the framework of a cultural system, a starting situation must also be described in terms of the presence or absence of other customs and their relation to the starting point of the custom in question.

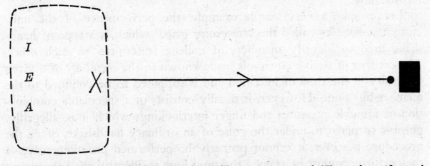

Starting situation in which interaction (I), environmental (E), and artifactual (A) elements are significant.

For the purpose of analyzing unit-customs we may reduce the principal features of starting situations to two. (1) If we are interested mainly in analyzing a custom from the point of view of learning and performance, we direct our attention to the fact that the starting situation is actually a configuration of stimulus and drive. The performer is taught to start the custom at the instant this particular configuration appears. (2) However, if we are interested primarily in analyzing a custom on the pattern level our attention is directed to the configuration presented by the presence or absence of human, environmental, artifactual, and cultural components and their relationships to the starting point. Looking at the matter from the latter point of view, we assume that the performer has already been (or can be) properly trained to recognize and respond to the proper stimulus configuration and to perform the custom properly. Leaving this aspect out of account, we are then interested in analyzing how the starting point is defined on the purely cultural level. Do other human beings have to be present in the starting situation? Who are they? What kind of environmental setting is required? Do artifacts have to be present, and what kind specifically? Are other customs present in the starting situation? How many and what are they? Which part of each custom is present: starting point, course, end point? Just where does the starting point of our custom stand among these several components? By answering these questions we are able to describe a starting situation from a strictly cultural point of view, as distinguished from the psychological point of view. If the performer of the custom misidentifies the stimulus configuration of the starting situation it is a psycho-cultural problem which presumably can be adjusted by training, or by attention to perceptive and structural defects in the performer. If, however, the starting point is wrongly placed by the pattern in the configuration of components, this is a purely cultural matter which must be corrected by repatterning.

Let us take a very simple example, the performance of the unit-custom sometimes called the "fraternity grip," which is a type of handshake used to identify members of college fraternities to each other. The *content* of such a custom is made known to the members of a given fraternity at the time of initiation and is supposed to be confined to the membership alone. However, it usually consists of a specifiable combination of knuckle pressures and finger interlockings which it is, allegedly, possible to perform under the guise of an ordinary handshake. Since the procedure is secret, it cannot properly be performed promiscuously, so the performers must be trained to know how to identify the appropriate starting point. Furthermore, this particular type of custom involves no cultural equipment, so that the definition of the starting point is somewhat simplified. We may assume that the principal *drive* involved is an acquired motivation based primarily on the drive for response, and that our fraternity man who is about to perform the custom is desirous of receiving favorable response from another member of dear old Kappa Eta Pi. An appropriate configuration of *stimuli* may involve a third party who serves as introducer. The man with whom our subject is to perform the custom presents an appearance of grooming and dress supposedly characteristic of the members of Kappa Eta Pi generally, and his features are arranged in a manner indicating friendliness and expectancy, rather than withdrawal or hostility. The introducer says to our subject, "I want you to meet Joe Burns who I understand is a member of your club at good old Siwash." It is to be noted that this introduction is a custom and that in this type of situation, the handshaking pattern is not properly started until *after* the introduction pattern has been performed. Thus we see in this very simple case that two customs are fitted together in a *time sequence*. It is also to be noted that Custom A (introduction) of this sequence serves as the cue-stimulus for the starting of Custom B (handshaking). The two alleged fraternity brothers now clasp hands and the performance of the course of Custom B begins. Any fraternity man knows that the handshaking pattern may be performed in a limited number of other types of situations, of which that described is only one, but in order to illustrate our point it is perhaps not necessary to describe these other situations in detail.

Another type of custom may involve cultural equipment in the specifications of its starting point. We may consider very briefly an example of such, the unit-custom called the "ground stroke" or "forehand drive" in the game of tennis. The content, that is, the responses involved in the proper performance of this custom, may be found in any handbook of tennis or may be learned, for a fee, from a competent tennis coach. There is one respect in addition to differences in content in which this custom varies considerably from that of handshaking, namely, that the "ground stroke" requires a number of items of equipment: a tennis ball, a racket, and an evenly level surface. This custom can of course be performed in solitude, as when a player practises his strokes against a wall or backboard, but let us consider it only in the setting of a tennis game in which two players are involved. In this case, the cultural equipment requires not only a level surface, but also that this be provided with a net, and that it be marked with lines according to the conventional specifications of the rules. For the sake of illustration we may assume that *prestige* is the drive, although in specific cases other motivations may be present.

We may take this opportunity to point out two functions which the cultural equipment plays in this type of situation. The equipment (*a*) forms part of the stimulus configuration, and (*b*) provides a necessary adjunct to the performance of the custom in question. Ground-stroking will not be appropriately performed unless the performer is present on a tennis court and it *cannot* be performed in the customary manner unless the performer is provided with objects called racket and ball, made to customary specifications. Thus the definition of the starting point involves a description of the cultural equipment involved.

As with handshaking, ground-stroking properly starts *after* the other player has performed an appropriate custom, namely hitting the ball to our side of the net and landing it within the conventional boundaries. The immediate stimulus for the start of the stroke, then, involves a ball in our court rising on the bounce to a certain height at a certain speed at

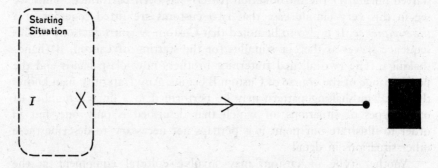

Diagram of a simple custom pattern with starting situation indicated in which interaction factor (I) is the only significant element, for example, shaking hands.

a certain distance from the net, the height of the net itself, and the position of our opponent on his side of the net. At this point performance of the pattern starts. Once again we see two customs, performed by two different individuals, linked together in a time-organized fashion. It is also obvious that the performance of this type of custom is dependent upon many other customs than that performed by the opposing player immediately before the start of ground-stroking by us. The material equipment is the result or *product* of a considerable variety of customary performances. Since most tennis players in our country do not themselves construct their courts, balls, nets, and rackets, it is obvious that the performance of a single unit-custom in a tennis game involves custom performances by quite a number of other persons, often specialists.

Our example of ground-stroking also illustrates the point previously made that a unit-custom is not necessarily merely a single stimulus-response unit translated to the social level. All who have learned this custom know that ground-stroking involves a great many muscle groups and their responses, which control the position of the feet, flexure of the legs, balance of the trunk, positions of right and left arms, grip of the fingers on the racket handle, and so on. These unit-responses may be recombined into other customs. But they must *all* be present in the performance of ground-stroking and the total combination constitutes a functional unit in the game of tennis.

There is also a type of custom which is organized to start in the absence of other customs, other persons, or cultural equipment. For example, the custom of picking fruit by hand may appropriately start when the stimulus configuration includes fruit in the appropriate state of

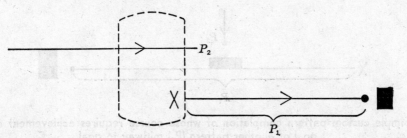

Starting situation of a simple custom pattern (P_1) which includes course of another pattern (P_2); e.g., voice solo starts after piano accompaniment is in course.

ripeness. The starting point is defined in terms of certain criteria of ripeness, and the practitioners of the custom are trained to discriminate situations in which these stimuli appear. No cultural equipment and no performance of other customs necessarily enter into the definition of the starting point.

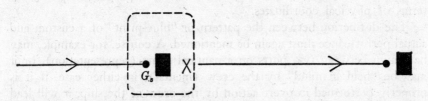

Starting situation in which achieved performance or goal (G_s) of preceding pattern is required.

Thus the starting point of a custom always involves a situation which is conventionally understood by fully trained members of the group to whom the custom is common. And the analyst must always specify this situation in terms of the criteria mentioned at the beginning of this section.

The course of a custom consists of a succession of patterned or projected events leading to the end point of the pattern. Thus each course may be said to have *direction*. In customs which involve a series of spatial changes in position, this feature may be fairly readily appreciated. The ground-stroking custom, for example, begins with the racket held at arm's length behind the body at about the height of the shoulder and continues through a series of coördinated movements involving various parts of the player's body until contact is made between the racket and the ball and then continues to the end of the "follow through," the purpose of which is apparently to leave the organism in a balanced position for the starting point of the next unit-custom it may be expected

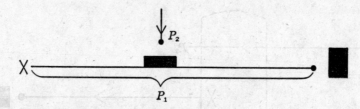

Simple custom pattern completion of whose course requires achievement of goal of another pattern (P₂) midway to goal.

to perform in the game. The problem of direction of pattern cannot be fully comprehended without a consideration of goals, which we shall discuss shortly. It is to be understood, however, that direction is not necessarily bound to the framework of physical space; it is direction within a system of culture with which we are concerned. Thus a representational custom, like a spoken sentence, may be "directed to the point," or not. A thought may be "a step toward" the solution of a problem, or not. In neither case, however, is the direction properly expressed in terms of physical coördinates.

The distinction between the pattern or "blue-print" of a custom and actual performance must again be mentioned. A course, for example, may be drawn between two ports on a nautical chart (representation), or it may be "held in mind" by the crew (mental); in either case, if it is properly performed in overt action by the crew of the ship, it will lead them to the distant port. But if, for one reason or another, the crew of specific ship A does not actually navigate this course, the patterning of the custom is not necessarily invalidated thereby.

A custom may be specified with respect to the *time* measurement of its course: thus one course may be slow, another fast (or, long or short, respectively in terms of elapsed time). It may also be described in terms of the presence and function, or the absence, of other cultural elements. A unit-pattern may require the presence of the end point of another unit-pattern along its course. There is a customary maneuver in parlor magic, for example, which involves a smooth sweep of the arm from overhead to a position in front of the body. Midway in the pattern, however, it is necessary for an assistant to slip a card into the hand as it passes downward. If the end point of the assistant's pattern does not touch the course of the magician's pattern at the proper point in its course, the magician's pattern misses its goal (exhibition of a supposedly missing card). Likewise a certain point in the course may serve as the starting point of a second custom-unit whose performance is necessary to the achievement of the goal of the first unit. For example, in our system of introducing men and women, the lady first raises her hand. At a certain point in her performance the man should begin the performance of his unit, namely raising his hand to meet hers. But he may be punished if he starts his pattern before the lady's pattern has reached a conventional

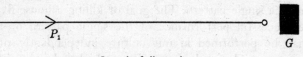

P_1 G

Simple full goal.

point in its course. Finally, a course may be so patterned that one or more other courses must run parallel to it; that is, the course lacks cultural function if it stands alone. For example, there are few musical compositions written as solos for the tuba; the course of any unit-pattern performed on the tuba most frequently must be accompanied by a concurrent course performed on at least one other instrument, if the tuba pattern is to achieve its goal (recognition, applause, and so forth).

The end point of a custom is the point in the course (*a*) at which no further activities are projected in the pattern. From the patterning point of view an end point should (*b*) be contingent to a specific *goal*.

In the handshaking pattern previously discussed, after the specified series of knuckle-twists have been performed, the custom is finished—it has reached its end point. This does not necessarily mean that the goal has been achieved. Let us say that the goal is favorable recognition of the performer as a bona fide member of Kappa Eta Pi. Suppose, however, that our man performs the custom incorrectly and does not receive the answering "grip" from his new acquaintance. Even if it is performed correctly the new acquaintance may not accord the recognition, friendliness, and intimacy desired. In any such case the pattern is performed (incorrectly or correctly) but the goal is not achieved. It is for this reason that we do not consider goals to be parts or attributes of unit-patterns. Nevertheless, if the custom is correctly patterned, it should lead to the goal if correctly performed.

Goals. Every unit-custom is designed, one might say, to reach a specific goal. But what do we mean by goals?

Goals may be classified as *simple* (achievable by performance of single pattern) and *compound* (fully achievable only by performance of two or more patterns); we may also classify goals as *full goals* (goal situation does not serve as patterned starting situation for following customs) and *subgoals* (achievement of subgoal serves as starting point for following pattern leading toward full goal). From these variations in function we derive the following basic types of goals: (1) simple full goals, (2) compound full goals, (3) simple subgoals, and (4) compound subgoals. Let us illustrate.

A *simple full goal* may stand either at the end of a single pattern or at the end of a pattern-sequence (which will be discussed below). Its distinguishing feature is that it is achieved upon the attainment of the end point of a single pattern. The goal of killing a house fly is achieved upon the successful performance of the single pattern of fly-swatting, which may be performed in our culture independently of any other custom-sequence. The goal of shooting a chicken hawk with a shotgun is supported by the single custom of pulling the trigger of the gun. However, this pattern is the final pattern in a sequence of patterns which includes loading gun, sighting gun, pulling trigger. In neither of these two examples is any subsequent pattern expected to start after the achievement of the goal. It is true that, having killed the fly, one may brush it off the table, and, having killed the hawk, one may pick up the carcass and carry it away, but in the overall pattern of the culture neither of these customs is linked in a necessary fashion to the goal. Goals of this sort which are not patterned to "touch off" or to "set the stage" for following patterns we call full goals.

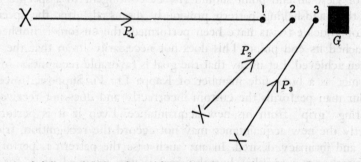

Compound full goal (G) achievable only after end points of three patterns (P₁, P₂, P₃) have been reached in ordered sequence.

Compound full goals are achievable only upon the attainment of the end points of two or more customs patterns. Again they are of two general types: (*a*) the goal may be supported by the simultaneous attainment of several end points, or (*b*) by several end points whose attainment is not necessarily simultaneous. The latter type of case is not to be confused with a pattern-sequence, which is discussed below. The first type is illustrated in the proper performance of symphony music. The goal of applause is achieved only if all players play their respective closing notes simultaneously; if the oboist intones his final note one beat too late, he may be said to have reached the end point of his particular pattern, but to have missed the goal badly. The other type of compound full goal allows some leeway in the timing of its supporting customs. For example, in our pattern of nominating office-holders by petition, it may be that 10,000 names are required, that is, 10,000 performances have to be made to achieve the goal, but until the 10,000th signing is finished the other 9,999 achieve nothing. Yet, the 10,000 performances cannot be made simultaneously, and a period of time is usually allowed for them.

Simple subgoals are those which are supported by single custom-patterns, but whose attainment merely serves to set up the starting situation for the start of one or more following patterns leading eventually toward a full goal. A loaded gun is one of several subgoals to the major goal of killing the game, and it is achieved by the performance of a single custom. Likewise a kissed baby is one of the goals subsidiary to being elected to Congress, whereas a kissed "date" is one of the subgoals to the full goal of getting married.

Compound subgoals require for their achievement the performance of a number of supporting customs, but are in turn followed by other customs in the overall patterning. In amphibious warfare, for instance, the "softening up" bombardment prior to landing troops involves the performance of a variety of patterns, including bombardment by aircraft, shelling by offshore naval craft, and perhaps a rocket barrage from landing craft. Once the subgoal has been achieved (the beach is "softened up," that is, the enemy is unable to make effective resistance in the immediate area of the bombardment), the total operation is still a long way, perhaps, from the final goal of conquest of the island which is being attacked. This particular subgoal is followed by the patterns involved in landing operations; once the beach is secured (another subgoal), another set of patterns comes into play, involving advance inland, and so on, until the pattern is followed through (in successful cases) to the full goal of conquest or control.

FUNCTIONAL TYPES OF PATTERNS

Just as goals may be classified into functional types in terms of the number and arrangement of patterns required for their achievement, unit-patterns themselves are of several types, depending upon complexity and ordering, that is, their functional positions in relation to other elements of a system. It is to be understood that unit-patterning may apply to each of our three types of customary activity—actional, representational, and symbolic.

Independent custom-patterns have been sufficiently well described. Each may be analyzed into starting point, course, and end point. But an independent custom-pattern is not involved in any high order patterning whereby it is functionally connected or coördinated with another custom-pattern. It leads directly to a simple full goal.

Sequential custom-patterns. This type occurs in pattern sequences, and its functional effectiveness depends upon its position in a sequence which consists of a series of patterns. Some patterns in such a train or sequence have no function independently; for example, loading powder bags into the breech of a 16-inch naval gun happens to be a custom-pattern which does not occur in any other sequence than that concerned with operating major naval ordnance. On the other hand another custom-unit, such as screwing a bolt on a nut, may be patterned to have a definite position in hundreds of different mechanical pattern-sequences.

Complementary custom-patterns. Another type of custom fits into an organization of cultural elements, but in a manner different from that of the custom-patterns involved in a pattern sequence. In the latter type the train consists of a sequence of custom-patterns linked together by subgoals. In the complementary type of pattern, on the other hand, the goal is not achievable by the completion of the single pattern alone. These are the types of patterns whose end-points support compound goals,

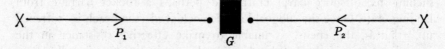

Goal supported by two complementary or reciprocal patterns (P_1 and P_2).

either of the full or subordinate variety. In the fraternity handshaking pattern, for example, the goal of the first performance is not achieved unless succeeded by the complementary pattern ("returning the grip") practised by the other party. In the process of laying railroads, a unit-pattern consists in lifting the rail by means of large tongs. One man, however, cannot achieve the goal alone; he must be assisted by a certain number of other men, all performing similar patterns concurrently, all directed toward the same goal. In football the goal of a given play is to advance the ball, but each player is assigned a particular unit-custom to perform which is complementary to those assigned to the other ten men of the team. Generally speaking the goal is achieved only if all unit-customs are performed properly.

THE PATTERNING OF COÖRDINATION

Unit-customs and goals are the fundamental units of culture, but they are usually organized with other comparable elements of the same kind into a *system* of customs and goals which is more or less integrated. In discussing compound goals we have already touched upon this matter, for a compound goal is supported, not by one pattern alone, but by two or more patterns which are more or less coördinated. On a relatively low level of organization, we frequently find patterns and their respective goals linked together.

Pattern sequences. Although patterns may appear singly in a system, they frequently appear in consecutive series which we may call pattern sequences. In a pattern sequence each unit pattern leads to a subgoal, the achievement of which should be followed by the starting point of a second pattern, and so on, until the full goal, which stands at the end of the sequence, is reached. In actual performance, a given individual or

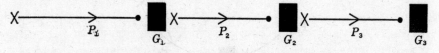

Pattern sequence with two simple subgoals (G_1 and G_2) and one simple full goal (G_3).

group may perform only one unit of such a pattern sequence, content with the satisfaction of the subgoal for one particular performance. Thus one may perform the tooth-brushing pattern by itself, reaching only the subgoal comfort resulting from removal of "film" on the teeth. On the other hand, if we are to believe the advertisements, the tooth-brushing pattern is so set up in our cultural system that, having performed it, a young lady, for example, may follow a pattern sequence of "making herself attractive," leading to a full goal of a marriage proposal.

One of the features of a culture's development seems to be increase in complexity. And one of the features of cultural complexity is the subordination of former full goals to the status of subgoals. Likewise, full goals become dependent upon an increasing number of patterns and an increasing intricacy of the ordering of their end points in relation to the full goals to which they lead. Thus, at a primitive level of culture, a unit pattern starting with the plucking of a berry from a bush may lead directly to the end point of popping the berry into the mouth and the achievement of the goal. On the cultural level of a metropolitan hotel, on the other hand, a hundred unit patterns, involving dozens of "middlemen" and batteries of cultural equipment, may intervene between the bush and the mouth. Thus a culture is "built" or developed not only by a constant addition of new unit-customs, but by linking an increasing number of unit-customs together into functional complexes.

Pattern sequences apparently show various degrees of complexity in the ordering of their patterns and may take several forms, of which the two most commonly observed are probably (*a*) the *linear pattern sequence* and (*b*) the *circular or repetitive pattern sequence*. The linear

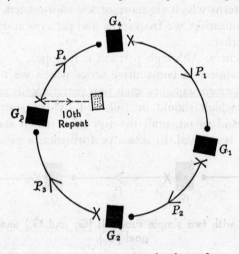

Example of a circular pattern sequence. Involved are four patterns (P$_{1-4}$) and four simple subgoals (G$_{1-4}$) which reach full goal (G) on tenth repeat of fourth pattern (P$_4$).

form of pattern sequence specifies that each pattern is to be performed only once in the series and, with proper ordering, the achievement of the full goal may be expected upon the performance of the last pattern in the series. Food preparation patterns are usually of this type. The reader may easily trace through for himself the unit-patterns and subgoals involved in "making coffee," for example, starting with the placement of the pot on the stove and ending with the full goal of having imbibed a cup of the brew.

In the circular or repetitive form, a pattern sequence consisting of, say, four unit-patterns and subgoals may have to be performed, say, ten times before reaching the full goal. It is possible to describe pattern sequences in algebraic formulae, but for present purposes it is sufficient if we have in mind the general idea. In everyday life in our society we frequently practise pattern sequences of the circular type. For example, the doctor advises you to treat a wound. The sequence may involve washing out the wound with antiseptic liquid, covering it with sulfa powder, and bandaging it. This sequence must be repeated once a day for four days. Upon completion of the fourth repetition, the bandages are removed and the full goal of a healed wound is achieved. Insurance salesmen are inured to the practice of circular or repetitive sequences, which are repeated until the prospect finally "cracks." The salesman may go through the series of procedures involved in calling at the prospect's office, getting by the secretary, presenting his sales argument, and so on, once a month for six months. On the sixth repetition the prospect finally signs on the dotted line for a $10,000 policy. Such patterns are part of the specialized culture of salesmen and the like.

Ordering of culture elements. Whenever the patterns for unit customs are linked together into a larger pattern the units must be arranged with respect to each other in some kind of order. The two outstanding criteria of order are *time* and *space*. Thus if units A and B are linked together, the overall pattern must specify whether A is to be performed before B, or vice versa, and what is the interval of time intervening, or if the two patterns are to run concurrently. Also the pattern specifies *where* the two patterns are to be performed with respect to their spatial relations with each other.

With respect to time-ordering, let us mention two types: *instantaneous* and *delayed*. In baseball, for example, pattern A (hitting grounder to infield) should be followed instantaneously by pattern B (hitter running to first base). In agriculture, on the other hand, we often find delays between patterns of a sequence. Fall ploughing (pattern A), for example, may be properly followed by spring planting (pattern B) only after an interval of six months. It is perhaps not necessary to detail numerous other examples in order to remind the reader that timing is a crucial factor in most cultural activity, and that the efficiency of many activities depends upon their being properly designed from this point of view and also that they be properly performed. We must not forget that these principles of ordering apply to mental and representational customs as well as to actional customs. The timing element is familiar enough in the question of cadence and rhythm in speaking and performing music (representational customs). It is also vital in the successful performance of mental complexes. For example, a lawyer is running over an argument "in his mind"; it is essential that he go over the premises first, then the deductions, before coming to the conclusion. Performing a mental sequence of this type in reverse order will usually result in confusion and ultimate heavy punishment.

HIGHER ORDER UNITS OF PATTERNED COÖRDINATION

We have seen some of the ways in which customs are patterned internally and how their relationships to other elements are coördinated on a relatively simple level. In considering the total culture of a given society or group we are almost always able to distinguish certain major units of culture. These are made up of unit-patterns functionally organized, and the organization involved may correspond to various levels of complexity. For convenience the various types of cultural organization may be described as follows.

Pattern sequences and compound goals. These are the simplest types of cultural organization, involving discrete elements, and have already been described.

Cultural complexes. The next larger unit of organized cultural elements is frequently described as a "complex." It involves a number of unit-patterns, subgoals, and goals organized together for a purpose which is functionally significant within the cultural system as a whole. A favorite example of anthropologists is the "horse complex" which has often been described. It will be noticed that a variety of artifacts with their associated customs are involved in this complex. Incidentally, the horse itself, a domesticated animal, is to be regarded as an artifact in this context.

Institutions. Goals, the patterns necessary for their achievement, and whole complexes may be organized into what we may call institutions. We use this term in a technical sense describing a type of cultural organization which involves cultural elements, cultural equipment, and complexes integrated about a generally recognized purpose or purposes which are understood by the members of a society. Thus, although a building, such as a banking edifice, is often spoken of as an "institution" in everyday speech, it should be clear that such a structure may be a part of the cultural equipment involved in, say, "the banking institution" in our culture.

Malinowski (1944, p. 52) has called institutions "concrete isolates of human behavior." The present definition differs from his mainly in the fact that it is exclusively cultural—we do not include the social group or groups, as such, among the attributes of an institution—what Malinowski calls the "personnel." Our position follows our general principle that culture is behavior whereas human beings and the groups into which they may be organized are the practitioners of cultural activity.

The *content* of an institution always includes all three major types of customs. (1) *Mental customs and systems* are represented by the *charter* (Malinowski's term) which is a universal aspect of institutions, and which may be thought of as a system of values to which the members of the group subscribe. The purpose or *raison d'être* of the institution is usually described or inferred in the charter, which often is a body of traditions viewed with a certain amount of awe and respect by the members of the group. Also included among the mental aspects of institutional content are the *rules and norms*, which, although they are supposed to be translated into action through their counterparts in overt customs, nevertheless are held as mental patterns by well-trained members of the group practising the institution. The rules are more specific than the charter and usually are concerned with the organization of the membership and the customary activities enjoined upon and permitted to the membership. (2) Actional customs include the overt patterned activities of the membership. In the family institution, for instance, they may be observed in the customary interactions of members of the family with each other and with non-members. (3) Representational customs may take the form of spoken representations of the mental and actional customs, respectively; they may be written and preserved in books or other documents, or they may be directed toward certain material objects, such as a cross or a wedding ring which have representative function. Most institutions include both spoken and materialistic representations, and, in literate cultures, they usually include the written type as well. They serve as symbols.

Associated with every institution is a body of *cultural equipment*, which may be used in connection with either the representational customs or the actional customs, or both. Thus in the family among ourselves, the wedding ring as an item of cultural equipment has only a representative function (representing the bond of marriage which binds the husband and wife and which is a symbolic pattern common to them both). The common dwelling of the family, on the other hand, is a piece of cultural equipment which serves primarily a utilitarian function, that is, it is associated principally with the actional customs of the membership. There is no hard and fast line between the two functions of cultural equipment—representational and actional. In the course of time a purely utilitarian item may come to have representational function. "Home, Sweet Home" refers not only to the customary activities associated with a house, but also to the mental patterns—the purposes, ideals, and values—of the family which occupies or occupied the home.

The *function* of an institution is the effect which it has in its culture and society when the institution is properly performed. The function may be patterned or it may be adventitious. For example, two major institutions may support one another, as the State and the Church in Medieval Europe, or they may conflict with each other as the Church and the State in the Soviet Union during the 1920's.

Thus every institution may be analyzed in respect to the following cultural categories:

Mental customs   Representational customs
Actional customs   Cultural equipment

The feature which distinguishes an institution from a mere congeries of customs and equipment is the fact that its constituent elements are *integrated* together to some extent and that such integration is on a relatively permanent, rather than a temporary, basis. Integration is achieved by arranging the patterns so that they support a major *institutional goal* or group of goals. The institutional goals may be made explicit in the charter, although only partially so and in some cases not at all. For example, in our own family institution one of the principal goals is the mutual sexual pleasure of the married pair, but this is seldom stated explicitly in representations of the charter, and if alluded to at all is usually disguised. Actually the goals of the family among ourselves are usually stated as the production, rearing, and training of children in socially approved ways; the provision of food, clothing, shelter, affection, and other necessities for the membership; the provision of social status for the membership and protection against attacks upon that status. A single complex may be incorporated in distinct institutions.

For example, the family in our culture includes the complex of "housework" and the complex of "child care." These complexes may also be organized into other institutions as well. "Housework," for example, has its place in the institution of hotel-keeping, and "child care" forms of a part of the institution of the orphanage, but we do not have to be social scientists to realize that, as organizations of culture, both hotel-keeping and the orphanage, are different from the family. For one thing, provision of love and affection are not among the recognized goals of these institutions.

Complexes, in short, lack the comprehensive goals which characterize institutions, the content of the complex is smaller, and the function and place of the complex in the culture as a whole is less stable and permanent. The institution, in short, is a small cultural system and it tends to have a life of its own, which may even be independent to some extent of the desires and drives of the practitioners of the institution. Institutions are known to exist in certain cultural systems consisting of goals so combined together as to produce a net result of early death for individuals, illness, and "unhappiness." The institution of commercial prostitution in certain sectors of prewar Europe seems to have been of this type. It involved not only sexual excess, but also intemperate use of drugs and drink and certain other complexes not generally conducive either to mental or physical health in the long run. In such cases, each supporting goal of the institution probably embodies the satisfaction of acquired drives, at least, yet the overall result is to satisfy only the desire for money of a small group involved. A group of goals such as drunkenness, narcotic stupefaction, and biologically excessive sexual indulgence may be expected to produce a state of affairs not desired by any of the practitioners, although each goal itself may satisfy an acquired desire. Yet the institution, once organized and operating, continues its existence regardless of its overall punishing effects. I mention this example because it illustrates the fact that an institution may link together patterns and goals which in themselves are learned and practised for their immediate satisfactions. The participants do not have to subscribe to, or even to be fully aware of, the actual ultimate results of institutional action. Thus the institution of capitalistic industry, for example, on occasion has had, among others, the effect of impairing the health of child and women workers. Yet many a participant in the institution has had no intention or even awareness that he was contributing to this effect. The bookkeeper in the front office may be a pillar of the church and interested in social welfare, without being aware that his job is linked up with many other patterns in an institution which causes adolescent boys to die an early death from silicosis. The bookkeeper follows the patterns assigned to him in order to earn the money with which he supports his family, his church, and his "welfare" activities. He does not have to be clear about the place of industry in his society and culture in order to play his rôle successfully.

Is an institution merely an arbitrary grouping of goals by the anthropologist or cultural analyst? It frequently falls to the analyst to place a label upon an institution and to assess its "meaning" in the cultural system. But an institution is "real" (that is, functionally existent) when it can be proved that the component goals, subgoals, associated patterns, and complexes are of such a type that they reinforce each other, that is, that the performance and achievement of one set renders more probable the expectation of the performance and achievement of each and every one of the other sets in the institution. Thus there is evidence which seems to indicate that in the "decadent" culture of certain categories of prewar Paris, for example, alcoholism (the achievement of drunkenness) was particularly consistent with the taking of drugs and with excessive sexual indulgence—each complex of the prostitution institution tended to support the other. On the other hand, drunkenness was ruled out of the industrial institution in France because it is inconsistent with the complexes involved in "precision manufacture," for example.

Thus the general principle which governs the integration of institutions and, in fact, all types of cultural integration, is *consistency*.

Orientations and objectives. The highest level of cultural organization we shall term the *orientation*. It is an organization of institutions plus, in some cases, uninstitutionalized cultural elements. The goal toward which an orientation is directed we term an *objective*. There is no definite number of objectives which a culture is supposed to possess, a priori, but, when they exist, they are supported by large segments of the culture. It is even conceivable that a culture have only one objective, and that the whole culture support it. There was a time when "winning the frontier" was one of the objectives of North American culture. From 1941 to 1945 "winning the war" was such. An objective is always supported by a large array of patterns, goals and subgoals, complexes, and institutions, all of which are integrated together to some degree into an orientation.

Value systems. A total cultural system is made up of elements of the types which we have just discussed. We shall consider in a later chapter certain principles of integration, but we should not fail to mention at this point that a cultural system as a whole is usually "laced together," as one might say, by a system of values. A value is the worth of a thing as compared with something else. It is obviously the result of training or experience and arises out of satisfactions associated with the thing valued. Psychologically there is no reason that a value be conscious or abstractly explicit to its holder. But in the same sense in which we consider a value system as part of a culture, it is to be regarded as a mental system—a set of ideas, often colored by emotion, which tends to unite the elements and major organized units of a cultural system in the minds of the practitioners of the culture. Certain aspects of the culture are emphasized; some are rationalized by the value system; almost all elements with which the value system deals are justified in one way or another; and a certain relatedness (in some cases actually specious) is set forth in this type of mental system.

It is to be emphasized that value systems, like all mental systems, may be either realistic or unrealistic. Furthermore, cultural values are by no means immutable. They can be changed. For example, the Japanese were represented as possessing an elaborate cultural value system built around the symbol of the Emperor who was regarded as a god. The cold fact seems to be that this system was erected in the 1860's by the architects of "modern Japan" and taught to the Japanese people. At the close of our war with Japan in 1945 the Emperor value system was only some eighty years old. It is an ironic reflection upon the cultural naïvete of policy makers in our own government that a considerable number of responsible officials of the Department of State seemed to have been convinced, or at least represented themselves as convinced, that this value system was unchangeable and immutable. At the same time, a knowledge of cultural organization was evinced by this group in their claim that, without the Emperor value system, anarchy and socio-cultural disorganization would be likely to result in Japan following the surrender. Whether old or not, the Emperor system apparently did serve to hold Japanese culture together.

It is sometimes held that value systems which exert an integrative influence in culture are inevitably of a religious or supernatural nature, as if only the belief in supernatural sanctions were sufficient to provide the starch and glue of a system of culture. It is to be admitted that such values are very effective, but an empirical examination of cultural integration in a later chapter will reveal the fact that "sacred," "religious," or "supernatural" values and value systems are not the only ones which may preserve the unity and consistency of a culture.

CHAPTER 23

Some Types of Cultural Integration

ONE OF THE most perplexing problems of social science, either from the descriptive, analytical, or "practical" point of view, is that of cultural and social integration. It is by no means difficult to conceive, in theory, of a perfectly integrated culture in which all the social entities are nicely balanced with each other and the various unit patterns, complexes, institutions, and orientations "gear into" each other smoothly and without friction or maladjustment. So far as we know, however, no such "ideal" state has ever been achieved in practice by any society, although the literature of utopianism, from Plato to the present day, has attempted to set forth—on paper—a multitude of schemes and plans whereby "perfect" integration could be achieved. Many such schemes suffer from the fact that they devote attention only to the mechanical organization of cultural patterns without giving serious thought to the psychological aspects of the learning and performance of the customs themselves. At any rate, in surveying the cultures of the world as they actually have existed or do exist, we are unable to point to any functioning culture which displays theoretically perfect integration, but we must be content to range them on a scale of relative perfection in this respect. Before turning to general principles, let us consider briefly two types showing relatively high integration.

SECULAR AUTHORITARIAN INTEGRATION

In large populations and comparatively complex cultures the nearest approaches to perfect mechanical integration of culture patterns have historically been made by authoritarian systems whereby the organization is decreed by a small group and ultimately perpetuated by force. Nazi Germany, for example, exhibited a higher degree of social and cultural integration than does the United States at the present time. The fact that our own seemingly loosely integrated system won out in the recent test of force during World War II, and the fact that the authoritarian principle is uncongenial to our set of values, should not prevent us from viewing such an attempt at organization dispassionately. Soviet Russia, apparently using a different system of mental patterns, seems to be striving toward a somewhat parallel unification and integration of its culture at the present time. Although these two cultures emphasize the secular, non-supernatural bases of authority, many essentially secular systems of authority in the past have reinforced and glossed over the fundamentally mundane source of integration by the development of patterns of belief and rationalization phrased in terms of the supernatural. All of the oriental despotisms, such as Assyria, Persia, India, and China, relied upon supernatural sanctions and rationalizations. The Inca culture of Peru was highly integrated, and the source of organization was the Emperor and the royal family, who were considered to be of divine origin. The emperor himself was supposed to be brother of the Sun, the supreme supernatural power. The European monarchies with their "divine right of kings" relied upon the same type of window-dressing. The personal adulation accorded to Hitler and Stalin, although usually phrased in strictly secular terms, is perhaps a variation of this theme.

The basic feature of such an organization of culture is the fact that in so far as the interrelation of patterns is controlled at all, it is decreed by a small secular group—a king and his advisers, a dictator and his cabinet, or similar secular oligarchy, in the interests of achieving a major orientation of the culture as this group sees it. Whatever supernatural sanctions may be used to bolster this power, the ultimate sanction is force. All such systems have been characterized by sizeable armies, police forces, spy systems, and other organisms whose principal function is the suppression of individual initiative (culturally speaking) and the enforcement of a general adherence to the cultural patterns as decreed (party line, the law, and so on).

Whether one likes such a system of cultural organization or not is frequently judged on the basis of one's attraction to the premises underlying the major cultural orientations toward which it is organized. Since we must recognize that such orientations may be entirely relative, we must postpone their consideration to a later section in which we attempt to deal with the scientific criteria of fundamental cultural values. In other words, we should not judge the success of this or that type of cultural integration solely on the basis of an evaluation of the goals or objectives toward which the authoritarian cultural system in question may be oriented. As a cultural system it is always possible that a given organization of custom may be highly efficient and well integrated, regardless of the fact that the objectives toward which it is oriented are, from any scientific or humanistic point of view, utterly reprehensible. Indeed, the seeming efficiency of some such systems has tended to obscure the distastefulness of the objectives in the minds of certain modern observers

more concerned with the mechanics of our own cultural system than
with the objectives it is supposed to achieve.

The *Inca system* of pre-conquest Peru is one of the best examples of
secular authoritarian integration which we have from non-literate
societies. Ample studies of the way in which the cultural patterns of this
society were organized exist, and in the following paragraphs we sketch
a few features of coördination in order to give the reader a passing notion
of the system. Unfortunately, the most prominent authoritarian systems
of contemporary times—the Nazi and Soviet systems—have not yet been
subjected to definitive scientific analysis.

INCAIC INTEGRATION [1]

At the time of the Spanish conquest in the first part of the sixteenth
century the empire and culture of the Incas occupied a continuous territory
stretching some 2,400 miles from the northern boundaries of present-day Ecuador to Central Chile, comprising both the coastal and highland-mountainous
areas between these limits, although the Incas were unsuccessful in penetrating
the jungle regions to the east. The fact that the territory occupied ranges
through all climatic zones from a desert sea coast to the highest mountain
peaks in the western hemisphere and the fact that the area was originally occupied by many tribes of somewhat diverse cultures and antecedents renders
all the more remarkable the organizing and integrating results achieved by the
Inca culture. In fact, it was not until the fifteenth century that large-scale
and permanent expansion and coördination of the Inca territory was begun,
and some of the outlying portions of the empire, for example North Ecuador,
were not incorporated until fifty or sixty years before the coming of the
Spaniards. The language of the empire was Quechua. However, the absorptive
power of the Inca system was so great that even these lately conquered regions
became thoroughly Incaized both in language and custom, and for the most
part remain so to this day after more than four centuries of European domi-
nation.

This system can perhaps be characterized in a word as an imperialistic
socialism. We shall not attempt to describe all details of the culture, but shall
endeavor merely to mention a few features which seem to have played a
significant part in cultural integration.

Inca technology rested on a horticultural base, and the principal interest
of the common man as well as one of the major objectives of the culture as
a whole was the welfare of the crops.

A wide variety of plants were domesticated in the region, but the only
truly domesticated animals of economic importance (dogs, llamas, alpacas,
guinea pigs) were not used for traction, with the result that all cultivation
had to be done by human power alone. Although the working of certain
metals (copper, bronze, gold, silver) on a handicraft (non-mechanized)
basis was fairly advanced, the culture lacked the wheel and any type of
machine based upon it. The Incas had no system of writing of which we
know and kept their records, which were mainly of a statistical nature, by
three methods: a system of knotted strings called *quipus*, clay relief maps,

and counting boxes made of clay in which small balls or other counters were moved from one compartment to another. The technological achievements of the culture were considerable, especially in the fields of engineering. Hard-surfaced roads with the necessary bridges connected all parts of the domain, and two parallel highways, one along the coast and the other through the sierra or intermountain plateau, ran the whole length of the empire. Hundreds of square miles of arable land were added to the natural resources by laboriously terracing the sides of mountains with heavy retaining walls of stone. Water was brought to these and other needful fields from long distances around and through mountains by means of elaborate canals and tunnels. Inca stone masonry in the construction of palaces and fortresses is justly famous, for in some cases it involved the moving and fitting of huge blocks weighing as much as fifty tons; the workmen had also mastered the art of cutting and fitting irregularly shaped stones together in massive walls without the use of mortar. The technological achievements of the culture, however, depended as a whole, not so much on ingenuity of processes as upon the organization of the human element: it was in the precise and ordered coördination of the activities of large numbers of human beings that the culture displayed its genius.

The most obvious expression of the unification and integration of the culture was the political organization, which was a pyramidal structure at the top of which stood the status of the emperor. The latter was an absolute ruler who claimed descent from the Sun, who was worshiped as divine during life, and who became the center of a cult after his death. The emperor's functions were defined as including an obligation to care for his people, but his power was unchecked save by custom and the fear of revolt. The new emperor was chosen by the old one from among his sons. The emperor had a large harem of secondary wives in addition to his chief wife, who in later times was always his full sister. All offspring and members of the royal family enjoyed special social positions, and upon the death of an emperor his descendants in the male line formed a special hereditary kinship group (ayllu) which was responsible thenceforward for the upkeep of their royal ancestor's palace and the maintenance of his cult. A special fringed headband and large earplugs were among the distinctive symbols of royal status.

Next below the royal family itself was the nobility, which consisted of two divisions: (a) hereditary kinsmen of the royal family, and (b) adopted or created nobles. The latter usually consisted of former rulers of subject states or their descendants, plus commoners who had distinguished themselves in war and other services to the state.

The bulk of the population consisted of commoners. The political unit in this group was the male taxpayer who was always head of a family. Thus population was organized on the basis of the number of taxpayers rather than the actual number of persons living.

The political administration was highly centralized, and embraced not only political affairs but practically the entire life of the average inhabitant. The empire was divided into four great quarters, and the official name of the empire was Tawantinsuyu, or Land of the Four Quarters. Over each of these large divisions presided a *prefect* who was always a nobleman, although the position itself was not hereditary. The four prefects maintained their headquarters in Cuzco, the capital city, and formed a sort of state council to advise the emperor. Each quarter was divided into a number of *provinces*, usually corresponding to the territories of conquered tribes which had been incorporated into the empire. Each province was in the charge of an *imperial governor*, who was also usually a noble, and who possessed judicial as well as executive powers. The provinces in turn were subdivided into *districts* of no more than 10,000 taxpayers. The districts were in turn composed of *communities* (ayllus), which were originally localized kin groups, but which the Inca system transformed into local administrative units. In the administrative hierarchy, under the provincial governor served a number of chiefs (curacas) of various ranks: highest were those who had charge of a group of 10,000 taxpayers (district chiefs), next came the chief over 1,000 (normally ten for each district), then the chief of 500, and finally the centurion or chief of 100 taxpayers, which group in later times was supposed to correspond to the local unit or ayllu. Below this latter status were two ranks of *foremen*, who were appointed by the chief of the hundred. These minor officials were responsible for the groups of fifty and ten taxpayers respectively. Thus the population of the Inca society was "regimented" in the literal sense of the term according to a decimal system of ascending units, starting with the small group of ten taxpayers at the bottom and proceeding through multiples of tens and fives to the emperor himself. This decimal classification was based on an exact head count recorded in Cuzco, which also served as the basis of taxation and army service. All births, deaths, and change in age grade were recorded by the foremen and sent to the provincial governor who embodied them in an annual report submitted during the festival of Raymi in December. The system was bolstered by an organization of inspectors or spies, responsible only to the emperor, who reported on the work of the administrative officials.

The administrative organization and other aspects of the culture were financially supported by a system of indirect taxation on land and labor, which was based on the premise that all land belonged to the emperor and individual citizens enjoyed only the usufruct of such ground as they were allowed to work. Money was unknown to commoners and no payments to the government took place in kind. The only form of taxation was in labor: commoners were expected to contribute services by work on the fields, service in the army, labor on public works, and personal service to the emperor and members of the nobility. The lands of each community were divided into more or less equal parts between the religion (the Sun), the state (emperor and his administration), and the ordinary commoners or taxpayers. So far as the latter were concerned, it was the duty of the local government officials to assign to each taxpayer and his family just enough land to maintain them. In later years land was reassigned each year on this basis, taking into account the number of dependent children and the changes in family composition which may have occurred during the preceding year by reason of births, deaths, and change in status of family members. All taxpayers worked not only the land assigned for their own use, but also the land belonging to the religion and the state; indeed, the latter portions of land had to be cultivated and planted first. Work of this sort was usually done in gangs of neighbors working in unison with singing and instrumental music. At the time of breaking the ground and planting, women worked with their husbands, and it seems that the work was not regarded as onerous, but on the contrary that it was a form of festival and social interaction of an agreeable sort.

Two types of storehouses were maintained in each district, one for the support of the religion and the clergy, the other for the support of the government. In time of famine or crop failure, the local chiefs were authorized to draw upon the government stores of food, textiles, and other necessities for distribution to the general population. In addition the produce from the government lands went to the support of the army, nobility, certain specialists and craftsmen, the sacred virgins, and all classes of the population who were not required to pay taxes in labor. Among the latter were the aged and infirm, widows, and government servants. The emperor also ordered a general distribution from time to time when the surpluses in the government warehouses were sufficiently large. As a result of these provisions, poverty and destitution were unknown in the Inca empire.

In addition to the stratification of the population by political status, a classification by age grades was also in force. This was primarily for the purpose of census-taking and tax assessment. Twelve different age grades were recognized, the most important of which was that of able-bodied adult, which an individual entered at marriage and in which he continued as long as able to do a full day's work.

Trade and commerce, except for local bartering of home-grown and home-made products among neighbors, was a monopoly of the government. A great deal of economic exchange took place between the various regions of the empire. Fresh fish were brought daily from the coast to the highland capital of Cuzco, coca (a mild narcotic containing cocaine) was brought from eastern tropical plantations and distributed throughout the empire, cotton grown on the coast was exchanged for wool (of llama, alpaca, vicuña, and guanaco) of the highlands, and so forth. But this was a matter, not of individual initiative, but of transfer from one government storehouse to the other. The basic idea was that every citizen's essential needs should be supplied, but that luxuries, such as fine textiles, precious metals and jewels, plural wives, and personal service, should be reserved to the royal family and in diminishing degree to the administrative hierarchy.

The coördination of patterns extended to what we would consider the private life of the average citizen. For example, the government regulated marriage, and arbitrarily supervised the careers of its women subjects. An imperial official annually visited each village and classified all girls who during the previous year had reached the age of ten. Those of outstanding beauty and physical perfection were sent to Cuzco or a provincial capital to be educated at the expense of the government. Those rejected for such status were given in marriage to eligible boys, who upon marriage would become taxpayers and family heads. Such marriageable boys and girls were lined up opposite each other in the village square and the local chief gave a girl to each boy in the name of the emperor.

At the time of marriage each couple was not left to fend for itself. A plot of ground and a dwelling house were provided, as well as the necessary utensils and two outfits of clothing, according to sex. If the available land of the community was exhausted or if the number of taxpayers in the local group exceeded 100 by many, the newly-wed couple might be required to move to some other area; but the government saw to it that each new family got a fair start. And at the annual redistribution of population and property, a suitable amount of land was added to the taxpayer's holdings to support each additional child. When the children grew up and established families of their own, the land holdings were again reduced, so that, in theory at least, the economic resources of the family were kept nicely in balance by government action.

The Chosen Women, those who were selected out in the annual inspection, were placed in convents or girls' schools in the provincial capitals or in Cuzco. There they spent four years learning to spin, weave, cook, make chicha (the standard beer of the empire), and other household tasks. Then they were reclassified. (a) Those called mothers (mamakona) were either dedicated to chastity and the service of the state religion, or were given as concubines to the emperor. (b) The others were given to the members of the nobility as wives. A few were set aside to be used in human sacrifice, although such offerings were employed only in times of greatest crisis, and they were considered especially fortunate, for they were guaranteed a life of ease and happiness in the next world.

Artisans, such as metal-workers and architects, and specialists, such as accountants and quipu-keepers, were also especially selected and educated and were exempt from the ordinary work taxes. Likewise, special educational institutions were provided for male members of the royal family and of the nobility. No formal education was provided for commoners. Levies for the army were selected as special servants of the state and were also free from the normal work service. The army was supplied from the government storehouses as long as it was operating within the territory of the empire, and a special transport service of llamas and men supplied it from government stores when operating outside the boundaries, so that the support of the military organization did not fall upon the shoulders of local residents of the region near operations. This, of course, was a feature of military supply which was not adopted by European armies until modern times, and it will be remembered that the arbitrary quartering and supplying of troups at the expense and inconvenience of ordinary citizens was one of the principal grievances of the American colonists in their revolution against England.

Although narcotics were available, their abuse never became an important problem. The use of coca was restricted to the royal family and the nobility. Tobacco, of which only the native wild varieties were used without attempts at special cultivation, was restricted to medicinal use in the form of snuff or powder. Distilled liquors were not known, but brewed chicha or beer was ubiquitous. Alcoholic intoxication, however, was permitted only in religious ceremonies, and ordinary habitual drunkenness on the part of a commoner was suppressed by heavy penalties, including death, in the case of unreformable individuals.

Religion, like everything else, was organized on a state-wide basis. In general it was characterized by emphasis on ritual and organization, rather than mysticism and spirituality, and, in the words of Rowe, "its chief interests were the food supply and curing." The official cult was presided over by a high priest, usually a brother of the emperor. And associated with him was a descending hierarchy of local priests, diviners, sacrificers, caretakers, and so on. Parallel to the male religious officials there was a group of nuns or consecrated women, selected from among the Chosen Women, and presided over by a high priestess thought to be the Sun's wife, who was usually a member of the emperor's family, or at least of royal blood. These females were vowed to perpetual chastity and spent their time making textiles for ceremonial priestly garments, preparing chicha for festivals, and other duties.

Although the Inca culture was so organized as to prevent the rise of or to lower most of the anxieties common to man in society, such as those concerning status, economic security, sex and mating, the culture actually possessed no technique adequate, in modern medical terms, for the prevention and cure of disease and bodily ailments. This fact is reflected in the persistence of a large body of beliefs and practices, not officially recognized by the state cult, having to do with magical curing, the processing and use of medicinal herbs, sorcery, witchcraft, and similar matters actually concerned with physiological maladjustments.

In this brief highlighting of certain aspects of Inca culture, we shall mention only one other major feature, namely, the general techniques whereby conquered populations were assimilated to the system with a minimum of disturbance. After the cessation of armed resistance the new territory was surveyed and a census was taken by age grades, the results of which were transmitted to Cuzco in his routine report by the commanding general, in the form of *quipus* and clay models. This report was studied by the emperor and his advisers and on the basis of it they ordered a reorganization of the population. Native ayllus were moved about and a provincial capital was erected together with the necessary administrative and religious buildings. The irreconcilable elements of the conquered population were moved to a distant location within the empire, while colonists, often consisting of surplus population of the established local groups within the empire, were brought in and settled. These colonizing groups are known in the literature as *mitamaes,* and their job was to serve as an example of Inca culture. They were supplied with lands and dwellings, as at home, and were encouraged to carry on their traditional Inca customs without necessarily attempting to mix with the local conquered population. Naturally, they spoke Quechua, the language of the empire, and refused to learn the native language of the subjected population. Also they practised Inca arts and crafts, as well as all other patterns of Inca culture, with the result that the native populations were forced to accommodate themselves to the colonists, rather than vice versa. The Quechua language was required. The emperor showed favor to the colonists by giving them presents and otherwise building up their prestige.

This perhaps is the technique of not too blood-thirsty conquerors everywhere. But the Incas showed their finesse by a policy of conciliation toward the victims of their aggression. The native chief, provided he showed any inclination to coöperate, was kept in office and made, at least nominally, a member of the Inca administrative hierarchy. In cases of proved loyalty such former enemies were absorbed into the Inca nobility. To insure the current loyalty of such defeated chiefs and the continuation of their function within the system, their sons were taken as hostages to Cuzco where they were educated as the sons of the Inca nobility. In the meantime, an Inca governor of the new province was appointed, the flocks and lands were marked and divided according to the going decimal system, the usual pattern of labor taxes was introduced, roads were built, and the customary storehouses instituted. The religion of the conquered tribe was not desecrated, but on the contrary was absorbed. The sacred shrines and images of the victims of Inca aggression were taken to Cuzco where they were worshipped when a delegation from the province visited the capital. At the same time it was made clear that the major Inca divinities would henceforward be considered supreme: shrines and the cult of Viracocha, the Sun, the Thunder, and other supernatural powers were established.

The result of such a policy was phenomenal. We can only regard it as a system which provided a nice balance between the basic and acquired drives of diverse peoples and the fundamental orientations and objectives of the Inca culture.

What were the fundamental objectives of the Inca culture? At this distance it is difficult to be definitive. But it seems that we may summarize them in the following terms. (1) The basic drives (that is, the fundamental physiological well-being of the average man) must be served in this culture through the organization of effort and mental pattern toward the achievement of good crops and herds. (2) This objective is balanced by the systematic elimination of possibly countervailing anxieties and other "distracting" cultural drives. For example, the drive for prestige was on the whole eliminated by the hierarchical stratification of the population and the limitation of special education to those socially able to perform the patterns thus acquired. The drive for security was satisfied in large part by the system of government patterns which assured personal and economic security to the average man through the system of shared labor and government warehouses, and so forth. (3) Anxieties and other drives concerned with the "supernatural" were for the most part provided with ready patterns of relief through the highly organized system of the cult which paralleled and was to some extent identified with the secular politico-social organization: each political official had his opposite number in a member of the religious hierarchy; few families existed which had not contributed at least one member to the Chosen Women. (4) A fine balance was maintained between force and the satisfaction of basic drives or desires. For example, the average man who "got out of line" was heavily punished; he who followed the patterns was rewarded with satisfaction of his basic desires, plus relief from the necessity of worrying about his economic or social future. (5) The whole system was centered upon the emperor as a symbol of both the mundane and supernatural unity of the culture. In effect the system contributed to a life of luxury and privilege for the royal family and the nobility. These advantages for one class or caste were paid off in the form of assurance of security for the common individual.

Although such a system required a strong military and spy organization, it is worth remarking that the average citizen seems to have been well content with his lot under the Inca régime. For example, the accounts of most of the chroniclers who accompanied the Spanish invaders indicate that work in the fields was not regarded as drudgery by the workers themselves. On the contrary, it seems to have been a pleasure, accompanied by music, singing, joking, and a feeling of community solidarity. This fact has often been contrasted with the situation at present, in which we find Indian descendants of the empire eking out a miserable and distasteful existence as peones on haciendas and plantations operated for profit by Europeans, usually of Spanish descent. All the evidence indicates that the Inca system did not exploit the worker in terms which may be compared to the modern definitions of profit. Although the emperor, royal family, and nobility unquestionably enjoyed privileges beyond those of the common citizen, the motivations of these categories were not those of unlimited "profits" in the modern capitalistic sense. The Inca definition of the situation was so different from that of modern capitalism that it is scarcely possible to describe it in modern terms. To be sure it involved privilege and material and spiritual welfare of the upper castes, but this objective was inextricably united with the welfare of the society as a whole, including the individual satisfaction of the common man and his family. The fact that the desires of the common man were limited by his restricted education and comprehension of the system, does not negate the fact that the system itself was, on the whole, exceptionally well developed for the satisfaction of human wants within the limit of the creation of such wants by the system itself. We have seen that all acquired drives of a cultural nature are the products of a cultural system, and the virtue of the Inca system lay in the fact that it did not create wants or drives for any person (social category or caste considered) which it, the system itself, was unable to satisfy reasonably.

Thus we are able to discern in the Inca system a nice balance between the creation of acquired drives and the provision of cultural patterns for their satisfaction. The ultimate resort in the system was force, and the whole structure reposed on a hierarchical organization supported by military organization and spies. Yet, so far as we can determine from the evidence at hand, the average inhabitant was socialized in such a way that the culture was able to meet his expectations. In short, the patterns of the culture fitted into each other nicely so that a smooth-working coördination resulted, with a minimum of internal inconsistencies and conflicts—so long as it did not have to contend with a foreign cultural component of resilient organization and proved virility. The downfall of the Inca system before a handful of Spanish adventurers may be laid to many factors. But among the most important will always be recognized (1) the insecurity of the pattern of successorship to the emperorship, whereby it happened that two sons of the old emperor, Huayna Capac, were able to divide the empire between them and to engage in a civil war at the time of the appearance of the Spaniards; and (2) the pyramidal structure of the politico-social organization itself, whereby it was possible for the Spaniards, by the relatively simple maneuver of removing the emperor as the kingpin of the system, to wreck the entire culture in a relatively short time.

In summary, the Inca system, whatever its shortcomings, shows us a form of essentially secular cultural organization in which the patterns of performance were fitted to each other through the mechanism of social stratification and consequent differential assignment of cultural patterns. Although a system of mental patterns united the secular agents and statuses with a supernatural system, the important features of Inca integration were at all times secular, and it is difficult, if not impossible, to see this as a "sacred" society, despite the pretentions of the priests and functionaries of the official cult. In the last analysis, in so far as there was conscious planning in the Inca system, it seems to have been the product of hard-headed administrators who, if they deluded themselves, were nevertheless able to grasp the essential requirements of an integrated culture from a shrewd practical point of view.

Weaknesses of the authoritarian type. On the basis of performance we may raise several questions concerning the desirability or efficiency of the authoritarian attempt at cultural integration.

1. First is the fact that practically all such organizations have been oriented toward an objective of subordinating the individual to the culture (or the "state"). In our culture, such an objective is generally repugnant, that is to say, inconsistent with the mental and representational patterns of the majority of our population. The fact that we in our culture consider the subordination of the individual to the goals of the culture as a whole to be reprehensible, does not of course prove scientifically that such a judgment is correct. More to the point in the present connection is to consider the results or effects of such authoritarian régimes. 2. Up to the present, such attempts at cultural integration have always involved suppressing or ignoring the basic drives or desires of a considerable portion of the population of their societies. Contemporary readers will doubtless be acquainted with the persecution of some six million Jews and millions of liberals by the Nazis, and the suppression of several million kulaks, or small farmers, by the Soviet régime is also familiar. Likewise the organization of the communist culture resulted in the frustration of desire on the part of the unreconstructed middle class of pre-Bolshevik days. It may, of course, be argued that in these modern instances, such persecution and suppression is a passing phase, and that a newer generation by proper training may be educated to perform its designated patterns with no feeling of frustration or resentment. All such systems in the past, however, have involved the "control" by force of considerable numbers of malcontents, slaves, prisoners of war, subject territories, disaffected elements of the population, and so forth. Apparently large numbers of the first generation of the Inca victims of conquest had to be forcibly "handled." This feature of such a system, whatever may be the efficiency exhibited in the more prominent aspects of the organization, is a serious maladjustment and sign of inefficiency in itself.

3. Perhaps more important, from the point of view of cultural organization itself, is the fact that all such authoritarian systems have shown themselves to be relatively impermanent. The reason for this seems to be that such an organization has always proved to be, by its very nature, comparatively rigid, and therefore unadaptable to changing conditions. The integration of such a culture is maintained by force, which attempts to exclude spontaneous change in response to new elements which appear in the natural or cultural environments. Change, if any, must come from the small authoritarian group "at the top." The great Inca Empire was unable to accommodate to the presence of a handful of determined and bellicose Spaniards, and, once the Emperor, who was the keystone of the system, was removed, the system was unable to operate. The Roman Empire fell apart because, among other

reasons, the directors of the system at Rome failed to appreciate new patterns of warfare, new patterns of organization, and new incentives which had developed among the "barbarian" tribes on the frontiers. There is considerable evidence that the common people, colonists on the frontiers and plebians of the cities alike, were at least vaguely aware of these newly emergent factors in the foreign cultural component of the culture of the empire, but the authoritarian form was too rigid to respond in time. The fact seems to be, in the experience of history at least, that the authoritarian type of integration has never been able to solve permanently a fundamental dilemma. (*a*) This type of integration is maintained by force and depends upon the attempted suppression of all spontaneous change. (*b*) At the same time it is faced with the necessity of making fluid changes to alterations in conditions, like any other culture. Up to now no successful compromise has been made by the authoritarian type between these two needs, namely, the maintenance of integration by the suppression of change, and the need for adaptable change in the system.

These would seem to be the fundamental weaknesses of this type of integration, regardless of our "feelings" regarding the rightness or wrongness of the objectives proposed.

SACRED DEMOCRATIC INTEGRATION

Another type of cultural integration of relatively high degree has been achieved in the form of a so-called "sacred society." Many an isolated "primitive" tribe has shown this type of cultural integration before it came in contact with European civilization or with other cultures. Robert Redfield and associates have specialized in contrasting this type of culture with the more heterogeneous organizations influenced by cosmopolitan cultural trends in Central America.

As an example, let us sketch briefly one such integrated culture, which has maintained its independence in Arizona for several hundred years. We refer to the culture of the Hopi Indians.

HOPI INTEGRATION [2]

The Hopi live in eleven villages on top of or below three adjoining mesas or table lands which rise steeply several hundred feet above the Arizona desert. At present they total about 3,500 persons, and there is very little admixture of white blood. The average elevation is about 6,500 feet above sea level and the territory is arid, watered by a few springs, intermittent streams, and occasional summer thunderstorms. The people live mainly by dry farming and one of the principal problems of the culture has to do with the natural environmental component of the situation—the danger of draught, sudden summer floods, and early frosts. Oraibi, which is situated atop the so-called

Third Mesa, is probably the oldest continuously inhabited town in the United States, for the archaeological material shows that it has been occupied since at least about 1150 A.D., if not earlier.

Corn is the main food crop although a number of vegetables and fruit trees are cultivated. Field crops are cultivated by men, and vegetable gardens by women. Seeds are sacred property of matrilineal households and inherited through the female line. The horticultural technology still relies, as in prehistoric times, primarily upon hand labor and the use of digging sticks. Handicrafts in weaving, basketry, and pottery are well developed, although the craftsmen combine such work with other duties and do not constitute a group of full-time specialists. Recently the Indian service has attempted to induce the Hopi to take up cattle and sheep herding, but this has not become an integral part of the culture as yet. Houses are made solidly of stone and adobe.

In contrast to the Inca, the Hopi are not organized into a hierarchical social system, nor do they have any centralized political control, either as a tribe or locally. The society is essentially unstratified and democratic, although not according to the same pattern as the town-meeting type of democracy with individual enterprise which is in our tradition. Hopi means "peaceful," and there is no record of aggressive military operations. Indeed the only bellicose patterns have had to do with defense against neighboring raiding tribes and in armed revolt against Spanish rule in 1680. No military organization exists at present.

The fact that they live in a relatively isolated area accounts to some extent for the fact that the Hopi have maintained their culture practically intact throughout the centuries, but isolation does not seem to be the principal factor, for they have been repeatedly attacked by nomadic tribes, they were conquered by the Spaniards in the sixteenth century, and they have been in contact with Americans for a hundred years. The durability of the culture reflects its close integration, and we shall endeavor to sketch only a few aspects of this integration.

To a Hopi life is not broken up into a series of more or less unrelated segments, but appears to be an integrated whole the various parts of which are obviously inter-related. If life thus appears as an organic whole, it also seems objectively true that the patterns of the culture are also closely bound together. What we in our culture call the sacred and the secular, the economic, the social, the political and so on, are fitted together into one unified and fairly consistent configuration.

The organization of society is based upon the kinship system, which however connects with other aspects of the universe as well. The kinship system is based on unilinear descent through the female line and the terminology is of the classificatory type. On this basis the society is divided into a considerable number of exogamous *clans*, each of which consists of one or several matrilineal *lineages*, the members of which believe themselves to be descended from a common ancestress. The lineage is headed by the oldest living woman and consists of her sisters and all their female descendants through the female line. The brothers of the head and all of the male descendants of females in the lineage are also members. The houses of the lineage are usually grouped together, and the husbands of the members, although they live with their spouses, look upon their mothers' or sisters' households as their real homes. The *household* itself consists of a woman and her husband and children. Each household is an economic unit with division of labor between the sexes. Ownership in Hopi theory is based on use, and the children and the household property, including seeds and garden land, are thought of as belonging to the lineage. Men own individually only their tools, clothing, ceremonial regalia, livestock, and fruit trees. One household in each clan is the "ancestral house" or chief household. The woman of this household is the "real" head of the clan, and her oldest brother is the "ceremonial" head of the clan. In this house are kept the sacred fetishes and ceremonial paraphernalia of the clan, and here meetings are held.

The kinship system is extended to the world of nature, for each clan considers itself related to a species of animal or plant or a phenomenon of nature (Cloud, Sun's Forehead, and so forth), which gives the clan its name, its character or "medicine," and its protection. A fetish is kept in the clan ancestral house symbolizing the supernatural relationship, and people refer to their supernatural partners by a kinship term. In addition to the primary partners, wuya (supernatural relatives), each clan usually has several other, secondary ones.

A group of clans sharing the same supernatural partners are considered to be closely related and are grouped into a *phratry*, the members of which are forbidden to intermarry. There are twelve phratries among the Hopi.

The customary patterns expected between statuses in this kinship are symbolized in the kinship terminology, which is of the classificatory type. This terminology applies to all members of one's clan or phratry and, through extensions and modifications, to all members of the society. Since each term implies a set of patterns of interpersonal relations, it signifies a pervading and integrated system of social organization at this level.

Women would seem to be in a very favorable position in this culture, and indeed the mother-daughter relationship is the cornerstone of the kinship system. The kernel of this aspect of Hopi cultural organization is to be seen in the complex of patterns and artifacts which may be called the mother-house-fetish complex.

But the culture is neatly balanced to afford male statuses an equally important and interlocking part in the cultural integration. For the men are mainly responsible for carrying on the ceremonial life which expresses the basic Hopi theories (mental patterns) concerning the unity of the culture and the universe.

The harmony of the universe and the welfare of the society are maintained by an annual cycle of ceremonies which are performed, each at its appointed time, under the charge of secret societies. Each major ceremony in the calendar is conducted by a secret society under the leadership of a priest who traditionally belongs to a certain clan. In the majority of cases these individuals are men. The societies and their ceremonies differ somewhat in the importance which is attached to them, and the chief priests may be ranked in accordance. However, such distinction in status is not phrased in terms of personal aggrandizement. "The emphasis is always on *responsibility* for tribal welfare attached to a rôle, rather than on the prestige or power of the individual who assumes it." [3] There are twelve of these societies among the Hopi at present, nine of which are open only to men. The other three societies, conducting minor ceremonies, are open to females as well as to men. One society takes in all males in the tribe, another all males and females. The others—secret societies properly speaking—are, however, open to voluntary joining by any one who satisfies the sex and age requirements, that is, there is no "blackballing." A boy, however, usually joins the societies of his godfather, a girl those of her ceremonial aunt. Both of these functionaries serve as sponsors. When preparing the annual ceremony the secret society meets in the *kiva*, to which the rite is attached. A *kiva* is a large, circular, underground chamber which, at such times, is closed to non-members of the society. At other times, however, it is used as a club and work room by all men, usually those living in the neighborhood. The *kiva* belongs to the clan which built it, not necessarily the same clan which has the chief priest of the society, and it is in charge of this clan's ceremonial headman, called the *kiva* chief. Important male statuses then, are clan chiefs, *kiva* chiefs, and chief priests of the secret societies. They choose and train their successors from among their sisters' sons.

Several other male statuses are also connected with this system. Each secret society controls a particular form of illness, and the chief priest of the society may function as a sort of chief *medicine man*. His powers, though, derive not from his own supernatural experiences but only from his knowledge of the rituals of the society.

The ceremonial of each pueblo, or community of the tribe, is reaffirmed at an annual meeting once a year of a council composed of the chief priests of the leading societies. The chief priest of the Winter Solstice ceremony (the most important in the calendar) is chief of this council and receives the title of *Village Chief.* In eight of the eleven Hopi villages he is also male chief of the Bear Clan, supposed to be the oldest of all the clans. In theory the Village Chief owns all the land of the village, and one of his functions is the settling of disputes over real estate. However, his principal job is praying for his people and advising them in the Hopi Way; to afford him time for such efforts the people cultivate the lands attached to the office by means of voluntary work groups. He also has certain unspectacular materialistic symbols of office which may be displayed on ceremonial occasions, but otherwise he follows the same patterns as other persons of his age and sex. The village council, or "Chiefs' Talk," makes decisions involving ceremonial life, based on common agreement, not on formal majority rule. It is not thought of as making laws, because the mythology and the Hopi Way of ethical conduct constitute the common law of the society and they are not considered to be the product of human beings. The council, however, does have some judicial functions, and it enforces its decisions through the *War Chief* and certain *kachinas*, who are men dressed to impersonate supernatural ancestral visitors. However, in the Hopi culture, the individual is expected to coöperate voluntarily, and law-enforcement patterns based on force are practically undeveloped. Gossip, ridicule, and accusations of witchcraft serve to put pressure on the wayward person.

When it has been impossible to reach agreement on some vital issue in the village council, the minority group may secede and form another village. This has happened only a few times in Hopi history. There is among the Hopi patterns no mechanism for tribal government, nor even for settling disputes among the villages. Occasionally intervillage feuds have broken out into violent conflict. Since 1937 under the provisions of the Wheeler-Howard Act a tribal council has been organized, but has not established itself as a significant body.

We have seen, then, that the integration of Hopi culture is manifested in a nice balance and interrelationship of the patterns of status and social intercourse. Over and above the exploitative patterns which are compatible to the rigorous natural environment and which involve an equitable division of labor between the sexes, two structures or major institutions of social organization are discernible. (1) The matrilineal kinship system, with its organization of individuals, households, lineages, clans, and phratries, is consistent throughout the culture and forms the basis for patterns, such as those in the economic field, regulation of marriage, etiquette, and social intercourse among all members of the society. Through the male members of the clan groups the kinship system gears into (2) the ceremonial-political institution, mainly in the hands of males, who carry on the ceremonials which manifest the details of the Hopi world view and also exercise theocratic political functions.

The solidarity of the culture, however, would not be plain without considering briefly the system of mental patterns whereby this orderly patterning of overt behavior is justified and rationalized. According to the Hopi view the whole universe, including human beings, other animals, the land, plants, and the supernatural, is an ordered functioning system. It operates under a set of rules which are known to the Hopi and to no one else. If a Hopi learns the rules, he can exercise some control over the universe by regulating his behavior, emotions, and thoughts in accordance with them. Practically every actional and representational pattern of the culture is therefore viewed with respect to its consistency with this scheme, and most of the representative patterns symbolize it to some extent. Thus the clans and phratries are linked to non-human partners, these in turn are linked with directions (there are six cardinal directions—space is six-sided), with particular colors, with some part of the year, and with phases of the cycle of reproduction and growth. The whole universe is grouped into categories of things, just as human beings are grouped into categories of kinsmen, and so forth. Thus a single individual does not operate of and for himself, but as the representative of his human group vis-à-vis other groups or categories of the universe, whether they be species of animals or plants, groups of divinities, forces of nature, or others.

The ideal relationship uniting these various categories or orders of the universe is thought of in terms of reciprocity. If A does something for B, it must be reciprocated if the universe is to continue to function. And it is the obligation of human beings to discover, learn, and apply these rules of interaction, not only in the interest of their group, but to prevent the universe from "running down." For example, everything has a "house," which, to the Hopi, is not only a protection from the elements, but a symbol of security. The Sun has a house at the two solstice points on the horizon, the clan has an original house (usually regarded as under the earth), and so on. As part of the reciprocity pattern, man builds houses or shrines for his non-human clan partners and for his gods.

In Hopi belief the other entities of the universe play their assigned rôles automatically, but man must learn his, which are expressed in a body of myth and precept called the Hopi Way or the Peaceful Way. This in effect consists of a code of rules or a set of patterns for acting, feeling, and thinking. The number of rules or patterns one has to learn increases with age and reaches its peak in ceremonial activity. One must not only *do* the right things according to the pattern, but he must have a "good heart," which means that he must not feel anger, fear, worry, or sadness. Witches, who are greatly feared, and despised, do not have good hearts—they are called "two-hearted" and believed to have both an animal and a human heart.

The public ceremonies are essentially a systematic, socialized set of patterns for maintaining the relations of man with other categories of the universe. Each one emphasizes a phase in the horticultural cycle, but at the same time embodies the total world view. The series begins with the Winter Solstice ceremony in December, emphasizing the importance of the Sun, a major deity, in the cosmic system. Magical rites are performed to turn him back on his northward course, and offerings of prayer sticks are made to all the orders of the universe. This is followed by the Bean Dance, various ceremonies in the summer (including the famous Snake Dance) concerned primarily with bringing rain, and so on. In many of these ceremonies not only the living Hopi participate, but also the dead. In the preparatory phases in the *kiva* or ceremonial room, the *sipapu* or sacred hole in the floor is always opened. This symbolizes the place from whence the ancestors of the Hopi tribe came out of the ground, and it is opened to facilitate communication with the underworld, or original source of the tribe. Dead Hopi are believed to live in a home in the San Francisco mountains. A special society is concerned with these beings, called *kachinas*. Members of the society dress in special costumes and impersonate the ancestors, who come once a year to assist in the initiation of boys and girls into ceremonial life.

Without going into more details, it should be clear that the mythology, world view, and ceremonial cycle all tend to reinforce a cultural environment which is a unified whole, a culturally constructed universe in which everything has its place, and a system of cultural patterns, every one of which has a function in terms of this system. Neither the dead nor the living are excluded, neither the animate nor the inanimate. And for the individual there are two essentials: (1) perform according to the expected pattern, (2) keep a "good heart."

This system has resulted in a remarkable stability of culture over long periods of time and a notable absence of overt aggressiveness in the typical individual. And all this has been achieved without patterns of "authority" as understood either in our culture or in the Inca culture, for example. It may be argued that isolation, relatively small population, and a complex of peculiar environmental conditions have made this possible. Undoubtedly all of the components in the situation must be considered, but the fact remains that other peoples living in essentially the same environment—such as the Navaho, the Apache, the Pima, and the Papago—have exhibited neither the degree of integration and solidity nor the permanence of culture shown by the Hopi. We conclude that there must be some basic principle of internal integration which we may discover in a cultural configuration which shows these traits.

NOTES TO CHAPTER 23

1. For more detailed summaries of Inca culture the reader is referred to Rowe, 1946; Baudin, 1940 (1928); Means, 1931; and references cited in these works.
2. For more detailed summaries of Hopi culture the reader is referred to Thompson and Joseph, 1944; Titiev, 1944; Murdock, 1934, pp. 324-358; and references cited in these works.
3. Thompson and Joseph, 1944, p. 45.

CHAPTER 24

The Integration of Cultural Systems

OUR INTEREST in the principles of cultural integration is not merely the excuse for an academic exercise, but is ultimately directed toward the solution of practical problems. We need to know the qualities of "good" integration and the principles underlying it, if we are to be in a position to suggest or to effect constructive changes in cases in which a society or group is suffering from cultural maladjustment because of faulty organization of its patterns.

We are here concerned primarily with the integration of *cultural systems*. To avoid misunderstanding a distinction must be noted between *cultural* and *social* integration. At a given point in time a high degree of cultural organization does not necessarily guarantee an equally high degree of social integration. The patterns, or blue-prints, for cultural activity may be well fitted together, admirably planned, and so forth, yet the population they are designed to serve may show a certain amount of disorganization. We may mention a few possible reasons for such a state of affairs, and we must be prepared to search for such factors in cases which are presented to us. (1) The cultural system, while well organized within itself, may not be compatible with its situation. It may not be adapted to the realities of the natural environment, the capabilities of the members of its society, or similar factors. (2) The members of the society may not have learned the patterns of the system completely. For example, there is usually a period of social disorganization in the freshman class at college during the first few weeks of the term, while the new students are learning the expected mode of life in a university community. Indian tribes in our own country have often gone through a period of disorganization and demoralization after being presented with a nicely-worked-out system of reservation life by the Indian service—partly because time is needed to learn the customs involved.[1] (3) "Personality" factors may also render a cultural system unworkable, in the sense that certain members or sections of a group refuse to follow the patterns, even though they know them. In so far as such "personality" factors are the result of inadequate socialization the matter can of course be corrected within limits.

515

SOME DETAILED ASPECTS OF INTEGRATION

Although many discussions of integration begin with a consideration of the overall cultural system, it seems most useful for us to start with the consideration of factors which can readily be discerned even in connection with relatively simple parts of a system, such as may be viewed in the everyday operation of customs. We shall mention four aspects of integration in this connection: relatedness, linkage, consistency, and balance. These principles may be and usually are involved in all levels up to and including the total system.

Relatedness. As a simple example, the writer may mention an experience which could doubtless be duplicated by many other participants in government activity during World War II. As a representative of one of the war agencies he was attached to a United States Embassy. Among other duties (cultural patterns) of his office was the making of certain investigations regarding the physical and social organization of various cities in the country in which he was working. Techniques were well developed, and the patterns were carried out without conflict between them, with the results passed through the Ambassador to headquarters in Washington. The Embassy at that time was a fairly large social group; its total staff numbered about four hundred persons, including the diplomatic staff, representatives of the armed forces, and employees of numerous "war agencies." All of these individuals and subgroups were of course governed by rules, regulations, directives, and the like, all of which can be considered cultural patterns. And during wartime, especially, much emphasis was placed on the fact that the patterns must be followed carefully, without deviations, and that conflict and delay were to be avoided at all costs. The Embassy operated with internal harmony, culturally speaking; there were no significant internal conflicts in pattern or behavior. But in some respects it was not a well-integrated cultural system. This is illustrated by the fact that about the time the author and his colleagues in his particular branch had completed the aforementioned investigations assigned to them, they discovered that almost exactly similar work had been assigned to and had been accomplished by two other units of the Embassy. In short, three groups within the organization had carried out parallel work, without mutual awareness. This was a tribute to the discretion with which each group did its job, but does not speak well for close cultural integration of the overall pattern in the Embassy. There was no conflict between groups or individuals, nor any inconsistency between the patterns practised; there was simply a lack of *relatedness*.

Something similar may often be observed in cultural systems serving whole societies. One or more complexes or institutions may become detached, as it were, from the total matrix of the culture, and the process may proceed to the point that the "matrix" itself loses whatever unity it had. This seems to be one of the features of modern urban culture.[2] Religious complexes and institutions, for example, in the modern overall configuration, have little connection with, let us say, certain economic institutions such as industry or with many of the recreational institutions. When we compare the detachment between our religious complexes with the manner in which the system of religious beliefs and practices of the Hopi touch almost every other aspect of their culture, we are forced to the conclusion that there is a certain lack of relatedness as regards this aspect of our system. In the American cultural system there has also been a traditional separation between the political aspects of the culture, and many other segments, especially the institutions of business. Although this gulf has been narrowed during recent years, the pattern is still reflected in the old shibboleth that "the best government is the one which governs least." This may be contrasted with the Inca system in which government patterns permeated even the culture of home life.

Redfield and associates have demonstrated this feature of modern urban culture, which he terms *heterogeneity*, by comparative studies in Yucatan, contrasting the heterogeneous modern urban center of Merida with the progressively more homogeneous, more Indian rural communities of the hinterland.[3] We shall return in more detail to the matter of relatedness in a few pages, but it will be recognized that a certain minimum degree of relatedness seems to be a necessary prerequisite to cultural integration. Complete relatedness of all parts of a cultural system is very seldom if ever achieved. Even in the examples of highly integrated configurations we have chosen, some unrelatedness between patterns exists. Among the Inca, for example, the diviners' and curers' procedures and statuses were outside the official religious complex and more or less detached from the system as a whole, although they were undoubtedly parts of the culture. Among the Hopi, such modern additions as cattle herding, lie for the most part outside and separated from the main unifying orientations of kinship and religion.

As a minimum guide to relatedness we may say that two or more parts of a cultural system (ranging from unit-patterns to major orientations) are related to each other if the performance of one has a *meaningful connection* with the performance of the other or others. On the level of mental patterns, this means that the items involved must be logically related to each other *or* otherwise associated. (Many such an association is by no means logical.) On the level of representational customs, relatedness requires that the symbols used are at least within the same "universe of discourse." On the level of actional patterns it means that the performance of the one custom, complex, or whatnot, effects the situation in a way significant to the performance of the other customs under consideration in the system. It must be borne in mind that the connections between two parts or aspects of a well-developed cultural system are often indirect and that they may lack obviousness, so that considerable analysis is required to demonstrate their relatedness. For example, a great many intervening connections stand between a farmer's customs for raising a wheat crop and the customs involved in dining in a metropolitan hotel.

In general it seems that lack of relatedness tends to appear in cutlures having a great many highly evolved specialties and/or in those societies containing a large number of constituent groups and categories without an overall structure of social organization. In our own society it is pointed out that occasionally scholars become so involved in their specialities that the connecting links with the general culture are lost—the "ivory tower" situation. Likewise, we often see cultural disintegration in mixed populations, composed of persons from two or more originally distinct cultures. The period of lack of relatedness is manifested in the interval during which the various subgroups are "milling about," as it were, having lost their old patterns of social structure and not having agreed on a new structure of coördination. In some cases such agreement is delayed for a long time, if indeed it is ever achieved. The confused situation in the immigrant sections of large American cities, the "heterogeneous" culture of modern Latin American cities in countries having significant aboriginal Indian cultures, and the cultural and social turmoil among the "displaced" populations of Europe following a major war are examples of such failure of coördination.

Although relatedness seems to be an essential feature of such integration as may exist in a culture, it has been pointed out that complete or total integration has up to now never been achieved by a functioning system. Every cultural system contains certain traits and complexes— and often larger units of organization—which are relatively unrelated to each other, at least for practical purposes. The patterns of Roman Catholic communion-taking, the custom of wearing clocks on one's socks, and the rule of driving on the right side of the road do not appear to be functionally related in our culture. To such unrelated items or subsystems Sorokin [4] has given the name of *congeries*. They exist within a total culture, but are unrelated. Sorokin has also rightly pointed out that the mere fact that an individual may practise a congeries of patterns does not prove that they are related in systematic fashion. Indeed, it seems that much seemingly illogical and disorganized behavior of individuals in our culture is due to the fact that they have made part of their cultural repertory a series of unrelated congeries. In the Amish culture (pp. 209-220) the farming complex seems to exist in a congeries relationship to most of the remainder of the culture; its connection with the religious institutions, rules for living, dressing, housing, and so on, seems to be more or less the result of historical accident. The main part of the culture shows a high degree of integration, but it would probably be practised without much modification if the livelihood complexes were weaving in village mills, handicrafts in small shops, or something else.

Functional linkage. In all cultures certain traits and other aspects are functionally linked together in such a way that the absence of one element may well render inoperative the other elements linked to it. This is sometimes called interdependence of cultural patterns and is probably to be considered a special type of relatedness. It is illustrated in the old rhyme which relates the sad tale whereby "for lack of a horseshoe nail a kingdom was lost." Various types of linkage have been discussed in a previous chapter dealing with technics. The higher the proportion of the total elements of a culture which are so linked together, the greater is the cohesiveness of the cultural system, and, other things equal, the greater the integration. Examples of linkage have been mentioned in passing on previous pages: plough agriculture is originally linked to patterns concerned with the domestication of draft animals; the possession and control of fire is a necessary prerequisite to the making of true pottery; most types of power-driven machinery depend upon the wheel; and so on.

In our own society most of us are aware of many linkages in the system and our dependency on them: a railroad strike, for example, renders inoperative thousands of complexes and institutions ranging from the manufacture of automobiles to dietary customs around the dinner table; a traffic snarl among ships in a port of embarkation may necessitate the complete postponement of an entire military campaign; a faulty pattern of instruction in high school may cause a whole class of graduates to fail in their first year in college. The failure of performance or the faultiness in design in any one of such linked patterns is usually manifested to the members of a society in the form of personal frustrations and social disorganization. However, one aspect of the matter is not so clearly understood, at least in our society. It is easy enough to see the importance of linkage on a single level of culture—for example, in an industrial "process." It is often not clear, however, that a successfully integrated system involves linkages not only among the elements of what might be called a linear series of patterns, but also requires linkage between the various levels and types of patterns. By way of illustration, it is obvious that a manufacturing institution may have to close down for lack of raw materials which in turn are lacking because of the failure of striking workers to perform the transportation patterns. On the other hand, the strike in many cases occurs or continues because there are no adequate patterns in the culture linking the work of the employees with their ideas (mental patterns) of a decent standard of living, or for expressing their grievances to employers, or for understanding their part in the general economic system, and so forth. To achieve a smoothly working, integrated system, in short, a culture must provide linkages not only between the patterns of action themselves but also between them and the ideational systems, patterns of feeling and attitude, means of expression (representational patterns), and so on. If, in our society, as much attention was given to working out strong functional linkages of this sort as is given to the mere linkage of patterns in actional series, we would doubtless suffer less frequently from that "lack of understanding" which produces partial paralysis and breakdown of the system as a whole.

Elton Mayo phrases this matter, in part, in terms of "communication." As a result of more than twenty years of investigation of industry which he has directed under the joint auspices of the Harvard School of Business Administration and various industrial concerns, he concludes that the difficulties of many an otherwise admirably planned industrial enterprise lie in neglecting to plan and develop patterns for communication between labor and management, between constituent members and groups of the workers, and between industry and the public. Modern industrial engineers, he points out, have reached a high degree of perfection in developing technical procedures and in linking operations together from the materialistic point of view. Much lowered efficiency, loss of production, and open conflict, however, is caused by the failure to provide patterns of mutual communication and action for the human element whereby individuals and groups of actual human beings engaged in these operations may be integrated into the whole.[4a]

Consistency.[5] Mere relatedness of cultural patterns does not automatically produce cultural integration. In the case of the Amish, we have seen that certain modern patterns, the use of automobiles and hard-surfaced roads for example, have come into direct relation—sometimes physically—with such patterns as the use of horse and buggy. The result has been a conflict in the actions of persons pursuing the respective patterns and conflict in the cultural system itself.

As a guide to a minimum definition of consistency we may say that two or more parts of a cultural system are consistent if the performance or achievement of one does not interfere with the performance or achievement of the other or others in question. Two patterns, for example, will be inconsistent if the performance of A impedes in any way the complete performance of B. Goals X and Y will be inconsistent if the achievement of one renders impossible or incomplete the achievement of the other.

Questions of consistency can often be brought into sharper focus by showing examples of inconsistency. Let us briefly discuss a few of the major types of consistency and their absence.

Consistencies of form. This concerns mainly the consistency between the various parts of a culture as previously analyzed. (1) First we may mention the question of consistency as between unit-patterns. One of the criticisms often leveled at coeducation is based upon alleged inconsistencies of pattern which the culture of such a situation sometimes reveals. It is claimed that patterns of courtship usually coexistent with the patterns of scholarship in college undergraduate culture are mutually inconsistent —the performance of one renders incomplete or inefficient the perform- ance of the other. (2) Consistency between a unit-pattern and the goal to which it leads is another aspect of ideal integration. In certain cate- gories of our society a common pattern for the "cure" (elimination of deleterious effects) of snake bite is to gulp immediately as much straight whiskey as one can swallow. Medical evidence indicates that the pattern in question is inconsistent with the goal, the neutralization of the snake's poison in one's body. Ingestion of whiskey not only does not neutralize the poison, but actually, by increasing heart beat and relaxing the blood vessels, aids in diffusing the poison through the body of the victim. Many "quack" cures illustrate the same inconsistency between pattern and goal. (3) Consistency within a pattern sequence is another desideratum of integration. Let us consider an example in which subgoals within a sequence are consistent, but the patterns involved for reaching them are not. In the "work-your-way-through-college" sequence, two inconsistent patterns frequently occur: work eight hours at night (subgoal: funds to pay expenses), appear in class next day prepared for recitation (subgoal: passing grade or better). Although the two subgoals in this segment of the sequence are consistent, the two unit-patterns in question are usually inconsistent, which probably accounts for the fact that a large number of students who try to follow this sequence are forced either to shift to another patterning or must drop out of school. (4) Consistency between goals is a fairly obvious requirement. Inconsistencies between goals may extend from the goals of simple unit-patterns to those between major objectives of the culture. However, they are usually more glaring in the higher levels of cultural organization than in the lower, for without a certain minimum consistency between the small goals of everyday life any culture would become paralyzed. However, many a woman has found that the goal of a weekly pay-check on a job and the goal of a well-kept house for her family are mutually inconsistent under usual circumstances. Objectives, such as "peace on earth, good will toward men" and "privilege for the élite" are often so inconsistent that their continuance in the same cultural system leads to violent revolution and revision of the system itself.

Consistency of order. (1) For integration there must be consistency of *time specification* as between the various parts of a cultural system. This is to say that the culture must be so planned that the various parts may be performed in a possible chronological order. Many patterns and goals are inconsistent if required to be performed instantaneously, but are perfectly consistent if performed in proper order. Thus one cannot bake a cake while one is playing bridge, but one pattern may be performed before the other. Two goals, such as drunkenness and consummating a business deal, cannot usually be achieved at the same time, although not a few groups in our society manage to achieve them in sequence. (2) Consistency of *place specification* is another obvious requirement for a smoothly performable culture. This is merely to say that a pattern cannot require its performers to be "two places at once."

Consistency of type. Actional patterns must show a certain consistency with representational and mental patterns, respectively, and vice versa. An inconsistency of this class exists when group fantasies render actional patterns inoperative. We see this sort of inconsistency in certain types of "nativistic movements" and other phases of acculturation: the symbolic patterns of "the good old days" are of such a nature that the performance of new actional patterns designed to cope with the present situation cannot be performed effectively, that is, are inconsistent. "Conservatives" in all cultures tend to exhibit this type of inconsistency or cultural maladjustment. Such maladjustment is sometimes labeled "lack of realism." At all events, there is an inconsistency between thoughts, fantasies, dreams—that is, mental patterns—and actional patterns.

Inconsistency between mental patterns and representational patterns occurs in all cases of "faulty expression." We are told, for example, that the heart of German culture is, in effect, a set of mental patterns of exquisite beauty. If this is in fact true, we can only conclude that the representational patterns, even within the culture itself, to say nothing of their relation with foreign cultures, seem to be woefully inconsistent. In American culture, the question of whether or not the set of culture parts collectively called the "movies" are consistent as representational patterns with the symbolic patterns of our culture has been seriously discussed, although not precisely in these terms.

The relations between representational patterns and actional patterns may be likewise inconsistent. In certain Latin cultures (individuals in

North America sometimes practise the same patterns) it is customary to substitute representational patterns for actional patterns with the result that certain actional patterns are rendered unperformable. For example, in one Latin American republic the present writer, at that time unacquainted with the local culture, was assured by the Minister of War that the Minister would immediately issue orders so that by the time the writer arrived at a certain river mouth a military boat with an outboard motor would be waiting to take the writer to a certain tribe of Indians. This statement (representational pattern) was made several times in the presence of the writer, the American Minister, and several other prominent personages. When the writer arrived at the specified river mouth some weeks later, he discovered that the Minister of War had performed no actional pattern consistent with the representational pattern whatever; the local garrison had received no orders, and, of course, no boat was present. In this case, we may speak of a segment of a pattern series. Minister says "I will order that boat to be ready when you arrive at such and such a river mouth." Writer says, "I will base my actions on this assurance." Follows a series of actional patterns performed by writer which leads him to specified river mouth. Once arrived there, however, he finds that his representational pattern ("I will base my actions on this assurance") is inconsistent with the actional pattern of Minister of War, as was also his original representational pattern. Result is that writer is unable to perform next pattern in train, that is, boating. Subsequent experience in this culture taught the writer that such inconsistency at that time was to some degree characteristic of the culture. (I am happy to hear that this type of inconsistency has since largely disappeared.) That such inconsistency may have a certain charm cannot be denied, but neither can it be denied that it produces maladjustments. Also we must recognize that a group of individuals may learn to live among lies. This is only to say that human beings are capable of making an adjustment to maladjusted cultural systems, but not to deny that systems which contain patterns for customary lying are inconsistent. Apparently, one of the difficulties of the late Mr. Chamberlain, Prime Minister of Great Britain, was the fact that he and his government were unable to make this type of adjustment to the representational patterns (lies) of Herr Hitler and the German foreign office.

Balance. In order to maintain its integrity, a system of culture seems to require a certain degree of balance; even though it also possesses relatedness, linkage, and consistency within itself an overbalance may send it crashing nonetheless. All terms which deal with this aspect of integration are borrowed from physics and it is difficult to think about such matters except in physical analogies. "Equilibrium" is a word which has been widely used in the social sciences in reference to the same problem, but it seems to suffer from the semantic difficulty that, to many people, it implies a condition of rest, complete static stability. Since no cultural system is ever completely static, we need a concept and vocabulary which can also be applied to dynamic conditions of a system.

To revert to a partially physical analogy for a moment, we might think of a group of mountain climbers going up the face of a cliff, fastened together by ropes. They represent a system in which they are in a state of relatedness, they are physically linked together, and their respective energies are put forth in a consistent manner, so the performance of one climber does not interfere with the others. However, a point may come when on a ledge or a ridge with all members straining in the same direction they suddenly lose their balance and the whole party falls into the abyss. The mere fact of being linked or fastened together may, in such a case, hasten their fall and insure the destruction of their system of relationships as a whole, rather than part by part.

The physical analogy may be suggestive in understanding cultural systems, provided we remember that cultural relations and cultural directions, rather than physical space and time, are the primary factors involved.

Within a cultural system balance of the whole requires a certain *reciprocity* between the constituent parts. We must try to rid ourselves, if possible, of the implications of mechanics which this word may have, as when we think of a "reciprocating engine." In a cultural system, reciprocity means that the performance of one portion of the system will aid the performance of other parts of the system, and vice versa; a mutual relationship of "helpfulness" exists between the patterns. In the cultures surveyed in the previous chapter we have seen, for example, how the patterns of work taxes for commoners made possible the economic support of the Inca state, which in turn was reciprocated with patterns assuring economic security of commoners. Among the Hopi the kinship organization provided the framework for membership in the religious organization whose patterns in turn served to buttress the kinship organization. All patterns for "division of labor" show some elements of reciprocity, of course. Whereas the principle of consistency holds that the performance of no parts of a cultural system shall hinder or interfere with other parts, the principle of reciprocity holds that the several parts must actually aid each other, either directly or indirectly.

The mere existence of a certain degree of reciprocity in a system will not, however, necessarily insure balance of the system as a whole. First, the reciprocity may not be system-wide. The procedures used in 1946 for disposing of surplus war property by the government showed nice reciprocity between the disposal agencies and private business, for example, but left the ordinary consumers "out in the cold." Thus we saw acres of automobiles and trailers either deteriorating or being destroyed, because of agreement by the government not to "flood the market" while consumers clamored for these articles, which were essential items of cultural equipment and otherwise unobtainable at the time. Other stocks of surplus goods were sold by the government only to dealers who retailed them to the taxpayers at prices far above what the government had either paid for them or obtained for them. To many consumers, conscious of the fact that the system required them to pay the taxes and buy the bonds to produce these goods in the first place, the disposal procedures seemed a rank violation of reciprocity. In the second place, reciprocity may not be equalized or even approach equalization within the system. Although it is one of the tenets of laissez-faire economics, for example, that everyone in a capitalistic system is paid according to his contribution to the system and that competition will eliminate injustices, a good many workers and middle-class persons are beginning to question the system. They are willing to admit that they are paid and that the patterns are to a degree reciprocal; but they ask, thinking of the payments to various executives and large stockholders: Does any man contribute enough to be paid $500,000 or $1,000,000 per year when the system pays a mere subsistence wage or a trifle more to the great bulk of the participants? Few students any longer deny that the present "concentration of great wealth" in the hands of a relatively few, and unequitable distribution of income represent a serious disbalance in our economic system, which, unless corrected to some extent, may lead to the collapse or destruction of the system itself.

Integration thus requires a certain balance of the patterns of a culture; it requires that one phase of life does not get "too far out of line" with other phases. Examples from history are numerous of systems which have disintegrated due to overemphasis upon one or the other aspect of the system. Pleasure is said to have become so dominant a feature of life in the latter days of Rome that large numbers of the population gave themselves over to idleness or amusement, to such an extent that it was no longer possible to perform adequately the patterns of maintenance, such as agriculture, construction, and defense. The great emphasis which our culture lays upon physical and mechanical aspects has often been cited as a serious disbalance of our patterns and institutions. This can hardly be doubted, when we are faced with the fact that we are in possession of cultural patterns capable of reducing most of modern civilization to a shambles and have trained considerable elements of our population to perform them, while at the same time we give relatively little emphasis to the training of people in the patterns of social and cultural adjustment which would render such destruction unnecessary.

MAJOR CULTURAL OBJECTIVES AND INTEGRATION

A considerable amount of descriptive, empirical evidence has been adduced to show that certain types of major cultural objectives seem to have more integrating power than others. Such objectives are goals around which entire systems of culture may be organized and integrated.

One such distinction is that made between the "sacred" and the "secular" type of culture which, in anthropological circles, has been emphasized in the researches of Redfield and his group.[6] This view is derived in some respects from the distinction raised by the German sociologist Tönnies [7] between community (*Gemeinschaft*) and society (*Gesellschaft*) and also from the differentiation underlined by the French sociologist Durkheim [8] between the sacred and the profane aspects of social (cultural) life. Redfield has shown quite convincingly that, in the series of four communities which he studied in Yucatan, at least, the "sacred" type of culture exhibits a much higher degree of total integration than the secular. The Hopi culture, which we have previously sketched, is a good example of the "sacred" type: the whole culture is tied together, as it were, by a system of mental patterns, projective patterns in truth, which rationalize, explain, and justify the overt aspects of the culture in terms of the relations of the people to the supernatural. The Hopi Way is an excellent charter, a superb binder, for the whole of Hopi culture. Associated with sacredness, Redfield sees homogeneity (relatedness) in the various constituent parts of the culture and group solidarity. This state of affairs is contrasted with the secular type of culture which exhibits heterogeneity and individualism. The "folk" type of culture, according to Redfield, usually exhibits the sacred type of organization, whereas the modern urban culture, in which most of the readers of this book participate, exhibits the secular, rather unintegrated variety. Redfield's analysis seems to be incontrovertible in the field of his investigations in Yucatan and Mexico. He himself is chary of generalizing to other situations. But his conclusions raise the question as to whether integration is possible only on the "sacred" basis of organization. Since our own culture is definitely not of the "sacred" type and shows very little possibility of developing in that direction at present, we are naturally interested in whether or not approach to integration may not be achieved on some other basis.

Value-objectives. If we raise our sights to take in the whole of the varieties of human culture there seems to be no reason to believe that religion or supernaturalism embodies the only type of objective which can dominate and integrate a cultural system. It must be admitted that the "sacred" type of integration has had considerable success in various cultures, like those of the Indians of Central America, the European cultures of the medieval period, the Hopi of the Southwest, and so on.

Is it religion or supernaturalism per se which produces integration in these cases, or is there some deeper principle at work? On theoretical grounds, the answer seems to be that an integration can be achieved around *any* type of major objective or group of them, and the facts seem to bear this out. Among the Incas, the well-being of the total society seems to have been the major objective, although it was symbolized in the person of the emperor and expressed occasionally in somewhat mystical terms. So far as our information goes, it seems that the body of mental patterns known as Marxian doctrine (as revised by Lenin and Stalin) provides the integration of the modern Soviet Union and the major objective is that set of conditions summed up in "the perfect communist society," "From each according to his ability, to each according to his need." The integrational success of this objective is not known in detail at present in terms of statistics or of cultural studies made by outsiders, but the performance of the Red Army during World War II indicates at least that the Soviet culture was not at that time "coming apart at the seams" as so many had predicted that it would. At all events, the Soviet objectives are certainly not religious, whatever else they may be, and the Soviet Union can hardly be described as a "sacred society" in the same general category to which this phrase customarily refers. The objective of economic ease and power (associated with the profits motive) seems to have high integrating value in large business organizations within our own society, although we must admit that it seems to fail in integrating the entire culture. If we may accept Benedict's analysis of Japanese culture, we see a system of custom highly integrated about a non-religious concept of "honor," symbolized in the person of the emperor. The system is bound together by an intricate web of reciprocal patterns phrased in terms of obligations.[8a] Without citing further illustrations it would seem that we must conclude that the specific content of the objective is not necessarily the crucial factor in integration.

Any objective would seem to be capable of integrating a cultural system, provided it possesses the power to *permeate* the major remaining portions of the culture and provided it possesses high *value* in the cultural system. In other words the objective should be tied up in some way (see preceding section) with most of the cultural activities specified in the patterns so that they actually are "directed" toward this ultimate goal and so that the members of the group understand the ultimate connection. Likewise, the objective must be linked with representational and mental patterns in such a way that the people regard it as valuable; in fact, a highly integrative objective usually appears as the most valuable goal of life; striving toward it seems to make life worth living; its existence as a goal provides a "reason" for the other activities specified in the cultural configuration. Supernatural salvation in the next world, a life of materialistic well-being in this life, the prospect of social and personal order and peace in a secular sense—all these and many other goals have shown success in cultural integration in the past.

Positive and negative sanctions. The fact that the major objective and its associated mental patterns in fact often constitute a mental system projected into the future seems to add to their effectiveness rather than the contrary. Acquired drives based on anticipation of future bliss or wealth, for example, can be very motivating, even though they are rewarded only piecemeal, or symbolically, or in fantasy. On the other hand some systems are so arranged that the rewards are tangible and empirical in the present, real world. The system which Confucius set up in China promised no rewards in the after-life, but held out the prospect of peace of mind and physical well-being in this existence.

In addition to acquired drives of the appetite variety which create a desire for the goals or objectives, an integrated cultural system also creates anxieties which may be raised if the patterns toward the goal are not followed by the people. Hellfire and damnation in the after-life, an old age of poverty and ill health, a life of annoyance and frustration, failure in hunting and agriculture, fear of destruction by a foreign enemy —these and other punishments are held out to raise the anxieties of the wayward individual who fails to follow the patterns. And, of course, physical punishment by police or other agents of the society always stands in the background, although, as we have seen, some systems make very little use of this sanction.

In the literature of social science these <u>rewards and punishments</u> are often spoken of as positive and negative sanctions respectively. The positive sanction motivates the members of society to strive toward the objective with the promise of reward; the negative sanction threatens punishment of one sort or another to those who would stray from the road or who would attempt to upset the integration of the system.

The success which religion and supernaturalism have had in integrating many cultures seems to be explained in large part by the characteristics of "projective systems" as discussed in Chapter 15. A projective system, if effectively inculcated in the population, creates for the average individual an "unseen world." This world which, though unseen, is felt to be ever present about us, operates according to rules and usually involves sanctions which are thought to be beyond the control of ordinary humans except by following the rules. If the system of mental customs which constitutes such a supernatural projective system is properly linked up with the other aspects of the culture, if it is related to and consistent with so-called mundane experience (including cultural experience), the members of society are often under compulsion to see a large part of everyday cultural behavior and artifacts as manifestations of the unseen world.[9] Or they may be convinced that what persons trained to some other cultures consider to be merely "secular" patterns have their roots in the unseen universe which is beyond the limits of direct, empirical contact. For people in such a culture, all or most customs may be seen as consistently related to the projective system and interpreted in terms of their effects in the supernatural sphere. The Hopi Way seems to be such a system which, on the whole, is consistently related to all other parts of the culture. Thus certain types of religious or supernatural systems of mental patterns possess high ability to permeate. Added to this, a religious system may incorporate the highest values of the culture, and by projecting them into the non-empirical world removes such values from empirical testing and criticism. This adds to stability and integration of the system. If "cleanliness is next to Godliness" the matter is settled for true believers without further discussion. If "the Lord loves a cheerful giver" that is sufficient reason for charity. This is quite a different point of view, of course, from that expressed in "honesty is the best policy"—meaning that it is the best way to get along in secular relationships. In a well-integrated "sacred" culture the basic policies are not determined by human action—they have already been settled in the unseen sphere which permeates all aspects of human life. Man's duty is to follow faithfully the patterns of the culture in order to keep in line with these foreordained directives, to escape the punishment which follows failure or deviation, and to receive the rewards which come either in this life or the next from activity consistent with the structure of the supernatural.

Cultural integration on such a basis has much to be said for it. As scientists, of course, we are not in a position to say whether this or that religious system is objectively "true" or "false." It is, however, apparent that this type of integration is probably not immediately achievable in our own culture. Two reasons may be mentioned. First, most of our religious and "sacred" culture consists of mental patterns which are not consistent with certain other large segments of the culture; it is very difficult to make an effective linkage between current religious concepts and the experimental method, for example, so that the one can meaningfully be discussed in terms of the other or vice versa. Second, the skeptical attitude and its associated pattern of having everything "proved" are firmly imbedded aspects of the culture and are grossly inconsistent with the "believing" attitude and the pattern of taking the unseen world on "faith." Skepticism is firmly linked with science, another fundamental aspect of the culture, and is also related to our mechanistic technology, which tends to train members of the society to "take apart" anything they do not understand in order to be able to "fix" it for practical purposes. By reinterpretation, the religious patterns can doubtless be more closely related to the other aspects of our culture, but the skeptical attitudes and questioning frame of mind are so strong a trend and have produced so many rewards that they seem to stand as an impenetrable bar to an overall integration of our culture by a projective system incorporating the features of religion as it has been traditionally known in our history.

This does not mean that religion has outlived its usefulness. It is still a very important aspect of our cultural life, which brings solace to many individuals frustrated by the inconsistencies of the culture and by other circumstances. The religious beliefs also have a strong integrative influence in certain categories and sections of the society. Our only point is that a "sacred" type of *overall* integration of Western culture does not seem possible without tremendous changes either in the culture as a whole, in the traditional religious patterns, or both.

PRACTICAL ASPECTS OF INTEGRATION

Complete cultural integration has never been achieved for a society as a whole, and there is considerable doubt that it would be altogether desirable. Some years ago Aldous Huxley wrote *Brave New World* which was in some respects a satire on utopias and the type of impractical "social planning" which is often associated with them. He pictured an imaginary society, stratified according to ability, which was in turn controlled by medical treatment of unborn embryos in such a way that just enough individuals for each social category were produced each year. Those who were destined to be workers, for example, were so treated that they were unable to develop the desires and ambitions which upper-class status could satisfy. A pair of wonderful drugs were used to eliminate fatigue, anxiety, and other drives which might occasionally arise in spite of the integrated patterning of the system itself. Thus every one had his place, all wants were satisfied, no yearnings or fears were developed, perfect peace and order reigned. The moral of the book was, however, that in such a system life lost its savor, living was no longer fun; there were no new goals beyond the horizon, no strivings, no hopes, no disappointments, no ambitions.

Such a degree of integration is probably beyond the limits of possibility at present and for most societies would not be worth achieving anyway. But lack of integration, conflict, and confusion are even more undesirable in the Western system of culture, especially as its area of influence tends to take in larger and larger portions of the planet. Planning for a greater measure of harmony between our conflicting patterns is not only possible, but apparently essential if we are to avoid a heavy price in destruction and blighted lives.

After the close of the Second World War many persons in all countries looked forward to the establishment of a world organization which could integrate the peoples of the globe around certain objectives, the most important of which was generally phrased as peace and tranquillity. If the desire for the achievement of this objective is strong and pervading, there are undoubtedly cultural techniques which can be developed for reaching it. Although the detailed discussion of such planning is beyond the scope of this work, the interested reader can well elaborate certain plans on the basis of principles laid down in the preceding chapters. He must always remember, however, that principles of culture must be applied in relation to already existing conditions of culture. "Principles" do not work in a void, or just because we want them to. We must have accurate, empirical knowledge of the cultural situations around the world and they must be analyzed in terms of a consistent theory. The same applies to any planning which may be done for the purpose of eliminating some of the conflicts and inconsistencies in our own national culture.

NOTES TO CHAPTER 24

1. Gillin, 1942.
2. See among numerous other works on this aspect of our culture, Angell, 1941.
3. Redfield, 1941; see also Wirth, 1938.
4. Sorokin, 1941; the concept is further developed in the preceding three volumes of this work.
4a. Mayo, 1945.
5. Parts of the following paragraphs originally appeared in slightly different form in Gillin, 1944. Thanks are expressed to Dr. J. Alden Mason, editor of the *American Anthropologist*, for permission to use this material here.
6. Redfield, 1941.
7. Tönnies, 1887.
8. Durkheim, 1915.
8a. Benedict, 1946.
9. For a psychological explanation, compare Sherif, 1936.

CHAPTER 25

Conditions and Processes of Cultural Change

WESTERN CIVILIZATION and, particularly, the North American varieties of it, have exhibited so many changes even during the lifetimes of persons now living that probably no readers of this book have to be convinced of the fact of cultural change. One has only to glance through an account of the twenties, such as Frederick Lewis Allen's *Only Yesterday*, to realize that the American culture has altered in two decades, not only in such obvious traits as fashions of dress, but also in more fundamental matters, such as the cultural definition of the relations between labor and management, or the worth of the individual. To go a little further back, if we read the romantic novels or the newspapers of the close of the Victorian period we realize that many of the fundamental values and aspirations common to persons of our society in those times have either disappeared or received new interpretations in our culture of today. It is a truism that the Victorian lady and gentlemen were different persons from their counterparts in the 1940's; they followed patterns which in some cases our own generation no longer knows how to practise (for example, where can one find men today outside a few specialized groups who know how to drive a four-in-hand, how to use a moustache cup, how to dance the polka?); their culture provided them with expectations and with goals which in some cases have been discarded today, in others transferred to the levels of fantasy or myth.

If such changes are familiar to us, we must recognize that something similar occurs in all cultures, although often at varying rates. There is no such thing as a completely static functioning culture, although in certain times and places the changes may be so slow as to be barely perceptible during a single lifetime, and people may come to believe that a final equilibrium has been achieved. Wherever we have data of history or archaeology covering any significant period of time in a society's past, however, we are forced to recognize the fact of change, even in nonliterate cultures. The warlike mounted tribes of the Plains Indians who presented such effective resistance to the encroachments of the American settlers in the nineteenth century, followed a significantly different mode of life two hundred years earlier. The glory of the Aztec capital which confronted Cortez in the early sixteenth century was unknown a century or two earlier. Even what we think of as the distinctive flavor of Eskimo life is apparently a development of the last few centuries previous to the European discovery.[1] Thus cultural change seems to be ubiquitous.

At the present period of history it is especially necessary that we arrive at some scientific understanding of the processes of cultural change, some grasp of the principles involved which would enable us to predict to a degree, if not to control, the changes in modes of life and thought which have increased in tempo throughout the modern world. Because of the vastly increased contact between peoples throughout the earth and because of the rapid rate of invention and discovery in technological fields, the study of cultural change becomes a practical matter of utmost significance. Let us turn, then, to a brief consideration of the underlying principles and processes in cultural change. Following this, in the next chapter, we shall deal with a particular form of cultural change which is of special significance in the modern world, namely, acculturation.

INNOVATIONS

Although cultures may be changed by learning and unlearning the patterns which compose them, it is obvious that the patterns will not be altered unless something new is presented and accepted by the society in question. At the outset, then, two problems present themselves: (1) under what conditions do new patterns appear?, and (2) under what conditions are new patterns accepted and learned?

Inventions and discoveries. All elements of culture content are, of course, originated by individuals in the last analysis. In many cases the individual is unconscious of the fact that he originated something and in other cases the new contribution seems to be so trivial that no immediate notice is taken of it and no effort is made to identify the originator. Thus we have no record concerning the individual or individuals who first discovered the malleability of copper ore or who first bent a piece of wood into a bow and used the elasticity of the material to project an arrow. But we may be sure that some individuals were involved. Thus we should dispose at once of the notion that innovations appear "automatically" or in some mystical or superhuman manner.

The two processes most usually invoked to explain innovations which appear internally within a functioning culture are invention and discovery. A convenient definition of these processes is that of Linton: "A discovery is any addition to knowledge, an invention (is) a new application of knowledge."[2] From this point of view invention is the important functional process in cultural innovation. In fact, practically all discoveries have to be followed or accompanied by inventions if they are to be culturally significant. For example, the discovery that steam tends to expand and therefore is a potential source of power was not culturally important until certain inventions, such as the cylinder, steam-tight piston, and valve, had been perfected to the point where the discovery of the properties of steam were humanly useful. The discovery that the atoms of a certain kind of uranium are fissionable was a basic finding; but the atomic bomb awaited a very complex series of inventions for the control of this process and the application of the energy so produced to certain human purposes. At the time of this writing we are awaiting still other inventions which will permit the application of this type of energy to more constructive purposes than the obliteration of cities.

In our culture we are often prone to think of innovations as occurring only in the realm of materialistic things, probably because of our emphasis upon technology and economic patterns. But it must be understood that innovations are invented or discovered in the non-material fields of culture as well. We should not be misled by the fact that individuals who have produced an acceptable new gadget or machine process are usually honored as "inventors," whereas those who have suggested new forms, say, of social organization have sometimes been castigated as "revolutionists." The realization that human beings in society adjust to nature and to each other by means of cultural patterns is a discovery in a field not exclusively technological. The application of this knowledge to such fields as labor relations and colonial administration involves inventions of a social or cultural nature. Non-technological inventions have had a profound influence, often more fundamental than those confined to technology. Representative democracy, the joint-stock company, the labor union, the experimental method in science, the elective system of taking courses in schools and universities are just as truly inventions as the steam engine or the internal combustion motor.

A distinction is usually made between *basic inventions* and *improving inventions*. Once an invention of the basic type has been made and accepted into a culture, a whole series of improving inventions usually follows in its wake. The basic invention of the wheel was, as every one knows, followed by literally thousands of inventions involving many improvements upon the form of the wheel itself and also its application to a wide diversity of uses. The first improvement seems to have been that which allowed the wheel to turn on its axle, then possibly the preserving of the life of the wheel by the addition of a metal rim, then its lightening by the substitution of spokes for the solid disk. Later we see the development of bearings, the invention of brakes, then pulley wheels, cog wheels, and so on. A basic non-material invention such as double-entry bookkeeping is followed by a whole series of elaborations or "improvements" designed to increase its efficiency or its application to a wider variety of situations.

Thus we see that discovery and invention are two important processes whereby new ideas, new artifacts, and new usages are presented within the framework of a culture.

Borrowing. Although all innovations appear originally as discoveries and inventions, the new patterns which are presented for possible acceptance by any particular culture may not have been originated within its own configuration. In other words, a culture may change by taking over something from other cultures, a process which is called *borrowing*. Through this process a society, provided it is in contact with other societies, does not have to depend entirely upon its own resources of originality, but may share in the innovations which have been made in alien cultures. The conditions which make for the acceptance or rejection of such foreign novelties will be discussed later. Other things equal, however, a culture which is in a position of having foreign traits presented to it at a high rate of frequency will naturally have more *potentialities* for changes than one which is isolated from such influences.

In summary, the first essential to cultural change is that there be "something new" presented to the practitioners of the culture. The sources of such potential novelties are discovery, invention, and presentation from foreign cultures.

Analysis of innovations. If we examine matters more closely we see that there are several ways in which "something new" may be added to a culture. In the first place, an innovation may be offered as something entirely unique, so far as the given culture is concerned; something for which there is no equivalent in the preëxisting system of customs and artifacts. On the other hand, the new item may be presented as an alternative to an element or complex already existing, in which case its acceptance depends upon its competitive worth. Pottery, for instance, has usually appeared as an alternative or competitor to other types of containers. In the case of the Anastasi sequence of culture in the Southwest, pottery appeared in late Basket Maker culture as a substitute or alternative for baskets. On the other hand, it would appear that the horse as a riding animal appeared among the tribes of the Plains as something radically novel, for which there was no analogy in their former culture.

If we delve into these matters still more deeply we must recognize that there are several distinct aspects of patterns in which novelties or innovations may possibly be offered. These may be thought of as the aspects of form, principle, function or purpose, and meanings. If we think of artifacts as objectifications of mental patterns and as adjuncts of actional patterns, it will be understood that innovations or modifications in the field of artifacts may also be included in our discussion of patterns. Thus innovation may take place in the form of a cultural item, in the principles involved in its performance and design, in the function, or in the meanings associated with it. On the other hand, an innovation may involve all four aspects. These aspects are essential not only in considering changes originating within a culture, but also in the problems of acculturation and other changes originating outside.[3]

The most radical type of cultural innovation would be one which involved newness in all four aspects. Such innovations are apparently very rare; at least there are few which have been adequately documented. The wheeled cart drawn by domestic animals, even in its first crude appearance in Neolithic times in the Old World, must have been a comprehensive invention of this sort. We know that, from the point of view of the native cultures of the Andean region, it was a complete innovation when first presented by the Spaniards. The form of the wheel had no artifactual prototype in the native cultures. The principle of rotary motion may have been aboriginally comprehended in the use of rollers, although the evidence is not clear; but at any rate, the combination of rotary motion with the suspension of the load above the ground on an axle was quite radical; furthermore, the principle of combining animal-power with rotary motion for traction purposes was totally novel. The function of transporting loads was, of course, already recognized in the culture and fulfilled by other patterns (for example, on the backs of men and llamas), but the transport of persons, which the cart and wagon also performed, was practically confined in aboriginal Andean culture to ceremonial travels of the Inca emperor and his immediate family and was accomplished by man-borne litters. Since nothing similar had previously existed in this culture, the meanings and associations attached to the cart were entirely new. For example, in most localities it perforce became associated with roads which went up and down grades without the use of steps, used on the previous Inca roads; it became firmly associated with European or cholo (mixed blood) status, and even to this day carries some of this meaning in the minds of Indians. The wheeled vehicle has not yet been as extensively accepted in this region as in some other parts of the world, a fact partly to be explained by its radicalness in terms of the native culture.

It is probably safe to say that most of what are ordinarily considered basic inventions involve a fundamental innovation in only one of the aspects mentioned, at least when they are first presented to the culture. If they are accepted, changes in the other aspects may quite likely occur. Since function or purpose is really a matter of felt need or drive, a new function usually gradually comes into being as a result of small cumulative changes in the cultural situation, rather than as a sudden innovation. On the other hand, at a certain point in the development of this process it is not unusual for individuals to arise who "point out" the new need which the bulk of society may have vaguely felt but not explicitly recognized. The formulation of such a need or function, even in the absence of patterns for its fulfilment, is of course a cultural innovation, if the formulation becomes part of the mental patterns of the group. The recognition of a need for a cancer cure and of a need for the abolition of international conflicts are now parts of our culture, of course. The mere fact that such functions are desired also serves to stimulate the discovery or invention of means for carrying them out.

From a statistical point of view most basic inventions probably involve fundamental innovations, either in principles or in form of patterns and artifacts, or both. Let us mention first the sort of invention which involves innovation in both principle and form. In many hunting cultures means are required for the purpose of casting pointed and shafted projectiles against game animals and/or enemies. The spear-thrower and its associated patterns seems to have been chronologically the earliest solution to this problem. The later bow-and-arrow fulfilled essentially the same function, but employed an entirely different principle, namely the elasticity of wood and string of some sort in place of directly applied muscular power of the human arm and centrifugal force. In the application of this new principle the form of the bow and the patterns of use turn out to differ radically from those of the spear thrower. On the other hand we may observe another type of invention in which the form of the artifact is held constant, but a new principle is introduced. For example, in some bow-using cultures—notably the Eskimo—it was discovered that the bow in essentially the same form as used for projecting arrows could also be used for turning a drill. The principle is that of rotary motion applied by twisting the bow string around the shaft of the drill. In such a case, of course, the form of the actional patterns used is different, depending upon whether the bow is used as a weapon or a tool; the form of the artifact, however, remains constant. In the case of the bow drill, however, it appears that neither the artifact (bow) nor the function (drilling holes in wood and bone) was new to the culture. The bow was previously present as a hunting weapon, whereas hole-boring had been previously practised by means of awls held in the hand. Therefore, we see a case in which the innovation consists in applying an old artifact to an old function by means of a new principle.

Innovations may also take place which at the start involve only a new meaning for already existing elements, that is, a new symbolic reference.

In 1946 an agitational group with many trappings of Fascism appeared in Georgia. It was called the Columbians. One of its artifacts was a shoulder patch, representing a jagged streak of lightning, worn on shirts of the members. According to press accounts this was an exact copy of shoulder patches used to identify one of the (now demobilized) United States army divisions which fought in World War II. The material artifact was the same, it was used in the same way, it had the same general function (individual identification with an organized, militant group), but the meaning was new. The jagged lightning now became associated with a rabble-rousing organization avowedly dedicated to "white supremacy," anti-Semitism, and anti-Catholicism, rather than with a military unit dedicated to the extirpation of such goals in Europe.

It is probably not necessary to discuss further examples. Our purpose is mainly to suggest that innovation in culture must be examined closely if we are to understand specific cases and if we are to be able to predict, at least in some measure, their outcome.

The innovator. Although the majority of the members of a society may be content with the current patterns, there are always some *deviants*, some persons who are not satisfied with the patterns enjoined by society as a whole. They are always trying to do it "some other way." Such individuals can only be explained in terms of a study of their personalities or personal histories. That is, their appearance and the form of their originality are not predictable on the basis of our knowledge of the patterns of their society, except that their innovations will usually have to be produced within the already existent framework of the culture. These deviants may have basic drives which are innately stronger than those of other persons, or they may have, through accidents of training or experience, developed acquired drives which are not satisfied by the available cultural techniques. Or they may be individuals with unusual sensitivity to stimuli and unusual mental ability which enable them to notice features of the situation which others pass by and to imagine new situations which more stodgy members of the society have never thought of. In some cases they are cripples or persons inherently unable to practise certain customs of the society (unable to perform the generally made responses). In sum, the innovating individual is one who, for some reason or other, is *dissatisfied* with current modes or who is able to appreciate *greater satisfaction* possible by some change. If his innovations are not taken over by other members of the society, he is often regarded as "queer," eccentric, or peculiar. The writer remembers one Carib man in British Guiana who was a crank in the matter of decorating himself for dances. On such occasions it is customary for men to plaster their foreheads with honey and to stick on a thick mass of white down feathers of the bush turkey. This fellow insisted on applying the decoration to the back of his neck "because it looked better and kept the feathers out of his eyes." Up to the time of my departure from the tribe this innovation had not been taken over by others and hence had not become a custom. But it is this kind of deviant who every once in a while turns up something which seems to offer advantages not provided in previously practiced patterns.

Successful innovators are not always cranks, nor are they often to be regarded as abnormal in any sense. In fact major discoveries or inventions always require a relatively high (1) ability to *notice* new things and combinations, plus (2) ability to *appreciate* their potentialties in terms of human usefulness. Originality of this sort, whether anonymous or famed, is the very cornerstone of cultural innovation. Every society interested in progressive change would be well advised to seek out and equip possible innovators, for, on the basis of our present knowledge, they are statistically rare in any population and their abilities are often allowed to go to waste for want of motivation and reward. Rigorous suppression of originality is socially stupid.

The ability to make discoveries and inventions is not necessarily correlated with the ability to win their acceptance from society. In our own society the laboratory inventor frequently must join forces with salesmen and promotors in order to put his inventions across. When an individual appears who combines originality with popular appeal and the ability to win substantial numbers of followers to his ideas, he usually effects a major change in culture—changes the course of history, as it is said. It is often pointed out that such "great men" are the children of their time, that their accomplishments are dependent upon the accumulation of a vast number of small innovations made by less spectacular individuals. This is true in practically all cases, but the truly great man is one who synthesizes the potentialities of his culture into a new combination and induces his people to follow the new patterns he develops. While we cannot rely exclusively on a "great man theory" of cultural change, we must recognize that many of the major changes in culture have been put in motion by outstanding individuals who themselves made original contributions, men such as Jesus, Mohammed, Hiawatha (supposedly the originator of the League of the Iroquois), and Pachacuti (supposedly the founder of the later Inca imperial system).

Factors stimulating and permitting innovations. *Accident* accounts for many innovations. Individuals are said to "stumble" upon an innovation which they realize offers a new satisfaction or is more rewarding than a previous pattern. Penicillin, for example, was accidentally discovered as a specific cure for certain bacterial infections when a medical man noticed that a certain type of mold growing on a bacterial "culture" seemed to inhibit the growth of the microörganisms he was trying to propagate with quite another purpose in mind. Accidental discoveries of this sort are often made through *play with technique*. Aniline dyes are said to have been invented by German chemists who were simply trying to see into how many chemical combinations coal-tar could be broken up. The first copper axes made in Europe were flat, but, probably due to play with the technique of hammering them, forms soon began to appear with flanges turned up along the edges and it was readily perceived that the split end of a wooden handle could be more securely held in place by the flanged type. From this presumably accidental invention numerous "improvements" were made. Another aspect of the same thing is illustrated by modifications resulting when a workman attempts to transfer an activity pattern from one form of material to another. For example, curvilinear designs may be easily painted on pottery, but when one tries to weave them into a textile they tend to become angular. Customary techniques suitable for house building with wood usually are modified when the builders turn to stone or steel. On the representational level, we have already mentioned the numerous alterations to which the early Semitic alphabet was subjected as it was applied to languages with differing phonemic systems.

Still another type of change which may be classed under the head of accident is due to faulty *imitation or poor memory*. In a community of Eastern Guatemala red water jars are made by the Indians and decorated with painted flower and animal designs in black. Among the latter are silhouetted designs of monkeys with tails. However during my stay in 1942 one of the women potters originated a style depicting an animal without a tail and with pointed ears. I saw some of her first specimens and asked what they were supposed to represent. It turned out that she was under the impression that she was drawing a monkey, but, having never seen a live specimen, had forgotten that they were supposed to have tails and short ears. The innovation caught on, and has now become an established style, although no tailless monkeys are native to the Western Hemisphere. In the same community the Indians have a brass band, but are unable to read music. Some one occasionally goes to the city, memorizes a tune, and comes back to teach it to the band, or a traveler passing through whistles a piece, which is copied by the musicians. During my 1942 visit I gave them the tune of "On Wisconsin." When I returned in 1946 I heard them playing what I took to be a new composition and asked the name of it. They were somewhat offended that I had not recognized "Adelante, Visconsin," which, in the interval, had passed through a considerable number of mutations, not to say mutilations. Innovations due to faulty imitation and faulty memory are apparently more likely to appear in a non-literate culture than otherwise.

Socially stimulated innovations are produced in certain societies. When a society feels a need for which there is no adequate customary satisfaction it may offer unusual *rewards* to innovators and thus stimulate them to search for new cultural solutions. Thus the Israelites of the eighth and seventh centuries B.C. felt a strong need for spiritual interpretation and gave a certain degree of honor and followership to the Prophets who could find ways of interpreting the Will of God in the interests of the society. The prophet cults, such as the Ghost Dance,[4] which sprang up among the reservation Indians in the latter nineteenth century in this country seem to have been a similar response to stress, in which a considerable number of individuals were stimulated to develop appealing new rituals which lowered the anxieties of the people. In the realm of material things we remember the rewards offered by the government during the First World War for the invention of an all-purpose motor, which resulted in the development of the Liberty Motor. At the present time several substantial money prizes, not to mention high prestige, are awaiting those who will perfect an effective procedure for the prevention and cure of cancer. Some cultures seem to have the effect of developing a "novelty drive," so that there is a felt desire on the part of members of the society for "new things." Any one who can satisfy this acquired drive is rewarded for his efforts, and this serves as a social stimulus for innovations. Our own society, especially in the realm of women's fashions and mechanical artifacts, is constantly demanding "something new and different." In fourth-century Greece, new philosophical ideas were roundly applauded and their originators usually heavily rewarded. In Elizabethan England the poet who invented new verse forms and original conceits received distinction and patronage. These examples show us that innovations may be socially stimulated, but they demonstrate also that the cultural system usually controls the type of innovations which are encouraged. Among ourselves poetic and philosophical inventions receive little reward, whereas Greece and the England of Elizabeth offered few prizes for new types of mechanical gadgets or industrial processes.

Finally, to mention no other factors, close contact with alien cultures and steady inflow of foreign cultural influences usually afford an enhanced supply of novelties which may be accepted or rejected by a culture. An "iron curtain" inhibits such presentations.

So far as the individual innovator is concerned, in addition to native ability to notice and appreciate new things, he must have motivation for doing so. The individual who is satisfied with things as they are will let his discoveries lie dormant.

Inhibitions to innovation. Provided the society is "normal" mentally, the search for or recognition of new items of culture can be choked off at the start by certain conditions which inhibit these activities. Lack of motivation or of felt need is probably the most fundamental factor. Certain societies have convinced themselves that they are satisfied with the culture which they have and that "new-fangled" ideas and processes are unnecessary. This state of affairs is symbolized in the hymn, "The Old Time Religion" which, it is proclaimed, "was good enough for granpappy, it was good enough for pappy, and it's good enough for me." Of course, such a feeling of complacency seldom if ever extends to the entire membership of a society, but the prevailing attitude may be such that individuals of originality see only indifference and possibly hostility as the reward for any innovations they might produce. Active hostility against new things may be incorporated in a culture, so that innovators are discouraged and punished, whatever may be the intrinsic merits of their offerings. It is natural for all cultures to suppress deviations to some extent, and this self-preservative tendency may simply be carried to the point where the door is shut on change, except of a surreptitious or "revolutionary" type. Punishments for innovation may take the form of loss of prestige or other social privileges, or they may involve direct infliction of pain. Numerous studies of the South show how such an innovation as rotation of crops (which is badly needed from any point of view) is discouraged by social pressure. The emotional atmosphere is fairly well portrayed in Ellen Glasgow's novel, *Barren Ground*. Direct physical punishment for innovations or deviations has usually been the foremost weapon of authoritarian régimes from those of Czarist Russia and Hitler to certain reactionary communities in the United States which have relied on instruments such as the police, the militia, the tar pot and feather barrel, and mob-inflicted torture or death. If one stands a good chance of being horse-whipped or castrated for suggesting a new idea for the improvement of the status quo, one usually keeps such originality strictly to himself. In the long run, societies using suppression of innovation of course suffer from backwardness and cultural poverty or stagnation.

Finally, we must mention that the orientation or ethos of the cultural system as a whole may tend to inhibit innovation in certain sectors while not interfering in others. In the Deep South, for example, such mechanical inventions as the machine cotton picker are not suppressed, whereas any individual who ventures to suggest a change in the wage or social system is fortunate if he is only socially ostracized. Taking our country as a whole, at a time when every day's newspaper reveals some new technological invention (such as rockets and airplanes capable of circling the globe non-stop), the same papers attempt to persuade the public that the very idea that wage increases should show some proportionate correlation with profit increases is contrary to the foundations of American culture. Admitted that such incongruities are often manipulated by self-seeking groups, the latter would not waste their time in "argument" if the former did not have some plausability in the framework of our culture—namely that technological innovations are on the whole encouraged, whereas innovations in the structure of human relationships are in many cases outside the realm of consideration.

ACCEPTANCE AND REJECTION OF INNOVATIONS

The mere production of a new potential contribution to culture does not, of course, insure its acceptance. The ability to innovate does not always go hand in hand with the ability to induce the society to change its practices and traditions. Mere newness in itself is not necessarily followed by cultural change.

Psychological conditions of change. As a general proposition we may say that a culture or a specific element of it will change if the following psychological conditions are fulfilled: (1) if the society in question is under drives ("feels needs") which are not satisfied adequately by the presently available cultural resources; (2) if new solutions are adequately presented so that they may be comprehended and grasped (adequate stimulus value); (3) if the practice of new patterns is teachable, that is, if the necessary responses can be made; (4) and if the new items show promise of or can be proved to deliver more reward and satisfaction than currently available items. These propositions should, perhaps, be further discussed in socio-cultural terms in order to clarify their application to actual situations.

Drive aspects of change. First, it is fair to assume that the basic drives are operative in any culture. If new customs are being introduced for their satisfaction, their acceptance depends upon whether or not the innovations have the effect of satisfying such drives more effectively than the old customs. For example, it is not very difficult to convince a native that a repeating rifle provides game and thus helps to satisfy hunger a great deal more effectively than a bow and arrow or a throwing stick. Second, we must consider the acquired drives which are already present in the culture. Prestige is often important, and if the innovation is introduced by an individual of high status and prestige there will be a tendency for other members of the society to copy this individual in order to satisfy their own culturally generated prestige drives. However, some cultures seem to inculcate nothing similar to the prestige drive. This apparently is one reason why so little acculturation has occurred among the Pueblo peoples, since prestige drive seems to be undeveloped by their own cultures. Third, it is always possible, through appropriate manipulation, to create new drives in the members of a society. One of the commonest methods is via the use of force, which of course tends to create anxiety drives of various types. After the advent of white men, the Lac du Flambeau Indians of Wisconsin soon became aware of the fact that failure to practise such white customs as wearing short hair (for men), living in a house, speaking English, wearing shoes, participating in a church, and so forth, led to removal of privileges (that is, resulted in punishment); thus they rapidly developed a form of status anxiety which drove them to learn and to practise those customs which were approved by white men.[5]

An example of the attempted use of force in creating anxieties motivating to the dropping of old customs and the acceptance of new ones in an acculturation situation is the following report on the Mescalero Apache, made by Lt. V. E. Stottler of the 10th Infantry and Acting Indian Agent, in 1896.

... The police force consists of 1 captain and 13 privates. Their duties consist in herding and butchering cattle, making arrests, collecting and returning children to school, working at the sawmill, cleaning ditches, or any work that may have to be done pertaining to the agency, reservation, or school. ... Several of them have been discharged for working against the policy of the agent, others for refusing to cut off their hair, one for letting a prisoner escape unnecessarily. I use the police as a means toward civilizing the tribe, and when a member fails to come to my way off goes his official head. ... I use the police in compelling the Indians (males) to cut off their hair. When the matter was first broached the police demurred, and I discharged the chief and one private, both school Indians, for refusing. I personally paid one tractable old fellow $5 to cut his hair and gave a relative of his a place on the force for cutting his hair, and then I appointed an Indian who had been a soldier and kept his hair short. This gave me three. ... One of my hardest working Indians asked for a wagon, which I refused to give until he cut his hair. He did not comply, but three other candiates for wagons came in and without any solicitation requested to have their hair cut. With two other soldier Indians with short hair, these three, and the three short-haired police, I saw I could have a leverage on the police. ... I sent the police ... to bring in every male Indian who had ever been to school and I compelled them to cut off their hair and abandon breech clout and blanket and put on hat, coat, vest, shirt, pants, and shoes. In ten days I had one-third of the males in this condition. The Department then at my request sent me a letter calling on the old ones to cut their hair and put on civilized clothing, and in three weeks 100 per cent had been transformed. Some demurred, but a little force and a judicious use of the guardhouse accomplished the end desired. They will be kept up to this mark. ...

... The drunken rows and brawls so frequent in the past have entirely ceased. The tiswin camps have been broken up. I inaugurated repressive measures by giving hard labor to the manufacturers, and after making a huge bonfire of all the effects in a camp where I found the liquor the making of it has ceased.... One of the Indians obtained some wine in Tularosa last fall, and I hear that occasionally the Indians on the outskirts get wine from Mexicans, but the grand old drunken carousals of other days have gone for good....

...There has not been an Indian dance on the reservation since I have been agent. Attempts have been made to hold them, but they have been nipped in the bud and apparently the desire for them has ceased....

...If they can not be taught to be industrious and have all the warpath spanked out of them, it were high time to give up the effort.

...I can point as an evidence of progress during the past year to the following: Every male Indian has his hair cut short and has adopted civilized clothing. Paint has ceased to be used in their toilet. They have ceased to hold their barbarous dances.[6]

The advertising fraternity in modern North America has, at considerable expense to the sponsors and as a result of much random trial and error, evolved a number of techniques for creating and arousing acquired appetites in potential consumers. It is illustrative to note some of the methods used. Let us say that the advertiser sets out to create an appetite for lizard meat. We perhaps have it dinned into our eyes and ears that this is more nourishing than any other meat product (appeal to basic drive of hunger); it contains vitamins (appeal to acquired drive already created by other advertisers); it will make us socially successful because all the "best people" use lizard meat on cocktail canapes (appear to acquired drive of prestige); we may not be able to hold our job and keep our friends if we do not use it (appeal to acquired status anxiety); it is more economical calory for calory (appeal to money drive and security drive); and so on and so forth. The creation of new acquired drives, in short, always necessitates some reference to the basic drives which underlie them.

Stimulus aspects of change. Adequate presentation of new items is a first step in change. Since the taking over of new customs often involves copying and imitation,[7] it is essential that the new patterns be presented in such a way that the members of the society not only want to practise them, but also so that they can "see" clearly what the new pattern is. For this reason it is often easier to present artifacts and overt behavior patterns than it is to present items which involve considerable symbolism, although such a generalization has its limitations. It is quite easy to demonstrate the patterns of use for a lawnmower, for instance, but the various adjustments required to make a threshing machine operate efficiently are not so obvious to casual observation. Artifacts and their associated patterns, in short, differ considerably in their demonstrability. The same is true of many overt patterns. Sleight-of-hand patterns are, of course, deliberately designed to inhibit successful imitation. Likewise, in the realm of certain other overt cultural patterns not so deliberately designed, considerable demonstration is needed. For example, one may work in the same office all his life with a good stenographer and wish very much that he could imitate her shorthand without grasping the patterns which she practices. Thus it is that patterns differ among themselves with respect to their intrinsic communicability—some are easier to "sell" than others. In addition the introducer must either be given or make for himself an opportunity to present his innovation and to attract the attention of an audience, that is, members of the society who might be induced to adopt it. It is for this reason, in addition to the prestige which they enjoy, that prominent personages in the local social system are usually good introducers: they are highly "visible" to other members of the society and their behavior and cultural equipment are widely known. Thus an obscure bookkeeper would hardly be considered the best medium for introducing new styles in men's dress, not only because his position carries little prestige, but also because relatively few persons pay any attention to him or his raiment.

In respect to those innovations which involve symbolization, adoption naturally depends largely upon the success with which the meanings are transferred. Even when the same language is used by both introducer and prospective adopters confusion may be caused by injudicious choice of words and phrases, as most advertising copy writers and salesmen have to learn early in their careers. One reason, perhaps, that new scientific concepts penetrate the colleges and schools so tardily is the failure of many teachers to explain them in terms understandable to the students. Considerably more difficulty is, of course, encountered when the new item must be translated from one language to another. Many areas of the world have therefore developed "pidgin" and "creole" dialects which serve to bridge the gap between European and native tongues.

The principle of generalization may often be used with success in presenting new stimuli. This principle, as we recall, operates so that responses will be made to new stimuli in proportion to their similarity to old and famliar stimulations. For example, such Christian religious figures as the Holy Virgin have on occasion been presented to native peoples in terms and appearance which enable the natives to see that perhaps the Virgin is not so different from the old Mother Goddess or to some other familiar figure of the native pantheon. It has been sagely pointed out that, if Fascism comes to the United States, it will probably be presented as anti-Fascism. New wine, in short, often stands a better chance of being drunk from the old familiar bottles.

Response aspects of change. The adoption of a new item of culture usually involves the learning and practising of patterns of response, either entirely new, or modified to some extent from previous patterns. Other things equal, a new item will be the more readily accepted if it contains response elements already learned by the members of society or if its form is similar to that of current customs. A new custom which utilizes the same muscle groups as the custom it is designed to displace is usually easier to establish than a complete novelty. The iron spade and its patterns of use, for example, found ready acceptance among peoples who had been used to using a digging stick with foot rest (as in parts of the Andean area), whereas it was less favorably received by peoples accustomed to the use of the hoe (as in parts of tropical Africa). Idea systems which involve figures and modes of thought already current find more ready adoption than those whose concepts are totally foreign. The set of beliefs concerning "evil winds" and "bad airs" which was carried to the New World by the colonizing Spaniards spread rapidly where the native thought system was already concerned with malevolent draughts (for example in Yucatan).

Reward as the crux of cultural change. We cannot expect an old custom to be supplanted, so long as it is rewarding to the drives involved, unless a new custom can be demonstrated to be more rewarding. Christian rituals, for example, are often rather intricate and therefore difficult to demonstrate, but even more difficult is it to prove to people unacquainted with the Christian tradition that they are rewarding. Likewise, the rewards from democratic political patterns are not always immediately obvious. On the other hand, the advantage of a steel tool over one made of stone can be appreciated at once, and the value of using a perfected power-driven vehicle over the use of the human organism or slow-moving animals does not require argument—if reward is the only factor involved. Of course, everywhere people want to escape or avoid pain and punishment, so that force is always available as a means of changing customs. Force, however, can seldom be relied upon alone as a motivation for permanent change in culture, because, once it is removed, the customs which were based upon its alleviation or avoidance will tend to be dropped for want of motivation. Force is only useful in establishing relatively permanent changes if acquired drives of a fairly enduring type can be created with its aid. We have seen in the Amish culture, for example, that militarism was very punishing to the ancestors of the Amish in Europe and a number of avoiding customs were built upon fear of it. Even now, the growing of moustaches, which were originally symbols of the dreaded military, is carefully avoided although the people have been free of any militaristic threat for more than a century. However, the custom of shaving the upper lip has now become a rewarding response to drives of prestige, as defined in the culture.

In summary, if one is setting out to change a pattern or a custom, several things must be taken into account. One must know what people want. One must be able to show them that the suggested innovation is more satisfying than anything they know. One must be able to present the innovation so that it can be clearly comprehended as a stimulus. And one must induce people to try it out. If the innovation is not designed to satisfy current wants or drives, it may be necessary to develop new acquired drives which it will serve.

SOME BARS TO CULTURAL CHANGE

In spite of contacts and other opportunities for borrowing of culture or presentation of internal innovations, we often see that a "receiving society" refuses to accept certain items. In other cases accepted items are taken into the culture only partially or in modified form. In practically all cases, unless the culture of the receiving society is completely destroyed, such borrowings as are made appear in the form of selections rather than indescriminate choices.

1. If any of the conditions of the learning and performance of new customs are nullified to any degree a block will be set up. It is, of course, the task of the social scientist to analyze such conditions in socio-cultural terms. These matters have been touched upon and illustrated in the previous section.

We may mention a few other forms which interference with psychological factors may take. *Isolation*, either geographical or social, is a bar to borrowing from outside the culture or between categories within it. It represents a failure of the stimulus aspect of cultural change. The failure of new ideas or patterns to arise within the culture likewise inhibits change. In short a society will not take over new patterns unless the latter are at least presented and they become aware of them. *Punishment* for newness is a frequent inhibitor of change. Rationalizations may be present in the culture which made the individual members of society fear that innovations may be dangerous. The Amish culture (pp. 209-220) presents some good examples of this. Punishment for borrowing may also come from outside the group, as discussed in section 2 below. The present culture, on the other hand, may posesss customs and equipment which already, at least in the view of the members of the society, satisfy the ends for which the new item is intended. The use of tobacco, especially in the form of smoking, has hardly penetrated among the Indians of highland Peru. It provides nothing in the way of relaxation and lift, which the use of coca, already present, does not already provide as well or better, from the point of view of the users. Generally speaking a new item which competes with an old one usually has to possess marked advantages in order to gain a following, except in those societies which have developed a "novelty drive." The new item not only has to prove more rewarding, but it usually also requires the learning of new patterns of activity. Many people are willing to get along with something not quite as good, if they do not have to spend time and effort necessary in mastering a new pattern. Plenty of typewriter keyboards have been invented which would be more efficient than the one currently in use among ourselves, but they are not taken into the culture because of the difficulty of retraining an army of typists. The same factor, on an even larger scale, seems to prevent the success of calendar reform; not only would millions of people in Western society have to learn new ways of thinking about periods of time within the year, but the coördination of events organized by the calendar system would probably be upset for a time.

2. Although no inhibition to the learning and performance of new customs may be present, a new item may be refused because of the difficulty or impossibility of integrating it into the preëxisting configuration. For one thing, the lack of the prerequisite technological knowledge and equipment may render the acceptance of a piece of machinery non-functional. For instance, machine-made cloth has been readily accepted by many tribes of New Guinea, but modern power-driven looms for making it can hardly be sold to them at the present time for obvious reasons. On the other hand, non-mechanically minded cultures have been known to take over some types of machinery and to fit them into a new function, as when an Indian tribe buys alarm clocks, not to tell time, but for the pleasure of hearing them ring or for their ornamental value. Again, the forms and interests of the receiving culture may be such as to render it difficult to establish a meaningful connection between a new element and the other patterns of the system. The Christian theological system, for example, does not seem to "fit in with" the supernatural system of the Pueblo Indians, such as the Hopi, so long as the latter system maintains its integrity. Aside from drives and other psychological factors involved, the forms of thinking and the directions of interest are so different in the two complexes that it is difficult to find a common meeting ground; there are no "hooks," one might say, by which any essential part of the Christian system can be attached to the native system or vice versa. Thus it becomes a case of either one or the other, and up to the present, the native theological system has won out among the Pueblos. Another aspect of the integrational factor is the fact that there may be a lack, for one reason or another, of bridging patterns which would render the new

element functional. A common form of this is the economic bar. The receiving culture is eager to take over education, new forms of dress, automobiles, and so on, but these traits may only be had for money beyond the resources of the receiving group. In many cases they either have not developed patterns for acquiring money, or have not been allowed to do so.[8] A superordinate society or category often manipulates conditions in this way in order to keep the would-be receivers "in their place," to preserve the wage incentive, and so forth. In Western society the differentiation in the subcultures of the various social classes is largely a matter of economic barriers, rather than failure of desire, presentation, ability to learn and perform the patterns. All situations which involve a differential distribution of privileges between groups inhibit certain types of changes in the groups of lower status. If Negroes in some parts of the South start taking over the country-club complex, the whites begin to regard them as "uppity." If Indians in Eastern Gautemala start learning to play pool, the equipment is removed from them and they are thrown off the premises. Thus gaps are maintained in some cases between a giving and a receiving culture which prevent effective borrowing and individuals attempting to bridge the gaps are punished.

Finally, the acceptance of a new item of culture may in actuality require a reintegration of large areas of the culture and therefore may be resisted; that is, it is inconsistent with the going patterns. The case of the calendar has been previously mentioned. This is also one of the factors apparently involved in the notorious resistance of military organization to innovations. It was only in the heat of crisis, when drive was high, that the Allied armies took over the complex of the paratrooper; for one reason, it required a major shake-up in the organization of both ground and air forces to be used effectively on a large scale. In our society, the legalization of lotteries as a means of raising money for public purposes is apparently resisted because it would require a considerable reorganization of moral systems, charity organizations, tax systems, and some areas of business.

UNEVEN RATES OF CHANGE

Because of the tendency for "improving" patterns to be built on and around a basic innovation, it often happens that one aspect or "department" of a cultural system develops at a faster rate than the others, following one or a series of basic innovations in that particular field. In an earlier chapter we have mentioned how the introduction of mechanization into manufacturing in a relatively short time changed the form of industrial institutions into what we know as the factory system.

Furthermore, it is quite obvious that the last 150 years have seen the heaping of one technological invention upon another in our culture with a resultant "overdeveloping" of the technological aspects of the culture, when compared with the developments in other departments which have taken place during the same period. If basic innovations and the subsequent elaborations based on them occurred at an even rate in all departments of a culture, this type of internal readjustment would probably not be necessary.

Any culture, as we have seen in the previous chapter, must maintain a certain degree of integration if it is to continue to function as a system. Innovations often have the effect of upsetting the previously existing integration, with a resulting tendency on the part of the culture, one might say, to repair the disturbance through internal readjustment. A recent illustration of adjustment to an innovation in our own culture is the introduction of the automobile as an almost universal item of equipment. There was a period during the early twenties when many of the older generation of that time doubted that the culture could withstand the strain of the new phenomenon. Whether the culture may be said to have survived the crisis in any ultimate sense or not, it is now clear that an astonishingly wide number of readjustments were made in our patterns of living. Almost every pattern of customary activity for the average person, from the manners of courtship, the organization of rural schools, marketing practices, to the form of funerals, was repatterned to some extent; new or more direct linkages were built up and others eroded away; the general flavor of American life changed with the passage from the horse-and-buggy era to that of rapid automotive mobility. Something similar occurred in the readjustment of the culture of the Plains Indian tribes following the introduction of the horse in the seventeenth century—although this innovation came from outside the native cultures and in its finally accepted form was less a product of internally produced innovations than was the automobile in American culture. Tribes which had previously been more or less isolated nomads, wandering on foot in restricted areas, now began to range over wide territory, bringing them into contact with others. Formerly horticultural tribes who borrowed the horse tended to slight cultivation and to give more emphasis to hunting. Indeed, the methods of hunting, particularly in connection with the buffalo, were revolutionized by the horse. The war complex as it was known in historic times was a product of the readjustment following the introduction of the horse. And many other aspects of Plains life can be shown to have been influenced by this innovation.[9]

When one part of a culture becomes overemphasized and out of balance with other parts, the condition of the latter is often described as *cultural lag*, and represents a type of cultural maladjustment.

It should be noted that an efflorescence of a certain department of a culture due to accumulation of innovations in its field, while others lag, tends to influence the orientations, objectives, and values of the total system. Thus the main interests and values of our own cultures have not always been in materialistic technology and economics. Less than 500 years ago post-mortem salvation of the soul was a consuming objective of European culture. As luck would have it (in the absence of a more detailed explanation), our culture developed a number of basic technological innovations which have been described in Chapter 18. These brought hundreds of improving inventions in their wake. As new successes were registered in this field more and more attention was drawn toward it. Some basic wants were satisfied by the new technology more handily than by preëxisting patterns; many new drives were generated and to some extent satisfied by the system. Thus the focus and objectives of the culture swung away from a preoccupation with the fate of the soul toward materialism. It is quite possible that, if some basic innovations of a non-material sort could be made *and accepted*, the process would be repeated although toward other dominating objectives.

Notes to Chapter 25

1. Speck, 1926.
2. Linton, 1936, p. 306.
3. Cf. Barnett, 1942.
4. Cf. Lesser, 1933; Wallis, 1943.
5. Gillin, 1942.
6. Report of the Commissioner of Indian Affairs, Washington, 1896, pp. 209-213.
7. Cf. Miller and Dollard, 1941, Chapter 16.
8. Gillin, 1945a.
9. Wissler, 1914.

CHAPTER 26

The Contact of Cultures

OF ALL THE aspects of cultural change which have most engaged the attention of anthropologists and others in recent times, those concerned with the contact of distinct cultures in various parts of the world are perhaps most outstanding. This is not to say that the problems arising from the contact of cultures in the modern world are by any means the most important, because we have already seen that innovations and changes arising within cultures themselves cannot be overlooked by serious students of these matters. In fact in the larger sense the whole modern problem of acculturation or culture contact is part and parcel of the greater problem of cultural change.

During the past four hundred years a series of innovations appeared in that culture which we call Western civilization which, in turn, led to the expansion of its area. First, the culture of the west spread from Europe to the Americas, to Africa, to Asia, and to other outlying parts of the world. Then the carriers of this culture came into increasingly intimate contacts with the bearers of native cultures, many of which were entirely distinct from anything known to the Europeans. As time has gone on this process of expansion and increased contact between the West and native cultures of other parts of the world has increased both in tempo and in volume. One of the outstanding results of World War II was the fact that large numbers of American soldiers and government functionaries of various types were brought into contact with peoples of varying traditions and customs residing all over the globe. The present era which is distinguished by its rapid means of communication and travel would seem to be one in which we shall see increasing intimacy between our own type of people and those who have been raised in a different tradition, whose customs conform to a different configuration, and whose ordinary habits of living are often, from our point of view, rather exotic.

This matter of cultural and social contact has often been approached from the point of view of "race." The older writers often talk as if the whole problem was one of adjusting people of different genetic constitution, one to another. To be sure it is true that when peoples of different blood or genetic make-up come together, miscegenation ordinarily results.

However, the results of miscegenation are, in the first instance, biological rather than cultural. The contact and mixing of cultures, on the other hand, must be studied on the basis of socio-cultural rather than biological principles.

In the first place, we must recognize that there are several types of contact between cultures of distinct cast or configuration. For example, different cultures may be in close first-hand contact. The members of their respective societies may see each other personally at relatively frequent intervals, or may even live side by side and rub elbows with each other. On the other hand, every one is familiar with the fact that societies may be in contact of a less intimate sort. For example, we are well aware of the fact that we acquire certain men's fashions from London, although relatively few Americans actually visit London regularly or know any Englishmen in what might be called a personal way. To take another example, the Negro peoples of tropical Africa now cultivate maize as a staple article of diet. It is one of the crops which plays the largest part in native agricultural economy in the Negro portion of Africa at the present day. Yet historical research shows us that this plant and the methods of cultivating it were originated in aboriginal America. The Negroes of Africa who today depend upon maize as the staff of life have in most cases never seen an Indian of the Western Hemisphere, nor were their ancestors in contact with the people who provided the original innovation which led to the cultivation of this major food crop. In this latter case we speak of a different type of cultural contact which in the literature of anthropology is usually called *diffusion*.

Very few cultures are completely isolated from others. But in some cases of long-standing contact, a system of more or less stabilized relationships has been worked out following an earlier period of readjustment, so that, at the present time, the fact of contact is of no great importance in considering change. For example, the Pygmies of Central Africa live in a sort of symbiotic relationship with the full-sized Negroes; their villages are often close by those of the larger Negroes and the two groups are in daily primary contact even though they follow different configurations of custom. The Pygmies supply game to their larger neighbors, and the Negroes provide their small friends with certain agricultural products and some protection against enemies. In certain parts of Guatemala a sort of stable relationship has been worked out between Indians and ladinos (Europeanized group), each group following a different pattern of life even though they may live together in the same town or community.[1] In such cases the process of change which undoubtedly set in when the two groups first came into contact has been slowed down or arrested, at least for the time being.

Diffusion. During the early part of this century a good deal of anthropological effort was devoted to proving the fact of diffusion, that is, that items of culture may be passed from one group to another. At the present time there is no longer any doubt that such a process takes place, and commonly. Diffusion is the name which is applied to that process of cultural transfer which may take place without direct or long-continued primary contact between the cultures involved. Thus Japanese culture was never in direct contact with the Indian cultures of aboriginal America, yet it eventually took over the custom of smoking tobacco as the result of a long-drawn-out process of diffusion which started when Europeans first "borrowed" the custom from Indians of the Atlantic seaboard and carried it to Europe. Of course such transfers often involve personal contact between *some* members of the source culture and the receiving culture either directly or through intermediaries. But in cases of diffusion the societies as wholes are usually not in direct or close contact. Diffusion by indirect contact without the instrumentality of persons may occur when traits are taken over through "silent trade," furtive theft, secret observation, or the printed word or other materialistic representations.

The process of diffusion is very important in explaining the richness of content which characterizes many of the world's foremost cultures, both present and past. It is probably not an exaggeration to estimate that perhaps 90 per cent of the elements of present-day North American culture were originated in societies other than our own, either in modern times or earlier. All of the great world civilizations owe much of their content to outside sources and received many of these outside influences by means of the process which we call diffusion.

Although "borrowing" may not be a good method of enrichment for the individual, it is a guaranteed and highly satisfactory method of enriching the cultural life of a people. Diffusion and acculturation are actually processes whereby different societies may "pool their cultural resources," and thus achieve a greater range of satisfactions than probably would be possible by their own unaided efforts.

Just as in the case of changes arising from innovations made within the culture, those stemming from innovations introduced from without may be accepted wholly or in a selective and partial fashion. The form of an artifact or activity pattern may be accepted, but its meaning (associated mental patterns) or function may be reinterpreted. When form and meaning diffuse or are borrowed independently of each other, we are witnessing the fact that material objects and actional patterns may pass cultural lines independently of representational and mental patterns which may be attached to them in the lending culture. When function does not pass over to the receiving culture, we usually have a case in which the integrational systems of the two cultures differ, with the result that the receiving culture is forced to assign, so to speak, the new item or complex to a more or less appropriate place in its own configuration, if the integrity of the latter is to be maintained.

We may cite a few examples. The Caribs of British Guiana have borrowed chickens from Europeans. However, the chickens are not used either for meat, feathers, eggs, or cock fighting as in the various European cultures from which they were borrowed, but are merely objects of conspicuous display. Every man takes pride in his chickens, boasts about them to other men, and people sit about and admire and compare the fowl belonging to various families. The ownership and care of domestic fowl, in other words, is a response to prestige drive and nothing else. To cite another example, automobile tires are in high demand by Indians in many parts of Latin America. The Indians do not own or drive automobiles, but cut up the tire casings to make sandals; in at least two communities with which the writer is familiar, the older art of making sandals from skins has been lost and the people have become dependent upon the supply of automobile tires—a fact which caused minor crises during the war when they became practically unobtainable in these regions.

The borrowing of mental patterns without associated actional patterns or artifacts is illustrated by the process which Kroeber has called *stimulus diffusion*.[2] Among the examples which he cites is the development of an acceptable system of writing for the Cherokee language by one of the tribesmen, known as Sequoya. This man had grasped the general idea of writing and saw the advantages of it for white men with whom he had come in contact, but he had not learned our system sufficiently to grasp its principles and details. However, he invented a syllabary (rather than an alphabet) for his native language. Another example is the development of porcelain in Europe during the eighteenth century. The idea of making porcelain was derived from China and specimens had been imported. In short, a portion of the porcelain complex was borrowed, but not the techniques of manufacture. But the Europeans decided to make it for themselves in order to save the cost of importation. A considerable amount of conscious experimentation was necessary before the process was finally perfected in Europe. Something similar occurs constantly in the modern world whenever a trade secret or military secret is inhibited from being diffused completely. As of this writing, the basic idea of atomic fission and several of the fundamental formulas have been diffused throughout physicist circles of the Western world, but the "know-how"—techniques for controlling and applying energy thus generated—have been kept secret in North America. We are assured that other countries will eventually work out techniques of application for themselves, even if they do not succeed in stealing the detailed patterns or in persuading the United States to share the secret aspects of the complex.

The diffusion process seldom produces rapid changes in the cultural situation of a receiving culture. It does not usually result in cultural shock to which a major overall adjustment of the receiving society system has to be made. The diffused elements are usually taken into the receiving culture in a selective fashion and at a relatively slow rate, so that the major patterns of integration are maintained. In this respect diffusion often differs from acculturation.

Acculturation[3] is commonly considered to involve continued and relatively close contact between societies of different custom or between their agents. Although we often think of acculturation in terms of a contact between Europeans and native peoples, in which the European is dominating, there are actually two types of acculturation which must be recognized: first the relatively balanced type, and secondly the relatively unbalanced type of acculturation. In the balanced type the cultures involved are in close contact, but the introduction of items from one to the other and the resultant modification of the cultures flows in both directions at approximately an equal rate. The changes which occur are mutually reciprocal in the large sense of the word. One culture does not dominate or impose its patterns on the other. The one culture is not superordinate to the other in the situation. The nation-cultures of Mexico and of the United States at the present time constantly influence each other, but they tend to stand in a balanced relationship—one does not dominate the other. Under such conditions acculturation may be said to be a balanced two-way process.[4] As between modern nation-societies, this process will probably become increasingly evident.

In the unbalanced type of acculturation, on the other hand, we typically find a strong society with a complex culture dominating a smaller society which has either a simpler culture or one whose patterns are unable to compete on equal terms. In the modern world this situation has been of considerable importance from a practical point of view as European nations have conquered and colonized outlying areas of the earth, and as European civilization has confronted the cultures of so-called simpler peoples. The adjustments, as every one knows, have often been painful and costly, not only for the natives but for the Europeans as well. Colonial powers, such as the British and the Dutch, have consequently supported studies of acculturation in their own interest, and they have encouraged the application of anthropology as a means of pacifying and of governing their colonial subjects with less loss of life and property than was common in an earlier day of reliance upon military conquest and subjugation.

Thus we see that diffusion and acculturation are two types of cultural transfer. The difference is perhaps illustrated in South America. According to the researches of Nordenskiöld,[5] the banana, which of course was an Old World plant, was carried to the Atlantic shores of Brazil in the early sixteenth century, probably by Portuguese explorers or colonizers. However, in the succeeding hundred years or so it *diffused* throughout a large area of the Amazon Valley long before any Portuguese or other Europeans appeared in those regions in person. Thus it was that Europeans ascending certain tributaries of the Amazon and contacting the Indian tribes for the first time were surprised to find these native peoples cultivating bananas. The banana, in short, was a culture trait which had been transferred from the cultures of the Old World, particularly Africa, to previously unvisited tribes of interior South America by means of the diffusion process. It will be noted that in the case of the interior tribes, the acceptance of the element did not involve any first-hand contact with the ultimate source in America, namely, Portuguese colonizers on the Atlantic coast. Acculturation of these tribes, on the other hand, has not actually begun in some cases even at the present time, four hundred years later, for many of the tribes which today cultivate the banana are not in direct contact with Europeans or representatives of European culture.

SOME DISTINCTIVE ASPECTS OF ACCULTURATION

We recall that in an earlier chapter we discussed the fact that every cultural system represents an adjustment to a total situation. Now the outstanding aspect of acculturation which distinguishes it from other processes of cultural change and transfer is that acculturation involves a particular type of situation. An acculturation situation, in other words, is always characterized by the introduction of a foreign cultural element represented by alien persons and their customs and artifacts into the situation of the receiving culture. It is for this reason that the subcommittee of the Social Science Research Council charged with the task of defining acculturation insisted that one of its characteristic features was long-continued first-hand contact between societies of distinct cultural configuration and tradition.[6]

When a society comes into direct contact of this sort with another group it is obvious that its former situation is changed by the mere presence of foreigners practising customs which are strange to that of the original society, and carrying with them artifacts, buildings, tools, and other material objects of culture which are strange to the situation as it previously existed. Therefore the old culture is of necessity required to readjust. In most cases, the old customs were not designed as adaptive responses to these new factors in the situation. Many of the features of the new situation have no parallel in the past. If the reader will turn back to the pages on which we have sketched the present situation of the Amish of Pennsylvania, he will grasp the problems which are presented to the Amish culture by the encroachment of Americans of a different type upon the area which was originally more or less exclusively occupied by the members of this religious sect.

Specific ways in which acculturation may alter situation. The advent of a group with distinct culture into the situation of a previously adapted culture is bound to have the effect of altering conditions to which the latter is designed to provide adjustment. If one is to understand the process in any specific instance, he must be prepared to analyze in detail the actual changes in conditions which are taking place. In general, acculturation contact may alter conditions in the following respects.

1. Conditions of natural environment may be changed so that the practice of the old techniques of exploitation, subsistence, and general adaptation becomes unrewarding. Organized hunting of the buffalo by whites with repeating rifles destroyed these animals on the Plains during the nineteenth century, with the result, of course, that the whole economy of many tribes whose source of subsistence and raw materials was largely these animals had to be abandoned and revised. Large-scale lumbering operations by whites in the north woods of the Lake states not only destroyed the original aspect of the forests, but also dispersed the game which the Indians hunted and trapped.[7] The new-comers may alter the physiography, as when they undertake to drain swamps or to produce artificial lakes by damming; they may also introduce new types of flora and fauna (for example, domesticated plants and animals) which in effect change the landscape fundamentally. The "Purple Land" of Uruguay and Argentina, with its modern herds of grazing cattle and fields of waving grain, is a vastly different environment from the open pampa covered with long grass and inhabited by wild game to which the culture of the Tehuelche and other aboriginal tribes was adapted.

2. Changes in social conditions or potentialities may result from acculturation contact. Most native peoples have suffered a decline in population following the first period of intensive contact with Europeans. In other cases, as in South Africa and New Guinea, young men are required to leave their native communities for work in mines or plantations. Thus the proportions of the sexes and of the age groups are altered in the native society. The same result may be effected by removal of the

children for education, as was the policy on many North American Indian reservations, or by conscription for military service, as in the French African colonies. The new-comers may, by force or otherwise, also change the physical distribution of the population. Thus, one of the basic policies of the Incas was to reshuffle the population of a conquered area, moving some elements back into the interior of the empire and reorganizing the remainder into the mathematically similar units characteristic of the Inca system. Such changes obviously may, and usually do, render the old patterns of custom and social organization inoperative for lack of proper numbers of performers or for lack of performers with the inherent qualifications (such as age or sex) demanded by the old patterns. For example, in South Africa many of the old ceremonial dances have had to be abandoned because the young men are away from home at the times they should be performed. Increased contact with members of the new-comer society also constitutes change in social conditions which may require alteration of the old patterns. Thus the new-comers may demand that they be treated with respect or they may refuse to interact with the natives on the basis of native patterns. Patterns new to the native culture must be developed to cope with the altered social definition of the situation.

3. Changes in cultural conditions usually occur which render the old customs unadaptive or for which there are no old patterns whatever. New artifacts may be introduced, new means of communications, new types of buildings to which adjustment must be made. The performance of actual behavior (strange customs) by strangers must also be reckoned with. Such behavior may be entirely new in the experience of the members of the receiving society and they are forced to work out some patterns for adjusting to it. The throes through which the British went during the recent war when first confronted with what they considered the informal, "free and easy" manners and speech of the American soldiers quartered in their country are a case in point.

4. Changes may take place, as previously mentioned, in the genetic character of the population, as a result of interbreeding. The resulting half-breed group represents a new factor in the situation, which must be culturally defined in some manner. The mixed blood status may be ignored, as seems to have been largely the case in colonial coastal Brazil, or members of the mixed-blood group may be placed in a special class or caste involving new patterns of interaction, as in the case with the "Eurasians" in India.

Any or all such changes in conditions may lead to the development of new acquired drives in the members of the society undergoing acculturation. In so far as such drives become common to the members of the group, they become cultural motivations, and new patterns of customary response for their satisfaction will tend to develop. The desire for money, for example, is almost always created in natives after they come in contact with Europeans; appetites for new types of food, new types of anxieties regarding supernatural and earthly security, new definitions of prestige are all common results of acculturation.

The confused period in acculturation. For every society undergoing acculturation there would seem to be an inevitable period characterized by some confusion and lack of stability in behavior, a period during which (1) old customs unadapted to new conditions are being extinguished and new customs are being tried out and developed with corresponding patterns, (2) new patterns, once worked out, are being integrated, and (3) the new patterns in the new integration are being learned and practised as activity.

Will a new culture, exhibited in adapted and predictable behavior result? This depends upon whether or not the situation, once changed, remains relatively stable. Rapidly recurring, capricious, and disorderly alterations of conditions will result in random behavior, social and cultural disorganization, apathy, or withdrawal. It is quite possible for the dominant society in an acculturation situation to manipulate factors, either by accident or intent, in such ways that the foreign cultural component never remains stable. This has actually happened to many reservation Indian tribes in our country during the time that our government policies, as mediated through the Indian Service and other agencies, varied and contradicted themselves almost from one year to the next. The Indians could not develop any stable patterns which gave satisfactions in a relatively permanent sense. In many cases, because of being punished for almost everything they *did* try, they simply gave up trying, with the result that they are described as "lazy," "shiftless," disorganized, and suspicious.

Incidents in acculturation. The apparent higher prestige and efficiency of whites often motivates imitation of them on the part of the natives at a certain stage, although those white traits are usually imitated which are in line with the orientations of the native culture. The Eskimo, for example, are natively oriented toward material inventions and gadgets. At the present time they are reported to use motor schooners for fishing and outboard motors on small boats and have learned without much difficulty to repair the engines. They are fond of gramophones and American musical records of the popular variety. One instance is reported of the use of the typewriter in imitation of American businessmen, with both the sender and the receiver of the typed notes being unable to read or write. There are instances of ivory carvers whittling out expert imitations of false teeth, and several Eskimo dentists have made a considerable business of gold-plating the incisors of their confrères. They are quick to adapt material things into their own way of life, as the shaman who had his igloo Delco lighted and acquired great prestige by "causing the moon to come in and out of his igloo" at his command.[8]

In other instances we see displacement of native crafts and custom patterns by European elements. In many parts of Africa,[9] for example, copper telegraph wire has displaced iron ornaments and the old techniques of ironworking have been lost. The tin can and the beer bottle have rendered obsolete the old crafts of pottery making, and the five-gallon gasoline tin becomes a general carry-all as well as being hammered out flat for roofing of the huts, so that the old art of thatching is abandoned. Watch crystals come to be used as ornaments in the lips and smoothly rubbed beer-bottle glass replaces the carved ivory skewers of former days. In Africa, also, prestige has been redefined. The old communal idea of gaining favor by giving away wealth is replaced by personal property and conspicuous personal consumption. Thus incidents occur like that of the native man who bought a pair of large army boots and constructed a high wooden platform in his house so that he could clump around ostentatiously before his guests. The drawing off of native men for work in mines and plantations has tended to destroy the extended family, the authority of the elders, the old marriage pattern, and the hold of the old religious concepts, with the result that a large black proletariat has developed in most of the South African cities. This group has tended to be incorporated into the general society as a caste of low status.

These and other instances which could be described almost indefinitely illustrate the rather groping and uncertain behavior which characterizes members of the subordinate or weaker society in an acculturation situation during the period before a new cultural adjustment has been made.

Selective and partial acculturation. In the European expansion into other continents the pioneer agents of European cultures were often *traders* and *missionaries*. They each carried with them special aspects of European culture to "sell" to the natives—the traders brought material products of our culture and the customs associated with them, the missionaries brought the concepts and rituals of the Christian religion. If they succeeded in modifying native culture, as they often did, they nevertheless usually failed to convey large sections of European culture. Contemporary European art, political customs and organization, and machine technology, for example, were seldom presented by traders and missionaries to the natives. When these pioneers were followed by military men and colonial administrators whose task it was to consolidate the territories in the interests of the European overlords, they also brought with them only certain parts of their culture for presentation to the natives. European women and women's culture have seldom appeared in numbers in colonial territories, so that native peoples have been effectively shut off from borrowing much they might offer. In the exchange of culture between modern societies, the same problem of partial presentation often arises. Latin American peoples, for instance, have complained that the only Americans they see in their countries are businessmen, missionaries, and diplomats. Of recent years, when our government has brought Latin Americans to the United States to acquaint themselves at first hand with our culture in its full functional setting, we have had considerable testimony from such visitors to the effect that they had never conceived that the "United States was like that." In short, North American culture as it actually works on its home grounds and as it is presented by certain of its representatives abroad seem to be two different things.

Finally there is always a tendency for a receiving society to remake a foreign cultural element in order to render it consistent or functionally congenial to its own overall system. The greater the ease with which this can be done, the greater the chances of acceptance of a new item. A rather trivial example of the refunctioning of a borrowed item is the widespread use of an American-made product called "florida water" among Indians and mestizos in parts of Latin America. This substance is made to be used as an eau de cologne for bathing and perfuming the head and face. However, it has been taken into Latin American lower-class culture as an essential ingredient of magical potions which are used in witchcraft and curing procedures, and which are either imbibed or blown from the mouth. At present the annual exports for this use from the United States are by no means trivial in terms of dollars and cents. In our own culture we have borrowed African dances and music (usually via the West Indies or Latin America) whose original function was religious. We have modified them in accordance with our system of musical notation and have adopted them as forms of recreation, since they would be repugnant to us in a religious setting.

NATIVISTIC MOVEMENTS AND OTHER REACTIONS TO CONTACT

Nativistic movements. The new situation created by acculturation contact is often punishing to the members of the subordinate society. The new patterns for which the group is groping during a certain stage either fail to provide customary satisfactions or are insufficiently mastered to provide adjustment. Under such circumstances there is often a perhaps natural tendency to look backward to the days when the old culture was in full function before it had been disturbed by contact with outsiders and their patterns. This tendency in many cases has resulted in a sort of revolt or reaction, generally described under the head of "nativistic movements."

In general, as Linton [10] has pointed out, these reactions do not aim to restore the whole of the former culture, but rather are focused on certain elements of it which serve to symbolize the former adjustment. Nativistic movements, however, do not arise in all acculturation situations. For example, if the two cultures in contact have worked out a stabilized symbiotic relationship one to the other, a reaction of this sort is unlikely to occur. It is usually when one group is dominated by the other without feeling inferior or when it is not allowed, in spite of desire, to participate freely in the dominant culture that a nativistic movement will arise. In short, such movements are in large measure a reaction to frustration and an attempt to evade such blockage to satisfaction either by fantasy or by revival of formerly satisfying patterns.

Two general types of such movements have been recognized, the revivalistic and the perpetuative. The Ghost Dance [11] movement which swept the Western Indians following 1870 was frankly revivalistic. The program of its major prophet called for exclusion of the whites, and a return to the ceremonial life (somewhat modified) of the old days. The perpetuative type of nativism attempts to preserve values and action patterns against the encroachment of another culture. Ghandi, for example, is a symbol of a movement to preserve the rural, non-industrial culture of India against the attacks of the West.

With each of these types of movement a choice of techniques is available. The reaction may take place on magical grounds or with rational methods. The magical revivalistic movements are usually the most spectacular. As Linton says,

They usually originate with some individual who assumes the rôle of prophet and is accepted by the people because they wish to believe. They always lean heavily on the supernatural. . . . Moribund elements of culture are not revived for their own sake or in anticipation of practical advantages. . . . Their revival is part of a magical formula designed to modify the society's environment in ways which will be favorable to it. . . . The society's members feel that by behaving as the ancestors did they will, in some usually undefined way, help to recreate the total situation in which the ancestors lived.[12]

Compensatory cultural adaptations. Another type of reaction developed by subordinate groups under acculturation appears in the form of compensatory cultural patterns which fall short of a full-blown nativistic movement. Such a reaction seems to be most frequent in cases in which the native culture has lost part of its old value system and yet has not been able to achieve integration through the adoption of values from the lending culture. Among many of the Indians of the United States a complex of patterns called the Peyote Cult has grown up.[13] This cult centers around the use of a narcotic cactus button, originally used by the Indians of Northern Mexico for ceremonial and religious purposes. At the present time, however, the cult in most places also incorporates certain aspects of the Christian religion, and the use of the narcotic is often preceded by the reading of selections from the Scriptures. The cult, in short, provides a mechanism for social cohesion and a set of values which bridge the gap between the native and the European cultural systems, while at the same time giving a *raison d'être* and a sense of unity to the acculturated Indian group. In Latin America much the same function is fulfilled among partially acculturated Indian groups by an institution called the *cofradía* or *hermandad*. This institution is originally derived from the Roman Catholic sodalities (layman's religious clubs) of colonial Spain. But, although ostensibly Christian, the local organizations in many parts of Latin America, notably Guatemala, usually incorporate, in addition to certain elements of orthodox Christianity, social activities modeled along native lines, certain curing practices derived from native culture, and quasi-political functions following for the most part the old native local patterns rather than the modern Republican forms. Again the cofradía is a mechanism for promoting social solidarity among the Indians or mestizos in distinction to the whites or representatives of purer European culture. It is quite probable that certain peculiar types of lodge organizations and religious groups found among the Negroes in the United States may be a manifestation of the same type of reaction. In summary, such reactions to acculturation serve the function of restoring a certain integration in the group, lost through the passing of old mental patterns, ceremonies, and value systems. Through them pride and esprit de corps are restored in the acculturated group.

ACCULTURATION AND THE INDIVIDUAL

The direct contact of cultures not only has noticeable effects upon the respective cultural systems themselves, but also, of course, upon the individuals involved. Since any culture tends to mould the personality of the individual who practises it, and since individuals are trained to practise expectable patterns systematically organized together, it follows that major change or disorganization of a cultural system in the process of acculturation will be reflected in the social personalities of the people. The personal syndromes which appear as a result of acculturation are many and varied. For example, the older generation after a recent contact often tends to live in the past and to reject the new culture, making only a surface adaptation to present conditions, if any. Thus, until recently, on many of the Western Indian reservations could be found old men and women who, on first acquaintance, gave the outsider the impression of a schizoid personality. Their eyes were turned inward, as it were; their thoughts dwelt in the past; they only grudgingly attempted to come to terms with the new dispensation and withdrew from it as much as possible.

A second manifestation appearing under certain circumstances might be called personality arrest or paralysis. Here it must be remembered that we refer mainly to the public or social personality. The average individual represses manifestations of individuality and seeks security in obscurity and the rather compulsive following of the restricted patterns which are open to him. Hence the "passive" and "animal-like" personalities which impress so many persons even when well acquainted with such groups as the Andean Indians of the present time. Unfortunately, to date insufficient work has been done on the analysis of this type of acculturated personality to permit more than a superficial description, although studies are now being carried on.

Finally, the "marginal man" is a personality type frequently seen in acculturation situations. Such an individual is one, we might say, who finds himself between two cultural configurations without being fully of either one. Park [14] first drew attention to this type of individual, and Tumin [15] has recently published an illuminating sketch of one who was among the present writer's informants in Guatemala. The marginal man is "emancipated" in the sense that he is not bound by the controls of behavior and the systems of value of either one of the cultures in which he operates; he oscillates between patterns; he is seldom sure of the "right" thing to do or think; he is often unsure of acceptance by either group. The result usually is a basic feeling of insecurity and anxiety often manifested in capricious and unpredictable conduct and judgments. In ordinary parlance, the marginal man cannot make up his mind; he lacks personal integration.

It is because half-breeds, mulattoes, mestizos, and the like, are so often marginal men psychologically and culturally, that many casual observers have inveighed against race mixture and miscegenation. It appears on the surface that the instability and unreliability of the marginal individual is a biological inheritance of the "worst features" of both his parent races. It is now clear, however, that the psychological characteristics of such individuals are not usually a function of their genetic make-up, but are due to the inconsistencies of their cultural training and social environment. Given a relatively stable and consistent culture and social situation, and the mixed blood develops as well integrated a personality as any one else, as the vast majority of mestizos in modern Mexico, for instance, show.

Although the above "types" of persons show certain neurotic trends and evidences of personal maladjustment, acculturation does not always and necessarily produce inhibited, warped, anxious, insecure personalities. Certainly the modern natives of Danger Island, in Polynesia, although their culture is about half indigenous and half European, show no outstanding abnormal traits, if we can rely on Frisbie's descriptions.[16] The diverse elements in their present culture seem to be well woven together, major frustrations and anxieties are absent, and this is reflected in an apparently integrated, non-compulsive, non-anxious type of personality.

TERMINATIVE PROCESSES OF ACCULTURATION

With respect to content and organization of culture the process of acculturation obviously means the introduction and acceptance of *some* foreign elements and, usually, the elimination of others, plus a certain disorganization and reorganization of the total configuration of the receiving system. So long as the situation remains unstable this state can continue indefinitely. However, the "normal" course of events following contact between cultures in the acculturation form usually involves one or more of a series of subsequent processes. We may mention a few.

1. A stabilized symbiotic relationship may develop in which the two cultures maintain their separate identities which continue to operate parallel to each other, but are, at the same time, linked together at certain points in such a way that the operation of the one culture is necessary for the operation of the other. Such a stabilization occurred between the Woodland Indians of North America and the French traders during the eighteenth century and continued, in most cases, well into the nineteenth. Likewise, the Colonial Quechua of the Andean area settled down into a mode of life considerably different in detail and overall organization from that of their Inca ancestors, but interwoven with that of the Spaniards and cholos of the area.[17] The writer has elsewhere analyzed a somewhat similar situation of cultural parallelism and symbiosis in Guatemala.[18] Such an arrangement often results in social stratification with the practitioners of the subordinate culture being assigned to inferior social classes or castes.

2. One culture in the contact situation may extirpate the other without absorbing significant elements from it. This may be attempted mainly by force, as when the Germans set out to obliterate Polish culture,

but more frequently weak or primitive cultures are wiped out through inability of their societies to make adequate cultural adjustments. The Tasmanian culture, for example, disappeared about 1870 without leaving any perceptible trace in the variety of European culture which succeeded it on the island. In such cases the subordinate culture is so made up and organized that it contains no patterns which can be made over for adjustment to the European; all of its patterns are so different, its organization so distinctly oriented that, strictly speaking, it is unable to acculturate and as a result goes down for inability of its society to come to terms with the new situation.

3. One culture may be eventually absorbed or assimilated into the other so that it loses its identity. This has been a process through which most immigrant groups have passed in the United States. The native cultures in most of Argentina and Uruguay came to a similar end. In this process the absorbing culture usually takes into itself various traits of the disappearing culture, so that the result is considerably different from what it was at the start. Thus the present culture of the United States has assimilated numerous elements from the Indians, and from all the cultures of the migrants who have come to America. The Latin American culture which is now emerging to the south of us likewise is neither purely Spanish colonial, modern European, nor aboriginal.[19] "Something new has been added" to each in the new blend. In general this process of blending of cultures bids fair to be of increasing importance in the modern world.

4. The assimilation and blending mentioned in the preceding paragraph often tends to be blocked if the carriers of the two cultures are of different physical type or appearance. Physical appearance serves as a symbol of cultural difference and tends to perpetuate it in the minds of members of the respective groups. Complete cultural assimilation and blending under such circumstances is therefore dependent upon a biological process of interbreeding which leads to *genetic amalgamation*. Once this has been achieved, cultural blending and amalgamation may follow. Thus Mexico, for example, already has a population the majority of which is mestizo, a fact which renders easier the absorption of desirable indigenous elements into the nation's culture.

SUMMARY

Change in culture can hardly be avoided in the long run. If we know the *conditions* under which a culture operates and the lines of its internal integration and coördination, we are able to predict within certain limits what form and direction cultural changes will take. As we perfect our knowledge and our techniques for specifying the conditions of compatibility and consistency, our predictions become more accurate. As prediction becomes possible, so control and manipulation of changes are possible. Indeed, a degree of somewhat haphazard manipulation and operation of changes is already practised by such groups as advertising experts, propagandists, and salesmen, all of whom customarily work for pay or profit in the interests of small numbers of the general population. If corporations and pressure groups are able to profit from such manipulations of custom, it would seem to follow that society as a whole could also profit from the application of tested principles of cultural change.

Planning of changes is thus a practical reality. It is in fact a cultural complex available to be taken over by our culture as a universal, integrated to the culture as a whole. Many and dire have been the warnings issued from certain quarters of what may happen to the "American Way of Life" if any one should ever attempt to plan it for the welfare of society. These warnings on the whole seem to emanate from parties who are not opposed to planning in itself—they employ it constantly in business, politics, and professions. They are not opposed to planning, but to who does it and why.

Reliable planning for the adjustment of cultural patterns which are in conflict depends upon carefully collected information and is involved in the question of objectives. It cannot be undertaken lightly; it cannot be done in an "off the cuff" manner. And if it is to be accomplished for the welfare of society as a whole it cannot be performed by the representatives of selfish or restricted elements of the population.

NOTES TO CHAPTER 26

1. Gillin, 1945a.
2. Kroeber, 1940.
3. For general reading on diffusion and acculturation see Dixon, 1928; Hallowell, 1945; Herskovits, 1938, 1945; Linton, 1939, Chapters 8-10 inclusive.
4. Northrop, 1946, Chapter 2.
5. Nordenskiöld, 1930.
6. Redfield, Linton, and Herskovits, 1936.
7. Gillin, 1942.
8. Godsell, 1940.
9. Barton, 1940.
10. Linton, 1943.
11. Lesser, 1933.
12. Linton, 1943, p. 232.
13. La Barre, 1938.
14. Park, 1928.
15. Tumin, 1945.
16. Frisbie, 1944.
17. Kubler, 1946.
18. Gillin, 1945a.
19. Gillin, 1947a.

PART V

Individuality and Conformity

CHAPTER 27

The Person and His Culture

THE ANALYSIS of cultural patterns and customs, institutions and systems, situations and artifacts, is of primary value to us as it helps us to understand actual human beings, their actions, and attitudes. Anthropology is thus concerned not only with peoples, but also with people; not only with personifications, but also with persons.

The individual may appear on the scene in a number of different lightings. (1) First, we may see him with all his individual peculiarities highlighted. Since no two individuals are ever exactly alike, there is something unique about every one. (2) Second, he may appear to us in terms of his likeness or similarity to other individuals or "types" of individuals. Since every one has something in common with some other individuals this aspect is bound to appear sooner or later. Psychiatrists and psychologists, for example, in the interests of the diagnosis and treatment of personal maladjustments, are often primarily concerned with the first aspect, that is to say, with the peculiarities and uniqueness of the individual. Social scientists, planners and advertisers, to cite a few groups concerned, are interested in understanding and predicting how "the average man" of a given group will react to various conditions.

In this chapter we are principally interested in understanding the relation of the individual to his culture. Many of the similarities in actions and attitudes which he manifests in common with others are due to common cultural conditioning and training; on the other hand, his peculiarities and idiosyncrasies may also be described in terms of his deviations from the norms and patterns of the society in which he finds himself.

THE PERSONALITY

Definition and manifestation of personality. We shall regard a personality, for present purposes, as an internal organization of emotions, attitudes, idea patterns, and tendencies to overt action. This internal organization is empirically manifested in a continuity which may be called the "style of life." [1] To be sure, the style of life may be relatively consistent or inconsistent within itself, it may be self-contained or expansive,

573

it may be well integrated or relatively disorganized, and so on. But, whatever it is, it constitutes the empirical evidence available for the study of the personality.[2]

Sources of content and organization. The content and organization of the personality seem to derive from three general types of sources: (1) constitutional, (2) personal-social, and (3) cultural.

1. *The constitutional set* of the individual provides him with the raw material, we might say, with which he has to work in constructing his personality. It determines certain limits of development. In some types of constitutional deficiencies and pathologies the constitutional factors may actually dominate the personality. For instance, feeble-mindedness sets such definite limits to personality development that no external factors are capable of breaking them down. But for the average, so-called normal person in most societies the constitutional factors may be thought of as providing a base with certain wide limits. In such "average" individuals the constitutional tendencies are amenable to considerable moulding, modification, and alteration.

The constitutional fountainheads of the person are of course to be sought inside himself, perhaps in his germ plasm, but the other two general sources contributing to the formation of the person exist in the form of influences outside himself. Indeed, the larger part of the process of personality formation in the average individual may be conceived as a process whereby these external influences are internalized and organized as a result of the individual's experiences with the external world. These experiences are of two types, unpatterned and patterned. Theoretically they might both be considered of equal importance were it not for the fact that all human beings are exposed to vastly more patterned experiences than to unpatterned ones.

2. *The unpatterned life experiences,* which provide a second source of personality, are of a more or less capricious or accidental type. They are not usually predictable except in an actuarial sense under the conditions in which the individual lives, and therefore are not controlled in advance. Experiences of this sort may include such episodes as a young child's being forced to sexual intercourse by a pervert, a seriously crippling or debilitating illness during the formative years, a terrifying exposure to darkness or to the sight of blood, desertion by parents early in life, the bad luck of having a brutal or drunken parent, not to mention many a seemingly minor occurrence. Kimball Young has called such unpatterned experiences the personal-social sources of personality. These experiences are not expected or foreseen within the cultural framework. When their impact or stimulus value is strong we must always consider the "twisting" or "warping" effects they may have upon the individual. Even

when they are not of a shocking or traumatic nature, the personal-social experiences probably have a cumulative influence on personality content and organization. It is for this reason that a scientifically recorded life-history is so important for the adequate understanding of the individual case. This is true not only in respect to individuals in our own culture, but also for members of illiterate and other non-European societies. Of recent years anthropologists and psychologists working in such situations have provided a considerable body of life-history material.

The constitutional and personal-social factors apparently account in large measure for the uniqueness which characterizes each individual, for deviations from the socially approved norm, and for much of the originality expressed by individuals.

3. *Patterned experiences* are the third source of personality content and organization and are to be found in the cultural background and surroundings of the individual. These are experiences which are controlled by the overall pattern of the culture and which impinge upon the individual through the agency of the members of the society, group, or social category in which he interacts. In all societies the greater part of life experience to which the individual is exposed is of this type—patterned, arranged, and structuralized by the culture. The individual in the process of socialization is either purposely trained or otherwise learns to react to these experiences in ways which are considered acceptable in cultural terms. If we may accept the view that postnatal experience is the major factor in producing the personality, it would seem to follow that the cultural factors are the most important so far as the average individual anywhere is concerned, because the influence of the culture pervades the great majority of life experiences in all societies.

In short, most individuals learn to be the kind of persons they become, and most of what they learn is cultural material conveyed to them by members of their groups and by artifacts and symbols.

Practical value of cultural background to understanding the person. Each culture seems to have the effect, which we might expect, of producing a certain similarity in personality among the individuals who practise the culture. These similarities among members of a social group have been called by such names as "basic personality structure," "national character," and the like, but they owe their existence to similarities in training and conditioning to which children of a given group are exposed. No society succeeds in overriding and eliminating all aspects of personal individuality. But, on the other hand, all societies take the view that, if an individual cannot be molded into minimum conformity to the standard pattern or patterns of the approved personality, he must be eliminated from full participation in group life.

Thus, if we know the cultural expectations respecting individuals and the personality-molding pressures present in a given culture, we can predict within a certain range of accuracy the way in which a representative member of the society in question will react, at least in situations which the culture recognizes.

In psychiatry, the branch of medicine which deals with mental illness, the importance of an understanding of the cultural background has recently come to be realized, at least in some quarters of the profession. A knowledge of the cultural background is usually crucial to the understanding of peculiarities and apparent pathologies of personality, as well to the understanding of the "personality type" generally common to the members of the group. Even in the case of the congenitally defective—with the exception of those unable to learn anything—and the mentally ill, the major part of the content of the personality manifestations is derived from the cultural environment. The mentally defective is of course constitutionally unable to internalize all or part of the patterns of his culture to the degree considered socially necessary. But such internalization of experience as he does make, although it may appear "stupid" and "silly," is nevertheless derived in large part from what his culture has to offer.

In some types of psychosis the organization of personality content is disturbed by non-cultural factors, as, for example, in paresis (disturbance due to inflammation or destruction of brain and central nervous tissue by the spirochete of syphilis), or in the traumatic psychoses (disturbance due to destruction of organic structures of the nervous system by such accidents as a blow on the head, injury to the spinal cord). But the *content* of the psychotic personality, however muddled, is usually in the main derived from the culture. Thus the schizophrenic who insists he is Napoleon does not conjure up the Napoleonic notion itself from his constitution nor from any strictly physiological disease process. Nor does the image of Jesus, which appears to the depressed case and scolds her for her sins, emerge full blown from the patient's physiological and neurological equipment. Such ideas and notions come to the individual from the group or groups in which he has been reared and has lived. We might say that in the psychotic they have come loose from the cultural web or matrix conventionally held by the group, or have been reinterpreted into psychological forms uncommon to the general run of the members of the group.

Thus, in the treatment of cases which afford any possibility of the reëstablishment of the personality integration, the psychiatrist should understand those cultural complexes which the patient had absorbed before he fell ill. What is the structure of attitudes and customs to which the patient has been conditioned in his family, play group, church group, neighborhood, clan, secret society, or what not? Until the patient fell mentally ill he was presumably carrying on his life by means of some sort of a complex of conventional understandings common to the members of the social sphere in which he had his being. The psychiatrist needs to understand this complex, if he is to try to fit the pieces back into place, if he is to reëstablish the patient's personal integration. Nor, in our society, has the physician any right to assume that the conventional understandings common to his own circle, as a middle-class, highly educated medical man, are necessarily the same as those of his patients who may come to him from various categories of our variegated society, each category with its own subculture, each with its own world view, each with its special customary way of solving certain problems and adjusting the lives of its members to the world in which they are supposed to live. The present writer, in his activities as consulting professor in the Department of Neuropsychiatry of the Duke Medical School, has had the opportunity to see more than a few cases of mildly disturbed individuals who have been brought to the psychiatric service from rural regions of the South. At first blush the manifest verbal manifestations of some of these patients has appeared to be so far removed from the norm expected of "adjusted" persons in our society as a whole, as to suggest a diagnosis of psychosis, or major mental illness. In one instance the patient was talking incessantly and in an intimate manner to Jesus; a young Northern intern assigned to the case concluded that a major disassociation or disorganization of the personality was evidenced and diagnosed schizophrenia (dementia praecox). Further investigation, however, revealed that the patient came from a rural Southern community where it was customary for every one to talk out loud to Jesus when in a crisis situation. The patient was actually suffering from what Karen Horney would term a mild situational neurosis,[4] induced by being abandoned by her husband and by failure to obtain a job.

Relations of the person to his culture. The difference between an *individual* and a *person* is that the latter is an individual who has been socialized, who has absorbed and organized internally to some extent the tenets of his culture so that he is recognized by other individuals as a personal integration, the cultural components of which, at least, are commonly understood in the group. As G. H. Mead puts it, "the self is not initially there at birth, but arises in the process of social experience and activity.... [The personality] is essentially a social structure and it arises in social experience."[5] The person not only has internalized and organized certain generally understood tenets of the culture, but he has also learned to play certain rôles and to adapt to recognized statuses designated by the culture of his society so that he becomes predictable and understandable to other members of the society, a person, in short.

Since the views and actions common to the members of a society are controlled by a cultural system, it thus appears that the first question one may ask regarding the individual's relations to his culture is, What has the culture, through its agents and surrogates, done to the individual in order to make him into this or that kind of a person? This is what we might call (1) the formative relation of the culture to the individual.

Simmons [6] has also pointed out that the person, once socialized and integrated, also stands in several other relations to his culture, or, to put it in other words, he plays several rôles vis-à-vis his culture. The person is always a *creature* of his culture, the relationship we have just mentioned. He may also be (2) a carrier of his culture, (3) a creator of culture, and (4) a manipulator of the culture. This is another way of stating the inextricable intertwining between individuals and culture: the individual is molded by his culture; the culture is maintained by and through the activities of individuals; the culture may be changed through innovations initiated by individuals.

CULTURAL FACTORS IN PERSONALITY FORMATION

The influence of the culture upon the content and structuralization of the person's outlook on life has been demonstrated in a number of ways. For example, the Indians of the Northwest Coast have developed an art style in painting, carving, and weaving which is far from "primitive," but which to an American eye is highly bizarre. Animals, for instance, are seldom distinguished by "realistic" traits, but by conventionalized signs; they often are depicted in semi-dissected form, as if they had been split and the two halves spread out on a flat surface. These art forms have so permeated the individual that even small children have great difficulty in seeing, to say nothing of drawing, familiar animals naturalistically.[7] Both perception and performance tend to remain within the cultural norm. Bartlett and Nadel [8] have shown by experiments on members of various African tribes that the cultural patterns have a strong influence on the restructuralization of memories, giving rise to "preferred persistent tendencies of the group." For example, if an individual of one of these tribes is asked to repeat a European story, he always tends to cast it with characters typical of his tribal folklore and to tell it in a pattern of sequence and with twists of plot characteristic of the native stories. In short the "press" of the culture is such that the average individual is stamped with ways of perceiving, thinking, and acting which are characteristic of his society and predictable.

Approved personality type. Some cultures are well enough integrated and the socializing pressures are sufficiently consistent to produce general personality types which are approximated by the majority of members of the group, age and sex differences considered. The first to draw attention to this matter in a systematic fashion was Ruth Benedict [9] who pointed out the differences among the approved personalities of the Pueblo Indians, those of the Plains, the Dobuans of Melanesia, and the Kwakiutl of the Northwest Coast. First, borrowing terms of Nietzsche, she makes a distinction between the "Dionysian" and "Apollonian" types of culture and personality. Most of the Indians of North America, except the Pueblos, she diagnoses as Dionysian; the individual periodically must "get outside himself," enjoy extraordinary experiences, escape from the regular sensory routine. Thus we find in the Plains the puberty dream and visitations by the supernatural induced in part by fasting; we find frenzied torture as in the Sun dance; we see the great development of war and the importance of the personal exploit; and, even when the Plains Indians have been pacified and reduced to reservations, we find that the Peyote cult, based on the use of a drug which induces hallucinations, spreads rapidly among the Plains people and other tribes, with the exception of the Pueblos. The latter, such as the Zuni and Hopi on the other hand, are "Apollonians." The approved person is one who is always moderate, never going to excesses; he is self-effacing, not boastful and personally aggressive; the very idea of "getting outside oneself" and indulgence in ecstatic experience is almost beyond the ken of the Pueblo individual. Benedict then points out that at least among the nobility or upper class of the Kwakiutl, the approved man was one who in our terms would be considered megalomaniac: he preoccupied himself with his greatness and his superiority over others; he destroyed large amounts of property in contests with rivals to validate his position; he was touchy and paranoiac about possible insults. Among the Dobuans, the average person was suspicious, untrusting, paranoid; men and women both devoted large energies to magical defense and attack; even fathers and sons, husbands and wives were on their guard against each other. In fact, Reo Fortune, who made the original field study of Dobu, reports that the individual who was considered most "queer" and different by the Dobuans themselves was a man who was always outgoing, friendly, and optimistic.

This work and other observations have shown that some cultures, at least, have the effect of creating a general type of personality manifestation which is approved in one society but which would be thoroughly discouraged in another. In our own cultural context, for example, the suspicion-laden Dobuan would probably be considered insane. On the other hand, the back-slapping go-getter who is one of the approved types among ourselves would find no understanding of his case among the Pueblo people. The question thus arises as to what constitutes "abnormality." Certainly it is in part a matter of cultural definition, because personal manifestations which are considered perfectly right and proper in one society in some cases are "very much off the beam" in another cultural context. Let us grant that societies differ with respect to the cultural definition of approved personality types as manifested overtly. How are such manifestations to be explained? Are they the result of *training?* Do populations differ sufficiently in respect to the *constitutional components* so that members of one society have a hereditary tendency to follow one pattern, members of another society have a native endowment fitting them for something else? Or does each culture simply place its stamp of approval on a given type of behavior among all those manifestations of which the population might be capable? In short, is the cultural influence primarily *permissive?*

There is probably some truth in all of these possibilities. However, that for which we have the least supporting evidence is the "constitutional" theory. From the operational point of view, therefore, we shall get farthest in understanding and planning at the present time if we examine the "training" and "permissive" theories. From what we know at present the various types of basic constitutional tendencies are distributed in roughly equal proportions in all societies of any size, and furthermore are usually sufficiently malleable on the average to permit moulding into a variety of overt manifestations.

Core and social personality. Before considering this matter further, however, a few other aspects of the matter should be mentioned. A distinction must be made between the *"core personality"* [10] and what we might call the *"public or social personality."* The core personality is the essential inner organization of the person and, as we have said, is compounded of constitutional, social-personal, and cultural factors. It represents the individuality of the person. In this respect no two persons are exactly alike anywhere, but core personalities can be grouped into general categories which cut across cultural boundaries and are found in all societies. Thus, everywhere we find individuals who are relatively outgoing ("extrovert"), others who tend to turn inward ("introverts"), some who have great energy, others with comparatively little, and so on. Nevertheless, in order to achieve social adjustment, the person everywhere has to wrap around his core personality the cloak of a public personality; he must learn certain manifestations which other persons can predict and depend upon; he must live up to certain expectations. It is the public personality which is, presumably, most affected by cultural factors.

Does society provide the individual with only one suit, so to speak, or with several? Is only one type of personality manifestation permitted, or may the individual "take off and put on" a series of personalities? It seems that a society usually demands a general design or "basic personality type" and also permits and requires a series of subsidiary manifestations which are associated with the different rôles played by the individual. The *rôle personality* is thus a specific manifestation within the boundaries of the design approved for the general public personality. We may take an analogy from clothing. In our culture all men are supposed to dress in trousers, shirt, and jacket, which combination may be distinguished from general costume design of other societies. On the other hand, the details of the basic design are grouped into a series of approved patterns which are considered proper for different occasions. Although the basic design is required in all of the following, the materials and details of cut vary as to whether one is dressed for a job as a field engineer, a farmer, an office worker, or whether the same individual is dining out formally or spending a quiet evening at home. Not only do clothing patterns differ through a series of jobs and defined situations, but also the individual is expected to manifest patterned actions which are considered appropriate to his different rôles. Although Benedict's *Patterns of Culture* was concerned mainly with drawing distinctions between the general personality types of different societies, she pointed out that individuals did not conform to it at all times and places. The boastful, egotistical Kwakiutl man can be quite abject when faced by sorrow; he plays a tender rôle in certain family situations; and he shows a certain shyness when making love. Linton emphasized that the person's manifestations from hour to hour, and at different times and places of his life cycle, are often controlled by the respective rôles which he has learned.[11] It is worth noting that persons will perform rôles in the expectation of receiving rewards given out to those who live up to the cultural expectations, even though they may not "feel" the rôle particularly congenial to them. For example, it was expected of boys in many North American Indian tribes at the time of puberty, that they go to some secluded spot, fast, and have a dream or a vision during which a supernatural creature, identified as the individual's guardian spirit, appeared to the dreamer and provided him with certain magical formulas and objects, sometimes called the "medicine." However, there are several well authenticated cases on record of boys who never succeeded in having a true psychic experience, but who nevertheless returned to camp with an invented account of their alleged experiences sufficiently convincing to satisfy adults. The "call" which is supposed to come to children in certain sections of our society and is supposed to induce them to join a church, may not always be "felt" by the individual, notwithstanding which he will "go through the motions." He plays the rôle of the emotionally moved convert.

Child care and socialization in the formation of the personality. The importance of the early years of life in the formation of the personality has received much emphasis recently, partly due to the attention which Sigmund Freud, the founder of psychoanalysis, drew to these matters. Freud's explanations were mainly biological and instinctivist, whereas many present-day students are inclined to see the influence of culture as at least equally important.

To put the matter as simply as possible, the child at the moment of birth is introduced into a learning situation consisting of human beings practising culture and using artifacts for handling children in ways prescribed by the group. The child has wants and needs, which these persons, acting as surrogates of the cultural system, satisfy in one way or another, if the child survives. The older persons also have mental patterns or ideas of what the child is supposed to be and they set to work with rewards and punishments to "raise him" so that he will turn out according to their expectations. Since in the typical case the nurses and other surrogates of the culture are following cultural patterns with some degree of consistency among them, the infant is subjected to a more or less systematic course of treatment from which he may begin to construct unconsciously a view of the world consisting of expectations of certain kinds of punishment and reward. The infant, in short, tends to look at the world in terms of his nurses, their cultural equipment and behavior regarding him, and the patterns they expect him to follow. Such a basic outlook on life is usually established before the child has developed either conscious memory or the ability to verbalize. Later he cannot remember how he "got that way" nor does he have the verbal connections with such experiences which would enable him to discuss them with himself or others.

Customary patterns of dealing with infants and children of course differ from one society to another. In order to generalize safely concerning the precise effects of specific patterns, we need more studies, but some hint of the trend of investigation may be offered.

Security. The early years of life are apparently more important in establishing a basic framework of *organization* in the person than in providing *content*. Detailed patterns of coördinated behavior—that is, content of personality—are learned after early infancy. One of the fundamental aspects of personal integration or organization seems to be the development of some sort of internalized system for personal *security*. This grows out of the fact that the infant is unable to satisfy for himself certain primary or universal drives, such as hunger and the temperature drives, but must depend upon others. The desire for response, even if it is acquired, is early established and must also be satisfied during the first months and years by responses of others. The question is, can the infant or can he not depend on what other people do? His security system rests upon such expectations and the reliability of the actions he performs to attract the attention and favorable response of others. In general, it is assumed that a consistent and regular type of child care is more productive of security feelings than capricious and unpredictable methods of handling children.

Let us mention a few details. Children in our culture are usually *carried* in an adult's arms or in a baby carriage. When carried in the arms, the infant is usually clothed and likewise the adult, so that direct bodily contact does not take place. Among the Hopi, children during the first year spend about twenty-three hours per day strapped to a cradle board, which does not restrict movement of the arms, but does keep the legs and trunk fairly well immobilized. They are handled and fondled very little by mothers or other adults. In Bali, on the other hand, the infants are carried in the arms of the mother against the body or on the hip. The child is naked and the mother also, above the waist. The infants have ready access to the mother's breast and close bodily contact with her. On the other hand, mothers typically pay little attention to the children, go on about their business, or give attention to other matters in what Bateson and Mead consider to be a "disassociated" manner.[12] What do such differences in pattern have to do with the formation of the basic organization of security within the individual subjected to them? Dennis reports that restraint of trunk and lower limbs among the Hopi seems to have no physical after effects and that children so handled are later just as active as children not so restrained in North American society.[13] However, steady support and regular scheduling of feeding, cleansing, and so on, seems to have the effect of providing a firm and expectable little world for the Hopi infant, even at the expense of some frustration of movement and of restricted personal contact and response with elders. The Bali techniques, on the other hand, provide for free physical contact and fairly reliable physical support and feeding, but leave psychological response fairly much to one side.

In the matter of feeding infants cultures vary, as also in respect to cleansing, and elimination, and so on.[14] We have space here to do no more than suggest to the reader certain of these problems upon which more research is needed. And, in fact, it would be an exaggeration to say that all questions of detail have been answered at present.

In general, however, the cross-cultural study of child care seems to indicate that basic security and integration of the personality are fostered by the following features of infant care, whatever may be the details of the cultural content involved. The régime to which the child is subjected should be (1) consistent rather than capricious or disorderly; otherwise the infant, lacking personal resources, is unable to build up any expectations upon which he can rely; he is unable to "relax." (2) Satisfaction of primary drives and needs should be provided with as little frustration as possible, but such frustration as is imposed should be systematic and consistent. (3) Dependence on others should be balanced with the development of the infant's own resources as he grows older and develops capacities. A certain degree of flexibility and self-reliance are desirable if in maturity the individual is to adjust successfully to changes in culture and other crises.

As agencies for developing integrated personalities capable of playing successful rôles in adult life, it appears that cultures which follow a consistent, continuous line of training from infancy to adulthood are more adequate than others. Mead [15] was one of the first to suggest, on the basis of material from other cultures, that the emotional crises of adolescence which had often been thought to be "inevitable" in our society are probably not due to physiological changes so much as to the fact that we abruptly jerk the individual from the rôles of childhood into the rôles of adulthood at this period without providing preparatory experience or training. In Samoa, children pass through adolescence without emotional upsets and without being aware that they are in a "dangerous" period; the cultural patterns gradually shift as one becomes older, and one steps from one series of rôles into another almost imperceptibly, so gradual is the transition. Likewise, Benedict [16] has drawn attention to some of the methods of socialization used in various societies to accomplish the inevitable changes in rôles which are involved in advancing age. For example, among the Pueblos it is customary to require the child to take responsibility for small tasks as soon as he is physically able to perform them and the responsibility is gradually increased as his capacities increase. If a child is capable of closing a door, no one helps him, once he starts to close the door; if he is able to take a flock of sheep out to pasture, he cannot expect an oldster to take over the job when he gets tired. Thus children learn not only physical patterns, but also develop a sense of the necessity of doing tasks; learn how this or that pattern fits into the scheme of things. Other societies effect the change of rôles by means of group initiation of whole age grades. The individual does not pass from childhood to adult status alone, but is reinforced by the presence of a group, all in the same predicament, all being instructed in the patterns of their new rôles. Mechanisms of "easy" transition would seem to produce personal stability, other things equal.

WHAT DOES THE SOCIETY EXPECT OF THE ADULT INDIVIDUAL?

Since the expectations of societies are on the whole controlled by the systems of culture under which they live, the question of the social expectations laid upon the adult individual may largely be referred to the culture. The ways in which any particular cultural configuration bears down upon or opens out before a person vary considerably, but are ultimately capable of analysis and manipulation.

Possibilities and ideals. Cultures differ considerably as to the correspondence they may exhibit between the mental patterns of what the socialized persons *should* be and the availability of actual actional patterns which determine what he *can* be. The mental patterns having to do with the desirable social personality are sometimes referred to as the *ideal personality type* and are displayed symbolically in various forms. In our own society, the nubile immature young woman is undoubtedly a symbol of the ideal female type; the virile man of wealth and/or talent who has been rewarded by a position of power seems to be the ideal type for males of the society as a whole. LaBarre has analyzed such types in terms of "social cynosure," [17] which, however, means mainly the most interesting type of personality or the type on which most attention is focused by the society as a whole. The concept of the ideal personality type may also be applied somewhat more narrowly to mental formulations of the desirable manifestations in certain categories, as when young medical students, for instance, yearn to be like a particular eminent physician who seems to embody for them the acme of what a doctor should be, or merely subscribe to a verbal formulation of the "perfect" physician, even though no actual individual seems to measure up to the ideal. Agreement in our society is fairly general concerning ideal types of categories or of groups. The definition of the ideal banker differs from that of the ideal labor leader, for example, and it makes little difference so far as the mental pattern is concerned whether an individual occupying one of these rôles at the present moment seems to display all of the characteristics of the ideal.

It is pertinent to inquire whether or not a given culture provides practical patterns whereby the average individual may transform himself into something approximating the ideal type or types or not. Or, on the other hand, does the culture maintain a sort of gulf or gap between the available patterns of action and the ideal type? In stratified societies based upon hereditary status such ideal personality types differ among the castes. Thus, in so far as training and experience may mold the personality, the requisite measures for producing individuals displaying the personal attributes of kings and nobles, let us say, are available, but only to a limited portion of the population, to the members of noble and royal families. Members of the lower categories are trained to know that such social personalities are not expected of themselves and that, in any case, the cultural means for developing them are not available. The level of aspiration is controlled and such choice as is available is definitely limited to the personality types considered appropriate to the social level in which one was born. Other societies, on the other hand, lay emphasis on acquired aspects of the social personality. Any of the ideal types approved by the society are in theory, at least, open to the populace. Among most of the Indian tribes of the Plains these types of public personalities were open, but limited in number, and no significant barriers were placed in the way of the average man in learning and organizing the characteristics conforming to the ideal. In most Plains societies, a man could be a warrior or a medicine man and the field was open to any one who possessed or could take on the attributes. A man had to be brave, daring, yet cunning, and self-confident. Male individuals who, perhaps because of constitutional tendencies or accidents of personal-social conditioning, were unable to fit themselves into these two molds, were relegated to the status of *berdache*, which also involved an ideal personality type. The berdaches were non-men who wore women's clothes and specialized in both household arts and hunting (but not in warfare); they were regarded as wise and clever, understanding and skilful; sometimes they were overtly homosexual, but not always. They were simply a special personality type approved by the society. Our own society, of course, recognizes a series of ideal types in addition to the general ideal of woman and the general ideal of man. On the whole, however, the opportunity to display the approved characteristics of the ideal types among ourselves depends on one's success in competition. Only a few individuals can display the ideal personalities at any given time; the remainder who cannot "make the grade" often feel themselves doomed to disappointment, feelings of inferiority, or to a passive rôle of identifying themselves mentally with the individuals who play the approved rôles and who apparently possess the proper personalities for playing them. Such a situation is productive of a certain degree of personal maladjustment, for the competitive system lays considerable stress upon training and trying. Many individuals who have spent years aspiring to be one of the approved types and training themselves to perform the patterns and organize them feel that they are failures. For aspiring individuals there are courses in "how to win friends and influence people." For those who have failed in the competition there are some cultural compensations: spectator sports, romantic movies and fiction, drinking and other distractions whereby attention may be drawn away from the unachieved goals, whereby the expression of the ideal personality may be accomplished vicariously or in imagination, whereby the sense of frustration may be deadened. Another compensation which our culture affords is the fact that a considerable variety of rôle personalities are approved. If one cannot develop the one, he may try to fit himself into another. However, since life-long training and experience up to the years of maturity is required of most such public personality types, such a change-over, particularly in the face of disappointment, is often more than the individual is capable of making. The competitive context of the culture thus undoubtedly robs many individuals of that well-rounded integration which security and opportunity for full expression confer. On the other hand, it stimulates many to develop facets of capability and features of personal integration which under a non-competitive system would probably remain dormant.

Several suggestions may be put forward for correcting our socialization patterns with a view to cutting down the psychological cost at the adult level. (1) Methods of providing basic security and integration in the child which do not depend entirely upon specific external supports seem to be indicated. In short, the individual provided with a solid internal security integration is not so easily thrown off balance by slings and arrows of outrageous fortune. The individual, on the other hand, who is "lost" without the support of family, of social position, of friends, of money, of certain beliefs in the supernatural which may be destroyed by experience—such an individual is more apt to collapse and to lose some integration when any one of such props is pulled out from under him. (2) Methods of training which acquaint the individual with cultural processes in general and with the wide variety of personal opportunities in our own society should have stabilizing effects upon the personality. The individual who understands that many types of personality are approved and that there are many roads to a certain contentment and well-being will not be so easily crushed by failure to achieve success, as the individual who feels that only one type of social personality can be achieved and that failure to play his chosen rôle successfully is the end of everything for him. The ability to analyze one's culture objectively is largely a matter of training and education. (3) Preselection of individuals in terms of their capacities and personal characteristics for certain rôles, which has been widely practised in industry and the armed services by means of "aptitude tests" and the like, is another method of avoiding the frustrations of the unsuccessful aspirant to a certain rôle. This method, of course, has nothing to do with socialization per se; it merely attempts to place the various individual products of socialization in their "proper" social statuses.

The child's world and the adult world. Kardiner,[18] with the aid of Linton and other anthropologists, has raised the question of the correspondence or consistency between the world of the infant and little child as manifested in the structure of social interaction and artifact presented to him, and the world of the adult who is called upon to take a mature rôle in society. These investigators have demonstrated that in certain of the simpler cultures, at least, the structure of the child's world tends to be "projected" into the cultural definition of adult existence; in other words, the adult sees his world in terms—often transformed and somewhat disguised—of life as he learned to know it as a child. Thus the Israelites of the Bible, for example, were introduced at birth into a socio-cultural situation dominated by the patriarchal father; and they lived out their adult lives in a belief system dominated by a patriarchal God. Children in the Marquesas are frustrated by irregular nursing and early weaning, since their mothers are anxious to maintain their sexual attractiveness; as adults they believe themselves to be plagued by female monsters or witches who withhold or snatch away the gratifications they desire. It is clear that such cultures, whatever else may be said of them, provide a certain strain of consistency in the life-way of the individual. The general methods learned in childhood for coping with recurring situations may be translated into similar methods when one becomes an adult. The general organization of the life situation remains fundamentally the same throughout life, and radical readjustments in customary responses do not have to be made as one passes through life. If placation and self-abasement works for children in relation to their parents, it works with the gods and rulers after one grows up, and so on.

Although in our own culture we find certain reflections of the childhood situation, one of our dilemmas is the fact that the home and family situation of the small child is unable to provide either a general atmosphere or a series of solutions to life situations which are generally applicable to the vastly varied world, created by our culture, which confronts the individual on the adult level. The family picture of life no longer corresponds to the definition given to it in the market place, the professions, the ordinary business of being an adult; the techniques of successful interaction in the home are not adequate in the office, the machine shop, or the political caucus, and the like. The fact has been often noted [19] that modern American urban homes are dominated by women and that the major part of the care and education of children up to the age of college entrance is in the hands of females. In the case of boys, particularly, it has been alleged that this represents a maladjustment in the preparation of the male personality for maturity. It is claimed that, instead of being trained in patterns which would fit them for the

THE PERSON AND HIS CULTURE 589

realities of life among adult men, their mothers attempt to develop them into the sort of persons the mothers wish their husbands were (but are not), that is, the female-defined ideal personality type of the male. And their teachers, usually spinsters who know little of adult men and their problems at first hand, try to inculcate equally unrealistic personality structures. What the possible results of these patterns of training may be in the general personality of American adults have not been definitely studied by any means. The reader may, however, wish to explore such matters further.

WHAT IS ABNORMALITY?

Since the culture pattern exerts so pervading an influence on the person, it is clear that, in one sense at least, the "normal" person may be considered one who is able to make adequate and approved adjustment to his culture and the conditions it imposes upon him. This is the cultural definition of personal normality, and of course it is distinctly relative. The well-adjusted person in one culture might not be fitted to another culture without a long period of retraining and reorientation. However, the misfit in one society might find another society congenial to him. The non-competitive non-compulsive individual is not highly approved in our society, but not a few such persons have found the Latin American way of doing things more to their liking. The question arises as to whether there is any such thing as absolute abnormality; is there any type of person who would not be able to adjust to any known culture, or is abnormality merely the bad luck of having been born and reared in the wrong culture?

Actually, it seems that we may distinguish two types of personal abnormality. (1) The one we may call cultural abnormality, (2) the other absolute abnormality. In the first type the individual happens to be in the wrong culture, but if placed in another situation is able to make a satisfactory adjustment. Much of the treatment of neurosis as practised by psychiatrists consists in "situational readjustment," that is, finding a cultural and social atmosphere in our own society which the maladjusted individual finds congenial—a change of job, a change of mate, a new neighborhood, and the like. This, of course, does not necessarily solve neurotic problems growing out of deep-seated "inner conflicts."

On the other hand there are undoubtedly certain types of individuals incapable of adjusting satisfactorily to any type of culture or to any social situation. The feeble-minded, particularly those of the grade of idiot or imbecile, are obvious examples. Some societies, on the other hand, do make places permitting social interaction for certain types of psychosis or mental illness. It has been pointed out that tribes of Siberia and

California, for instance, select out for the status of medicine man or woman individuals who are subject to epileptoid and cataleptoid seizures. Medicine men among the Tembu and the Fingo (Bantu) tribes of South Africa are often, according to Laubscher, schizophrenic. The accepted rôle of homosexuals in certain North American Indian tribes has already been mentioned, while from the Lango, of East Africa, to cite only one other instances, we hear of men who publicly live with other men and simulate menstruation.[20]

Yet when we admit that certain cultures apparently find places for some types of psychotics, there are other types of mental illness which apparently unfit the individual for any type of culture. We mention only a few examples by way of illustration. In advanced and profound catatonia the patient withdraws completely from the outer world and frequently lies for days rigidly immobile. Although such an individual may be an object of veneration or of idle curiosity in some societies, he is still an *object* rather than a person; he is incapable of interacting and adjusting to any pattern of social activity. In advanced general paresis the personality is frequently so destroyed or disorganized that the patient is unable to control elimination, to feed himself, and to speak a coherent sentence or even to pronounce words. So far as the present writer is aware, no culture has developed a social status, rôle, or personality type into which such cases could be fitted.

We may, therefore, speak of individuals of this sort as suffering from *basic or absolute psychosis*. At present, all the causes of such conditions are not known; in our society progress is being made in achieving remission of the symptoms so that some such basic psychotics can be restored to at least a limited social rôle. Taken together, the low-grade feeble-minded and the basic psychotics may be considered the type of persons who are *absolutely abnormal* regardless of the cultural or social circumstances in which they find themselves. In essence, absolute abnormality implies an inability of the person to interact socially and to learn culture, or an inability to perform cultural patterns sufficiently consistently and meaningfully for other individuals to interact with him according to any known type of cultural system.

Cultural influences in maladjustment. If we understand that a culture may provide opportunities and patterns of interaction for individuals who, because of their personal characteristics, would be unable to function in certain other circumstances, it follows that a culture may also have the effect of creating conditions conducive to maladjustment in certain types of persons. We have already alluded to the maladjustment resulting in some individuals in our society by reason of our incessant cultural harping on ambition and success. It is also significant that the cultural structuralization of different situations in our society seems to set up distinctive patterns of strain and pressure upon the individual. Thus schizophrenia is more common in urban situations than in the country, whereas manic-depressive psychosis is proportionately more prevalent in rural areas. Schizophrenia is in one sense a withdrawal of the person into himself—the "shut-in" personality, and it may be argued that this is a sort of adaptation peculiarly appropriate to the hurry, rush, and variety of situations requiring special adjustments which confront the individual in modern city life. Rural life is, on the other hand, more monotonous, so that it may be argued that the individual tends to seek variation from the routine and indulges in cyclic episodes of hyperactivity and depression. Likewise the probable influence of differential socio-cultural demands and pressures are reflected in the facts that in Massachusetts at least (also probably true of our country as a whole) men are more susceptible to mental disease than women; that the insecurity and anxiety of unemployment bring mental breakdowns in their wake; that foreign-born citizens faced with the necessity of adjusting to new patterns show more mental illness than native born; that divorced persons show the highest rates, followed in order by the single, the widowed, and the married.[21] These are at present only suggestions, but they illustrate one type of influence which cultural conditions may have upon the development of abnormality.

A number of societies have developed what appear to be psychoses or neuroses more or less peculiar to themselves. The *witigow* psychosis, for instance, is found among the Algonkian peoples of Northeast North America. It is characterized by an obsessive craving for human flesh and exaggerated delusions of traffic with cannibal monsters. The fact that the people are hunters who recurrently suffer from meat scarcity and consequent anxiety seems to be connected with these manifestations.[22] Arctic hysteria or *piblokto* is found among Siberian tribes and the Eskimo and is especially common among females. Symptoms include hypersuggestibility, a tendency to repeat everything said and done by others present. Sexual delusions are often involved. *Amok, latah,* and *young-dah-hte*[23] are conditions especially recognized among Malays, Southeast Asiatics, and Indonesians. Latah is primarily a female condition characterized by sexual delusions and hypersuggestibility, but the individual is thrown into the state by some untoward incident. Young-dah-hte is much the same, but is chronic. Amok, on the other hand, is said to occur principally among men and is manifested by acute aggressive tendencies under the guise of indiscriminate attack upon any one who comes in contact with the patient. Although these conditions have not been exhaustively studied at present, it seems reasonably clear that they are, in part at least, manifestations of reactions to anxieties and frustrations induced by the culture. For example, on the basis of Jochelson's description of arctic hysteria among the Yukaghir of Siberia, one concludes that the following anxieties are involved. Hunger anxiety seems to be a factor, since the condition becomes more prevalent during famine; sex anxiety seems to be involved in the tendency of affected women to repeat obscene phrases and to try to get at men's genitals. The suggestibility characteristic of arctic hysteria seems to be a touch-off for suppressed anxiety reactions of types mentioned.

Hallowell, in describing the Berens River (Algonkian) Indians of Canada, provides a clear analysis of the manner in which culture "not only defines each situation for the individual, but structures it emotionally." This culture, for example, defines snakes, toads, and frogs as stimuli which arouse fear in "normal" members of the society. Yet the neurotic, "in addition to sharing the culturally constituted fears of his fellows, has fears which in quantity and quality differ from those of the culture pattern." [24]

Culture and the problem of neurosis. Freud developed the concept that neurotic manifestations in individuals were evidence of inner conflicts between emotions and drives within the individual which are inconsistent with each other and therefore partly repressed into the unconscious, because they cannot all be given free expression. He considered one of the most universal of these conflicts to be what he called the Oedipus Complex and he thought it to be common in some degree to all mankind: there is a "natural" tendency for a boy to "hate" his father and to feel a sexual love for his mother. Society, however, does not permit the expression of these emotions; the boy must act as if he loved and respected his father and must show no sexual interest in his mother. The conflict between these "natural" drives (as Freud saw them) and the demands of society are too much for some individuals to resolve for themselves, with the result that they become recognized neurotics.

Malinowski, in his studies of the Trobriand Islanders was perhaps the first to recognize that such conflicts and the resulting "complexes" may be the result of pressures laid upon by the individual by the family configuration and social organization. Since social structures differ from society to society, psychological complexes and conflicts do also. In a matrilineal society, such as the Trobriands, repressed sex attraction is more likely to exist between brother and sister than between mother and son, while repressed hostility is more apt to be felt by a boy toward his maternal uncle than toward his father. [25] In these studies Malinowski laid the basis in comparative ethnological data for much of current psychoanalytic theory of the "Neo-Freudian" variety which has come to see the source of many a neurotic conflict in our own society in the socio-cultural situations to which individuals are exposed, particularly during the formative years. Thus, instead of "universal" neurotic complexes in which we are supposed to share willy-nilly, many an expert has come to think in terms of the "neurotic personalities of our time." And since this view holds that the cultural pressures which produce the neurotic are in many respects cut from the same pattern as those which produce the "normal" personality of the same society, the concepts of the cultural structuralization of psychic life have provided useful tools for the analysis of personality types and character structures of modern nation-societies, such as Japanese, German, and North American.[26]

Although culture is not the only factor in "abnormality" and maladjustment, it is one factor which is clearly amenable to change and manipulation. A close study of cultural demands upon the individual is a necessary preliminary to the reduction of personal and social maladjustment.

NOTES TO CHAPTER 27

1. The concept of "the style of life" was originated by Alfred Adler.
2. For a discussion of the various approaches to the analysis of personality, see Kimball Young, 1940.
3. For reviews of life-history material and other data on personality among "primitive" people, see Kluckhohn, 1945; Gillin, 1939.
4. Horney, 1937.
5. Mead, 1934, pp. 135, 137.
6. Simmons, 1942, p. 388.
7. Anastasi and Foley, 1936, discuss the influence of culture on children's drawings in 41 cultures.
8. Bartlett, 1932, 1937; Nadel, 1937, 1937-1938.
9. 1934, and a number of previous papers.
10. Cf. Linton, 1945b.
11. Linton, 1936, Chapters 8, 26.
12. Bateson and Mead, 1942.
13. Dennis, 1940.
14. On various aspects of child care in cultures other than our own see Mead, 1928, 1930; Mead and Bateson, 1942; Dennis, 1940; Simmons, 1942; Thompson and Joseph, 1944; Opler, 1941; Whiting, 1941; Ford, 1941; Gorer, 1938; Du Bois, 1944; Kardiner, 1939 and 1945 (with Linton's summaries of Tanala, Comanche, Marquesas).
15. Mead, 1930.
16. Benedict, 1938.
17. La Barre, 1946.
18. Kardiner, 1939, 1945.
19. For example, Mead, 1942.
20. These and other instances are cited in Gillin, 1939, with bibliographical references there.
21. Dayton, 1940.
22. See Gillin, 1939, for documentation of some of these culturally structured "abnormalities" occurring outside our own society.

23. Still, 1940.
24. Hallowell, 1938.
25. Malinowski, 1927a, 1927b.
26. Horney, 1937; Mead, 1942; Gorer, 1943; Fromm, 1941; Maslow, 1943; Erickson, 1942; La Barre, 1945a; Benedict, 1946; and others.

PART VI

Epilogue and Prologue

CHAPTER 28

Current Trends in Cultural Anthropology

To the outsider it doubtless often appears that attempting to identify current trends in modern anthropology is somewhat the same problem as beset the bewildered Britishers of Malaya when the Japanese first opened their campaign of infiltration in 1942. The anthropologists seem to be turning up on all sides, going in all directions at once, and with no well-defined center. The same may be in some degree true of the other social sciences as well, or of social science in general. But the fact that anthropology has boldly defined its domain as "the study of man and his works" has provided the practitioners of this science with a self-granted license which the followers of the more narrowly defined social sciences sometimes feel that they do not enjoy.[1]

Of course it is one thing to lay claim to so vast an area and quite another thing to occupy it effectively. The fact is that the anthropologists, who are relatively few in number, cannot pour out over the terrain like a Mongol horde, but have to hack paths through the jungle, making relatively small clearings here and there which enable us to see how the land lies. For the field of "man and his works" is not a plane unobstructed surface whose area can be occupied merely by squatting down at will and whose topography can be understood at a glance from a single vantage point. In his efforts to explore and clear the jungle of fact and appearance which covers the land of his choice, the anthropologist has many competitors and collaborators—namely, other social and biological scientists of all types.

The most significant scientific trend of the present day, it seems, is the fact that at last these scientific frontiersmen are becoming aware of each other's existence and joining forces in their tasks. The science of man in any form is very young and the wilderness was entered by scientifically equipped explorers only a relatively short time ago. In the early pioneering stages each little group shouldered its own brand of axe, bush knife, and rifle and set off by itself, cutting its way up some particular stream of interest or grubbing out the undergrowth atop its own ridge of theory. As in the days when small groups of colonists were granted, to themselves and their heirs in perpetuity, a frontage on the

Virginia shore stretching vaguely inland "to the western sea," the pioneering scientific parties had little notion how far their respective provinces stretched, but each maintained a fierce, albeit theoretical, proprietary interest in its own particular claim.

Most of the scientific colonists eventually moved inland, made clearings, erected neat settlements, put up fences around green pastures and settled down to a fairly civilized type of activity. If there is one thing which distinguished the anthropologists, it seems to have been that they were the Daniel Boones among the scientific settlers. They did not like to settle down in towns nor to build fences, but were always charging off into new tracts of forest, leaving only blazed trails behind them. On the whole they lived so isolated a life that neither they nor their more settled brethren enjoyed much contact or interchange with each other. Of recent years the frontier has caught up with the anthropologists and has given them credit for their explorations in the wilderness. As a result the anthropologists have become aware of some of their own former naïveté. They are beginning to learn that a hoe can be as useful an implement as a long rifle, that certain types of game can be raised in barnyards as well as shot on the wing, and that a jack of all trades should also master a few. So long as these developments do not smother forever the spirit of the pioneer, they are all to the good.

If we may now discard the metaphorical language, we can deal more specifically with certain selected developments in cultural anthropology. The developments in physical anthropology, which is actually a biological science, will be ignored for present purposes except where their relation to social science is particularly clear or striking.

Cultural anthropology is essentially the study of customs, their form, meaning, use, function, their organization and interrelation, their manifestations or results in human groupings and in artifacts and other material products. This is the central core of interest, whether the student happens to work with materials which can be classified as archaeological, linguistic, historical, ethnological, or ethnographical.

HISTORICAL APPROACHES

Previous to the 1920's, cultural anthropology in all parts of the world as well as in North America was dominated by historical interests, whether purely antiquarian, archaeological, evolutionary, diffusionist, or particularist in the sense of regarding each culture as the product of a unique combination of historical forces. The theory of evolution and a series of quite remarkable archaeological and paleontological finds had infused the spirits of the last quarter of the nineteenth century with a vast yearning for "origins," "beginnings," and "stages of development." If the story of Genesis was not a literal account of man's start, then the new science of anthropology could surely provide one. The anthropologists of Europe and America were not men to shirk so earnest a plea, and were not long in developing theories and explanations. Thus theories of evolution in culture sprouted forth vigorously from a soil enriched, unfortunately, all too often only by droppings from the sacred cow of Darwinianism. We should not be flippant about these early efforts, but one of the fundamental errors of the evolutionary anthropologists was to equate by analogy the processes of development in one order of phenomena, namely cultural activity, with those governing development in a significantly different order of phenomena, namely, biological organisms. We know now that in so far as either one is related to empirical data, a cultural theory can never be made to have more than a superficial resemblance to a biological theory.

Evolutionary theories.[2] L. H. Morgan was the outstanding North American evolutionary ethnologist; the names of Tylor, Westermarck, Frazer, Lang, and others are linked with this movement abroad. When constructing their proofs of evolutionary sequences in culture, these men worked with the so-called comparative method, which is essentially an arm-chair procedure consisting of combing published sources more or less indiscriminately for ethnographic items which are then hung upon convenient hooks of the theoretical clothes rack. Although Morgan and Westermarck both did notable field work, Frazer and the majority of his confrères in the use of the comparative method never saw a primitive society, much less an individual member of one. The method had the usefulness of providing us with encyclopedic collections of ethnographic materials, but two primary criticisms must be leveled at it. First, little discrimination was used in the choice of source, and, second, no care at all was taken to preserve or to consider the native context of the customs abstracted from the sources. It was naïvely assumed that the form of a cultural item alone was of significance, and that a similarity in form between items in two or more cultures ipso facto signified equivalence of the items in question. Thus, polyandry, for example, among the Todas would be considered equivalent to polyandry among the Tibetans, and wife-lending among the Chukchi would be the same thing for purposes of evolutionary theory as wife-lending among the Southeastern Bantu of Africa. No doubt the drinking of tea in the United States would be considered equivalent to the tea-drinking complex of Britain. The doctrine of survivals likewise played a crucial part in the comparative method, an intellectual trick whereby certain current customs could be considered as "evidence" of earlier evolutionary stages in the history of the culture under consideration. Thus Morgan was the first to recognize classificatory kinship terminologies as distinct from particularizing terminologies. But he was unable to recognize any present social functions in such terminological classifications of kinsmen, and leaped to the conclusion that they represented survivals of earlier stages in marriage or relations between the sexes. The fact that the Hawaiians, for example, make no distinction except that of sex between their relatives of the same generation was to him conclusive evidence that they had formerly enjoyed or endured a state of promiscuity or, at the least, of group marriage.

The essential idea of the evolutionary approach was that culture develops through a series of stages. This, so far as we know now, is true. But, in its classical form, the evolutionary theory held that *all* cultures inevitably must pass through the *same* stages of development. Investigation has shown that such a hypothesis is not true to fact. On the contrary some cultures have "skipped" one or more of the "inevitable" stages, because of the operation of the diffusion process, because of peculiarities of the natural environment, and for other reasons. Among the early anthropologists associated with the evolutionary theory of cultural development, Edward B. Tylor has probably had the most lasting influence, partly because he was not obsessed by the evolutionary frame of thought alone. His book, *Primitive Culture*, is one of the classics of the science of man.

Diffusionist theories.[3] As the extreme evolutionists became confounded in the contradictions of increasing field data, carefully collected, certain extreme diffusionists stepped forward to press a somewhat contrary view. The latter, instead of claiming that all cultures automatically develop sooner or later through a preordained series of evolutionary stages, proclaimed that the content of all but a few cultures of the earth had been borrowed or otherwise spread from some favored center or centers of cultural development. The most extreme brand, the so-called Heliolithic school, which saw in Egypt the cradle of all world culture but which made its own headquarters in Britain, has for some years been safely interred and perhaps is better forgotten. It was promoted chiefly by W. J. Perry, G. Elliot Smith, and W. H. R. Rivers.

A somewhat subtler brand of diffusionism, the Kulturkreiselehre, was active in Vienna previous to the Anschluss and has attracted a good deal of attention as a startlingly new and scientific contribution to anthropology during the last couple of years among the previously rather intellectually isolated South Americans. Its founders were Fritz Graebner of Cologne and Father Schmidt of Vienna and Zürich. Aside from the fact that nine or more centers of diffusion are posited, the most difficult aspect of this theory to accept is the idea that whole complexes of culture show such cohesion among their elements that they are transmitted more or less intact to all parts of the globe, to and through peoples of the most varying traditions, and without, in many cases, too much attention to the known facts of chronology. This cohesiveness of elements in a complex is explained on the basis of Graebner's well-known criteria of form and quality, and the claim is made that it is precisely those elements which have no functional connection with each other which mutually adhere and diffuse in spite of all conditions. It is difficult to see how any one other than what Malinowski has called a "museum mole" could hold to such a postulate. Although the epithet was applicable in a jocular sense to Graebner, it must be admitted that certain members of this group, such as Schmidt, Koppers, Frobenius, Foy, and Ankerman, have done creditable field work. Likewise the distinguished Swedish ethnographer of South America, Nordenskiöld, was strongly influenced by the theory. In other words, we must grant that, whatever its absurdities, this theory does not in practice seem to inhibit workmanlike if rather formal jobs of descriptive ethnography. It is chiefly when the protagonists start lifting material from the literature or from the museum case that the spell of the Magic Circle (Kreis) seems to lay hold of them. Perhaps this is in part because of the fact that the theory itself is an extremely well-reasoned and logically tight structure which as an intellectual tour de force could only be admired could one grant its basic postulates and reconcile its conclusions with the results of empirical observation.

American historical approach.[4] The Kulturkreiselehre never succeeded in gaining converts of consequence in North America, in part because this country already had a fairly well advanced school of historical anthropology which had been developed, beginning about 1900, under the leadership of Franz Boas at Columbia University. Boas was a man of both broad and profound interests and he trained a group of students who dominated American cultural anthropology until the 1930's. Among them were Kroeber, Dixon, Lowie, Spier, Sapir, Wissler, Speck, Tozzer, Goldenweiser, Radin, and Mason. Boas himself made contributions of the first order in physical anthropology, as well as in cultural anthropology including linguistics, and he insisted rigorously upon two aspects of method which went far to place the study of cultures on an empirical basis. First, he emphasized the necessity of first-hand collection of data in the field, thus deflating the rôle of the arm-chair specialist. Second, he required that nothing be taken for granted, that is, that no neat framework of theory be imposed upon the data as they were collected. The interests of this group were historical, but each culture was studied intensively as a special case. The object was to uncover all of the supposedly significant cultural facts explaining the development of the present configuration of a culture as found by the field worker. Diffusion was recognized as a major factor in explaining the content of a culture, but empirical evidence was demanded.

Unfortunately Boas never made explicit his comprehensive theoretical position with respect to culture, and most of his group showed themselves somewhat naïve in those matters which do not touch upon the historical aspects. Boas and some of his followers often showed an intuitive grasp of certain aspects of functional dynamics which has enabled them to argue that they foreshadowed the functionalists, but the fact remains that the movement as a whole was obsessed by a phobia of generalizations, which impelled the majority of its members to confine their theoretical discussions to relatively narrow problems. Yet Boas was a prolific stimulator of students. Out of the group came, for example, the refinement of the culture area and age-area concepts. And at least three of Boas' later students, namely Sapir, Margaret Mead, and Ruth Benedict, achieved prominence in work oriented toward the psychological aspects of cultural dynamics with generalizable implications. In general, however, the movement militantly disdained theoretical generalizations other than those of an historical order (mainly deductions drawn from empirical trait distributions in North America). This had the effect of producing anthropologists, each one of whom knew a great deal about the tribe or area in which he had specialized and who could command a body of carefully collected data from other specific cultures provided by similarly trained colleagues, but who knew little about culture as culture or what makes it work.

Common features of the historical approaches. In general, all those schools of anthropology which emphasized the historical or developmental aspects of culture held one point of view in common, either implicitly or explicitly. They all tended to see culture mainly as an additive *product* of man's activities, a sort of deposit or exudation as it were of social life, but composed of more or less discrete and interchangeable units. Not only were the elements of culture taken to be somewhat lifeless and passive digits, but the members of the society which produced them were themselves either ignored for analytical purposes or regarded merely as interchangeable ciphers of no significance to the understanding of culture. In short, the historical schools are not to be criticized for being historical, for every scientist realizes the importance of studying preceding events, so far as they can be ascertained. The almost exclusive preoccupation with these matters, however, led the historicists to ignore almost completely some of the most crucial aspects of culture in human life. They seldom if ever considered a culture as a dynamic system with internal and external strains and consistencies of its own. They ignored almost completely the mutual influences of culture and actual human beings on each other.

The result was a vast accumulation of facts, but no explanations, at least in terms of known facts from other sciences. Even in the elaborate distributional studies of diffusion by some of the Boas group, the attempts at explanation are flat, unrealistic, and naïve. In such a book as Dixon's *Building of Cultures*, for example, the various types of materialistic diffusion and invention are admirably classified from a logical point of view, but no satisfying explanation is advanced as to why such events take place. They just happen. It was as if culture were something special, apart from other objects of scientific inquiry, with laws of its own which merely had to be stated somewhat clumsily and which required no bridging postulates to other scientific systems. Thus, even the Boas group, despite its admirable field techniques and its much practised ability to demolish the theoretical pretensions of extreme evolutionists and diffusionists, was methodologically limited and theoretically inept. A very great service was rendered by pointing out what culture is *not*— it is not biological; it is superorganic (Kroeber); it is not determined in detail by geographical influences (Goldenweiser); it is not a product of race (Boas and others); and so on. But none of the older anthropologies told us convincingly what culture *is* and why.

FUNCTIONALISM

It was on the horizon of this rather provincial bailiwick of anthropology that there appeared in the 1920's two prophets of Functionalism, Malinowski, an Anglicized Pole, and Radcliffe-Brown, an Australianized Britisher.[5] The two gentlemen did not appear in person in the strongholds of American historicism until the later twenties and in the thirties, but their publications began to attract attention in the early twenties and won some converts. Both admitted to having been inspired by Durkheim and his French school of sociology, which was a hazardous thing to admit, for in those days it was fashionable for anthropologists to describe sociologists in general as fellows who talked learnedly about nothing. But American anthropologists were impressed by the fact that both had performed adequately in the collection of field data—Malinowski in Australia and New Guinea, Radcliffe-Brown in Australia and the Andaman Islands. The trouble was that both wanted to lay down hypotheses of general, world-wide significance for culture, hypotheses which could be tested empirically.

It cannot be said that Functionalism appeared as a unified movement. In fact, throughout their careers (Radcliffe-Brown is still alive and functioning in England) neither Radcliffe-Brown nor Malinowski seemed much aware of the other's existence as a functionalist, in print at least.

The only mutual references to be found in their writings are passing or defensive notes. Both were men of considerable vanity and each would have liked to cherish the belief that he was the originator and fountainhead of the movement. This was a worthy ambition which, so far as I am aware, did no one any harm. Both developed groups of disciples in this country and the British Empire.

The main interest of the Functionalists was the study of cultures as going concerns practised by living societies, and not only a few cultures considered as unique cases, but all cultures. They sought general principles or laws applicable to the cultural life of human beings everywhere, even in our own society, and they started with the assumption that each culture was an organic whole, to use Malinowski's favorite phrase, or a configuration, which had to be understood to grasp the significance of single items, whether they were customs, artifacts, or words. Thus a single item or part of culture might be unique, not because of its historical position, but because of the functional part which it played in the particular culture where it existed. At the same time the function it served might well be universal.

One of the fundamental tenets of the new movement was that no elements of culture exist in living cultures as survivals, in the strict historical sense of being non-functional remnants of by-gone customs. On the contrary, any element of culture which is practised by a society owes its existence to the fact that it performs a function in the culture as a whole.

At the beginning the Functionalists were heavily critical of the historical schools and their historical sequences, at best somewhat indefinitely established. Since the American historical school had spent a good deal of its effort in demolishing theory builders in the past, its members were not long in bringing out their well-sharpened weapons and launching a counter-attack against the upstarts. For a time the anthropologists of the country were drawn into three groups, the two opposing armies and a third eclectic group who refused to leave the proclaimed no man's land between the skirmish lines.

The Radcliffe-Brown division of the Functionalist band was, and to some extent continues to be, more narrowly sociologistic than the Malinowski division. Function to Radcliffe-Brown was mainly a matter of the structural dynamics of social organization, or perhaps it is fairer to say that functional problems were approached primarily in terms of such analysis, and human social behavior was interpreted primarily in the light of such studies. Thus, kinship structures were thoroughly studied by this group which for the first time clearly demonstrated them to be frameworks of social organization. Morgan, an evolutionist, had looked at kinship terminologies and seen them mainly as survivals of a more primitive stage of marriage; the American historical school had classified them and deduced from their geographical distributions former historical connections between tribes; but Radcliffe-Brown and his students studied these outlandish sets of verbalizations, not only as words, but also in terms of the organized, patterned behavior of the categories and individuals to whom they were applied within a society. The social structure and the patterns of interaction associated with it formed the main interest of the Radcliffe-Browne Functionalists.

Malinowski and his closest followers give the impression of somewhat wider cultural interests. Function for Malinowski was broadly the fulfilment of need. Although until his last years at Yale, under the influence of the psychologists there, he was never very precise about the nature and derivation of the needs of which he spoke, it is clear in all of his earlier work also that the needs were to be ultimately derived from the requirements of the human species and organism. As Malinowski himself said many times, his approach was essentially pragmatic. He took the whole culture as the proper subject-matter for the field investigator and sought the functional interrelations of cultural elements not only in a demonstration of their interconnectedness with each other, but also with the adaptive and survival requirements of human beings and groups in the total situation. A custom, for example, was functional if it provided something that actual people wanted or needed; the job of the anthropologist was not only to discover what this want or need might be, but also to explain why it existed in a given situation and whether it was universal or restricted.

CURRENT TRENDS

These brief characterizations of movements in cultural anthropology can, of course, be criticized as inadequate in any absolute sense, but they perhaps serve the purpose of setting the stage for the appreciation of the significance of certain current innovations in anthropological work and interest.

During the period when the functionalists and the historicists in North American cultural anthropology were sniping at each other, a certain amount of bitterness was generated in some quarters (although not on the whole by the leaders themselves) and some individuals took up extreme positions which were actually untenable on broad scientific grounds. Thus a few of the new Functionalist converts categorically repudiated historical studies of all types, while others ridiculed their colleagues who spent any effort on the study of artifacts and the material products of cultural activity. Historicists on the other hand did not hesitate to dub as chimerical many of the functional connections alleged by their opponents or to accuse the latter of tautology.

Such a situation was bound to be resolved sooner or later by men of good will, but the unification of point of view was tremendously hastened and stimulated by the publication in 1936 of a book by Ralph Linton, entitled *The Study of Man*. Linton not only reconciled to a degree the theoretical and operational preoccupations of both schools, but also presented a consistent and highly stimulating, if informal, theory of culture of his own. With consummate skill Linton wove certain current cultural concepts as well as new postulates of his own devising into a fabric of theory which provided not only a plausible basis for the understanding of much existent data, but also fertile hypotheses for further research. For example, the concept of social status was not previously unknown in social science, but Linton pointed out that a status must be defined in terms of the patterned behavior expected of its human occupants. His classification of customs into universals, alternatives, and specialities, together with the corollaries, while perhaps implicit in some previous writing, had never been stated explicitly in anthropological literature. And so on.

Also of great importance was the fact that Linton made clear the crucial importance of psychological studies to cultural understanding. First, psychology must supply the anthropologist with principles for the explanation of the process of the acquisition and performance of customs by individuals. Previously it had been deemed sufficient for social scientists merely to repeat sententiously that culture is learned, and to let it go at that. Second, personality psychology must be linked with cultural studies if any real understanding is to be had of the person or of his influence in cultural dynamics, for as Linton insisted, culture exists in the minds of men and has no other existence. Although to explain the process of learning, Linton employed in *The Study of Man* a form of Behaviorism now somewhat antiquated, the fact that he indicated so strongly the necessity of coming to grips with these problems scientifically, rather than merely giving lip-service to them, has had a strong influence on subsequent work.

Let us now turn to a brief review of movements already under way or in course of development in modern cultural anthropology. But before proceeding with this it is well to bear in mind that earlier anthropologists were neither fools nor villains, regardless of the fact that they occasionally fell into what, from the standpoint of 1948, seems to be serious errors. We recall the adage that "the verities of one age are often the absurdities of the next." The anthropological pioneers were usually doing their best with the scientific concepts and tools at their command to produce some kind of understanding of human cultural life. The scientific possibilities of today would not be within our ken but for the work which they and other scientists did to clear the way. Thus science progresses from one generation to the next, building on earlier contributions, profiting from earlier errors. A generation from now, it is to be hoped that the anthropology of the 1940's and 1950's will appear comparatively primitive in the light of the great advances in the understanding of human relations which we trust will have been made by that time.

Closer integration of scientific methods and theory. The movement led by Boas was in a sense a reaction away from "too much theorizing" as displayed by arm-chair anthropologists. At the time it seemed to American anthropologists that what was needed were more "facts" and less "theory." Leaving out of account for the moment questions of specific subject-matter, we may mention that one of the significant movements in contemporary anthropology and related sciences is a growing competence in handling theories and using them for scientific purposes. To put it in general and simple terms, it is now realized that the alleged opposition between "facts" and theory" is somewhat like the discarded distinction between "mind" and "body"—they are false dichotomies in the world of scientific endeavor. If we consider facts as empirical phenomena and theories as mental systems of concepts, these two aspects of scientific activity cannot be usefully separated in any scientific attempt to arrive at reliable generalizations and predictions, whether it be in anthropology or any other science. No phenomenon is a "fact" until it has meaning for the observer in terms of a body of concepts which are related together in some more or less orderly fashion—in other words, in terms of a theory, either implicit or explicit. Phenomena which we observe never actually "speak for themselves." On the other hand, there is no way of testing the pragmatic validity of a theory except by appeal to empirically observed phenomena, that is, by testing against the "real world" as known through our senses. Thus a theory serves as a guide to observation and understanding, while observed data serve as checks on beliefs and propositions held by the observer.

Although even an uneducated observer sees the world in terms of some kind of a theory or set of beliefs in the light of which he interprets his observations, many such mental systems are scientifically useless if not harmful.

This is not the place for an extended discussion of scientific theory, but every student should understand one or two aspects of a scientifically useful formulation of theory. First, the propositions or hypotheses should be stated explicitly and unambiguously so that the observer does not confuse himself or others regarding the objects of his inquiry. Second, the postulates should be related together in orderly fashion, preferably using one or other of the systems of logic available in our culture; this requirement is for the purpose of saving labor and avoiding confusion. It often happens that if one finds one proposition to be empirically "true," it will follow logically that various other propositions in the theoretical system are either true or false. Unless they are clearly stated and arranged in logical fashion, however, a great deal of effort and time may be wasted before such a result becomes apparent. Third, the propositions contained in a system of theoretical thinking should be stated in such a way that they are empirically verifiable; that is, they are testable. If a given proposition, after adequate testing, does not seem to conform with observations, it can then be reformulated or discarded. Unverifiable theories are of no more use than frankly "unrealistic mental systems." Fourth, the theoretical propositions in one science eventually should be stated in such terms that they can be meaningfully discussed in terms of the propositions current in other sciences. If no "bridging propositions" were possible between anthropology and psychology, for example, each would be the poorer for want of understanding which could be contributed by the other.

It has now become commonplace in anthropological work to state explicitly the theoretical propositions guiding the investigator and also the methods and techniques used in pursuing the investigation. As theories thus become open to check and test by others, less effort is spent on the game of building and demolishing theories for their own sake. A theory is either scientifically useful or it is not, and personal vested interests of the orginator come to disappear as this point of view is appreciated. At the same time, increasing attention is being given to methods and techniques of investigation with a view toward perfecting them not only for the first investigator, but also the second, third, or any other number of investigators who may wish to check findings. Improvement in field techniques has been particularly noticeable in ethnology and social anthropology, with increased attention to systematic note-taking, interviewing techniques, improved use of photography, sound recorders, and more attention to statistical methods and the principles of sampling and so forth in the recording and analysis of cultural patterns.

Organization of cultural materials. One of the barriers in the way of developing sound generalizations in cultural anthropology has been the great size and scattered nature of the materials which have already been recorded on cultures throughout the world. The average investigator trying to test even a simple proposition on a world-wide, cross-cultural basis has been forced to spend an inordinate amount of time accumulating bibliography and references, unpublished field notes, and personal observations of other workers who have touched the same problem. In fact, not a few reputations in anthropology have been built upon the labor and ingenuity shown by their owners in piling up references and digging up obscure sources. Of recent years a number of efforts have been made to organize the available materials physically so that less scientific effort will have to be spent on the mere mechanics of assembling the recorded sources and more effort put into extracting meaningful conclusions from them. We may mention two or three specific successes in this respect. The Cross-Cultural Survey at Yale University has already been discussed on pp. 196-197. It is a physical assemblage of recorded material on nearly 1,000 cultures of the world, copied and arranged in files according to a detailed universal outline. Several important contributions based upon its use have already appeared, and we may expect many more in the future. Another move in this direction is the Microfilm Collection of Materials on Middle American Cultural Anthropology, originally started at the University of Chicago. Field notes and other unpublished materials are arranged in more or less uniform categories, and recorded on microfilm, which is available to interested workers at a nominal cost. This method has the advantage that the collected and organized material becomes available to scientific workers anywhere, whereas the Cross-Cultural Survey must be used in New Haven because of its enormous bulk. Unfortunately Social Science Abstracts ceased publication during the 1930's. At the present time, there is a great need for an adequate abstracting service covering the periodical literature of the world in cultural anthropology and the other social sciences.

Psychology and culture. A growing partnership between psychology and cultural anthropology has marked the activity of recent years. The readers of this book should be familiar with anthropological adaptations of learning and behavior theory in explaining the dynamics of customs. Freudian theory, particularly of the "Neo-Freudian" variety, has found a congenial application in certain aspects of cultural studies, especially in those having to do with socialization of children and the study of cultural influences in the developed personality. Psychological techniques of study and testing have also been adapted to certain purposes of anthropological field work. For example, the Rorschach or "ink-blot" test has been taken over by a number of ethnologists as a culture-free method of assessing fundamental personality structure in persons of extra-European culture. For similar purposes some types of free-drawing tests have been found useful, particularly in judging the personality development of children in other societies. Adaptations of Murray's thematic apperception test, to mention only one other, have been made for use in other cultural situations and applied systematically to members of foreign societies.

The influence of psychological theory and technique is thus apparent in the work of many anthropologists at the present time, for example, the late Edward Sapir, Ruth Benedict, Margaret Mead, Ralph Linton, Morris Opler, Cora Du Bois, Weston La Barre, Jules Henry, John Whiting, A. I. Hallowell, George Devereux, G. P. Murdock, C. S. Ford, Clyde Kluckhohn, Scudder Mekeel, and others.

This new psychological interest is of course a reflection of the recognition and formulation of problems, which, if not entirely new, had never been fully explored or exploited by cultural anthropologists. We may mention a few very briefly: (1) The dynamics of customs as actually practised. How do they develop? How are they maintained? How are they lost? How do they change? And why? (2) The psychological orientations of cultures considered as total functioning systems. Why do some cultures point toward one goal? Why do some point toward another goal? (3) The person in culture. How does the culture influence the development of his personality? What is "abnormal," considering the problem from the cross-cultural point of view? And so on. (4) The psycho-cultural aspects of cultural change and culture planning. Psychology and anthropology have thus aided each other.

Personality and culture. The relationship between the individual and the culture of the society in which he lives has tended to occupy more and more attention on the part of anthropologists, working in conjunction with psychologists and psychiatrists. This has been discussed briefly in Chapter 27.

Application of anthropological approach to modern situations. Recent years have seen the methods of investigation and the "cultural" approach of the field ethnologist more and more applied to studies of our own society. The older type of sociological surveys and studies of restricted segments of social life are still useful, but in many cases took the cultural system for granted. It is now realized that we must understand the totality of our culture as a functioning system no less than the cultures of "primitive" peoples, and that the methods which have worked so well with the latter are applicable with suitable modifications to ourselves. This trend was started by the Lynds—who were trained as sociologists but well indoctrinated in cultural anthropology—in their studies of "Middletown." Among recent work of the same sort by trained social anthropologists are the series of reports on "Yankee City" by W. L. Warner and associates; studies of Southern communities by Davis and the Gardners and by Powdermaker; the study of "Plainville, U.S.A." by James West (a pseudonym).

Mixed and emerging cultures. As the area of European culture expands and comes into contact with the ways of life of other peoples, new cultures are arising in various parts of the world, cultures which are not the "pure" descendants of any of their ancestral cultures, but fusions, mixtures, new configurations containing elements derived from various sources. A knowledge of this process whereby new cultures are created is necessary, not only to our understanding of historical events, but also to laying plans for international coöperation in the present, and for laying out practical projects for the future. The increasing amount of work being done on description and analysis of these cultural changes and mixtures by cultural anthropologists is perhaps a reflection of these needs, and has been discussed in Chapter 26.

Applied cultural anthropology. Up to the present the applications of principles and knowledge derived from the study of cultures have been confined principally to government administrative fields involved in relations with subject or minority peoples, and to a limited number of applications in the field of industrial relations and personnel. The applications by our own government and by European colonial powers have been previously touched upon. Several countries of Latin America, faced with the problem of integrating large segments of native cultures and population into a national unity, have turned enthusiastically to applied anthropology and the more fundamental field studies upon which it is based. Mexico was the first to develop a full-blown program for the purpose of creating national unity without destroying the values of the indigenous ways of life, and it has been followed by official programs which are now functioning in Peru, Guatemala, Colombia, and Brazil (which had previously developed a credit-worthy Indian Service). These programs and further efforts in other Latin American countries have been aided by the program of the Institute of Social Anthropology of the Smithsonian Institution, which has collaborated with the local scientific institutions in establishing modern university instruction and methods of field work in social anthropology, and the Inter-American Indigenous Institute, a coöperative venture with headquarters in Mexico, which was established by multilateral treaty signed by the United States and most other Western Hemisphere countries. The latter is primarily concerned with promoting practical programs for the adjustment of indigenous peoples to modern conditions.

Somewhat similar functions with respect to native adjustments in Africa are fulfilled by the International Institute of African Languages and Cultures, with headquarters in London, and branches in the United States and elsewhere. In 1946 a Pacific Institute was formed in Washington, D. C., one of the purposes of which is supposed to be to advise the Navy Department and other branches of the United States government on the problems of administrating islands of the Pacific which have come under our control as a result of World War II. All of these organizations involve geographers, economists, historians, and other social scientists, but applied anthropology plays a large part.

In industry, the application of cultural anthropology has appeared usually under the guise of "human relations." The idea is to work out smoother and more efficient patterns of relationship between workers on the job and also in their community life. The pioneer study of the Western Electric Company's Hawthorne plant by Roethlisberger and Dixon has attracted considerable attention, and current work in this line is reported in the quarterly publication, *Applied Anthropology*. At least one trained social anthropologist, Dr. Eliot D. Chapple, has set himself up as a professional consultant to industry and business on problems of personnel and management. As the principles of culture become clearer and the basis which they give for the prediction and control of human behavior are appreciated in business, it would not be surprising to see increasing application in the interests of profit. Just as most large businesses now employ qualified economists, the day may not be distant when a trained anthropologist will be an essential part of the organization. Whether this will make life any more enjoyable for the mass of customers depends on the definition of objectives.

The manipulation of culture in the interests of restricted sections of our society can be as potentially dangerous as placing the control of atomic energy in the hands of socially irresponsible men. Thus "applied anthropology," unless done on a widely socialized basis and with due regard to human goals and objectives, is not to be indiscriminately applauded. Unless the knowledge which has been gained about the ways of man in culture can be applied for the elimination of human suffering, and the fulfilment of healthy human potentialities on a scale in which every man has his fair chance to participate, it were better to have no science of culture at all.

Rapprochement between cultural and physical anthropology. Although it cannot yet be said to have reached overwhelming proportions, there is evidence of a significant coöperation in certain quarters between various aspects of physical and social anthropology. In this book we have endeavored to make it clear that the organism is the vehicle and originator of culture; that culture and the organism mutually influence one another in certain ways which are significant to the understanding of both. Not only in the field of cultural theory and analysis but in various other fields of interest, specialists in the organism and specialists in culture are finding common ground: the new science of psychosomatic medicine, growth studies and their relation to educational policy, the problem of diet and cultural efficiency, the applied science of industrial relations, and so on. The whole man is becoming more and more the object of interest, rather than only one aspect of him.

THE PROSPECTS AND DANGERS OF HUMAN ENGINEERING

Planning for human welfare is undoubtedly possible. We need to know more about human beings and their culture, but we already know enough to eliminate some of the maladjustments which we have created for ourselves.

But tinkering with peoples' lives is a dangerous business and should not be embarked upon without careful consideration of the possibilities. Knowledge of how human beings and their cultures operate is as necessary for self-protection from unscrupulous tinkerers as it is for improvement of undesirable conditions. It is theoretically as easy to plan and engineer a slave society as a free society—unless the prospective slaves know what is going on and how to prevent the fate which is planned for them.

It is therefore clear that the technical aspects of changing and manipulating customs and the patterns on which they are based are by no means beyond our ken, but that any such engineering is inevitably tied up with the objectives or goals which it would serve.

This is not the place for an extended philosophical consideration of what is "good" and what is "bad." Without attempting further documentation or defense, we may, however, offer as propositions the following goals toward which cultural systems could be orientated. In other words, we suggest that customs and culture which promote these goals are desirable for Western civilization, not only in our own country, but throughout its area. If any one can prove scientifically that these goals are not desirable or that others are more so, he is free to do so.

1. Culture should provide for the highest degree of physical health and well-being of the members of the population which it serves, not only a few members, but all. This means that the desirable culture is adjusted to limit and eliminate disease, stunted growth, starvation and malnutrition, injurious accidents, and homicide among the entire population.

2. "Happiness" is indefinable in an absolute sense and we therefore should not rate it as a realistic cultural goal. But the desirable culture would *eliminate mental suffering* or reduce it to a minimum consistent with social life. This means that unnecessary frustrations, needless tensions and anxieties, baseless angers and aggressions would not only not

be generated by performance of the culture, but satisfactory means for their lowering would be readily available to all. Cross-cultural evidence shows that this objective is possible.

3. The desirable culture would be so integrated as to serve both the society as a whole and the individual member of society. Since social life seems to be necessary for human survival, certain cultural measures are necessary for its preservation. But culture must be so arranged that the society (or the "state") does not become the absolute master of its component individuals. In the last analysis human beings are to be regarded as more valuable than any social or cultural forms. The latter exist as instruments of human beings for the ultimate end of *realizing the utmost of human potentialities.*

4. Participation in the rewarding patterns of culture should not be withheld from any member of society except on the basis of his scientifically proven inability to learn and to practise them. In other words, cultural opportunity should be open to all. Restriction, discrimination, or exclusion from the culture or any part of it on the basis of family origin, racial type or ancestry, and other culturally irrelevant criteria is regarded as inconsistent with the goals of a desirable culture. Furthermore, it is practically inefficient because of its wastage of human resources. Participation in culture on the basis of ability does not mean absolute cultural equality for all members of the population, of course. Absolute cultural equality for all individuals does not seem to be one of the realizable goals of any society.

5. A desirable culture would be capable of changes compatible with changing conditions. Furthermore, the requirement of equal opportunity for participation implies that all members of the society served by the culture would have a fair chance to contribute to changes and to decide upon their implementation.

In short, a desirable culture would be oriented toward the greatest possible elimination of human suffering and the greatest possible realization of human potentialities of the species and of the individual consistent with the continued survival of the species and of society. Mention of such goals is not mere cloudy utopianism. They are realistic in the scientific sense and, so far as science is concerned, they seem to be realizable. Any such democratic ideals, of course, which look toward full participation by all individuals according to their abilities, depend upon education in the fundamental sense. The ordinary man, if he is to help to create and to enjoy the benefits of a more satisfying culture, must be aware that he is an organism with certain potentialities and that culture, as patterned and performed in interaction with other human beings, can and will be his servant, if he understands how to use it.

NOTES TO CHAPTER 28

1. For reviews of scientific interests and theories as they have developed in cultural anthropology the following are useful: Lowie, 1937; Penniman, 1936.
2. See, for example, Morgan, 1877; Stern, 1931; Tylor, 1878, 1924; Marett, R. R., 1936.
3. See, for example, Smith, G. E., 1911, 1915; Perry, 1923, 1924; Schmidt, 1939; Graebner, 1911; Kluckhohn, 1936.
4. For a sympathetic review of the life and work of Boas, see Kroeber, and others, 1942, which also contains a complete bibliography of his writings. It should be clear to the reader that in the text we refer to a "Boas group," a group of influential anthropologists who received training or inspiration from Boas, but we do not dub this coterie a "school."
5. Lowie, 1937, gives extensive, if rather unsympathetic, treatment to both Malinowski and Radcliffe-Brown; for a full comprehension of these men's respective positions, an exploration of their writings is essential; brief notions of their position may be obtained in Radcliffe-Brown, 1933, Introduction, and in Malinowski, 1944.

Bibliography

Abstract of S-R Sessions of the Monday Night Group, 1938-1939 (mimeographed). New Haven: Institute of Human Relations.

ABT, Isaac A., ed. 1923. Pediatrics. Philadelphia: Saunders.

ADAM, William. 1943. The Keilor fossil skull: palate and upper dental arch. Mem. Nat. Mus. Melbourne, 13:71-78.

ADAMS, Romanzo C. 1937. Interracial Marriage in Hawaii. New York: Macmillan.

ANASTASI, A., and FOLEY, J. P. 1936. An analysis of spontaneous drawings by children in different cultures. Jour. Appl. Psychology, 20:689-726.

ANDREWS, J. M. IV. 1943. Evolutionary trends in body build. Papers of the Peabody Mus., 20:102-121.

ANGELL, Robert C. 1941. The Integration of American Society. New York: McGraw-Hill.

ANNA, M. 1940. Notes on the preparation of food in Buganda. Primitive Man, 13:26-28

Anon. 1939. Pain: history and present status. Amer. Jour. Psychol., 52:331-347.

APPLETON, V. B. 1927. Growth of Chinese Children in Hawaii and in China. Amer. Jour. Phys. Anthrop., 10:237-252.

APPLETON, V. B. 1928. Growth of Kwantung Chinese in Hawaii. Amer. Jour. Phys. Anthrop., 11:473-500.

ARISTOTLE. Politics. (B. Jewett, tr. and ed.)

ARMSTRONG, H. G. 1940. Principles and Practice of Aviation Medicine. Baltimore: Williams and Wilkins.

AULMANN, G. 1932. Geglückte Nachzucht eines Orang-utan im Düsseldorfer Zoo. Zool. Garten, Leipzig, 5:81-90.

BAILEY, J. 1863. An account of the wild tribes of the Veddas of Ceylon. Trans. Ethnol. Soc. London, n.s., 2.

BARKER, R. G., and STONE, C. P. 1936. Growth in height and weight in college and university women. Science, 89:59-61.

BARNES, Ralph M. 1940. Motion and Time Study. New York: Wiley.

BARNETT, H. G. 1942. Invention and cultural change. Amer. Anthrop., 44:14-30.

BARTLETT, F. C. 1932. Remembering. New York: Macmillan.

BARTLETT, F. C. 1937. Psychological methods and anthropological problems, Africa, 10:400-420.

BARTON, D. R., 1940. The vanishing African. Natural History, 45:304 ff.

BASH, K. W. 1939a. An investigation into a possible organic basis for the hunger drive. Jour. Comp. Psychol., 28:109-135.

BASH, K. W. 1939b. Contribution to a theory of the hunger drive. Jour. Comp. Psychol., 28:137-160.

BATCHELOR, J. 1927. Ainu Life and Lore. Tokyo.

BATESON, Gregory, and MEAD, Margaret. 1942. The Balinese Character. New York: N. Y. Acad. Sci.

BAUDIN, Louis. 1940. El Imperio Socialista de los Incas. Santiago de Chile: Zig-Zag. (Spanish translation of French original in Travaux et Mémoires de l'Institut d'Ethnologie, Vol. 5, Paris, 1928).

BAUMAN, J. E. 1923. The strength of the chimpanzee and the orang. Sci. Monthly, 16:432-439.

BAUMAN, J. E. 1926. Observations on the strength of the chimpanzee and its implications. Jour. Mammalogy, 7:1-9.

BEARDSLEY, Grace Hadley. 1929. The Negro in Greek and Roman Civilization. (Johns Hopkins University Studies in Archaeology, No. 4). Baltimore.

BECKETT, W. H. 1944. Akokoaso, a Survey of a Gold Coast Village. London: Percy Lund, Humphries. (Monographs on Social Anthropology, No. 10.)

BEHANAN, K. T. 1937. Yoga: a scientific evaluation. New York: Macmillan.

BENEDICT, F. G., and CATHCART, E. P. 1913. Muscular Work: A Metabolic Study with Special Reference to the Efficiency of the Human Body as a Machine. Carnegie Institution of Washington. Publ. No. 187.

BENEDICT, Ruth. 1934. Patterns of Culture. Boston: Houghton Mifflin.

BENEDICT, Ruth. 1943. Race: Science and Politics. New York: Modern Age.

BENEDICT, Ruth. 1946. The Chrysanthemum and the Sword: Patterns of Japanese Culture. New York: Houghton Mifflin.

BENSON, Stella. 1941. The Faraway Bride. New York: Readers' Club.

BERRY, Brewton. 1940. The concept of race in sociology textbooks. Social Forces, 18:411-417.

BEST, C. H., and TAYLOR, N. R. 1937. The Physiological Basis of Medical Practice. Baltimore: Williams and Wilkins.

BEST, E. 1934. The Maori as he was. Wellington, N. Z.

BIDNEY, David. 1944. On the concept of culture and some cultural fallacies. Amer. Anthrop., 46:30-44.

BINGHAM, H. C. 1928. Sex development in apes, Comp. Psychol. Monog., 5, No. 23.

BIRKET-SMITH, Kaj. 1935. The Eskimos. New York: Dutton.

BISHOP, C. W. 1942. Origin of the Far Eastern Civilizations: A Brief Handbook. Smithsonian Institution, War Background Studies, No. 1, Washington.

BLACK, Davidson. 1925. Asia and the disposal of the primates. Bull. Geol. Soc. China, Pekin, 4:122-83.

BLACKWOOD, Beatrice. 1935. Both Sides of Buka Passage. Oxford: Clarendon Press.

BLOOMFIELD, Leonard. 1933. Language. New York: Holt.

BOAS, Franz. 1894. The half-blood Indian: an anthropometric study. Popular Science Monthly, 14:761-770.

BOAS, Franz. 1911. Changes in bodily form of descendants of immigrants. Sen. Doc. 208, 61st Cong. 2d Session, Washington.

BOAS, Franz, ed. 1911. Handbook of American Indian Languages. 2 vols. Bulletin 40, Bureau of American Ethnology. Washington.

BOAS, Franz, and others. 1938. General Anthropology, Boston: Heath.

BOGORAS, W. 1904-09. The Chukchee. Amer. Mus. Nat. Hist. Memoires, II. New York.

BONGER, Willem Adriaan. 1943. Race and Crime. New York: Columbia University Press.

BORING, E. G., LANFELD, H. S., and WELD, H. P. 1939. Introduction to Psychology. New York: Wiley.

BOWLES, G. T. 1932. New Types of Old Americans at Harvard and at Eastern Women's Colleges. Cambridge: Harvard University Press.

BRELSFORD, V. 1933. Lukambo: a description of the Baila custom. Journal of the Anthropological Institute, 63:433-438.

BROWN, A. R. 1922. 2nd ed. 1933. The Andaman Islanders. Cambridge: Cambridge University Press.

BROWN, Burniston G. 1938. A report on three experimental fire-walks by Ahmen Hussain and others. University of London Council for Psychical Investigation. Bull. 4.

BRUNTON, Paul. n.d. The Quest for the Overself. London (1938?).

Buld, A., Smith, L. G., and Shelley, F. W. 1943. On the birth and upbringing of the female chimpanzee, "Jaqueline." Proc. Zool. Soc., London 113A (½):1-20.

Burke, A. 1903. The fire walkers of Fiji. Frank Leslie's Monthly, April 1903.

Burlingame, L. L. 1940. Heredity and Social Problems, New York: McGraw-Hill.

Butt-Thompson, F. W. 1929. West African secret societies, London: Witherby.

Calmette, A. 1924. Sur l'utilization des singes en médicine expérimentale (Laboratorie Pasteur de Kindia [Guinée Française]), Bull. Soc. Path. Exotique, Paris, 17:10-19.

Cameron, T. W. M. 1929. The species of Enterobius Leach in Primates, Jour. Helminthology, London, 7:161-82.

Cannon, Walter B. 1929. Bodily Changes in Hunger, Fear, and Rage. New York: Harpers.

Cannon, Walter B. 1939. The Wisdom of the Body. 2nd ed. New York: Harpers.

Carpenter, C. R. 1934. A field study of the behavior and social relations of the howling monkeys (Alouatta palliata), Comp. Psychol. Monog., 10:1-168.

Carpenter, C. R. 1940. A field study in Siam of the behavior and social relations of the gibbon (Hylobates Lar.), Comp. Psychol. Monog., 16.

Carpenter, C. R. 1942a. Societies of monkeys and apes, in Redfield, 1942.

Carpenter, C. R. 1942b. Sexual behavior of free ranging rhesus monkeys (Macaca mulatta). I. Specimens, precedures and behavioral characteristics of estrus. II. Periodicity of estrus, homosexual, autoerotic and non-conformist behavior. Jour. Comp. Psychol., 33.

Carpenter, Thomas M. 1941. Energy metabolism, in Annual Review of Physiology, pp. 131-150. Palo Alto: Stanford University Press.

Cassirer, Ernst. 1944. An Essay on Man. New Haven: Yale University Press.

Casson, Stanley. 1939. The Discovery of Man: The Story of Inquiry into Human Origins. New York: Harpers.

Castner, J. C. 1900. A story of hardship and suffering in Alaska. Compilation of Narratives of Explorations in Alaska, pp. 686-909. Washington: Government Printing Office.

Chapple, E. D. 1939. Quantitative analysis of the interaction of individuals. Proc. National Acad. Sci., 25:58-67.

Chapple, E. D., and Arensberg, C. M. 1940. Measuring human relations: an introduction to the study of the interaction of individuals. Genet. Psychol. Monog., 22:3-147.

Chapple, E. D., and Coon. C. S. 1942. Principles of Anthropology. New York: Holt.

Chase, Stuart. 1938. The Tyranny of Words. New York: Harcourt, Brace.

Childe, V. Gordon. 1945. Directional changes in funerary practices during 50,000 years. Man, 55:12-19.

Clark, W. P. 1885. The Indian Sign Language, Philadelphia.

Clavel, D. 1885. Le tatouage aux illes Marquises. Rev. d'Ethnog., 3rd ser. 3:134-149. Paris.

Cobo, Bernabé. 1890-95. Historia del Nuevo Mundo. Sevilla.

Conzemius, Eduard. 1932. Ethnographical Survey of the Miskito and Sumo Indians of Honduras and Nicaragua. Smiths. Inst., Bur. Amer. Ethnol., Bull. 106. Washington.

Coon, Carleton S. 1939. The Races of Europe. New York: Macmillan.

Corbin, K. B., and Gardner, E. D. 1937. Decrease in number of myelinated fibers in human spinal roots with age. Anat. Rec. 68:63-74.

Costango, A. 1939. Pigmentazione degli occlii e dei capelli e selezione naturale. Metron, 13:109-133.

Covarrubias, M. 1937. The Island of Bali. New York: Knopf.

Cowdry, E. V., ed. 1942. Problems of Ageing; Biological and Medical Aspects. 2nd ed. Baltimore: Williams and Wilkins.

CRAVIOTTO, René O., *et al.* 1945. Nutritive value of the Mexican tortilla. Science, 102:91-93.

CRÉVAUX, J. 1883. Voyages en l'Amérique du Sud. Paris.

CREW, F. A. E. 1927. The Genetics of Sexuality in Animals. Cambridge: Cambridge University Press.

CULWICK, A. T. and G. M. 1936. Ubena of the Rivers. London: Allen and Unwin.

CUNNINGHAM, A. 1921. A gorilla's life in captivity, Bull. N. Y. Zool. Soc., 24:118-24.

CURWEN, E. C. 1937. Querns. Antiquity, 11:133-151.

CURWEN, E. C. 1944. The problem of early water wheels. Antiquity, 18:130-146.

DAHLBERG, Gunnar. 1942. Race, Reason, and Rubbish. New York: Columbia University Press.

DAMON, Albert, and RANDALL, Francis E. 1944. Physical anthropology in the army air forces. Amer. Jour. Phys. Anthro., n.s. 2:293-316.

DANCE, Charles. 1881. Chapters from a Guianese Logbook. Demerara (British Guiana).

DANKS, B. 1892. New Britain and its people. Australian Assoc. Adv. of Sci. Proc.

DARBY, Hugh H., and CHILDS, Dorothy. 1941. Seasonal fluctuations in estrogen secretion. Science, 93:115.

DARWIN, Charles. 1859. The Descent of Man. London.

DARWIN, Charles, 1871. Selection in Relation to Sex. 2nd ed. London.

DAVENPORT, C. B. 1917. Inheritance of stature. Genetics, 2:313-389.

DAVENPORT, C. B., and STEGGERDA, M. 1929. Race Crossing in Jamaica. Carnegie Inst. of Washington. Publ. 395. Washington.

DAVIS, Allison, and DOLLARD, John. 1940. Children of Bondage. Washington: National Education Association.

DAVIS, Allison, GARDNER, B. B., and GARDNER, Mary. 1941. Deep South. Chicago: University of Chicago Press.

DAY, C. B. 1932. A Study of Some Negro-White Families in the United States. Cambridge: Peabody Museum.

DAYTON, Neil H. 1940. New Facts on Mental Disorders. Baltimore: Thomas.

DEACON, A. B. 1927. The regulation of marriage in Ambrym. Journal of the Anthropological Institute, 57:325-342.

DEEGAN, William. 1941. Fifty-nine year survey at Yale reveals freshmen are becoming younger, heavier, and taller. Research Quarterly, Vol. 12, No. 4, December, 1941.

DE GOEJE, C. H. 1910. Beiträge zur Völkerkunde von Surinam. Int. Archiv f. Ethnographie. Vol. 19.

DE HAAN, J. A. Biernens. Fahlbegriff und Handlungsrythmus bei den Affen. Zool. Jarhb. Abt. Allg. Zool. u. Physiol., 54:267-88.

DEMBO, Adolfo, and IMBELLONI, J. 1938. Deformaciones intencionales del cuerpo humano de carácter étnico. Buenos Aires: José Anesi.

DENNIS, W. 1940. The Hopi Child. New York: Appleton-Century.

DEVEREUX, George. 1942. The mental hygiene of the American Indian. Mental Hygiene, 26:71-84.

DEWEY, John. 1938. Logic: The Theory of Inquiry. New York: Holt.

DIAMOND, Moses. 1944. Dental anatomy. 3rd ed. New York: Macmillan.

DICKENS, Dorothy, and FORT, Robert N. 1942. Geophagy (dirt eating) among Mississippi Negro school children. Amer. Sociol. Rev., 7:65-69.

DILL, D. B. 1938. Life, Heat and Altitude. Cambridge: Harvard University Press.

DIXON, R. B. 1915. Indian Population of the United States and Alaska. Washington: Bureau of the Census.

DIXON, R. B. 1928. The Building of Cultures. New York: Scribner's.

DOBRIZHOFFER, Martin. 1822. An Account of the Abipones, an Equestrian People of Paraguay. London: Murray.

DOBZHANSKY, Theodosius. 1941a. The race concept in biology. Sci. Mon., Feb. 1941, 161-265.

DOBZHANSKY, Theodosius. 1941b. Genetics and the Origin of Species. 2nd ed. New York: Columbia University Press.

DOBZHANSKY, Theodosius. 1944. On species and races of living and fossil man. Amer. Jour. Phys. Anthrop., n.s. 2:251-265.

DOLLARD, John. 1937. Class and Caste in a Southern Town. New Haven: Yale University Press.

DOLLARD, John, MILLER, Neal E., DOOB, Leonard W., MOWRER, O. H., and SEARS, Robert R. 1939. Frustration and Aggression. New Haven: Yale University Press.

DOUD, Harold. 1942. Six months with the Jap infantry. Infantry Journal, Vol. 50, No. 3, pp. 28-36. (March, 1942).

DOVER, Cedric. 1937. Half-Caste. London: Secker and Warburg.

DRAPER, George. 1930. Disease and the Man. London: Kegan Paul, Trench, Trubner.

DRAPER, George, DUPERTIUS, C. W., and COUGHEY, J. L. 1944. Human Constitution in Clinical Medicine. New York: Hoeber.

DUBLIN, Louis I. 1942. Longevity in retrospect and in prospect, in Cowdry, 1942, pp. 91-110.

DUBOIS, Eugène. 1922. The proto-Australian fossil man of Wadjak, Java. Proc. I. Akad. Wetesch. Amsterdam. Sec. Sc., Vol. 23, Pt. 2, pp. 1013-1051.

DU BOIS, Cora. 1944. The People of Alor. Minneapolis: University of Minnesota Press.

DUNN, L. C. 1923. Some results of race mixture in Hawaii. Eugenics, Genetics and the Family, 2:109-124.

DUNN, L. C., and TOZZER, A. M. 1928. An Anthropometric Study of Hawaiians of Pure and Mixed Blood. Papers Peabody Mus., 11:90-211. Cambridge.

DURKHEIM, Emile. 1915. The Elementary Forms of the Religious Life. Tr. G. W. Swain. New York: Macmillan.

EAST, Rupert. ed. and tr. 1939. Akiga's Story: The Tiv Tribe as Seen by One of its Members. London.

EDWARD, A. S. 1941. Effects of the loss of one hundred hours of sleep. Amer. Jour. Psychol., 54:80-91.

EKHOLM, Gordon F. 1946. Wheeled toys in Mexico. American Antiquity. 11:222-228.

ELDER, James H. 1934a. Auditory acuity in the chimpanzee, Jour. Comp. Psychol., 17:157-83.

ELDER, James H. 1934b. Upper limit of hearing in the chimpanzee, Amer. Jour. Physiol., 112:109-15.

ELDER, James H., and YERKES, R. M. 1936a. The sexual cycle of the chimpanzee, Anat. Rec., 67:119-43.

ELDER, James H., and YERKES, R. M. 1936b. Chimpanzee births in captivity: a typical case history and report of sixteen births, Proc. Roy. Soc. London, B, 120:409-421.

ELFTMAN, H. 1944. The bipedal walking of the chimpanzee. J. Mammal., 25:67-71.

ERICKSON, E. H. 1942. Hitler's imagery and German youth, Psychiatry, 5:475-493.

Ethnogeographic Board. 1944. Survival on Land and Sea. Publications Branch, Office of Naval Intelligence. United States Navy. Washington.

EWING, H. E. A revision of the American lice of the genus Pediculus, together with a consideration of the significance of their geographical and host distribution, Proc. U. S. Nat. Mus., 68: Article 19:1-30.

EYRE, E. J. 1845. Expeditions of Discovery into Central Australia and Overland from Adelaide to King George's Sound. 1840-41. London: T. and W. Boone.

FARABEE, W. C. 1918. The Central Arawaks. Univ. Penn. Mus., Anthro. Publ., 9. Philadelphia.

FAY, T., and SMITH, G. W. 1941. Observations on reflex responses during prolonged periods of human refrigeration. Arch. Neurol. and Psychiat., 45:215-222.

FINLEY, John P. 1913. The Subanee, Carnegie Inst. of Washington, Publ. 184. Washington.

FISCHER, Eugen. 1913. Die Rehobother Bastards und das Bastardierungsproblem beim Menschen. Jena.

FISHBERG, Maurice. 1905. Materials for the physical anthropology of the eastern European Jew. An. N. Y. Acad. Sci., 16:155-297.

FITCH, Lyle. 1937. Inheritance of white forelock. Jour. Hered., 28:413-414.

FITZROY, Robert. 1939. Narrative of the Surveying Voyages of His Majesty's Ships Adventure and Beagle. Vol. 2. London.

FLEMING, R. M. 1939. Physical heredity of human hybrids. Annals of Eugenics. 9:55-81.

FORD, Clellan C. 1941. Smoke from their Fires. New Haven: Yale University Press.

FORD, C. S. 1945. A comparative Study of Human Reproduction, Yale Univ. Publ. Anthrop., 32. New Haven: Yale University Press.

FORTES, M., and EVANS-PRICHARD, E. E., eds. 1940. African Political Systems. London: Oxford University Press.

FRANCIS, Carl C. 1940. The appearance of centers of ossification from 6 to 15 years. American Journal of Physical Anthropology, 27:127-138.

FRANCIS, Carl C., and WERLE, Peter P. 1938-39. The appearance of centers of ossification from birth to five years, 24:273-300.

FRANK, L. K., and KISER, L. K. 1943. Human conservation. The Story of our wasted resources. Washington: Government Printing Office.

FRISBIE, Robert Dean. 1944. The Island of Desire. New York: Doubleday, Doran.

FROMM, Eric. 1941. Escape from Freedom. New York: Farrar and Rinehart.

FULTON, J. F., and KELLER, A. D. 1932. The Sign of Babinski: a Study of the Evolution of Cortical Dominance in Primates. Baltimore: Thomas.

FURNESS, W. H. 1916. Observations on the mentality of chimpanzees and orang-utans, Proc. Amer. Phil. Soc., 55:281-90.

GARTH, T. R. 1931. Race Psychology, a Study of Racial Mental Differences. New York: McGraw-Hill.

GATES, R. R. 1929. Heredity in Men. London: Constable.

GATES, R. R., SNYDER, L. H., and HOSTON, E. A. 1943. Medical genetics and eugenics. Philadelphia Women's Medical College of Philadelphia.

GEDDES, Patrick. 1885. An Analysis of the Principles of Economics. Edinburgh.

GENNEP, Arnold van. 1909. Les rites de passage. Paris: E. Nourry.

GESELL, Arnold, and others. 1940. The First Five Years. New York: Hoeber.

GESELL, Arnold, and HALVERSON, H. H. 1936. The development of thumb opposition in the human infant, Jour. Genet. Psychol., 48:339-61.

GILBERT, J. A., and PATRICK, G. T. W. 1896. On the effects of loss of sleep. Psychol. Rev., 3:469-483.

GILBRETH, F. B. 1911. Motion Study. New York: Van Nostrand.

GILFILLAN, S. F. 1920. The coldward course of progress. Pol. Sci. Quart., 35.

GILLIN, John. 1934. Crime and punishment among the Barama River Carib of British Guiana. Amer. Anthro., 36:331-44.

GILLIN, John. 1936a. The Barama River Caribs of British Guiana. Papers of the Peabody Museum, Vol. 14, No. 2. Cambridge.

GILLIN, John. 1936b. The configuration problem in culture. Amer. Sociol. Rev., 1:373-86.

GILLIN, John. 1939. Personality in preliterate societies. Amer. Sociol. Rev., 4:681-702.

GILLIN, John. 1942. Acquired drives in culture contact. Amer. Anthro., 44:545-54.

GILLIN, John. 1944a. Cultural adjustment. Amer. Anthro., 46:429-47.

GILLIN, John. 1944b. Custom and range of human response. Character and Personality, 13:101-134.

GILLIN, John. 1945a. Parallel cultures and the inhibitions to acculturation in a Guatemalan community. Social Forces, 24:1-14.

GILLIN, John. 1945b. Personality formation from the comparative cultural point of view. Sociological Foundations of the Psychiatric Disorders of Childhood, pp. 13-27. Langhorn, Pennsylvania: The Woods Schools.

GILLIN, John. 1947a. Modern Latin-American Culture. Social Forces, 25:243-248.

GILLIN, John. 1947b. Moche: a Peruvian coastal community. Smithsonian Institution, Institute of Social Anthropology, Pulb. 3. Washington.

GILLIN, John, and RAIMY, Victor. 1940. Acculturation and personality. Amer. Soc. Rev., 5:371-380.

GILLIN, John Lewis. 1906. The Dunkers: A Sociological Interpretation. New York: privately printed as a Ph.D. thesis in Columbia University.

GILLIN, J. L., and GILLIN, J. P. 1942. An introduction to Sociology. New York: Macmillan.

GIRARD, A. 1939. Vieulles coutumes bulgares: les danseurs du feu. Illustration, 203:180-181, June 3, 1939.

GODSELL, Philip H. 1940. The Eskimo goes modern. Natural History, 45:38 ff.

GOLDENWEISER, Alexander. 1913. The principle of limited possibilities. Journal of American Folklore, 26:259-290.

GOLDENWEISER, Alexander. 1937. Anthropology. New York: Crofts.

GOLDSTEIN, M. S. 1943. Demographic and bodily changes in descendants of Mexican immigrants with comparable data on parents and children in Mexico. Inst. of Latin-American Studies. Austin, Texas.

GOODENOUGH, Florence. 1934. Developmental Psychology. New York: Appleton-Century (2d ed., 1945).

GOODMAN, Leroy, and WISLOCKI, George B. 1935. Cyclic uterine bleeding in a New World Monkey (Ateles geoffroyi), Anat. Rec. 61:379-87.

GORDON, F. F. 1930. Physical measurements of 1000 Smith College Students. Amer. Jour. Public Health, 20:963-968.

GORER, G. 1934. Africa Dances. New York: Knopf.

GORER, G. 1938. Himalayan Village. London: Joseph.

GOULD, G. M., and PYLE, W. L. 1897. Anomalies and Curiosities of Medicine. Philadelphia: Saunders.

GRAEBNER, Fritz. 1911. Methode der Ethnologie. Heidelberg: C. Winter.

GREENBAUM, Lucy. 1945. In marriage it's a man's market. New York Times Magazine, June 17, 1945, pp. 14-15.

GREGORY, W. K. 1916. Studies on the evolution of the Primates. Bulletin, American Museum of Natural History, 25:239-255.

GREGORY, W. K. 1922. The Origin and Evolution of Human Dentition. Baltimore: Williams and Wilkins.

GRETHER, W. F. 1939a. Color vision and color blindness in monkeys. Comp. Psychol. Monog., Vol. 15, No. 4, Ser. No. 76, 1-38.

GRETHER, W. F. 1939b. Chimpanzee color vision. I. Hue discrimination at three spectral points, Jour. Comp. Psychol., 29:167-77.

GRETHER, W. F., and YERKES, R. M. 1940. Weight norms and relations for chimpan- Phys. Anthr., 27:181-97.

Silent Trade: a Contribution to the Early History of
reen.

n Unknown Land. London: Seeley.

las naciones situadas en las

Selk'nam. Mödling bei

GUTHE, C. E. 1918. Notes on the cephalic index of Russian Jews in Boston. Amer. Journ. Phys. Anthrop., 1:213-223.

GUTHRIE, E. R. 1935. The Psychology of Learning. New York: Harper.

HALL, A. Daniel. 1936. The Improvement of Native Agriculture in Relation to Population and Public Health. London: Oxford University Press.

HALLOWELL, A. I. 1938. Fear and anxiety as cultural and individual variables in a primitive society. Journal of Social Psychology, 9:25-47.

HALLOWELL, A. I. 1939. Sin, sex and sickness in Salteaux belief. Brit. Jour. Med. Psych., 18:191-197.

HALLOWELL, A. I. 1940. Aggression in Salteaux society. Psychiatry, 3:395-407.

HALLOWELL, A. I. 1941. The social function of anxiety in a primitive society. Amer. Soc. Rev., 6:869-881.

HALLOWELL, A. I. 1942. The Rôle of Conjuring in Saulteaux Society. Philadelphia: University of Pennsylvania Press.

HALLOWELL, A. I. 1945. Sociopsychological aspects of acculturation, in Linton, 1945a, pp. 171-200.

HAMBLY, W. D. 1934. The Ovibundu of Angola. Field Mus. Nat. Hist. Publ. 329, Anthrop. Series, Vol. 21, No. 2.

HAMILTON, G. V. 1914. A study of the sexual tendencies of monkeys and baboons, Jour. Animal Behavior, 4:295-318.

HAMLETT, G. W. D. 1939. Reproduction in American monkeys. I. Estrus cycle, ovulation and menstruation in Cebus. Anat. Rec., 73:171-87.

HANDY, W. C. 1922. Tattooing in the Marquesas. Bernice P. Bishop Mus., Bull. 1. Honolulu.

HANKINS, F. H. 1931. The Racial Basis of Civilization. New York: Knopf.

HARDY, James D., and DuBois, E. F. 1940. Differences between men and women in their response to heat and cold. Proc. Natl. Ac. Sci., 26(6):389.

HARDY, James D., MILHORST, A. T., and DuBois, E. F. 1941. Basal metabolism and heat loss of young women at temperatures from 22 ° C to 35 ° C. Jour. Nutrition, 21:383.

HARLOW, H. F. 1932. Comparative behavior of primates. Jour. Comp. Psychol., 14:241-252; (with H. Uehling and A. H. Maslow).

HARLOW, H. F., and BROMER, J. A. 1939. Comparative behavior of primates. VII. The capacity of platyrrhine monkeys to solve delayed reaction tests, Jour. Comp. Psychol., 28:299-304.

HARRIS, R. D. 1926. The San Blas Indians. Amer. J. of Phys. Anthro. 9:17-63.

HARTMAN, C. G. 1932. Studies in the reproduction of the monkey Macacus (Pithecus) *rhesus*, with special reference to menstruation and pregnancy, Carnegie Inst. Washington, Publ. 433, Contrib. to Embryology, 23, 1-162.

HENRY, Jules. 1941. Jungle People. New York: Augustin.

HERRERA, Antonio. 1728. Historia general de los hechos de los castellanos en las islas y tierra firme del mar océano. Madrid.

HERSKOVITS, Melville J. 1928. The American Negro. New York: Knopf.

HERSKOVITS, Melville J. 1930. Anthropometry of the American Negro. New York: Columbia University Press.

HERSKOVITS, Melville J. 1938. Acculturation. New York: Augustin.

HERSHOVITS, Melville J. 1940. The Economic Life of Primitive Peoples. New York: Knopf.

HERSKOVITS, Melville J. 1945. The processes of cultural change, in Linton, 1945a, pp. 143-170.

HILDÉN, Kaarlo. 1938. On ███████████ een age and the occurrence of the Mongolian eye-fold. Soc. ███████ ██ 7(6).

HILGARD, Ernest R., an███████████████ ████ditioning and Learning. New York: Appleton-███████

HIRSCH, N. D. M. 1927. Cephalic index of American-born children of three foreign groups. Amer. Jour. Phys. Anthrop., 10:79-90.

HOFMAYR, Wilhelm, 1925. Die Schilluk. Mödling bei Wien: Anthropos.

HOGBEN, Lancelot. 1932. Genetic Principles in Medicine and Social Science. New York: Knopf.

HODGE, F. W., ed. 1907. Handbook of the American Indians North of Mexico. 2 Vols. Smiths. Inst., Bur. Amer. Ethnol. Bull. 30. Washington.

HOKE, R. E. 1922. Improvement of speed and accuracy in "typewriting." Johns Hopkins Stud. Educ. No. 7, pp. 1-142.

HOLLIS, A. C. 1905. The Masai: Their Language and Folklore. Oxford.

HOLT, E., and McINTOSH, R. 1940. Holt's diseases of infancy and childhood. 11th ed. New York: Appleton-Century.

HOOTON, E. A. 1931. Up from the Ape. New York: Macmillan.

HOOTON, E. A. 1939. The Twilight of Man. New York: Putnam.

HOOTON, E. A. 1942. Man's Poor Relations. New York: Doubleday, Doran.

HOOTON, E. A. 1946. Up from the Ape. Rev. Ed. New York: Macmillan.

HORNEY, Karen. 1937. The Neurotic Personality of Our Time. New York: Norton.

HORWITZ, E. L. 1944. Race attitudes, in Characteristics of the American Negro (O. Klineberg, ed.). New York: Harpers.

HOSE, Charles. Natural Man. London: Macmillan.

HOST, Franz. 1874. Die Missionen und die Matacos Indianer im Gran Chaco. Globus, 25:24-26.

HOWELLS, W. W. 1944. Mankind So Far. New York: Doubleday.

HRDLICKA, A. 1908. Physical and Medical Observations among the Indians of the Southwestern United States and Northern Mexico. Bur. Amer. Ethnol. Bull. 34. Washington.

HSIAO, T'uvy Fei. 1944. Peasant life in China. Chicago: University of Chicago Press.

HSIEN, Chin Hu. 1944. The Chinese concepts of "face." Amer. Anthrop., 46:45-64.

HULL, C. L. 1932. The goal gradient hypothesis and maze learning. Psychol. Rev., 39:25-43.

HULL, C. L. 1935. The conflicting psychologies of learning: a way out. Psychol. Rev., 42:491-516.

HULL, C. L. 1937. Mind, mechanism and adaptive behavior. Psychol. Rev. 44:1-32.

HULL, C. L. 1943. Principles of Behavior: an introduction to behavior theory. New York: Appleton-Century.

HUNTER, Helen Virginia. 1940. The Ethnography of Salt in Aboriginal North America. Philadelphia.

HUNTINGTON, Ellsworth. 1924. Civilization and Climate. New Haven: Yale University Press.

HUNTINGTON, Ellsworth. 1945. Mainsprings of Civilization. New York: Wiley.

HUXLEY, T. H. 1894. Man's Place in Nature and Other Anthropological Essays. London: Dent.

IM THURN, Everard. 1883. Among the Indians of Guiana. London.

INGALLS, Albert G. 1939. Fire-walking. Scientific American, 160:135-138. (March 1939.)

ITO, P. K. 1942. Comparative biometrical study of physique of Japanese women born and reared under different environments. Human Biology, 14:279-351.

JACKSON, C. M. 1931. Changes in stature, weight, and body build of female students at the University of Minnesota during a period of 18 years. Anat. Rec., 49:71-80.

JENNESS, D. 1928. The People of the Twilight. New York: Macmillan.

JENNINGS, Herbert S. 1930. The Biological Basis of Human Nature. New York: Norton.

JENNINGS, Herbert S. 1935. Genetics. New York: Norton.

JENNINGS, Herbert S. 1941. The laws of heredity and our present knowledge of human genetics on the material side, in Scientific Aspects of the Race Problem, pp. 3-76. New York: Longmans, Green.

JOHNSON, Wendell. 1946. People in Quandaries. New York: Harpers.

JOHNSON, Winifred B., and TERMAN, Lewis M. 1940. Some highlights in the literature of psychological sex differences published since 1920, Jour. Psychol., 9.

JOHNSTON, H. H. 1908. George Grenfell and the Congo. London: Hutchinson.

JOHNSTON, H. H. 1919-1922. A Comparative Study of the Bantu and Semi-Bantu Languages. Oxford: Clarendon Press.

JONES, F. Wood. 1926. 3rd ed. Arboreal Man. London: Arnold.

KARDINER, Abram. 1939. The Individual and His Society. New York: Columbia University Press.

KARDINER, Abram. 1945. The Psychological Frontiers of Society. New York: Columbia University Press.

KATZ, S. E., and LANDIS, C. 1935. Psychologic and physiologic phenomena during a prolonged vigil. Arch. Neurol. and Psychiat., 34:307-316.

KELLOGG, V. L. Ectoparasites of the monkeys, apes, and men. Science, 38:601-02.

KELLOGG, V. L. Ectoparasites of mammals. Amer. Naturalist. 48:257-79.

KELLOGG, W. N. and L. A. 1933. The Ape and the Child. New York: McGraw-Hill.

KENNEDY, Raymond. 1937. A survey of Indonesian civilization. Studies in the Science of Society (G. P. Murdock, ed.). New Haven: Yale University Press. Pp. 2-91.

KIIL, W. 1939. Stature and Growth of Norwegian Men During the Past Two Hundred Years. Oslo: Norse Akad. Sc.

KIRCHOFF, P. 1932. Die Verwandschaftsorganization der Urwaldstämme Südamerikas. Zeitschrift für Ethnologie, 63:85-193. Berlin.

KLEITMAN, Nathaniel, and associates. 1933. Studies on the physiology of sleep. Amer. Jour. Physiol., Vols. 104-107.

KLEITMAN, Nathaniel. 1939. Sleep and Wakefulness. Chicago: University of Chicago Press.

KLINEBERG, Otto. 1935a. Race Differences. New York: Harpers.

KLINEBERG, Otto. 1935b. Negro Intelligence and Selective Migration. New York: Columbia University Press.

KLINEBERG, Otto. 1941. Mental testing of racial and national groups, in Scientific Aspects of the Race Problem, pp. 253-294. New York: Longmans, Green.

KLINEBERG, Otto. 1944. A science of national character. Jour. Social Psychology, 19:147-162.

KLINEBERG, Otto. 1945. Racial psychology, in Linton, 1945a, pp. 63-77.

KLINEBERG, Otto, ASCH, S. E., and BLOCK, H. 1934. An experimental study of constitutional types. Genet. Psychol. Monog., 16:145-221.

KLUCKHOHN, Clyde. 1936. Some reflections on the method and theory of the Kulturkreiselehre. Amer. Anthro., 38:157-196.

KLUCKHOHN, Clyde. 1941. Patterning as exemplified in Navaho culture. Language, Culture, and Personality, pp. 109-130. Menasha, Wis.: Banta.

KLUCKHOHN, Clyde. 1944. Navaho witchcraft. Papers of the Peabody Museum of Harvard University, Vol. 22, No. 2. Cambridge.

KLUCKHOHN, Clyde. 1944. The influence of psychiatry on anthropology. One Hundred Years of Psychiatry. New York.

KLUCKHOHN, Clyde. 1945. The personal document in anthropological science, Bull. Soc. Sci. Res. Council, 53:70-176.

KLUCKHOHN, Clyde, and MOWRER, O. H. 1944. "Culture and personality": a conceptual scheme. American Anthropologist, 46:1-29.

KLUVER, H. 1933. Behavior Mechanisms in Monkeys. Chicago: University of Chicago Press.

Koch, F. C., and Smith, Phillip E., eds. 1942. Sex hormones, Biological Symposia IX. Lancaster: Jaques Cattell Press.

Koch-Grünberg, T. 1910. Zwei Jahre unter den Indianern. Berlin.

Kohler, W. 1925. The Mentality of Apes. New York: Harcourt, Brace.

Kohts, N. 1923. Untersuchungen ueber die Erkenntnisfahigkeiten des Schimpanses. Moscow.

Kohts, N. 1928. Recherches sur l'intelligence du chimpanzee par la methode de "choix aprés modele." Jour. Psychol. Norm. Pathol., 25:255-75.

Kollmorgen, Walter M. 1942. The Old Order Amish of Lancaster County, Pennsylvania. U. S. Dept. Agr., Bur. Agr. Econ., Rural Life Studies: 4 (Processed). Washington.

Kollmorgen, Walter M. 1943. The agricultural stability of the Old Order Amish and Old Order Mennonites of Lancaster County, Pennsylvania. Amer. Jour. Sociol. 49:233-241.

Korzybski, Alfred. 1933. Science and Sanity. Lancaster: Science Press.

Kretschmer, E. 1925. Physique and Character. New York: Harcourt, Brace.

Krige, J. D. 1943. The Realm of the Rain Queen: A Study of the Pattern of Lovedu Society. New York: Oxford University Press.

Kroeber, A. L. 1909. Classificatory systems of relationship. Journal of the Anthropological Institute, 39:74-84.

Kroeber, A. L. 1925. Handbook of the Indians of California. Smithsonian Institution, Bureau of American Ethnology, Bulletin 78, Washington.

Kroeber, A. L. 1928. Sub-human cultural beginnings. Quart. Rev. Biol., 3:325-42.

Kroeber, A. L., ed. 1932. Walapai Ethnography. Mem. Amer. Anthro. Assoc. 42. Menasha, Wis.

Kroeber, A. L. 1938. Basic and secondary patterns of social structure. Journ. Anthrop. Inst., 68:299-309.

Kroeber, A. L. 1940. Stimulus diffusion. American Anthropologist, 42:1-20.

Kroeber, A. L. 1944. Configurations of Culture Growth. Berkeley and Los Angeles: University of California Press.

Krogman, W. M. 1943. What we do not know about race. Sci. Mon., 47:97-104.

Krogman, W. M. 1944. Physical anthropology at work. Sci. Mon., 58:468-469.

Krogman, W. M. 1945. The concept of race, in Linton, 1945. Pp. 38-62.

Krzywicki, Ludwik. 1934. Primitive Society and Its Vital Statistics. London: Macmillan.

Kubler, George. 1946. The Colonial Quechua, in Steward, 1946, vol. 2.

La Barre, Weston. 1938. The Peyote Cult. Yale University Publications in Anthropology, 19. New Haven: Yale University Press.

La Barre, Weston. 1945. Some observations on character structure in the Orient: the Japanese Psychiatry, 8:319-342.

La Barre, Weston. 1946. Social Cynosure and Social Structure. J. Personality, 14:169-183.

Landes, Ruth. 1938. The Ojibwa Woman. New York: Columbia University Press. (Col. Univ. Contrib. to Anthrop., 31.)

Langer, Susanne K. 1942. Philosophy in a New Key: A Study in the Symbolism of Reason, Rite, and Art. Cambridge: Harvard University Press.

Langley, S. P. 1902. The fire walk ceremony in Tahiti. Smiths. Inst., Report for 1901.

Lasker, Gabriel Ward. 1945. Migration and physical differentiation: a comparison of immigrant with American-born Chinese. Manuscript.

Lasker, Gabriel. 1945. Chinese physical development. Far Eastern Survey, 14:260-262.

Lattimore, Owen. 1932. The Gold Tribe, "Fishkin Tartars" of the Lower Sungari. Mem. Amer. Anthro. Assoc. 40. Menasha, Wis.

Laufer, Berthold. 1930. Geophagy. Field Mus. Nat. Hist. Anthrop. Ser., Vol. 18, No. 21, Publ. 28.

LAWRENCE, W. E. 1937. Alternating generations in Australia. Studies in the Science of Society (G. P. Murdock, ed.). New Haven: Yale University Press. Pp. 319-354.

LAWSON, A. and MOON, H. P. 1928. A clay adjunct to a potato dietary. Nature, 141:40.

LESSER, Alexander. 1933. The cultural significance of the Ghost Dance. American Anthropologist, 35:108-115.

LEVCHINE, A. 1840. Déscription des hordes et des steppes des Kirghiz-Kazakas. Paris.

LIEB, C. W. 1926. Effects of an exclusive long-continued meat diet. Jour. Amer. Med. Assoc., 87:25-26.

LINDERMAN, F. 1930. American. New York: John Day.

LINNÉ, Carl von. 1735. Systema Naturae sive segna tria naturae systematice proposita per classes, ordines, genera & species. Lugduni Batavorum.

LINTON, Ralph. 1924. Totemism and the A.E.F. American Anthropologist, 26:294-300.

LINTON, Ralph. 1933. The Tanala of Madagascar. Field Mus. Nat. Hist., Anthro. Studies, 22:1-334.

LINTON, Ralph. 1936. The Study of Man. New York: Appleton-Century.

LINTON, Ralph. 1938. Society, culture and the individual. Journ. Abn. and Soc. Psychol., 33:425-436.

LINTON, Ralph, ed. 1939a. Acculturation in Seven American Indian Tribes. New York: Appleton-Century.

LINTON, Ralph. 1939b. Analyses of the Marquesans, Tanala of Madagascar, and Commanche of the Southern Plains, in Kardiner, 1939.

LINTON, Ralph. 1940. Crops, soils and culture in America. The Maya and Their Neighbors, pp. 32-40. New York: Appleton-Century.

LINTON, Ralph. 1943. Nativistic movements. Amer. Anthro., 45:230-239.

LINTON, Ralph. 1944. North American cooking pots. Amer. Antiquity, 9:369-380.

LINTON, Ralph, ed. 1945a. The Science of Man in the World Crisis. New York: Columbia University Press.

LINTON, Ralph. 1945b. The Cultural Background of Personality. New York: Appleton-Century.

LITTLE, Clarence C. 1923. Animal sex ratios, in Abt, 1923, Chapter 2.

LOWIE, R. H. 1920. Primitive Society. New York: Boni and Liveright.

LOWIE, R. H. 1929. Relationship terms. Encyclopedia Britannica, 14th edition, Vol. 19, pp. 84-89.

LOWIE, R. H. 1935. The Crow Indians. New York: Farrar and Rinehart.

LOWIE, R. H. 1937. The History of Ethnological Theory. New York: Farrar and Rinehart.

LOWIE, R. H. 1941. The intellectual and cultural achievements of human races, in Scientific Aspects of the Race Problem, pp. 191-252. New York: Longmans, Green.

LUNDMAN, B. J. 1940. Ueber die Körperhöhensteigerung in den nordischen Ländern nach dem Weltkriege. Zeit. f. Rassenk., 11:1-5.

LYND, R. S. 1939. Knowledge for What? Princeton: Princeton University Press.

MAHONY, D. J. 1943a. The problem of antiquity of man in Australia. Mem. Nat. Mus. Melbourne, 13:7-56.

MAHONY, D. J. 1943b. The Keilor skull: geological evidence of antiquity. Ibid., 79-82.

MALINOWSKI, B., 1927a. The Father in Primitive Society. New York: Norton.

MALINOWSKI, B., 1927b. Sex and Repression in Savage Society. New York: Harcourt, Brace.

MALINOWSKI, B. 1929. The Sexual Life of Savages in North-Western Melanesia. 2 vols. New York: Liveright.

MALINOWSKI, B. 1944. A Scientific Theory of Culture. Chapel Hill: University of North Carolina Press.

MALLERY, Garrick. 1881. Sign language among the North American Indians. First Report, Bureau of American Ethnology. Washington.

MAN, E. H. 1882-1883. On the aboriginal inhabitants of the Andaman Islands. Jour. Roy. Anthro. Inst., London, 12:69-175, 327-434.

MARETT, J. R. de la H. 1936. Race, Sex, and Environment. London: Hutchinson.

MARETT, R. R., ed. 1908. Anthropology and the Classics. London: Oxford.

MARETT, R. R. 1936. Tylor. New York: Wiley.

MARKHAM, S. F. 1942, 1944. Climate and the Energy of Nations. New York: Oxford University Press.

MARTIN, Rudolph. 1928. Lehrbuch der Anthropologie in systematischer Darstellung, 3 vols. Jena.

MASLOW, A. H. 1936-1937. The role of dominance in the social and sexual behavior of infra-human primates, Jour. Genet. Psychol., 48:261-77, 310-38, 49:161-98.

MASLOW, A. H. 1940. Dominance-equality and social behavior in infra-human primates, Jour. Soc. Psychol., 11:313-24.

MASLOW, A. H. 1943. The Authoritarian character structure, Journ. Soc. Psychol., 18:401-411.

MASON, O. T. 1907. The Origins of Invention. New York: Scribner's.

MASSAM, J. A. 1927. The Cliff Dwellers of Kenya. London: Seeley, Service.

MAY, Mark A. 1930. A comprehensive plan for measuring personality. Proc. and Papers, Ninth Int. Cong. Psychol., pp. 298-300. Princeton.

MAYO, Elton. 1945. The Social Problems of an Industrial Civilization. Boston: Graduate School of Business Administration, Harvard University.

McCLELLAN, W. C., and DUBOIS, E. E. 1930. Prolonged meat diets with a study of kidney function and ketosis. Journ. Bio. Chem., 87:651-668.

McCLURE, M. T. 1936. Greek genius and race mixture, in Studies in the History of Ideas, Vol. 3. New York: Department of Philosophy, Columbia University.

McCOWN, T. D., and KEITH, A. 1939. The Stone Age of Mount Carmel. 2 vols. New York: Oxford University Press.

McDERMOTT, William C. 1939. The Ape in Antiquity. Baltimore: Johns Hopkins University Press.

McLESTER, James S. 1939. Nutrition and Diet in Health and Disease. Philadelphia: Saunders.

MEAD, G. H. 1934. Mind, Self, and Society. Chicago: University of Chicago Press.

MEAD, Margaret. 1928. Growing up in New Guinea. New York: Morrow.

MEAD, Margaret. 1930. Coming of Age in Samoa. New York: Morrow.

MEAD, Margaret. 1935. Sex and Temperament in Three Savage Societies. New York: Morrow.

MEAD, Margaret. 1935. Sex and Temperament in Three Primitive Societies. New York: Morrow.

MEAD, Margaret. 1940. The Mountain Arapesh. II. Supernaturalism. Anthr. Papers Amer. Mus. Nat. History, Vol. 37, Pt. 3. New York.

MEAD, Margaret. 1942. And Keep Your Powder Dry. New York: Morrow.

MEANS, P. A. 1931. Ancient Civilizations of the Andes. New York: Scribner's.

MEREDITH, H. V. 1941. Stature and weight of private school children in two successive decades. Amer. Jour. Phys. Anthrop., 28:1-40.

MERKER, F. 1904. Die Masai. Berlin.

MÉTRAUX, Alfred. 1942. The Native Tribes of Eastern Bolivia and Western Matto Grosso. Smiths. Inst., Bur. Amer. Ethn., Bull. 134. Washington.

MILES, C. C. 1935. Sex in social psychology, in A Handbook of Social Psychology, Carl Murchison, ed., Worcester: Clark University Press. Pp. 689-797.

MILES, W. R. 1933. Age and human ability, Psychol. Rev., 40:99-123.

MILES, W. R. 1942. Psychological aspects of aging, in Cowdry. 1942, pp. 756-784.

MILLER, Carey D. 1927. Food values of poi, taro, and limu. Bishop. Mus. Bull., 37. Honolulu.

MILLER, Neal E., and DOLLARD, John. 1941. Social Learning and Imitation. New Haven: Yale University Press.

MILLS, C. A. 1942. Climatic effect on growth and development with particular reference to the effects of tropical residence. Amer. Anthrop., 44:1-13.

MOHR, G. J., and GUNDLACH, R. H. 1927. The relation between physique and performance. Jour. Exper. Psychol. 10:155-157.

MONTAGU, M. F. Ashley. 1942. Man's Most Dangerous Myth: The Fallacy of Race. New York: Columbia University Press.

MONTAGU, M. F. Ashley. 1944a. Physical anthropology, in Glasser, Otto, ed., Medical Physics, Chicago: Year Book Publishers.

MONTAGU, M. F. Ashley. 1944b. On the relation between body size, waking activity, and the origin of social life in the primates. American Anthropologist, 44:141-45.

MONTAGU, M. F. Ashley. 1945. An Introduction to Physical Anthropology. Springfield: Thomas.

MONTGOMERY, H. C. 1940. Analysis of world's fairs' hearing tests. Sci. Mon., 50: 335-339.

MORGAN, Clifford R. 1943. Physiological Psychology. New York: McGraw-Hill.

MORGAN, L. H. 1877. Ancient Society. New York: Holt.

MORGENSEN, A. H. 1932. Common Sense Applied to Motion and Time Study. New York: McGraw-Hill.

MORLEY, Sylvanus G. 1946. The Ancient Maya. Palo Alto: Stanford University Press.

MORRIS, J. R. 1922. Our Japanese Letter. Phila. Public. Ledger, May 14, 1922.

MORTIMER, Hector. 1940. The genitonasal and genitoaural relationships, Laryngoscope, 50:349, 1940.

MOWRER, O. H. 1930. A stimulus-response analysis of anxiety and its role as a reinforcing agent. Psychol. Rev., 46:553-565.

MOWRER, O. H. 1940. Anxiety reduction and learning. Jour. Exper. Psychol., 27:497-516.

MUMFORD, Lewis. 1934. Technics and Civilization. New York: Harcourt, Brace.

MURDOCK, G. P. 1934. Our Primitive Contemporaries. New York: Macmillan.

MURDOCK, G. P. 1940. Double descent. American Anthropologist, 42:555-561.

MURDOCK, G. P. 1945. The common denominator of cultures, in Linton, 1945. Pp. 123-142.

MURDOCK, G. P., and others, 1945. Outline of Cultural Materials. Rev. ed. New Haven: Yale University Press.

MURPHY, G., MURPHY, L. B., and NEWCOMB, T. M. 1937. Experimental Social Psychology. Rev. ed. New York: Harpers.

MUSTERS, George Chaworth. 1873. At Home with the Patagonians. 2nd ed. London: Murray.

MYRDAL, Gunnar. 1944. An American Dilemma. 2 vols. New York: Harpers.

MYRES, John L. 1941. Nomadism. Journ. Anthrop. Inst., 61:19-42.

NACCARATI, S. 1921. The morphologic aspect of intelligence. Arch. of Psychol., 6, No. 45.

NACCARATI, S., and GARRETT, H. W. 1924. The relation of morphology to temperament. Jour. Ab. and Soc. Psychol., 19:254-263.

NADEL, S. F. 1937. Experiments on culture psychology. Africa, 10:421-435.

NADEL, S. F. 1937-1938. A field experiment in racial psychology. Brit. Journ. Psychol., 28:195-211.

National Research Council. 1943. The Problem of Changing Food Habits. Bull. 108. Washington.

NEWCOMER, M. 1921. The physical development of Vassar College students. Quart. Publ. Amer. Statist. Assoc., 81:535-538.

NISSEN, H. W. 1931. A field study of the chimpanzee. Comp. Psychol. Monog., Vol. 8, No. 1.

NOBACK, C. R. 1939. The changes in the vaginal smears and associated cyclic phenomena in the lowland gorilla (*Gorilla gorilla*). Anat. Rec., 73:209-21.

NORDENSKIÖLD, A. E. 1882. The Voyage of the Vega Around Asia and Europe. New York: Macmillan.

NORDENSKIÖLD, Erland. 1920. The Changes in the Material Culture of Two Indian Tribes Under the Influence of New Surroundings. Comparative Ethnographical Studies, 2. Goteborg: Erlanders.

NORDENSKIÖLD, Erland. 1930. Modifications of Indian Culture Through Inventions and Loans. (Comparative Ethnographical Studies, 8.) Goteborg.

NORTHROP, F. S. C. 1946. The Meeting of East and West. New York: Macmillan.

NUTTALL, C. H. F. 1904. Blood Immunity and Blood Relationship. Cambridge: Cambridge University Press.

OPLER, Morris Edward. 1941. An Apache Life-Way. Chicago: University of Chicago Press.

OSGOOD, Cornelius. 1937. The ethnography of the Tanaina. Yale Univ. Publ. in Anthrop. No. 16. New Haven.

PAINTER, T. S. 1924. Studies in mammalian spermatogenesis. IV. The sex chromosomes in monkeys. Jour. Exper. Zool., 39:433-451.

PAINTER, T. S. 1925. A comparative study of the chromosomes in mammals. Amer. Naturalist, 59:385-409.

PANIKKAR, K. M. 1918. Some aspects of Nayar life. Journal of the Anthropological Institute, 48:254-293.

Papers Presented Before the Monday Night Groups (mimeographed). New Haven: Institute of Human Relations.

PARK, R. E. 1928. Human migration and the marginal man. Amer. Jour. Sociology, 33:881-893.

PAVLOV, I. P. 1927. Conditioned Reflexes. (G. V. Anrep, tr.). London: Oxford University Press.

PAVLOV, I. P. 1928. Lectures on Conditioned Reflexes. (W. H. Gantt, tr.). New York: International.

PAVLOV, I. P. 1932. Neuroses in man and animals. Journal American Medical Association, 99:1012-1013.

PEAK, H., and FLEURE, H. J. 1927-1936. The Corridors of Time. 9 vols. New Haven: Yale University Press.

PEARSON, C. H. J. 1928. Effect of age upon vibratory sensibility. Arch. Neur. and Psychol., 20:482-496.

PEARSON, W. W. Natives of E. Mira and St. Mathias, Anthro. Rep., Territory of New Guinea.

PENDERGAST, W. 1936. Inheritance of short stubby hands. Jour. Hered., 27:448.

PENNIMAN, A. V. 1936. One Hundred Years of Anthropology. Cambridge: University Press.

PERRY, W. J. 1923. The Children of the Sun. London: Methuen.

PERRY, W. J. 1924. The Growth of Civilization. London: Methuen.

PIERSON, Donald. 1939. The Negro in Bahia, Brazil. American Sociological Review, 4:524-533.

PIGAFETTA, Antonia. 1906. Magellan's Voyage Around the World. Cleveland: Clark.

POLIAK, S. 1932. The main afferent fiber systems of the cerebral cortex in Primates. Univ. Calif. Publ. in Anatomy, Vol. 2.

POPPER, Julio. 1891. Apuntes geográficos, etnológicos e industriales sobre la Tierra del Fuego. Bol. Inst. Geog. Argentia, 12:130-170.

POWDERMAKER, Hortense. 1932. Life in Lesu. New York: Norton.

POWDERMAKER, Hortense. 1939. After Freedom. A Cultural Study of the Deep South. New York: Viking.

PRICE, A. Grenfell. 1939. White Settlers in the Tropics. New York: American Geographical Society.

PRICE, Bronson. 1931. A perceptual test for comparing the performance of age groups: preliminary report. Psychol. Bull., 28:584-585.

PRICE, H. 1937. Duda Bux. Spectator, 808, Apr. 30, 1937.

PRICE, Weston A. 1939. Nutrition and Physical Degeneration. New York: Hoeber.

PRYOR, J. W. 1923. Differences in time of development of centers of ossification in male and female skeletons. Anatom. Record, 25:257-64.

RADCLIFFE-BROWN, A. R. 1930-1931. The social organization of Australian tribes. Oceania, Vol. 1. Melbourne, Australia.

RADCLIFFE-BROWN, A. R. 1933. The Andaman Islanders, 2nd ed. Cambridge: Cambridge University Press.

RADCLIFFE-BROWN, A. R. 1940. On social structure. Jour. Roy. Anthrop. Inst., 70:1-12.

RADCLIFFE-BROWN, A. R. 1941. The study of kinship systems. Journ. Anthrop. Inst., 61:1-18.

RAIMONDI, A. 1904. El Perú. 5 vols. Lima.

RAINEY, Froelich. 1941. Native economy and survival in arctic Alaska. Applied Anthropology, 1:9-14.

RAUM, O. F. 1940. Chaga Childhood, London: Oxford University Press.

Recommended Dietary Allowances. 1943. Reprint and Circular Series, National Research Council 115, Jan.

REDFIELD, Robert. 1941. The Folk Culture of Yucatan. Chicago: University of Chicago Press.

REDFIELD, Robert, ed. 1942. Levels of Integration in Biological and Social Systems (Biological Symposia, VIII), Lancaster: Jacques Cattell Press.

REDFIELD, Robert. 1943. What we do know about race. Sci. Mon., 47:193-201.

REDFEILD, Robert, LINTON, R., and HERSKOVITS, M. J. 1936. A memorandum for the study of acculturation. Amer. Anthro., 38:149-152.

REDFIELD, Robert, and VILLA, R. A. 1934. Chan Kom, a Maya Village. Carnegie Inst. Washington., Publ. 448. Washington.

REED, S. W. 1943. The Making of Modern New Guinea. Philadelphia: American Philosophical Society.

REICHARD, Gladys A. 1944. Prayer: The Compulsive Word. New York: Augustin (Monographs of the American Ethnological Society, 7).

RHINE, J. B., PRATT, J. G., SMITH, B. M., STUART, C. E., and GREENWOOD, J. A. 1940. Extra-Sensory Perception After Sixty Years. New York: Holt.

RICHARDS, Audrey I. 1936. Land, Labour, and Diet in Northern Rhodesia. London: Oxford University Press.

RISLEY, H. H. 1901. Census of India: 1901, Part I. Calcutta.

RIVERS, W. H. R. 1906. The Todas. London: Macmillan.

ROBACK, A. A. 1944. A Dictionary of International Slurs. Cambridge: Sci-Art Publishers.

ROBERTS, F. H. H. 1935. A survey of southwestern archaeology. American Anthropologist, 37:1-35.

ROBERTS, L. J. 1944. Scientific basis for recommended dietary allowances. N. Y. State J. Med., 44:59-66.

ROCHEFORT, César de. 1665. Histoire naturelle et morale des illes Antilles de l'Amerique. 2nd ed. Rotterdam.

RODENWALT, Ernst. 1927. Die Mestizen auf Kisar. 2 vols. Batavia: G. Kolff & Co.

ROMER, A. S. 1941. Man and the Vertebrates. 3rd ed. Chicago: Chicago University Press.

ROQUE, P. 1939. La marche sur le feu au Japon. Illustration, 23:392, July 15, 1939.

ROSCOE, J. 1911. The Baganda. London: Macmillan.

ROTH, W. R. 1924. An Introductory Study of the Arts, Crafts, and Customs of the Guiana Indians. Bureau of American Ethnology, Annual Report, 38:27-745. Washington.

ROTHMAN, S. 1941. Physiology of itching. Physiol. Rev., 21:377-381.

ROWE, J. W. 1946. The Inca culture at the time of the Conquest. in Steward, 1946.

RUSSELL, R. V. 1916. The Tribes and Castes of the Central Provinces of India. 4 vols. London: Macmillan.

SAPIR, Edward. 1921. Language: An Introduction to the Study of Speech. New York: Harcourt, Brace.

SARASIN, P. and F. 1893. Die Weddas von Ceylon und die sie ungebenden Völkerschaften. 2 vols. Wiesbaden.

SAUER, Carl O. 1944. A geographical sketch of early man in America. Geog. Rev., 34:529-573.

SAVILLE, Marshall H. 1913. Precolumbian decoration of teeth in Ecuador. Amer. Anthro., 15:377-394.

SAYCE, R. U. 1933. Primitive Arts and Crafts, Cambridge: Cambridge University Press.

SCAMMON, Richard E. 1923. A summary of the anatomy of the infant and the child, in Abt, 1923.

SCHAPERA, I. 1930. The Khoisan Peoples of South Africa. London: Rutledge.

SCHEINFELD, Amram. 1939. You and Heredity. New York: Stokes.

SCHEINFELD, Amram. 1944. Women and Men. New York: Harcourt, Brace.

SCHMIDT, Carl F., and COMROE, Julius H., Jr. 1941. Respiration. Annual Review of Physiology, pp. 151-184. Palo Alto: Stanford University Press.

SCHMIDT, Wilhelm. 1939. The Culture Historical Method of Ethnology. Tr. S. A. Sieber, New York: Fortuny's.

SCHNEIDER, E. C., and CRAMPTON, C. B. 1940. A comparison of some respiratory and circulatory reactions of athletes and non-athletes. Amer. Jour. Physiol., 129:165-170.

SCHOFIELD, Richard. 1921. Inheritance of webbed-toes, Jour. Hered., 12:400-401.

SCHOKKING, C. P. 1934. Another woolly hair mutation in man, Jour. Hered., 25:337-340.

SCHOMBURGK, R. H. 1837. Diary of an ascent of the Rio Berbice. Journ. Roy. Geog. Inst., 7.

SCHULTZ, A. H., 1936. Characters common to higher primates and characters specific for man. Quart. Rev. Bio., 11:259-283, 425-455.

SCHULTZ, A. H. 1931. The density of hair in primates. Human Biology, 3:303-311.

SCHULTZ, A. H. 1940. Growth and development of the chimpanzee. Carnegie Inst. of Washington, Publ. 518, Contributions to Embroyology, 28:1-63.

SCHULTZ, L. 1907. Aus Namaland und Kalahari. Jena.

SCOTT, J. C., and BASETT, H. C. 1941. Temperature regulation. Annual Review of Physiology. Palo Alto: Stanford University Press.

SELIGMAN, C. G. and B. Z. 1911. The Veddas. London: Cambridge University Press.

SELIGMAN, C. G. and B. Z. 1932. Pagan Tribes of the Nilotic Sudan. London: Rutledge.

SELTZER, C. C. 1945. The relationship between masculine component and personality. Am. J. Phys. Anthrop., 2:33-47.

SHAPIRO, H. L. 1929. Descendants of the Mutineers of the Bounty. Bishop Mus. Mem. 11, No. 1. Honolulu.

SHAPIRO, H. L. 1931. The Chinese population in Hawaii. New York: Amer. Council, Inst. Pacific Relations.

SHAPIRO, H. L. 1936. The Heritage of the Bounty. New York: Simon and Schuster.

SHAPIRO, H. L. 1939. Migration and Environment. A Study of the Physical Characteristics of the Japanese Immigrants to Hawaii and the Effects of Environment on their Descendants. New York: Oxford University Press.

SHAPIRO, H. L. 1945. Society and biological man, in Linton, 1945, pp. 19-37.

SHARP, R. L. 1940. An Australian aboriginal population. Human Biology, 12:481-507.

SHATTUCK, George C. 1938. A medical survey of the Republic of Guatemala. Washington: Carnegie Institution of Washington.

SHELDON, W. H., STEVENS, S. S., and TUCKER, W. B. 1940. The Varieties of Human Physique: An Introduction to Constitutional Psychology. New York: Harpers.

SHELDON, W. H. 1942. The Variety of Temperament. New York: Harpers.

SHEPARD, W. T. 1910. Some mental processes of the rhesus monkey. Psychol. Monog., 12:1-61.

SHERIF, Muzafer. 1936. The Psychology of Social Norms. New York: Harpers.

SIMMONS, Leo W. 1942. Sun Chief: The Autobiography of a Hopi Indian. New Haven: Yale University Press.

SIMMONS, Leo W. 1945. The Role of the Aged in Primitive Society. New Haven: Yale University Press.

SIMPSON, C. G. 1940. Los indios Kamarakotos. Rev. de Fomento, Ano III. Caracas. Venezuela.

SMITH, Grafton Elliot. 1911. The Ancient Egyptians and Their Influence upon the Civilization of Europe. New York: Harpers.

SMITH, Grafton Elliot. 1915. The Immigrations of Early Culture. New York: Longmans, Green.

SMITH, Grafton, Elliot. 1926. Vision and evolution. West London Medical Jour., 31:97-117.

SMITH, Grafton Elliot. 1927. Essays on the Evolution of Man. London: Oxford University Press.

SMITH, S. A. 1918. The Fossil human skull found at Talgai, Queensland. Phil. Trans. Roy. Soc. London, Ser. B, 208:315-387.

SNYDER, L. H., and CURTIS, G. M. 1934. An inherited hollow chest. Jour. Hered., 25:445-447.

SOARES DE SOUZA, Gabriel. 1851. Tratado descriptivo do Brazil em 1587. Rev. Inst. Hist. Geog. Brazil., 14, Rio de Janeiro.

SOMBART, W. 1924. Der Moderne Kapitalismius. 2 vols. Munich and Leipzig: Duncker and Humbolt.

SOROKIN, P. 1941. Social and Cultural Dynamics. Vol. 4. New York: American Book Company.

SPECK, F. G. 1915. The family hunting band as the basis of Algonkian social organization. Amer. Anthro., 17:289-305.

SPECK, F. G. 1918. Kinship terms and the family band among Northern Algonkians, Amer. Anthro., 20:143-161.

SPECK, F. G. 1926. Culture problems in Northeastern North America. Proc. Amer. Philos. Soc., 65:272-311.

SPENCER, B., and GILLEN, F. G. 1927. The Arunta. 2 vols. London: Macmillan.

SPENSE, K. W. 1934. Visual acuity and its relation to brightness in chimpanzee and man. Jour. Comp. Psychol., 18:333-61.

SPIER, Leslie. 1925. The distribution of kinship systems in North America. University of Washington. Publications in Anthropology, Vol. 1. Seattle.

SPIER, Leslie. 1929. Growth of Japanese children born in America and in Japan. Univ. Wash. Publ. Anthrop., Vol. 3, No. 1, pp. 1-30.

STAPLES, Ruth. 1932. The responses of infants to color. Jour. Exper. Psychol., 15:119-141.

STAYT, H. A. 1931. The Bavenda. London: Oxford University Press.

STEFANSSON, Vilhjalmur. 1922. The Northward Course of Empire. New York: Harcourt, Brace.

STEFANSSON, Vilhjalmur. 1935-1936. Adventures in diet. Harper's Magazine. 171:668-675; 172:46-54, 178-189.

STERN, Bernard J. 1931. Lewis Henry Morgan, Social Evolutionist. Chicago: University of Chicago Press.

STEVENSON, H. N. C. 1945. Case of applied anthropology in the reconstruction of Burma. Man, 45:2-5.

STEWARD, J. H. 1936. The economic and social basis of primitive bands. Essays in Anthropology Presented to A. L. Kroeber, pp. 331-350. Berkeley: University of California Press.

STEWARD, J. H. 1937. Ecological aspects of Southwestern society. Anthropos, 32:87-104.

STEWARD, J. H. 1938. Basin-Plateau Aboriginal Socio-Political Groups. Smithsonian Institution, Bureau of American Ethnology, Bull. 120. Washington.

STEWARD, J. H., ed. 1946. Handbook of the Indians of South America. Smiths. Inst., Bur. Amer. Ethn. Washington: Government Printing Office.

STILL, Neil A. 1940. New Facts on Mental Disorders. Baltimore: Thomas.

STRANDSKOV, Herluf H. 1945. Birth sex ratios in the total, the "white" and the "colored" U. S. populations. Amer. Jour. Phys. Anthrop. n.s. 3:165-175.

STRAUS, S. L., Jr. 1934. The structure of the primate kidney. Jour. Anat., 69:93-108.

SULLIVAN, Louis R. 1920. Anthropometry of Siouan tribes. Nat. Acad. Sci. Proc., 6:131-134.

SUMNER, W. G., KELLER, A. G., and DAVIE, M. R. 1928. The Science of Society. 4 vols. New Haven: Yale University Press.

SUNDSTROM, E. S. 1927. Physiological effects of tropical climates. Physiol. Rev., 7:320-363.

SUSKI, P. M. 1933. The body build of American-born Japanese children. Biometrika, 25:323-352.

SUTTIFF, W. D., and HOLT, Evelyn. 1925. The age curve of pulse rate under basal conditions. Archive internal medicine, 35:224.

TALLGREN, A. M. 1937. The method of prehistoric archaeology. Antiquity, 11:152-161.

TAX, Sol. 1941. World view and social relations in Guatemala. Amer. Anthr., 43:27-42.

THOMAS, W. I. 1937. Primitive Behavior. New York. McGraw-Hill.

THOMPSON, Helen. 1936. The dynamics of activity drives in young children. Psychol. Bull., 39:751.

THOMPSON, Laura, and JOSEPH, Alice. 1944. The Hopi Way. Chicago: University of Chicago Press.

THORNDIKE, E. L. 1901. The mental life of the monkey. Psychol. Rev., Monog., Suppl., 3:1-57.

THORNDIKE, E. L. 1911. Animal Intelligence. New York: Macmillan.

THORNDIKE, E. L. 1935. The Psychology of Wants, Interests, and Attitudes. New York: Appleton-Century.

THORNDYKE, Lynn, 1923. A History of Magic and Experimental Science During the First Thirteen Centuries of Our Era. 2 vols. New York: Macmillan.

THORNDYKE, Lynn. 1929. Science and Thought in the Fifteenth Century. New York: Columbia University Press.

THURNWALD, Richard. 1932. Economics in Primitive Societies. London: Oxford University Press.

THURNWALD, Richard. 1935. Die Menschliche Gesellschaft. Vols. 1-5. Berlin and Leipzig: de Gruyter.

THURNWALD, Richard. 1937. The spell of limited possibilities. Amer. Sociol. Rev 2:195-203.

TILNEY, F. 1928. The Brain from Ape to Man. New York: Hoeber.

TITIEV, Mischa. 1943. The influence of common residence on the unilateral classification of kindred. American Anthropologist, 45:511-529.

TITIEV, Mischa. 1944. Old Oraibi: a study of the Hopi Indians of the Third Mesa. Papers of the Peabody Museum of Harvard University, Vol. 22, No. 1. Cambridge.

TOLSTOI, E. 1929. Effects of an exclusive meat diet on chemical constituents of the blood. Jour. Biol. Chem., 83:753-758.

TOMILIN, M. I. 1936. Length of gestation period and menstrual cycle in the chimpanzee. Nature, 137:318-19.

TOMILIN, M. I., and YERKES, R. M. 1935. Chimpanzee twins: behavioral reactions and development. Ped Sem. and Jour. Genet. Psychol., 46:239-63.

TÖNNIES, Ferdinand. 1887. Gemeinschaft und Gesellschaft. Leipzig: Fues.

TORDAY, E., and JOYCE, T. A. 1906. Notes on the ethnography of the Ba-Huana. Jour. Anthro. Inst., 36:272-301.

TOYNBEE, Arnold J. 1934-1939. A Study of History. Vols. 1-5. London: Oxford University Press.

TOTHILL, J. D., ed. 1940. Agriculture in Uganda. London: Oxford University Press.

TREGEAR, E. 1904. The Maori Race. Wanganui, N. Z.: Willis.

TSAI, L. S. 1935. Dietary factor in race regeneration. T'ien Hsia Monthly, Shanghai, 1:151-165.

TSANG, Y. 1938. Hunger motivation in gastroectomized rats. Jour. Comp. Psychol., 26:1-17.

TUMIN, Melvin. 1945. Some fragments from the life history of a marginal man. Character and Personality, 13:261-296.

TURNER, Ralph. 1941. The Great Cultural Traditions. 2 vols. New York: McGraw-Hill.

TURNEY-HIGH, Harry H. 1942. The Practise of Primitive War. Missoula: University of Montana.

TYLOR, E. B. 1878 (1865). Researches into Early History of Mankind and the Development of Civilization. London: Holt.

TYLOR, E. B. 1924. Primitive Culture. 7th ed. New York: Brentano.

UNDERHILL, Ruth M. 1939. Social Organization of the Papago Indians. New York: Columbia University Press.

VAILLANT, George. 1941. The Aztecs of Mexico. New York: Doubleday, Doran.

VALDIZÁN, Hermilio, and MALDONADO, A. 1922. La medicina popular peruana. 3 vols. Lima.

VANCE, Rupert B. 1935. Human Geography of the South. 2nd ed. Chapel Hill: University of North Carolina Press.

VAN RIPPEN, Bene. 1917. Pre-columbian operative dentistry of the Indians of Middle and South America. Dental Cosmos. Cambridge, Mass.

VEBLEN, Thornstein, 1899. The Theory of the Leisure Class. New York: Macmillan.

VIOLA, G. 1933. La Constituzione Individuale. Bologna: Cappelli.

VIRCHOW, Hans. 1903. Das Skelett eines verkrüppelten Chinesinen-Fusses. Zeit. f. Ethn., 25:266-316.

VIRCHOW, Hans. 1905. Weitere Mitteilungen über Füsse von Chinesinen. Zeit. f. Ethn., 27:546-568.

VIRCHOW, Hans. 1929. Das Os centrale carpi des Menschen. Morphologische Jahrbuch, 63:480-530. Berlin.

WAFER, Lionel. 1729. A new voyage and description of the Isthmus of America, giving an account of the author's abode there. 3rd ed. London: Collection of Voyages, Vol. III, pp. 261-463.

WALKER, C. R. 1945. Anthropology as a war weapon. Amer. Mercury, 59:85-89.

WALLIS, W. D. 1943. Messiahs: Their Role in Civilization. Washington: American Council on Public Affairs.

WARDEN, Carl J. 1940. The ability of monkeys to use tools, Trans. N. Y. Acad. Sci., 2:109-112.

WARDEN, Carl J., JENKINS, Thomas N., and WARNER, Lucien H. 1940. Comparative Psychology. New York: Ronald.

WARDEN, Carl J., JENKINS, Thomas N., and WARNER, Lucien H. 1936. Comparative Psychology. Vertebrates. New York: Ronald. pp. 363-420, 526-535.

WARMELO, N. J. van. 1932. Contribution Toward Venda History, Religion and Tribal Ritual. Union of South Africa, Dept. Native Affairs, Ethnol. Publ. 3: Cape Town.

WARNER, W. L., and LUNT, P. S. 1941. The Social Life of a Modern Community. New Haven: Yale University Press.

WEBER, Mac. 1922. Wirtschaft and Gesellschaft. Tübingen: Mohr.

WEIDENREICH, Franz. 1940. Some problems dealing with ancient man. Amer. Anthro. 42:375-383.

WEIDENREICH, Franz. 1943. The skull of Sinanthropus pekinensis, a comparative study of a primitive hominid skull. Palaeontologia Sinica, 127:1-484.

WEIDENREICH, Franz. 1945. Giant Early Man from Java and South China. (Anthrop. Papers, Amer. Mus. Nat. Hist., Vol. 40, Pt. 1). New York.

WEIDENREICH, Franz. 1945a. The Keilor skull: A Wadjak type from southeast Australia. Amer. Jour. Phys. Anthrop., n.s. 3:21-32.

WEIDENREICH, Franz. 1945b. The paleolithic child from Teshik-Tash cave in southern Usbekistan (Central Asia). Am. Jour. Phys. Anthrop., n.s. 3:151-164.

WEISS, L. 1927. Kretschmer's "Körperbau und Charakter," eine kritische Betrachtung der disherigen Ergebnisse. Zentralblatt für die gesamte Neurologie und Psychiatrie, 46:625-670.

WEST, James. 1945. Plainville, U. S. A. New York: Columbia University Press.

WESTERMARCK, Edward A. 1922. History of Human Marriage. 3rd ed. New York: Macmillan.

WESTERMARCK, Edward A. 1906. Origin and History of Moral Ideas. 2 vols. New York: Macmillan.

WESTERMARCK, Edward. 1926. Ritual and Belief in Morocco. 2 vols. London: Macmillan.

WEYER, E. 1932. The Eskimo. New Haven: Yale University Press.

WHIFFEN, Thomas. 1915. The Northwest Amazons. London.

WHITE, Leslie A. 1939. A problem in kinship terminology. American Anthropologist, 41:566-573.

WHITING, John W. M. 1941. Becoming a Kwoma. New Haven: Yale University Press.

WHITNEY, David D. 1942. Family Treasures: A Study of the Inheritance of Normal Characteristics in Man. Lancaster: Jaques Cattell Press.

WHITNEY, Leon F. 1939. The sex ratio in dogs. Jour. of Heredity, Sept. 1939.

WHORF, B. L. 1936. The punctual and segmentative aspects of verbs in Hopi Language, 12:127-131.

WILDER, Russell M. 1945. Misinterpretation and misuse of the recommended dietary allowances. Science, 101:285-828.

WILLIAMS, F. E. 1930. Orokaiva Society. London: Oxford University Press.

WILLIAMS, George D. 1931. Maya-Spanish Crosses in Yucatan. Papers Peabody Museum, Vol. 13. Cambridge.

WILSON, Elsie A. 1945. Basal metabolism from the standpoint of racial anthropology. Amer. Jour. Phys. Anthrop., n.s. 3:1-20.

WIRTH, Louis, 1938. Urbanism as a way of life. Amer. Jour. Sociol., 44:1-24.

WISSLER, Clark. 1914. The influence of the horse in the development of Plains culture. Amer. Anthr., 16:1-25.

WISSLER, Clark. 1923. Man and Culture. New York: Crowell.

WISSLER, Clark. 1930. Growth of children in Hawaii: based on observations by Louis B. Sullivan. Mem. Bernice P. Bishop Mus., 11:107-257 (No. 2).

WISSLER, Clark. 1942. Human cultural levels, in Cowdry, E. V., 1942, pp. 77-90.

WOLFE, A. B. 1933. The fecundity and fertility of early man. Human Biology, 5:36-39.

WOLFE, John B. 1936. Effectiveness of token rewards for chimpanzees. Comp. Psych. Monogr., 12, No. 60, pp. 1-7.

WOOLLARD, H. H. 1927. The differentiation of the retina in primates. Proc. Zool. Soc. London.

WUNDERLY, J. 1943. The Keilor skull; anatomical description. Mem. Nat. Mus. Melbourne, 13:57-70.

YEATS-BROWN, F. C. P. 1935. Yoga explained. London: Gollancz.

YERKES, R. M. 1933. Genetic aspects of grooming, a socially important primate behavior pattern. Jour. Soc. Psychol., 4:3-25.

YERKES, R. M. 1939a. Sexual behavior in the chimpanzee. Human Biology, 11:78-111.

YERKES, R. M. 1939b. The life history and personality of the chimpanzee. Amer. Naturalist, 73:97-112.

YERKES, R. M. and A. W. 1929. The Great Apes. New Haven: Yale University Press.

YERKES, R. M. and A. W. 1935. Social behavior in infrahuman primates, Handbook of Social Psychology (C. Murchison, ed.), 973-1033. Worcester: Clark University Press.

YERKES, R. M., and LEARNED, B. W. 1925. Chimpanzee Intelligence and its Vocal Expression. Baltimore.

YERKES, R. M., and NISSEN, H. W. 1939. Prelinguistic sign behavior of the chimpanzee. Science. 89:585-87.

YERKES, R. M., and TOMILIN, M. I. 1935. Mother-infant relations in chimpanzee, Jour. Com., Psychol., 20:321-58.

YOUNG, Kimball. 1940. Personality and Problems of Adjustment. New York: Crofts.

YOUNG, P. T. 1941. The experimental analysis of appetite. Psychol. Bull., 38:129-164.

YUN-JUEI, Tao. 1935. Zeit. f. Morphologie und Anthropologie. pp. 349-408.

ZNANIECKI, Florian. 1944. Las sociedades de cultura nacional y sus relaciones. Jornadas, 24 (Colegio de Mexico, Centro de Estudios Sociales). Mexico.

ZUCKERMAN, S. 1930-1931. The menstrual cycle of the primates. Proc. Zool. Soc. London, 1930:691-754; 1931:325-343, 593-602.

ZUCKERMAN, S. 1932. The Social Life of Monkeys and Apes. New York: Harcourt, Brace.

ZUCKERMAN, S. 1933. Functional Affinities of Man, Monkeys and Apes. New York: Harcourt, Brace.

Student Problems in Anthropology

GENERAL TEXTBOOKS IN ANTHROPOLOGY: Ralph Linton, *The Study of Man* (D. Appleton-Century), 1936; Franz Boas and others, *General Anthropology* (Heath), 1938; A. A. Goldenweiser, *Anthropology* (Crofts), 1937; Eliot Chapple and Carleton S. Coon, *Principles of Anthropology* (Holt), 1942; A. L. Kroeber, *Anthropology* (Harcourt, Brace), 1923 (supplement bound in, 1931); R. H. Lowie, *An Introduction to Cultural Anthropology* (Farrar and Rinehart), 2d Ed., 1940.

PROBLEMS FOR STUDENT REPORTS

Note: Bibliographic references given for each of the following topics are merely suggestive, for the purpose of "getting started." It is expected that each student will gather more material on his own initiative. Among the standard periodicals of anthropology in English are the following: *American Anthropologist, Journal of American Folklore, American Journal of Physical Anthropology, American Antiquity, Southwestern Journal of Anthropology, Primitive Man, Applied Anthropology, Acta Americana, Man* (British), *Journal of the Royal Anthropological Institute* (British). Much anthropological material is also published in the standard sociological and psychological journals, such as *American Journal of Sociology, American Sociological Review, Social Forces, Character and Personality, Journal of Applied Psychology*, and others. Among the well-known series in anthropology are the following: *Papers of the Peabody Museum of Harvard University, Bulletins of the Bureau of American Ethnology* (Smithsonian Institution), *Publications of the Institute of Social Anthropology* (Smithsonian Institution), *Anthropological Papers of the American Museum of Natural History* (New York), *Columbia University Contributions to Anthropology, Yale Anthropological Studies, University of California Publications in American Archaeology and Ethnology, Research Series of the Middle American Research Institute* (Tulane University), *University of New Mexico Publications in Anthropology, Viking Fund Publications in Anthropology* (New York), *Publications of the Division of Historical Research of the Carnegie Institution of Washington, Reports of the U. S. National Museum, Anthropological Series of the Field Museum of Natural History* (Chicago), *Yale University Publications in Anthropology, University of Chicago Publications in Anthropology*, and so forth.

1. FOSSIL MAN AND HUMAN EVOLUTION: E. A. Hooton, *Up from the Ape* (Macmillan), 1931, rev. ed., 1946; W. W. Howells, *Mankind So Far* (Doubleday, Doran), 1944, Parts I and II.

2. HUMAN RACES: Chapters by Shapiro, Krogman, Klineberg, in Ralph Linton, ed., *The Science of Man in the World Crisis* (Columbia), 1945, pp. 19-77; Howells, *Mankind So Far*, Part III; M. F. Ashley Montagu, *The Fallacy of Race* (Columbia), 1943; Otto Klineberg, *Race Differences* (Harper), 1934.

3. CONSTITUTIONAL TYPES: W. H. Sheldon and others, *The Varieties of Human Physique* (Harpers), 1940; *Physique and Temperament* (Harpers), 1943; E. Kretschmer, *Physique and Character* (Harcourt, Brace), 1925.

4. COMPARATIVE CULTURES: G. P. Murdock, *Our Primitive Contemporaries* (Macmillan), 1934; Forde, C. Daryle, *Habitat, Economy, and Society* (Harcourt, Brace), 1937.

5. LEARNING AND CULTURE: Neal Miller and John Dollard, *Social Learning and Imitation* (Yale), 1941.

6. HUMAN ABILITIES AND CULTURE: G. P. Murdock, "The Common Denominator of Cultures," in R. Linton, ed., *The Science of Man in the World Crisis;* John Gillin, "Culture and Range of Human Response," *Character and Personality*, 13:101-134, Dec. 1944.

7. DIFFUSION OF CULTURE: R. B. Dixon, *The Building of Cultures* (Scribner's), 1928; A. L. Kroeber, *Anthropology;* W. D. Wallis, *Culture and Progress* (Whittlesey House), 1930; R. U. Sayce, *Primitive Arts and Crafts* (Cambridge), 1933.

8. COMPARISON OF CULTURE AREA CONCEPT WITH REGIONAL CONCEPT: Clark Wissler, "The Culture Area Concept in Social Anthropology," *Amer. J. Sociol.*, 32:881-892, 1927; A. L. Kroeber, *Natural and Cultural Areas of Native North America* (University of California); Howard Odum and H. E. Moore, *American Regionalism* (Holt), 1938.

9. ORGANIZATION OF CULTURAL SYSTEMS: J. Gillin, "Cultural Adjustment," *Amer. Anthrop.*, 46:429-446, 1944; B. Malinowski, *A Scientific Theory of Culture* (University of North Carolina), 1944, pp. 43-144.

10. COMPARATIVE SEX AND REPRODUCTIVE PATTERNS OF MANKIND: C. S. Ford, *A Comparative Study of Human Reproduction*, Yale Univ. Publ. in Anthropology, No. 32.

11. COMPARATIVE KINSHIP SYSTEMS: Gillin and Gillin, *Introduction to Sociology*, Ch. 9; L. Spier, *The Distribution of Kinship Systems in North America* (Univ. Washington Publ. in Anthropology, No. 1); R. H. Lowie, *Primitive Society* (Liveright), 1920.

12. COMPARATIVE ECONOMIC SYSTEMS AND PATTERNS: Ruth Bunzell, "The Economic Organization of Primitive Peoples," in F. Boas, *General Anthropology*, Ch. 8; M. J. Herskovits, *The Economic Life of Primitive Peoples* (Knopf), 1940; R. Thurnwald, *Economics in Primitive Societies* (Oxford), 1932.

13. COMPARATIVE RELIGIOUS SYSTEMS AND PATTERNS: R. H. Lowie, *Primitive Religion* (Boni and Liveright), 1924; P. Radin, *Primitive Religion* (Viking), 1938; W. D. Wallis, *Primitive Religion* (Crofts), 1940.

14. COMPARATIVE TECHNOLOGIES: R. U. Sayce, *Primitive Arts and Crafts* (Cambridge); Lewis Mumford, *Technics and Civilization* (Harcourt, Brace), 1934.

15. THE INDIVIDUAL IN CULTURE

    a. MATERIALS AND METHODS: J. Gillin, "Personality in Preliterate Societies," *Amer. Sociol. Rev.*, 4:681-702, 1939; Clyde Kluckhohn, "The Personal Document in Anthropological Science," in *The Use of Personal Documents in History, Anthropology, and Sociology*, Bull. 53, Soc. Sci. Res. Council, 1945. R. Linton, *The Cultural Background of Personality* (Appleton-Century), 1945.

    b. SPECIFIC CULTURES (each one of the following is a report):
        (16) Socialization in New Guinea: J. W. M. Whiting, *Becoming a Kwoma* (Yale), 1941.
        (17) Socialization in New Guinea: Margaret Mead, *Growing up in New Guinea* (Morrow), 1928.
        (18) Hopi: Leo Simmons, ed., *Sun Chief* (Yale), 1941; Laura Thompson and Alice Josephs, *The Hopi Way* (University of Chicago), 1945; W. Dennis, *The Hopi Child* (Appleton-Century), 1939.
        (19) Navajo: Walter Dyk, *The Son of Old Man Hat* (Harcourt, Brace), 1938, *A Navaho Autobiography* (Viking Fund), 1947; A. and D. Leighton, *The Navaho Door* (*Harvard*), 1944, pp. 95-134.
        (20) Apache: Morris Opler, *An Apache Life Way* (University of Chicago), 1941.
        (21) Lepcha: Geoffrey Gorer, *Himalayan Village* (Michael Joseph, London), 1938.
        (22) Kwakiutl: C. S. Ford, *Smoke From Their Fires* (Yale), 1941.
        (23) Alor: C. Du Bois, *The People of Alor* (University of Minnesota), 1944.

    c. THE CONCEPT OF "BASIC PERSONALITY STRUCTURE": Kardiner, A., *The Individual and His Society* (Columbia), 1939; *The Psychological Frontiers of Society* (Columbia), 1945.

24. PSYCHOLOGICAL ORIENTATIONS OF CULTURES: Ruth Benedict, *Patterns of Culture*, 1934.

25. FOLK CULTURES

    a. Robert Redfield, *The Folk Culture of Yucatan* (Chicago), 1941.
    b. (26) Robert Redfield, *Tepoztlan* (Chicago), 1930.
    c. (27) Alfonso Villa R., *The Maya of East Central Quintana Roo*, Carnegie Inst. of Washington, Publ. 559.
    d. (28) Conrad Arensberg, *The Irish Countryman*, 1937; C. M. Arensberg and S. T. Kimball, *Family and Community in Ireland* (Harvard), 1940.

26. ACCULTURATION AND CULTURE CONTACT: M. J. Herskovits, *Acculturation* (Augustin), 1938; A. I. Hallowell, "Sociopsychological aspects of acculturation," in R. Linton, ed., *The Science of Man in the World Crisis*, 1945, pp. 180-200; J. Gillin, "Acquired Drives in Culture Contact," *Amer. Anthrop.*, 44:545-554, 1943; R. Linton, *Acculturation in Seven American*

Indian Tribes (Appleton-Century), 1939; B. Malinowski, *The Dynamics of Culture Change* (Yale), 1945, Part I.

27. THEORIES OF CULTURE: R. H. Lowie, *History of Ethnological Theory* (Farrar and Rinehart), 1937; B. Malinowski, *A Scientific Theory of Culture* (University of North Carolina), pp. 145-176; P. Radin, "History of Ethnological Theories," *Amer. Anthrop.*, 31:9-33, 1929; A. R. Radcliffe-Brown, "On the Concept of Function in Social Science," *Amer. Anthrop.*, 37:394-402, 1935; A. L. Kroeber, "History and Science in Anthropology," *Amer. Anthrop.* 37:539-569, 1935; David Bidney, "On the Concept of Culture and Some Cultural Fallacies," *Amer. Anthrop.*, 46:30-44, 1944; Ernst Cassirer, *An Essay on Man* (Yale), 1944.

Index